Ramesh Menon has written modern renderings of the *Mahabharata*, the *Ramayana*, the *Bhagavadgita*, the *Siva Purana*, the *Bhagavata Purana* and *The Complete Mahabharata*: *Adi Parva*.

DEVI

THE DEVI BHAGAVATAM RETOLD

RAMESH MENON

RUPA

Published by
Rupa Publications India Pvt. Ltd 2006
7/16, Ansari Road, Daryaganj
New Delhi 110002

Sales centres:
Bengaluru Chennai
Hyderabad Jaipur Kathmandu
Kolkata Mumbai Prayagraj

P-ISBN: 978-81-291-1554-6
E-ISBN: 978-81-291-2177-6

Twenty-sixth impression 2024

30 29 28 27 26

Typeset by Mindways Design, New Delhi

Printed in India

To Sri Ramakrishna Paramahamsa

Author's Note

This is an abridged, modern rendering of the sacred book of the Goddess. My only source for this retelling was *Srimad Devi Bhagavatam*, as translated in full by Swami Vijnanananda (1921).

I have shortened the original translation considerably in order to reach a wider modern readership. However, I have included all the main legends of the Devi, and many other stories, upakathas that I thought held literary interest and illumined the Indian spiritual tradition in general.

I have attempted to recreate in contemporary English the mystery, grandeur and enchantment of the *Devi Bhagavatam*, to the extent possible. However, this is scripture retold and my approach remains primarily one of bhakti, of devotion, as was that of the ancient Rishis who received and transmitted this mystic lore through the ages.

Acknowledgements

My thanks to Jayashree Kumar and Deepthi Talwar, both of whom copy-edited the text painstakingly, and did a fine job. Katya Osborne also worked on portions of the book; my thanks to her as well.

OM Ganeshayah Namaha. OM Saraswatheyah Namaha.
OM Sri Lakshmiyahah Namaha. OM Umayah Namaha.
OM Devi Bhagavati.

ONE

ONCE MORE, THE MUNIS OF THE SIX ILLUSTRIOUS FAMILIES ARE GATHERED in the Naimisa vana, sacred forest sanctified for ancient revelations. In their midst sits Suta Romaharshana, peerless Pauranika, who has learnt his lore from Krishna Dwaipayana, the awesome Veda Vyasa himself.

Saunaka, the eldest among the Munis, says, "Profound Suta, we Brahmanas have come to your feet today in terror of the advent of the kali yuga. We have heard that listening to the holy Bhagavatam of the Devi can free us from samsara, this endless round of births and deaths. Master, we would hear the immortal Devi Bhagavatam from your lips."

Suta says, "Fortunate am I that the wise want to hear the Purana from me. Brahmanas, I bow at the lotus feet of the Mother of the universe before I begin. *AUM.*

Everyone knows that Brahma created the worlds. Yet Brahma is born in the lotus that sprouts from Vishnu's navel. Then again, Narayana rests upon his serpent Ananta, who lies upon the ocean Ekarnava. We ask ourselves, from what primal source has this infinite sea come? And we turn for sanctuary to the source, the Mother of all things, the Devi."

Thus begins Suta Romaharshana, in his voice that is quiet as an ocean deep. He pauses, his eyes shut, his body still. After a moment, Saunaka murmurs, "My lord Suta, when we grew afraid of the looming kali yuga, we went to Brahma in his palace at the heart of a wondrous Brahma-vana. He plucked a mystic wheel from his mind and cast it down into the world. He said to us, 'Munis, where this wheel falls, there remain, until the feral kali yuga ends and a blessed satya yuga dawns over the world again. The wheel will protect you, for the kali will not enter its confines.'

The wheel from the Pitamaha's mind fell here, in this Naimisa vana, and when we entered within its boundary, the luminous thing melted into the ground like violet fire. So here we remain, in this auspicious forest, waiting for the kali to end. And we are fortunate indeed that you have come among us Master, to bless our long wait with the precious Purana."

Suta draws a deep breath and, his eyes still shut, continues, "Hear of the birth of Vyasa's son, Suka Deva, who first expounded the Purana in the world, as he heard it from his father. Once, Vyasa, the son of the fishergirl Satyavati, sat in his asrama on the banks of the golden river Saraswati, when he saw two sparrows feeding their newly hatched chick. Never had Vyasa seen such adoration in any living creatures as he saw in those parent birds, as they thrust the food they softened in their own beaks into their child's gaping mouth. Never had he seen such love, such ecstasy, such devotion.

Vyasa thought, 'If these sparrows, who will never see their child again once he can fly, love their young one so much, how much more will a man who expects the world of his son. Ah surely, to caress and nurture one's own son is the greatest joy that exists in this world.

Moreover, how can a man die in peace unless he has a son to whom he can leave his wisdom and his earthly possessions, a son who will touch fire to his corpse and perform his last rites, so that his soul can rise up to heaven?'

Vyasa decided that no man can be fulfilled unless he has a son, and his mind turned to how he himself could become a father without delay. The good Muni set out for Meru, to perform tapasya so he would be blessed with a son. When he arrived on that holiest of mountains, he built an asrama for himself, then wondered, 'Which God shall I worship now? Which one will grant me my desire most swiftly? Shall I pray to Vishnu, Brahma, Siva, Indra, Surya, Ganapathy, Agni, Karttikeya, Varuna?'

Suddenly he heard someone softly plucking on a vina, and saw that the wandering Rishi Narada had arrived there, as though by chance. Vyasa warmly welcomed Narada with madhurparka and arghya, and then they sat together on darbhasanas.

Narada said, 'Dwaipayana, you seem careworn. Tell me, what troubles you?'

Vyasa smiled wanly and replied, 'Muni, the man who has no son leads an aimless life and I am uncertain which God I should worship to have a son of my own.'

Narada laughed delightedly, 'Dwaipayana, knower of the ambrosial Purana, once my father Brahma asked Vishnu the very same question. At once Narayana lapsed into yoga, a deep trance. Amazed, Brahma said, "Lord of the universe, what samadhi are you plunged in? Whom do you worship, O Cause of causes? At your word, the sun ranges the sky, fire burns, and the wind blows. I, who am the Lord of Creation, was born in the lotus sprung from your navel. Padmanabha, you are the greatest of all the great, yet here I find you at worship. Who is worthy of your devotion, Narayana?"

Vishnu said with a smile on his perfect face, "Brahma, indeed you create, I preserve, and Rudra destroys the universes. Yet, without Shakti, the three of us would be inert, powerless. Maha Shakti, the Goddess, is the highest power of all, and she animates the rest of us. It is her I worship, Brahma, who else? It is by her wish that I incarnate as Matsya and Kurma, Varaha, Narasimha, and all the rest. It is by her will that I once had my head severed, and a horse's head set upon my neck.

There is none I know of higher than Parashakti, and it is upon her that I meditate," ' said Narada to Vyasa, adding, 'so, friend Dwaipayana, you had also best worship the Devi for your boon.'

After a while Narada left, and Dwaipayana, sitting in padmasana, began to worship the Devi Bhagavati," says Suta Romaharshana to the Munis of the Naimisa, athirst for his Devi Purana.

TWO

SAUNAKA'S RISHIS SAY TO THE SUTA IN SOME SURPRISE, "MY LORD! YOU SAY Narayana's head was severed? We have never heard anything so astonishing in all our lives. Tell us, Romaharshana, how did such an incredible thing happen?"

Suta smiles, "Once, when he had fought the Danavas, Madhu and Kaitabha, for ten thousand years without pause, Vishnu grew tired. He sat in padmasana in a forest, leant his head on his mighty bow, the Saringa, and fell asleep. Meanwhile, Indra and the Devas, Brahma and Siva arrived in Vaikunta to worship Vishnu, who is their Lord. But they did not find him in his city of miracles. When they sought him in the secret vana in which he had taken refuge, they found him in the swoon of yoganidra. They sat down around the sleeping Blue God, and were concerned to see the protector of the universe like that, plunged in a strange stupor.

Indra said, 'How shall we awaken Narayana from his slumber?'

Siva answered, 'He will be annoyed if you dare to rouse him. But, truly, we do urgently need to see him.'

At which, Brahma created a hive of termites called vamris, and loosed them on the Saringa against which Vishnu rested his head as he slept. If the insects ate through one end of the bow, the other would rise, dislodging Vishnu's head and waking him.

But the vamris said to Brahma, 'How dare we disturb the sleep of the Lord of the worlds? To disturb blessed sleep is a sin equal to tearing a husband from his wife. Moreover, what do we gain by this crime against Narayana?'

Brahma immediately replied, 'If you do this you shall have all the ghee that falls outside the pit of the homa for yourselves. So, hurry and rouse Padmanabha.'

The greedy vamris devoured one end of the bow. The bowstring of the Saringa gave way with a report like a star exploding. The sea rose in tidal waves, mountains shook, meteors fell screaming from the sky, the sun fell below the horizon, and evil omens filled the four quarters.

The alarmed Devas saw that Vishnu's head had been severed from his blue neck by the whiplash of the bowstring, and was nowhere to be seen. They began to beat their breasts and wail, 'Lord! Narayana! Invincible One, you have been decapitated today and we are to blame.'

Even Siva seemed stricken, and Brihaspati, who is the guru of the Devas and the embodiment of wisdom, advised, 'These tears are of no use now. When fate tries us, we must exert our intelligence to save ourselves from danger.'

But Indra cried, 'Fie on your intelligence! Narayana's head has been struck off by our folly. Ah, fate is all-powerful, and we are helpless against it.'

Brahma said, 'Indeed, fate is unequivocal, and all that are born must suffer. Only Mahamaya, the Devi, can help us now. Let us worship her.'

Brahma summoned the Vedas, who were there, incarnate, and commanded them, 'Sing the hymn of the omniscient Bhagavati now.'

And the resplendent Vedas did so at length, fervently calling out many of her thousand names. Then they sobbed, 'Bhagavati, Mother, are you angry with the ocean's daughter Lakshmi that you have killed her Lord today? Hari's head has vanished like a dream Devi, and no one but you can make him live again.'

Then a voice more exquisite than beauty itself spoke to the Devas from the sky, 'All will be well again, Suras. Golden Vedas, I am pleased with your worship. But nothing in this universe happens without a good reason; once Vishnu looked at his wife Lakshmi's face and laughed. And Lakshmi was distraught because she thought he had seen something ugly in her perfect features. She became suspicious that he had another woman or he would not laugh at her like that. Sorrow turned to wrath as the tamo-shakti possessed her.

As she cursed him, "May your head fall off!" she even thought it would be better to be widowed than have her Lord take another wife.

It is by that curse that Vishnu's head fell into the salt sea today; and from another curse, as well.

Once, the Asura Hayagriva performed a tapasya for a thousand years. He neither ate nor slept, but chanted my names ceaselessly, until at last, I stood before him in my tamasic body. I saw he truly loved me; for, when he saw me his eyes filled with tears of joy. I said to that Demon, "Hayagriva, I am pleased with you. Ask me for any boon you like."

He said, "Mother, let death never approach me. Let me be invincible against the Devas and Asuras, let me be an immortal yogi."

"Asura, birth follows death, as death does birth, ineluctably. You cannot be immortal, ask for another boon," said I to Hayagriva.

The canny Asura replied, "Then, Devi, let me find death only at the hands of one who has a horse's face like me."

So I blessed him, "Let only a horse-faced one kill you, Hayagriva."

Pleased no end, he went back to his kingdom, and ever since he has been the scourge of all the living. And no one can kill him, because none of the truly mighty has a horse's face. So, Devas, find a horse's head, fix it to Vishnu's neck, and let him rid the worlds of Hayagriva.'

With this, the invisible Devi fell silent. Indra said to his consummate artisan Viswakarman, 'Give the Lord a horse's head, so he can kill Hayagriva.'

Viswakarman found a fine stallion, severed its head with his axe, and attached the horse's head to Vishnu's throat with sacred mantras. At once blue Narayana stood up, neighing so loudly it seemed the sky would be shattered by that sound. The horse-headed God flew at the horse-faced Demon, Hayagriva, and tore him limb from limb," says Suta Romaharshana, once to Saunaka and his Munis in the blessed Naimisa.

THREE

SAUNAKA ASKS, "GENTLE SUTA, YOU SPOKE OF A LONG BATTLE NARAYANA fought against the Asuras Madhu and Kaitabha. Tell us about that war."

Suta says, "Once, after a pralaya, the universe lay dissolved in the single, primordial sea: Ekarnava. Vishnu lay asleep on his serpent-bed, upon the interminable coils of Anantasesha of a thousand hoods. My master, Rishi Vyasa, says that two Asuras were born from the wax in the sleeping Vishnu's ears, and they were dreadful to behold.

Madhu and Kaitabha grew to manhood in the plumbless Ekarnava, which are the waters of infinity, containing all places, all ages and all souls. They grew swiftly, and were soon as immense as they were powerful and hideous. They spoke to each other, wonderingly, "What is this marvellous sea, upon what foundation does it rest? Who made this ocean, and who made us? Who are our father and mother?" But they could find no answers to these questions.

One day, from inscrutable intuition, Kaitabha said to Madhu, 'Brother, the Devi is the cause of this sea, and of us as well.'

As soon as the words were out of his mouth, the two Asuras heard the blessed Vagbija in the air, the seed of all mantras, who is the Devi Saraswati herself. When that mantra receded, the horrible wax Demons began to chant it themselves, until, in a blaze of lightning above them, they saw the brilliant, embodied form of Devi Saraswati. The Asuras chanted on, and were one in spirit with that Devi for a thousand years.

At last, the Adi Shakti was pleased with Madhu and Kaitabha, and an extraordinary voice spoke to them, 'I am pleased with you, Danavas, ask me for whatever you want.'

'Devi, grant that we will only die when we will it ourselves.'

'So be it,' said the asariri, with the hint of a smile.

Madhu and Kaitabha's roars of joy shook their home, the infinite sea, from end to end. They dived under the water in delight and began to play, both gently and viciously, with the denizens of the deep. They flew up into the air, and played with the rainbow-hued birds there.

Then, one day, Madhu and Kaitabha saw an immense golden lotus in the sky, and sitting in it, steeped in dhyana, four-faced and white-bearded, lustrous Brahma, the sire of everything. The excited Demons called out to the Pitama, 'Come, let us fight! Or else relinquish your lofty place and flee from us.'

Brahma flickered all his eyes open and saw the Asuras, each big as ten Merus. He shuddered at how terrible they were, and wondered, 'I am not certain how strong these monsters are. I hesitate to fight them. I think I will rouse Narayana from his sleep and let him kill them.'

Brahma plunged down the stalk of the golden lotus, and besought Vishnu anxiously, calling him by many of his august names and begging him to quell the arrogant Demons. But nothing stirred; it seemed Vishnu had not heard Brahma. He could hear Madhu and Kaitabha roaring for him, so his lotus stem shook like any flower in a gale.

Brahma decided Narayana must be plunged in the yoga nidra, the trance of the Devi. He began to worship Adi Shakti, the ancient Mother: 'Bhagavati, you hold Vishnu in your deepest power, so that he does not stir although I have called his every name with such fervour. Madhu and Kaitabha mean to kill me, Devi, and terror grips my soul. Save me from fear, Mother, or kill me with your own hands!'

The Devi, in her inert form of sleep, withdrew from Narayana, leaving in turn his eyes, mouth, nose, heart and finally his whole body. The Blue God stirred on his serpent-bed; he yawned. In moments, Vishnu's form was again as splendid as a thousand suns, where a short while ago it had been muted and quenched. Narayana opened his lotus-eyes and saw Brahma Prajapati standing before him, trembling.

Vishnu spoke to Brahma in his voice like soft thunder, 'Why have you abandoned your dhyana, Pitama? Why do you tremble?'

Brahma whispered, 'I am in terror of my life, Padmanabha. The Asuras Madhu and Kaitabha want to kill me.'

Mahavishnu said languidly, 'Fear them no more, I will kill them for you.'

At that moment, Madhu and Kaitabha arrived there, roaring. The Demons trod water easily, and their savage faces lit up when they saw Brahma.

Madhu hissed, 'So! This is where you have come to hide, coward. Come and fight. We will kill you first, and then this blue fellow lying on the snake.'

Kaitabha sneered, 'Either fight, or say you are our slave and we will let you live.'

Vishnu roared like the thunder of the storm that ends the worlds. 'Come and fight me, Asuras!'

His eyes rolling, Madhu sprang at Narayana, while Kaitabha stood back. They fought on Ananta, they fought on the waves of Ekarnava, they fought under the water and in the sky, furiously, striking each other with stupendous blows, the Blue God and the Demon born from his earwax.

Brahma returned to his lotus and peered down from safety at the duel, while Adi Shakti, the Devi, watched from everywhere. The battle was ferocious, and both Demon and God tired quickly. Suddenly Madhu stepped away from Narayana, and at once Kaitabha sprang forward to engage him.

Thus the two Demons fought Mahavishnu turn by turn, and at times both together. Vishnu battled the sinister brothers without rest for five thousand years, and he grew tired. Seeing the God wane, the Asuras crowed in triumph, 'Vishnu, if you are vanquished, join your palms and raise them over your head to say you are our slave. Otherwise, we mean to kill you first, and then to drink Brahma's blood.'

Vishnu saw the Danavas treading water, easily, and replied, 'No warrior will fight a tired enemy, a frightened one, one who has no weapons, or a child. For five thousand years, we have fought and each of you rested, while the other one faced me. But I have had no rest, Asuras, and I am tired. So let me draw breath for a while, and we will fight again.'

Madhu and Kaitabha nodded their macabre heads solemnly, and allowed Vishnu the rest he wanted. They stood back from him, arms folded across chests like continents, still treading water. Vishnu fell into deep dhyana. As he meditated, he learnt of the Devi's boon to the Asuras, of ichchamrityu: to die only when they themselves willed it.

The Blue God was perturbed; for who wants to die, even in the direst circumstances? He realised how vain his battle with the wax-Demons had been. Narayana folded his hands and worshipped the Devi Bhagavati feverishly. 'Mother, I am exhausted, and the Danavas who have your boon are ready to kill me. I am helpless, Devi, save me.'

Devi spoke to Narayana out of the air, 'Fight again without fear, Hari. I will seduce the Asuras with a look from my eyes, so you can kill them.'

Vishnu went back to fight, and the Asuras welcomed him fondly. Soon they began to strike one another again, with blows that are beyond describing. Now, Madhu and Kaitabha were both rested and they fought Narayana together. He quickly found their combined strength more than he could bear and, reeling from their blows, he looked imploringly up to the Devi to save him.

She manifested herself before the Asuras' eyes then, and she was enticement personified! Ah, her red eyes shot shafts of unfamiliar lust at the Danavas. The enchanted Asuras had eyes only for the Devi now. They stood gazing at her like men in a salacious dream, aroused past endurance and not knowing what to do.

Seeing his chance, Vishnu said, 'Warriors, I am so pleased with the fight you gave me, I will grant you any boon. Only ask me, Asuras.'

Standing before the alluring Devi, the Asuras wanted to impress her, and replied haughtily, 'Who are you to grant us a boon? We are not beggars that we want anything from you. On the other hand, you ask us for a boon, Vishnu, and we shall grant it in our munificence.'

Their eyes never left Bhagavati's ravishing form. Vishnu replied, 'If you are so pleased with me, Asuras, grant that I kill you both.'

At once, the Devi vanished, and the Demons realised they had been tricked. They hung their black heads, and green tears trickled down their awful faces. Then Madhu had an inspiration. Brightening, he said, 'We know you never lie, Narayana. We have need of the boon you promised us earlier.'

'Ask me,' said Vishnu, for he had indeed promised.

'We will let you kill us, but it must be on solid ground where there isn't a drop of water,' said Madhu; and of course there was no dry place in the dissolution.

Hari said, 'So be it,' and he expanded his own thighs, so they were a bright, dry island floating upon the sea of Ekarnava. The Asuras grew so they were ten thousand yojanas each. But Narayana made his thighs twice as vast. With nothing else for it, Madhu and Kaitabha laid their heads on Vishnu's thighs as on an executioner's block, and, with his Sudarshana Chakra the Blue God struck those heads off their immense trunks in an eruption of gore.

Those Demons' marrow, their meda, flowed out of them and mixed into the sea. Later, when the sea became earth, it was called Medini, and was inedible because of the marrow of Madhu and Kaitabha," Suta, wonderful raconteur, tells the Munis of the Naimisa vana.

FOUR

IN THE VANA, THE RISHI SAUNAKA SAYS, "SUTA, NOW RETURN TO YOUR tale of how Veda Vyasa's son, Suka Deva, was born."

"On Mount Meru, Vyasa immersed himself in worshipping the Devi; the sacred syllable Vak never left his lips. He prayed for a son as pure, as lively, and as powerful, as the elements themselves. He worshipped Devi, and Siva, the granter of boons. For a hundred years, never eating, Vyasa sat in a magical forest of karnikara trees on Meru, where Gandharvas and Kinnaras, the greatest Munis, the Adityas, Vasus, Rudras, Maruts, and the Aswin twins came.

Vyasa's tapasya was so intense that, soon, his hair stood on end and resembled tongues of flame. The subtle fire of his penance swept through the universe, and Indra in heaven grew afraid. The Lord of the Devas went trembling to Siva, and said, 'If Vyasa's tapasya continues, he will replace me as king in Devaloka.'

Siva laughed and said, 'The Muni is only praying for a son. He has worshipped the Parashakti and me for a hundred years; it is time I gave him what he wants.'

Siva appeared in glory before Vyasa, and said, 'Dwaipayana, I bless you with a son as pure as fire, earth, air and ether, a boy who will be wise and brave, and full of mercy.'

Vyasa's cry of delight rang among the golden peaks of Meru. He went back to his asrama, and now he felt the exhaustion of his long tapasya. He felt as hungry as a man who had not eaten for a hundred years. Vyasa fetched his arani sticks and began rubbing them together to make a fire, so he could cook himself some food.

As he rubbed, he wondered, 'How will I have a son when I have no wife? But how can I marry, when I know perfectly well what bondage even the most chaste woman is? Perhaps, my child will be born like fire is from these sticks.'

Even as he was lost in these reflections, he saw a woman who was seductiveness embodied. She was Ghritachi, queen of the Apsaras. The lovely nymph trod air before the Rishi's eyes, and wore a diaphanous garment that barely covered her shimmering nakedness. She smiled at Vyasa. The continence of a hundred years erupted in his blood, and the Muni was afire.

Ghritachi began to unwind the sheer raiment she wore. Her breasts came into view, and Vyasa felt like a lost man. He struggled desperately with himself, but each moment his flesh was proving stronger than his poor spirit. Vyasa shut his eyes but he saw her behind his eyelids. He told himself that if he took the Apsara, as every cell in his body wept to, he would find not happiness but sorrow for himself. Why, poor Vyasa even reminded himself of Pururavas and Urvashi to save himself from folly," says Suta, pausing, with a slight smile on his austere face.

Into his brief silence, one of Saunaka's Rishis asks, "Who were Pururavas and Urvashi, good Suta? Why was Vyasa reminded of them when he saw Ghritachi? Tell us now, before we forget to ask later."

"I heard this tale from my master Veda Vyasa," says Suta. "Brihaspati, as you know, is the guru of the Devas, he is also their priest. Once, his lovely wife Tara saw Soma, the Moon, and was smitten by that Deva. Soma saw Tara, and he too lusted madly after her. He flowed in through her window one night, and they fell together upon her bed while her husband Brihaspati was away. Their lovemaking was so rapturous that Tara eloped with the Moon and began living in his home. And he, expert lover, pleased her in every imaginative way that her austere husband had neglected to do.

Poor Guru was beside himself at not seeing his young wife. He would do anything to have her back. He sent his sishya Angiras to Soma, begging him not once, but many times to return Tara. When Soma sent Angiras back empty-handed, again and again, Guru went himself in a rage to confront the sinning Moon.

'I am your master,' Brihaspati cried in fury to the arrogant Soma. 'You are committing a mahapaapa. Vicious Soma, return my wife to me or I will curse you.'

Soma answered insouciantly, 'Guru, anger is a great sin also. Tara will surely come back to you. What harm is there if she stays in my home for a few days more? After all, no one forces her to remain. She stays here by her own choice, to enjoy herself a little.'

Brihaspati went back, his heart in anguish for his young wife, his mind tormented with visions of her in the Moon's arms, in every posture of flaming love. But in a few days, he was back at Soma's gates, roaring at the guards when they barred his way. Brihaspati cried, 'Give my Tara back to me, or I will turn you into ashes!'

Soma came out and said haughtily, 'Devaguru, why waste your breath? Tara is too young for you; she is too beautiful. What will you do with a woman like her? She is too spirited for your ascetic ways, old one. Better, marry yourself an uglier, less passionate woman. From what she tells me, you know nothing of making love, and she wants to be made love to all the time.'

Soma laughed in his master's face, 'Moreover, you are so full of lust yourself that your curse will hardly affect me. Do what you like, Tara stays here with me.'

Trembling, Brihaspati crept away from there. He went to Indra's palace. Concerned to see his master so distraught, Indra asked, 'What ails you Master, when all the Devas are your sishyas?'

In a low voice, Brihaspati confessed, 'Soma has abducted my Tara, and refuses to return her to me. Indra, help me.'

Outraged, Indra sent a clever messenger to Soma. The messenger said to the Moon, 'My lord Indra says to you, "Soma, what sin is this you commit against our own guru? You have twenty-eight delectable wives. Menaka and her Apsaras are yours to enjoy. Return Tara to her husband. When a lord of heaven commits such a sin, shall lesser beings not imitate him? Dharma will be lost to creation. Relent, Soma, give Tara back." '

But Soma was addicted to Tara's velvet body, her long caresses. He replied roughly to Indra, 'My Lord, such pure advice from you of all people! But Indra, Tara loves me, how can I abandon her? How will Brihaspati's home be a happy one, when his wife will always be thinking of me? The truth is our perfect Guru made love to his younger brother Samvarta's wife. Ever since, Tara has been unhappy. And, my Lord, how does the thousand-eyed Indra give such fine advice about chastity, when all the worlds know how he got his thousand eyes? I will never give Tara back.'

Indra's thousand eyes turned crimson as kimsuka flowers when he heard Soma's message. He summoned his awesome host to attack the renegade Moon. But Sukracharya, the guru of the Asuras, saw a chance to pit the demons' ancient enemies against each other. Moreover, Sukra hated Brihaspati. He flew straight to Soma, and offered him the legions of darkness, to resist Indra.

When Siva learnt of Soma's perfidy, he came to fight at Indra's side. War broke out, the first between the Devas and Asuras, and it lasted a thousand years. Blood to fill a sea was spilt on diverse fields.

Finally, Brahma went to Soma and said, 'If you do not stop this madness and give Tara back, I will have Vishnu raze your army. As for you, Acharya Sukra, I am astonished at you.'

Shaken at Brahma's anger, Sukra relented and advised the Moon to return Tara. He said to Soma, 'Your father, the Maharishi Atri, sent me. He says you must give Tara back.'

It was the only argument that would have persuaded the Moon. Tara was sent back to an ecstatic Brihaspati, who welcomed her home with tears in his eyes. But she was pregnant by Soma. The armies of the Devas and Asuras disbanded, and went back to wherever they had come from. Siva left with his ganas for Kailasa, and Brahma went home to Brahmaloka.

Brihaspati was delighted to have his wife home again, and spent some tender months with her. Then, she gave birth to a splendid child, and the Devaguru was beside himself with joy. But suddenly, there arrived a messenger from Soma, who said, 'The child is mine. Give him to me.'

Brihaspati replied, 'He looks like me; he is my son. He stays with me.'

Again, teeming armies gathered and they prepared for war. Brahma arrived in Brihaspati's home, and asked Tara privately, 'Tell us, woman, whose is this child? Only you can prevent another war.'

Bending her head in shame, Tara said softly, 'He is Soma's son.'

Brihaspati would not allow that child to remain an hour in his home, and Soma took him in great joy. Tara was punished for her sin by being parted from her son, and wept bitter tears. Soma named his son Budha and set him up in the sky. The armies of darkness and light disbanded again, and a dreadful war was averted," the Suta says.

Puzzled, the Munis ask, "But, what has this to do with Pururavas and Urvashi, peerless Suta?"

"Why, the ancient king Pururavas was Soma's grandson. He was Budha's son."

FIVE

SUTA SAYS, "IN ANCIENT DAYS, THERE WAS A KING CALLED SUDYUMNA, who was a man of dharma, restrained and righteous. Once, Sudyumna went hunting in the forest with some of his courtiers. He went on horseback, carrying the exceptional bow, the Ajagava, and wearing precious ear-studs that sparkled like bits of a star. It was a great hunt, and buck and rabbit, pheasant and teal, bison, panther and rhinoceros were their game.

After a week's hunting, the king arrived at the heart of an enchanted forest that grew in the shadow of blessed Mount Meru. Mandara, asoka, bakula, sala, tala, tamala, champaka, panasa, nipa, madhuka, yuthika, and countless other fine trees grew here, and an extravagance of flowers and fruit adorned their branches. Crystalline lakes with water birds and lotuses dotted this forest; bamboo thickets seemed to play soft aeolian music. It seemed the birds of this vana had more mellifluous throats than any other birds in the world.

The forest beckoned with an exhilarating magic, and Sudyumna rode his horse eagerly into it, his courtiers after him. Suddenly, his body tingled with the strangest sensation he had ever felt, and his horse below him was restless. Sudyumna thought he was fainting. When the feeling passed, he found that he had become a woman and his horse a mare, whinnying in surprise! And so, too, with all his nobles and their mounts."

The Munis cried, "Ah, passing strange! How did this happen?"

"Once, in ages gone by, some Rishis like yourselves went to that same vana to worship Siva, who they had heard was there. But when they came upon the Lord, in a glade beside a glassy pool, they saw in alarm that Parvati sat quite naked in his lap, and Siva and she were making love. When she saw the Munis, she gave a cry, leapt up from Siva's lap, and pulled on her clothes in mortification. She stood there trembling for shame, although the Rishis had fled.

Siva called her to him again, but she glanced fearfully into the trees and would not come. Siva laughed, and said, 'Let any man who enters this forest be turned into a woman, so you need not be afraid of being seen naked by another man. Now come back to me.' And she did.

The curse remained on the forest, and anyone who knew of it would avoid that vana. But Sudyumna and his party were far from home, and now they found they had become women. In anguish, the king decided he could not return to his kingdom; he would be a laughing stock, and how would he rule? Sudyumna now called herself Ila. She gave women's names to her companions as well, and they built an asrama for themselves and began living in that forest, praying for a cure to their strange affliction.

It happened that Soma and Tara's son, Budha, who was roaming the worlds for adventure, arrived in that forest. Being a Deva, he was not affected by Siva's curse. But when he saw the gorgeous Ila bathing in a lotus pool, he was struck by love's lightning. She came out after her bath, and saw him there, gazing entranced at her.

He was the first man she had seen after she was transformed, and he was a splendid Deva. Ila stood wet before Budha, and a fine flush crept over her naked skin. And he, wild one, did not hesitate a moment to lay her down in the soft moss beside that breeze-swept pool. Ila became pregnant by Soma's mercurial son, and in time, she gave birth to a fine prince, Pururavas. After the birth of her son, Ila grew more anxious than ever about the future.

Meanwhile, the people of Sudyumna's kingdom believed their king had been killed by wild animals. Great Vasishta, Brahma's son, was the kulaguru to Sudyumna's royal line; and he had kept order in the kingdom by telling the people their king was not dead and would return to them soon. Now Ila sent word to his guru in secret. When Vasishta learnt what had happened in the enchanted forest, he knew by mystic intuition whose curse afflicted Sudyumna. Vasishta performed a yagna to Siva.

The Lord appeared to the Muni in splendour. 'What boon would you have of me, Brahmarishi?'

Vasishta begged him, 'Let Ila be a man again.'

Siva pronounced, 'He cannot entirely become a man again. But let him be Sudyumna for one moon, Ila for the next, and so on.'

Thus, Sudyumna came home and began to rule his kingdom again. But every other month, he would go into a retreat and not be seen. No one knew why their king did this, and the people were disturbed. Meanwhile, Pururavas grew into a magnificent young prince, and everyone thought he was the king's child by some woman he had met in the forest. Which was not entirely untrue.

When Pururavas came of age, Sudyumna gave the kingdom into the young man's able hands, and went away into vanaprastha. Narada came to Ila's asrama, and taught her the Devi mantra of nine syllables. When she had chanted the mantra, both as Sudyumna and as Ila, for a long time, one day the Goddess stood irradiant before her. Ila Sudyumna prostrated herself at the apparition's feet, and Bhagavati drew her bhakta unto herself, and gave her blissful moksha.

Pururavas ruled wisely and justly. It was said of him that he knew all men's minds, but none knew his. He preserved the dharma in his kingdom, and his people were devout and prosperous. Ila's son was a fearless warrior, as well, and great was his domain.

Pururavas' fame as a matchless king of the earth spread even to heaven, and the Apsara Urvashi was enamoured of him. It so happened that, by a twist of fate, a Brahmana had cursed Urvashi to spend some years on earth. She arrived in Pururavas' court; and which mortal man could resist the unearthly nymph? As soon as he saw her, the king wanted her for his wife. He had never seen any woman who could remotely rival that Apsara's beauty.

Urvashi made two conditions, 'I have two lambs I entrust to you. Let no harm ever befall them. Secondly, my eyes must never see you naked, my lord, even while we are making love. As long as both these conditions are honoured, I will stay with you. But break either one, and I will vanish from your life.'

Pururavas accepted her conditions without a moment's hesitation, and Urvashi lived with him. That king had never experienced love such as she gave him, and soon he could not stay away from her for even an hour. Pururavas neglected his kingdom and his dharma, and his people suffered from his neglect. No longer would their noble sovereign even deign to come into his court; instead he appointed his ministers to attend to his tasks, while he lay in Urvashi's arms all day in a lascivious enchantment, although he kept heavy blinds drawn across his windows and no taper burned in his room unless he was fully clothed.

The years passed on earth, which are days in heaven. Then, Indra noticed that the lovely Urvashi was missing from Amravati. He called some Gandharva elves and said, 'It seems as if Devaloka is not beautiful anymore that Urvashi is not with us. I would be pleased if you went into the world and stole two ewe lambs from Pururavas' palace.'

Visvavasu, lord of the Gandharvas, took some of his ethereal people and arrived in Pururavas' palace. They came in the dark through a crack in the twilight. They waited until the palace slept, and crept into the king's private garden. It was midnight, and the elves heard the intimate sounds of love floating down from the king's open window above them. They seized the two lambs and flew up into the sky with them.

But the little creatures bleated loudly, and Urvashi jumped up from her bed even though Pururavas lay under her. She screamed at the king, 'My lord, you have betrayed me! Thieves are stealing my lambs, which are like my own daughters.'

It was dark in that room, and Pururavas sprang up to see who had taken his lady's lambs. He ran to the window, and leapt out to chase the elves. Just then, the Gandharvas in the sky cast glimmering moondust down from their fine hands, and the Apsara Urvashi saw Pururavas stark naked as he ran after the thieves.

That king was such a splendid kshatriya that the Gandharvas hastily abandoned the lambs and fled. But when Pururavas brought the little beasts back, he was just in time to see his Apsara vanish into the sky. That king roared his anguish to the stars, but to no avail. He ran through the earth like the blind wind, tears streaming from his eyes; but nowhere did he find his love. At last, he came panting to holy Kurukshetra, and there he saw Urvashi as a luminous mist before him.

Pururavas roared, 'How could you abandon me? Ah, this body of mine, that you once loved, will fall dead without your caresses. Come back, Urvashi!'

But she scoffed at him, 'What lover are you, that couldn't keep your word to me? What wisdom do you have that you rant like a mad man now? Go back to your kingdom, mortal, our paths have forked forever. You are too far beneath me to even dream of me again.'

The king felt as though she was slicing his heart with a knife; but the Apsara vanished coldly before him, and he never saw her again," says the Suta. "So, Vyasa, who knew this ancient tale, was aware of how fickle and heartless the Apsaras of heaven are in their dealings with all men, especially men of the earth. And though his flesh screamed to possess the Apsara Ghritachi, he struggled manfully to master his desire."

SIX

"VYASA STOOD TREMBLING BEFORE THE APSARA, STILL RUBBING HIS ARANI sticks together in a daze. She mistook his arousal for anger. Growing afraid that he might curse her, Ghritachi became a suka bird and flew away. Vyasa gave a moan of anguish, but with his tapasvin's powerful imagination he still saw her before him, half-naked and ravishing, and unable to help himself, he began to fondle her in his fantasy.

Indeed, so strong was that Rishi's desire that he possessed Ghritachi the Apsara in his mind as assuredly as if he actually had her in the flesh. He could feel her satin skin against his hands, he could smell the delicate musk of her body. He could feel her moistness on his fingers, while he rubbed the arani sticks together dreamily. Then, an ineffable surge of rapture swept over the Muni, and his seed spurted from him on to the arani sticks.

The innocent Vyasa hardly noticed his ejaculation, but went on rubbing the aranis together. The next moment, instead of fire, a flame-like boy sprang up from the tinder-sticks! That child was radiant and he resembled Vyasa in every feature. Dwaipayana was amazed. Without laying hands on a woman, he had a son who shone like agni. This must be Siva's grace, he thought. His boy stood before him like a glowing treasure.

Munis, it is told that Ganga herself flowed in that asrama, and Vyasa performed his lustrous son's first ablution with her sacred water. It is told that Tumburu's Gandharvas sang in heaven and Apsaras danced, when the precious Suka was born. The Devas and Vidyadharas chanted the Vedas at his birth, and, in a few moments, that child was a beautiful youth, his bright hair down to his shoulders; and a brahmana's danda and a kamandalu floated down from the sky for him.

Vyasa performed his upanayana, and all the Vedas and Puranas revealed themselves to the wind-clad youth, and remained with him as they did with his father. Vyasa called his brilliant son Suka, for the bird that Ghritachi had turned into. Brihaspati became Suka's guru, and the boy lived in his father's house after he took a vow of brahmacharya. When Suka had mastered the Vedas, in their every nuance, he gave guru-dakshina to his preceptor and returned to his father Dwaipayana's asrama.

Vyasa sniffed his boy's head, and embraced him. Father and son lived together in joy. One day, the Muni Vyasa decided it was time for Suka to take a wife. He said, 'Child, it is time you marry and bless your father's life.'

Suka wondered at this. He sensed dark attachment in Vyasa's heart. 'Muni, you are the Rishi who divided the holy Veda. Why do you ask me to marry?'

'My son, you were born after a tapasya of a hundred years. You were born by Rudra's blessing. I will ask some king of the world to give you enough wealth to lead a comfortable householder's life. But you must fulfil my dreams for you.'

Suka said anxiously, 'Father, there is no joy in the world that is not tainted with sorrow, and most of all, in family life. The wise do not call this true joy. Muni, if I marry, my wife will certainly dominate me. How can such a man be happy? A man cast into prison can hope to be free some day. But a man bound with a wife and children shall be a prisoner all his life.

The human body is a despicable thing, full of excrement and urine, whether it be a man's or a woman's. The mating of such bodies can only be an act of hell. I wasn't born of a woman, Father, how can I hope to find happiness in a woman's arms? No such base pleasure can ever compare with the bliss of the atman, the ecstasy of dhyana.

When I first read the Vedas, it struck me that the karma-marga they advocate is a way of himsa, of violence. I asked my master Brihaspati to show me the true wisdom. But I found he was also entangled in the delusions of samsara, bound by many attachments and ignorance. So I came back to you, hoping you would show me the way to light, to moksha.

There is no real joy anywhere in the world of samsara, but only in the atman. Men who look to find satisfaction in this world are like worms that copulate in the midst of excrement. Great scholars of the Vedas and Shastras are the most deluded of all! None so stupid as these bookish hypocrites, who, for all their learning, are more attached to the world than anyone else.

The home is called griha because it binds a man so finally. It is the darkest prison. What joy can one hope to find in such a place? I am afraid, my father, to marry.'

Vyasa replied, 'The home is no prison, and the householder whose mind is unattached can always find moksha. Indeed, the householder supports the rest of the world; there is no asrama, no stage of life, as noble as the grihasta's. How else would the greatest of the great like Brahmamuni Vasishta marry? Moreover, every stage in life is transitory, and a man may leave any one of them whenever he chooses.

Suka, my son, set aside this needless anxiety, and marry. Father sons as bright as yourself, who will spread the dharma through the world. When old age comes to you, you can renounce your family and become a sannyasin. The wise who know insist that the young man who does not take a wife is maddened by his desires. Only when the desires begin to fade with satiety and age, should a man think of hermitage.

Just think of Viswamitra. He sat in tapasya for three thousand years, and glowed like fire. But he carried unfulfilled desires within him, and when he saw the Apsara Menaka, he fell prey to her charms. Desire is so powerful that not the greatest man can resist her in her season.

My father, the Rishi Parasara, could not help himself when he saw the fisherman's daughter, Matsyagandhi my mother. He lay with her on a dwipa, an island in the river, for which I am called Dwaipayana. Why, Brahma himself was ravished when he saw his daughter Sandhya within the golden lotus. When your time comes, you will also succumb. I beg you, Suka, marry a wife from a good family. This is the true path.'

But Suka was not convinced. 'Marriage is a leash. It binds a man like a dog, and he can never escape. To marry is to plunge oneself into a sea of anguish. Marriage is the root of greed for wealth, from which a man will harm even his own blood. Even Indra, Lord of the worlds, is not as happy as a beggar who owns nothing except his freedom. Who is happy then?

What can I say about this world's agonies? There is anguish at birth, anguish in sickness, and in death. But the cares of family life are worse than all these. Women, Father, are like leeches that suck a man's blood. But men are fools to let themselves be deceived by a woman's appearance. A wife is like a thief you keep in your own house. She steals your wealth with soft words, and your very strength as your seed.

Yet men become entangled with women as a lamb with a butcher. No woman ever gave a man any pleasure, only every misery one can imagine. So, Father, don't tell me to marry, but rather teach me the way to the bliss of the atman.'

When Vyasa heard what Suka said, tears streamed down his austere face and he began to tremble as if he ran a fever. His son said, 'Ah! Maya deludes even the great Vyasa, the divider of the Veda, the composer of the profound Puranas. You worshipped her for a hundred years, and she has you firmly in her coils now.

Why, Maya holds Brahma, Vishnu and Siva in her power, and the entire universe. But in truth, there is no father or son: all this is illusion. Tell me, Vyasa Muni, how I can find moksha for myself.'

His father murmured, 'You had best study the Bhagavata Purana. Once, at the end of the kalpa when the universe lay dissolved, Narayana lay upon the ocean of eternity as a small child. He lay on a floating pipal leaf, and wondered, who has created me a child? Who am I?

A voice spoke to him from the sky, "All that I see is myself, only I am eternal."

The child wondered who spoke. Narayana, the child, began to chant the mantra the voice had spoken. "All that I see is myself, only I am eternal." Suddenly, the Devi Bhagavati appeared before him as Mahalakshmi. Narayana was astonished to see the exquisite Goddess standing on the water at his side. He saw her shaktis around her—Rati, Bhuti, Buddhi, Mati, Kirti, Smriti, Dhriti, Sraddha, Medha, Svadha, Svaha, Kshudha, Nidra, Daya, Gati, Tushti, Pushti, Kshama, Lajja, Jrimba, Tandra and the rest.

All the Devis wielded divine weapons, and had dazzling forms. They wore wonderful raiment and were adorned with unearthly ornaments. Vishnu was perplexed. Where had the women appeared from, who was he that lay on the pipal leaf on an endless sea? Is the Devi my mother, wondered Vishnu, or some sorceress? Why has she appeared here now?

Lakshmi Devi smiled at the infant Vishnu, and said, "Have you forgotten me, my Lord? But there have been countless pralayas before this one, and countless times you have lain exactly thus on the leaf, and I appeared as I am now before you. You have forgotten.

When you and I are one, Brahma will be born again from the lotus that grows from your navel. He will sit in dhyana for a thousand lotus-counts of years, and then, begin to create. First, he will emit the three realms,

Swarga, Bhumi and Patala. Then he will make the pancha mahabhuta, the five elements, and the universe from them.

You, Narayana, will preserve the universe. Then Rudra will leap from Brahma's brow, howling. After a fervid tapasya, Rudra is given the Samhara Shakti, with which he destroys the universe when another kalpa ends. I have come so we can begin the new kalpa. Take me unto yourself to be your Vaishnavi Shakti."

Vishnu said, "Beautiful one, who spoke the mantra I heard earlier? I am obsessed with the need to know, even as a poor man is with wealth."

Lakshmi Devi answered him, "It was the Adi Shakti, the Cause of causes, that spoke to you. The Mother must be pleased with you that she taught you the mantra that is the seed of the Purana. Cherish that mantra in your heart, like your very life."

It was at this point that Brahma arrived in terror of Madhu and Kaitabha, and Narayana slew those demons. Then Vishnu began once more to murmur the mantra the Devi had given him. Brahma was astonished, and asked, "Whom do you worship, Padmanabha, you who are the highest God?"

Narayana replied, "The Adi Shakti, the Devi upon whom this sea rests, who is its source and mine as well. This mantra is the bija of the Devi Purana which will come to be as the kalpa unfolds."

As Brahma sat in his golden lotus, he, too, began to recite the Devi's bija-mantra. Later, the Pitama taught that mantra to his son Narada, who taught it to me. It is from that secret, fathomless mantra that I have wrought the mystic Devi Bhagavatam. Suka, my son, imbibe this Purana and darkness will leave your heart, and a sun of wisdom will rise over your life.'

Thus, Vyasa's son Suka Deva came to study the eighteen thousand slokas that are the Devi Bhagavatam. He committed the Purana to memory, why, he even taught it to some disciples like me; but Suka himself was not satisfied.

Vyasa Muni saw his son disconsolate, and asked him, 'My child, why are you so full of care, like a man who is deep in debt? It seems your heart gives you no peace, and nothing I say can change that. In the city of Mithila, lives a king who is also an enlightened Muni. His name is Janaka. Go to him, Suka. He will deliver you from your confusion, for he is a jivanmukta, a liberated one.'

Suka cried, 'Incredible! He is a king, Father, who rules a kingdom. How can Janaka be enlightened? It is like a barren woman having a son, or darkness and light existing in the same place. But I must go and see for myself. Give me leave.'

Suka prostrated himself at Vyasa's feet. With tears in his eyes, Vyasa Muni raised up his son and embraced him. He said, 'Go then, if you must. But swear you will return to me when you have seen Janaka, and then remain here with me always. Ah, my son, you are the light of my life. How will I live if I don't see your face?'

Thus, Suka Deva set out from his father's asrama for Mithila, the Rajarishi Janaka's city," says Suta Romaharshana in the Naimisa vana, where Saunaka's Munis hang on his every word as if his Purana was their very soul.

SEVEN

"WONDERING AT THE MARVELLOUS WORLD THAT UNFOLDED BEFORE HIM as he went along, Suka made for Mithila which was a long way from his father's asrama. It was another practical education for the brilliant Muni. He passed over white mountains and came down into jade plains. He forded great blue rivers, and crossed many climes and kingdoms. He encountered all manners of men on his way, from every occupation and every walk of life. He passed through deep jungles, where he saw only Rishis who lived in tapasya. Among these, he saw men that worshipped Siva and Shakti, Ganapathy and Surya, Indra and Vishnu, and many other Gods as well.

After a year Suka arrived at the gates of Janaka's Mithila. He saw how magnificent was the city before him and how contented its people seemed. But a huge guard stopped him at the gates, and asked rudely, 'Who are you, stranger? What brings you to Mithila?'

Suka was astonished and made no reply, but he smiled to himself. The guard said sternly, 'By king Janaka's command, no one may enter his city without declaring himself properly. You may not pass.'

Now Suka began to laugh softly. He said, 'I have crossed Meru and the Himalayas, countless jungles, rivers and kingdoms to come here. Now I see how deluded I was, and it was my own father who deceived me. The prarabdha karma of other births made me walk all this long way here, and now I cannot even see Janaka of Videha.

Mithila is no tirtha, nor does any Veda personified live here to warrant my having taken such pains to come to this city.'

As Suka spoke, the traveller's dust seemed to fall away from his body, and the guard saw that his skin shone like a God's. The man relented. He said, 'Brahmana, forgive me if I offended you. You may enter, for I see you are a blessed soul.'

'There is nothing to forgive; you merely did your duty. And how could you tell that I was not a thief or an enemy?'

Suka went in to Mithila and saw a bustling city full of people, all vigorously plying their various trades. He wandered the streets a while, in mild amusement at the frenetic activity around him, all born of attachment. He saw men bargaining, arguing, some even coming to blows; and none of them seemed to realise what they did, nor how far from contentment they were. After a time, Suka came to Janaka's palace.

Here also a guard barred his way. Suka shut his eyes, and stood still as stone before the swarthy fellow. The guard saw in alarm that the stranger's body began to shine with uncanny light, as Vyasa's son was plunged in dhyana. Bright as a sliver of sun shone Suka, and in a moment, a minister ran out of Janaka's palace and ushered the Muni past the awe-struck guard and into the king's harem.

The king's women received him and when they saw how illustrious he was, and how young and handsome, their hearts were all aflutter. But Suka was beyond the temptation of the women. They fed him with rare delicacies on which he nibbled politely, then showed him into an elegant apartment where a bed of swans-down was made up for him. They fluffed the pillows but lingered on in that chamber; for they were aroused and would serve him more intimately.

Smiling, the serene Suka washed his feet carefully. He slipped the ascetic's ring of kusa grass onto his finger, then sat on the floor at the foot of the bed in padmasana, shut his eyes, and was lost in dhyana again. The women saw how candescently his body began to blaze, and growing afraid, they left him alone.

Suka meditated on the supreme Brahman for three hours, then rose and slept for six more. He awoke in the last yaamas of the night, and sat in dhyana again for another three hours. Came the Brahma muhurta, the hour before sunrise, and Suka bathed in cold water, while the rest of Mithila slept, and yet again, he sat meditating.

Later that morning, Janaka came to meet Suka. The king came with his court priest, and with arghya and padya for the guest. When they had greeted each other formally, Janaka asked, 'Holy one, I see you are free of desire. Why has a Rishi like you sought me out?'

Suka replied, 'My father Vyasa said to me, "Child, take a wife, because grihasthasrama is the best stage of life. But I believe that marriage is bondage and want no part of it. Vyasa said that being married one could still be detached. He sent me to you, saying you ruled a kingdom and were yet a jivanmukta. My lord, I want moksha, and nothing but moksha will satisfy me.'

Janaka said, 'Moksha is hard to attain. A man must first experience the four stages of life: of a student, a householder, a renunciate, and, finally, an ascetic, before he comes to freedom. No man who has not experienced grihastha and vanaprastha can become a sannyasin.'

Suka said, 'But if a man has vairagya, and is detached even before he lives through grihasta and vanaprastha, can't he become a sannyasin straightaway?'

Janaka said gravely, 'You are my guru's son and I tell you the truth. If a man enters sannyasa with his desires unfulfilled they are liable to waylay him without warning. He who makes his bed on a cliff can fall to his death, but the man who sleeps on flat ground is in no such danger. Desire is powerful; a man never relinquishes his cravings. The only way to free oneself of desire is the slow and gradual path prescribed in the Veda.'

The king smiled, and Suka saw how full of grace he was. Janaka said softly, 'Sinless one, look at me. I live in the world in the thick of every activity, yet nothing binds my spirit and I am a free man. Bright youth, this world of illusions cannot deceive the soul. When the heart is pure and calm, then all the world is untainted and tranquil. The enemy is not outside; every demon lives in one's own heart.

The mind binds a man, not his circumstances. The atman is beyond everything the mind perceives; the atman can never be bound. When the mind sees the atman everywhere, then the mind becomes free. The wise man experiences the four asramas of life so that he can cleanse his mind until it grows still and he sees the truth that is immanent. But how will the mind recognise the truth when it is found, unless it has first known the world of illusion and despair?

Once the mind discovers the soul, it comes to enlightenment, from which there is no return. An illumined man is freed forever.'

But Suka argued, 'But, my lord, the dharma of the Veda is at times the way of himsa, of violence. The Veda extols wine and meat, even gambling. And how can any man who becomes attached to the pleasure of coition, ever hope to be free?'

'The Veda advocates these only as sacrifices, to purify the mind. It does not say that a man should become dependent on them. He should act, while being free from desire for the fruit of his actions. The Veda only says that the himsa committed by a man when he worships God is no himsa, and no sin accrues from it. What I am saying is not a matter for debate, Brahmana. When a man is a jivanmukta nothing he does binds him, because all that he does is worship; and he sees no death, but only the eternal Soul everywhere and in all things.'

Suka said doubtfully, 'My lord, the mere mention of a lamp in a dark room does not dispel its darkness. A householder lives in the thick of the deluded and violent night of samsara. How can he be free?

When you are a king, O Janaka, and enjoy the wealth and power of a kingdom, how can you be a jivanmukta? Don't you think of this great Mithila as being your own? Don't you make a difference between pleasure and pain, the garland of flowers and a serpent? But the true mukta is beyond every attachment. I fear it is a royal vanity that makes you think of yourself as being a mukta. Why, even ascetic Munis, who subsist on roots and fruits of the earth, fall prey to this world's maya.'

Janaka smiled tolerantly at the young man. He said, 'You speak cleverly, Suka. But the truth is that you are full of doubt and anxiety, while I am not. I have no doubt that I am free, and not your cleverest arguments can change that. Remember that it is you who have journeyed all the way here to seek the peace of your heart. I, Suka, am already at peace, and I stay here in my kingdom with no desire.

Do you think that if you live in the heart of a forest, you will be free of the doubts that torment you? Why, the jungle is as full of bondage as my Mithila. The vana is made of the five elements as much as is the city. How will you be any freer in the vana than anywhere else? Freedom is of the spirit, and the spirit can be free anywhere, or bound anywhere. Moksha is within you. Indeed, what you imagine to be a less conducive circumstance to attain moksha may well be the very one that sets you free.'

Perhaps because the time had come, Suka suddenly felt his doubts melt away from him. Janaka had said nothing to him that Guru Brihaspati and Vyasa had not. Yet the manner in which the lord of Mithila argued, and, most of all, his cheerful detachment, struck a deep chord in Suka Deva. Vyasa's son felt like a man who had set down a great burden that he was hardly aware he had been carrying. He smiled radiantly at Janaka, and said with feeling, 'Sadhu! Sadhu!'

Suka prostrated himself before the king, took the dust from his feet, and walked out of Mithila feeling happier than he had for a long time. Vyasa ran out of his asrama in delight when he saw his son had returned. He clasped Suka in his arms and covered his face with kisses. Suka stayed with his father, and Vyasa saw that a profound transformation had come over his child. The youth was at peace now, and quietly pursued his study of the dharma Shastras. He did not argue with his father any more, but seemed content to learn from him with a tranquil spirit. And whenever Suka sat in dhyana, he saw Janaka's serene, smiling face before him, and this filled him with untold peace.

After some weeks, Vyasa cautiously broached the subject of marriage to his son. Suka smiled and said, 'As you wish, Father. If it will make you happy, I am ready to enter grihasthasrama.'

Vyasa was overjoyed. Suka was married to a chaste girl called Pivari, who was also a Rishi's daughter. She was a devoted wife and bore him four sons, Krishna, Gauraprabha, Bhuri and Devasruta, and a daughter called Kirti. Vyasa watched his son's family in quiet delight, and Suka was so happy that if he ever looked back to the time when he had stubbornly refused to marry, he would laugh to himself that he had been so afraid.

In time, Suka's daughter Kirti was married to king Vibhraja's son Anuha. Their son was Brahmadatta, who became lord of the earth. Narada taught Anuha the mayabija, and that king was enlightened and left his kingdom to become a hermit.

As for Suka, he never gave up his quest for moksha. Indeed, as Janaka had hinted to him, being a husband, father and grandfather only made him seek the truth more fervently than ever. In time, Suka climbed Mount Kailasa, alone, and sat in profound meditation. In due course he acquired occult siddhis. Bright as a star, that Muni rose bodily from Kailasa, cleaving the crown of that most sacred mountain. He was so radiant that it was as if another sun had appeared in the sky. In a moment blessed Suka vanished entirely, for he had become one with the infinite, formless Brahman. The seeker had become all times and places, and all things. He was free.

But Vyasa was devastated at losing his son. He roamed the earth like a mad man, calling out Suka's name. At last, he came to Kailasa, and saw its cloven peak. His eyes streaming tears that froze on his hollow cheeks, Vyasa cried in anguish, 'Suka! Why have you abandoned me?'

An echoing voice spoke then, out of all the elements, earth and air, ice, rock, sun and tree, saying, 'Father, you and I are one. Why do you weep for me?'

And this echo can be heard even today on Kailasa's summit. But Vyasa, the father, was not consoled. He sank down on his knees and sobbed, 'Oh, my son! My son!'

It is told that kindly Siva appeared then before the distrait Vyasa. The Lord said, 'Vyasa, your son has attained the highest truth. You must not grieve for him. Why, now you are known in the world as Suka's father.'

But Vyasa was inconsolable. He wept ceaselessly, calling his son's name over and over again. Merciful Siva then showed Vyasa a mysterious shadow-form of Suka's, glowing like a piece of the moon. Siva said the Muni could see this bright shade whenever he wanted. Somewhat mollified, Vyasa went back sadly to his asrama. For dharma called him there as well."

Saunaka asks, "What dharma was it that called Dwaipayana back to his asrama?"

Suta says, "Vyasa had other disciples, whose tutelage was not complete. Asita, Devala, Vaisampayana, Jaimini, Sumantu and the rest waited for him. When they had learned all that he had to teach them, they went down into the world to spread the Sanatana dharma among men.

When Vyasa Muni was alone again, the pang in his heart ravaged him once more. Everywhere he looked, he saw his son's face and he knew he must leave this asrama or lose his mind. One day, Dwaipayana remembered his mother Satyavati, who had given birth to him on an island in the river; perhaps she could comfort him in his grief. Vyasa wended his long way down from the sacred mountain and arrived on the plains of Bharatavarsha. He came to the banks of a midnight-blue river, to the very place on the Yamuna where he had been born.

There he saw his grandfather, the fisherman's, hut deserted. He saw some Rishis and asked them where his mother Satyavati was. They told him that she had been given in marriage to the great Kuru king, Santanu of Hastinapura. Vyasa felt destiny stir in his heart, as if he had some momentous thing to accomplish in the world of men. He made his way again to his old asrama on the banks of the Saraswati and began living there, waiting for a sign of what he must do next.

He spent some months by the golden river, and Suka's memory tormented him less jaggedly on it banks. One day, as he sat in dhyana, he clearly heard his mother's voice calling him urgently with the mantra he had given her when he was born. It was the first time she had called him since the day she bore him on the island, and he went eagerly to Hastinapura where he would become embroiled in a fate he could never have imagined.

His mother was calling him to become a father again, to sire the heirs of the Kuru kingdom on her widowed daughters-in-law, Ambika and Ambalika, because the great Bheeshma would not break his solemn vow of celibacy. And, of course, the sons Vyasa fathered on those young queens were the blind Dhritarashtra, and the pale Pandu; and in the dark, on Ambika's maid, he sired the wise Vidura." says Suta Romaharshana in the Naimisa vana.

EIGHT

ONE OF SAUNAKA'S MUNIS ASKS, "TELL US ABOUT VYASA'S MOTHER Satyavati, and how Dwaipayana was born to her."

Suta begins, "I worship the Devi Bhagavati, the Mother of the universe, before I relate this tale.

Once, there was a king of Chedi called Uparichara. He was a devout sovereign, and Lord Indra of the Devas gave him a marvellous vimana. This crystal ship flew anywhere at the king's thought, and that lord of the earth became known as Uparichara Vasu, for he ranged the sky in his magic vimana.

Uparichara had a ravishing wife called Girika, and she bore him five fine princes. One morning, when she knew it was her fertile time, queen Girika came to her husband and asked him to make love, because she wanted another son. But he had sworn to go out to the forest that day, to hunt meat for a yagna he was to perform for his ancestors in heaven. Girika begged him to stay, but the king felt the cause of his dead fathers was more pressing.

Uparichara set out for the vana, with his bow in his hand and the image of his wife in his heart. She had come to him that morning wearing a transparent robe, and nothing beneath it. The king had not been with her for ten days, and he did not realise how much she had aroused him. When he had missed two fine stags with his arrows, Uparichara came to a lotus-laden pool in the depths of the forest, and with his queen's enticing form before his mind's eye, ejaculated onto a pipal leaf.

The king was anxious that his royal seed should not be wasted. He spoke a potent mantra over the folded leaf, to preserve his retas, and called his hunting falcon down from the air. He gave the falcon his seed, and said, 'Fly, friend, take this to my queen as swiftly as you can.'

As the falcon sped through the sky towards Chedi, a fishing eagle perched in a tree on the banks of the Yamuna saw him. The eagle mistook the pipal leaf for a shred of flesh and flew at the falcon. The birds fought briefly in the sky, and the leaf fell out of the falcon's beak and down into the river.

Now, it happened that a year ago the Apsara Adrika had flown down from heaven to swim in the Yamuna. It was the twilight hour, and when she had been in the water for a while, she saw a Muni at his sandhya vandana at the river's edge. The austere one sat motionless, his eyes shut fast. Adrika saw how radiant he was, and she wanted him.

She swam under water close to where the Rishi sat, and playfully seized his ankles to pull him into the river. Adrika thought that when he saw how beautiful she was he would gladly make love to her in the Yamuna. She could not have been more mistaken. The Muni's eyes flew open, and he cursed Adrika, 'You dare disturb my dhyana? Be a fish from now!'

At once, the Apsara had golden scales and a fish's form. The Muni strode away from the river without saying when the curse would end. Neither he nor she realised that fate had a design to fulfil. So Adrika stayed in the river, swimming here and there, and devouring other fish when she felt hungry. Soon she forgot that she was an Apsara, and thought of herself as just a fish.

When the fishing eagle set on Uparichara's falcon, the pipal leaf with the king's seed plunged down into the midnight-blue water of the Yamuna. Adrika saw the leaf strike the water's surface, and the king's seed being washed off. As it sank, with a flick of her tail she darted at that shimmering seed and swallowed it. The Apsara became pregnant by the king's retas.

In ten months, she was so big she could hardly swim, and one day, she was snared by a fisherman in his net. He was delighted by her size, as she lay gasping for breath on the sand. The fisherman cut that great golden fish open with a stone knife. There was a flash of light and he saw the spirit-form of a heavenly nymph rise out of the dead fish and fly up into the sky.

The man was blinded for a moment, but when he looked again into the fish's belly, his mouth fell open. Two brilliant human infants, a boy and a girl, lay there gazing back at him. The next day that fisherman arrived in the palace of the king of that land, and told Uparichara Vasu how he had discovered the marvellous children. The fisherman begged to be allowed to keep one of them.

The king guessed how those twins had been conceived, and his queen was still anxious to have another son. Uparichara Vasu kept the little boy, and let the fisherman take the girl to raise. That prince born from a fish's body was named Matsyaraja, and in his time, he would rule his father's kingdom as ably as Uparichara had. The fisherman raised the little girl as his own, and a fortune-teller who read the lines on her palm said that she would one day be the queen of a great kingdom. The fisherman lived with that prophecy clasped to his heart, and would not give his daughter to any man who came asking for the dark girl's hand. That child's body always smelled of fish, and her father called her Matsyagandhi," tells Suka.

NINE

SAUNAKA URGES SUTA ROMAHARSHANA, "MASTER, TELL US HOW YOUR guru Vyasa was born."

Suta says, "Some years later the celibate Parasara, immortal Muni on his pilgrimage, arrived on the banks of the Yamuna at Matsyagandhi's father's hut. It was a crisp winter morning, the sun shone pale and ethereal and the river sparkled as if with a million jewels. The fisherman in his hut sat at his morning meal of last night's fish and rice, when the austere figure loomed suddenly in his doorway.

'Take me across the river quickly, I am in a hurry!' said Parasara ungraciously.

It was not the first time the profound one had passed this way and the fisherman recognised him. But he thought that it was not proper for him to abandon his meal, which was part of God's grace. So he called out to his daughter.

'Matsyagandhi, take our Muni Parasara across the river.'

She appeared at the corner of the hut, sixteen, and comely as a bit of winter sun. Budding breasts strained against her green blouse. Eyes like small pools set wide in her lean, dark face regarded the Muni frankly. When he saw her, something stirred deep within the great Parasara. Without a word, Matsyagandhi led the radiant one to the wooden boat moored at the riverbank.

As the Rishi followed the girl the smell of her body invaded him, the raw smell of fish with which she was born. Instead of being repulsed, Parasara lost his heart to her. He, who had felt no twinge of desire in the company of fawning Apsaras in Devaloka, was overcome by the earthy whiff of the fishergirl.

When she helped him into the boat, he retained her hand in his longer than he should have. She looked sharply into his face, quietly freed her hand, and cast off.

But he would not be so easily denied. As they moved out, Parasara reached for her hand again and clasped it on the oar. She smiled at him, huge eyes twinkling. She stopped rowing, though they were now in midstream and drifting. But she did not withdraw her hand.

She rather liked the gentle old man. She was attracted by his elegant presence, and his dignity, which presently suffered somewhat for his excitement. His hand trembled on hers. He leant forward awkwardly to try to kiss her. She smiled, dazzling him, and she stroked his gnarled hand without inhibition.

In her husky voice, which inflamed him even more, she said, 'Holy one, why do you want to do this? You are a high brahmana descended from Brahma, and I am the daughter of a nishada; this isn't proper between us."

Then she trembled, thinking—suppose he cursed her! At that moment, her father hailed them faintly from the bank. He stood washing his hands outside the hut and wanted to know why they had stopped. Parasara released the girl's hand. She rowed again, while the Rishi kept watch on the fisherman, who stood staring after them, his eyes shaded. Again, Parasara took Matsyagandhi's dark, small hand.

She giggled, 'Brahmana, aren't you repelled by my smell, for which I am called Matsyagandhi? Holy one, you know it is said in the Vedas that one shouldn't have sexual intercourse during the day. And besides, my father can see us."

For, when Parasara was near enough to kiss her, she was reminded sharply of his great age, and both aroused and dismayed by it. But he waved a wiry arm above his head in an occult mudra. At once, they were shrouded in a dense mist, and the fisherman could not see them any more.

Darkness surrounded the boat on the river.

'Is that night enough?' said Parasara. Little Matsyagandhi gasped. She trembled, now as much with desire as awe. Yet, being a virgin and afraid of this unlikeliest suitor, she said, 'Yogin, I know the seed of a man of power like you never fails. You will enjoy me and go your way. But I will become pregnant. What will my fate be? My virginity will be ruined; I will be the laughing stock of the world. And my father, oh, whatever will I tell him?'

He cried hoarsely, 'Give me your love freely and you will be famed forever among the Rishis and the Devas! You will be known as Satyavati in heaven. Look."

Again a wizardly mudra from him, and she saw her body aglow with a new beauty. Her limbs were lustrous, her features made finer by his power, and the smell of her was transformed so that now she smelt of wild jasmine, lotus, and other subtler fragrances, not of this world. In a moment, they spread from her for a yojana. The original scent of her, fishy musk, had not vanished, but became a sublimely erotic perfume: which made his ardour fiercer!

Still she hesitated. She restrained his wandering, lustful hand, so he cried, 'Say whatever you want and it shall be yours. Ah, quickly, you are driving me mad!'

After a moment's reflection, she said, 'If neither my father nor any person on earth comes to know of this, if my virginity is not ruined, if the son born of our love is a magician like you, and if I always smell as I do now, then take me, holy one, and gladly.'

Parasara of fame in the three worlds laughed like rolling thunder. He said, 'You will have a son more famous than I. For I sense that it is God's will that I, Parasara, have been smitten by Kama's lust today. Be assured all your conditions will be fulfilled. And more, your son shall be the greatest poet the world has seen."

He took her in his arms in that boat rocking softly on the Yamuna, while all around them his magical mist held up its opaque curtain. Impatient for him now that her fears had been allayed, she rowed to an island in the stream and moored there. And they lay together, unlikeliest lovers, heating the pale sands dry.

At last, after he drank deeply of her youth, and she of his age, Parasara rose away from her to bathe in the Yamuna. Then, with a last kiss on top of her head, he walked upon the water and out of her life.

And in that mystic dimension, no sooner had she conceived than she was in labour.

Her delivery was miraculous, and she felt no pain. Her boy, bright as a star, handsome as Kama Deva, was born a full-grown and evolved Muni, with a kamandalu in one hand, a smooth staff in the other, and his matted, tawny hair shining in an unearthly halo. That newborn and exceptional Rishi said calmly to his mother, 'We must go our separate ways. But whenever you want to see me, only think of me and I will appear before you.' And he walked away from her.

Since he was born on the dwipa in the Yamuna, the marvellous one was called Dwaipayana. But later, he was to divide the holy Veda in four, and compose the sacred Puranas from ancient revelations. He was to become renowned as Veda Vyasa, or just Vyasa.

Vyasa taught me this ancient lore. It is from him I learnt about the Devi Bhagavati, the highest Goddess," says the Suta.

TEN

SAUNAKA ASKS ROMAHARSHANA, "MOST ERUDITE SUTA, WHEN WAS THE Devi Bhagavatam first narrated in this world of men?"

The Suta says, "It was thirty-six years after the Mahabharata yuddha, on the tenth day of which this dark kali yuga fell on the earth. Vyasa Muni's grandson, the Pandava emperor Yudhishtira, and his brothers heard that their Incarnate cousin Krishna had left the world. The Pandavas crowned Arjuna's grandson Parikshita in Hastinapura, and then they too left this world.

For sixty years, Parikshita ruled wisely; until, one fateful day, he went hunting in the forest. After a long chase, he finally shot a fine sambur stag with an arrow. But the deer bolted into the dense vana, and Parikshita chased him a long way in vain. At last, tired and thirsty, he saw a Rishi's asrama in the heart of the jungle.

Parikshita walked into the hermitage and saw a Muni lost in meditation, as he sat on a deerskin spread on the ground. The exhausted kshatriya asked, 'Can I have some water to drink?'

The Rishi had taken a vow of mowna, and did not say a word or even open his eyes. The king asked again, 'Muni, can you give me some water to drink?'

Still the ascetic made no sound or movement. Parikshita saw a dead serpent lying nearby. In anger he picked it up with his bow, draped it around the silent Rishi's shoulders, and stalked out of the asrama. He went home to Hastinapura and thought nothing more about it.

But that peaceful Rishi had a son called Sringi, who was a quick-tempered young hermit. Some friends told Sringi that someone had draped a dead snake round his father's neck as he sat in samadhi. Sringi's eyes blazed. Trembling with rage, he took up holy water in his palms, and breathed a curse, 'Let the man who did this vile thing be bitten by the serpent Takshaka and die a week from today!'

Another Muni who heard him knew by sacred intuition that Sringi had cursed Parikshita. He went to the Kuru king the same day, and told him what had happened. Parikshita was dismayed, but he was determined not to yield unresisting to Sringi's curse. He ordered a lofty tower, seven storeys tall, to be erected overnight.

Parikshita stationed his finest warriors to guard the entrances to the tower. He also gathered mystics around him, men who knew the occult powers of gemstones, mantras, and the healing herbs. And he ensconced himself on the seventh storey of that tower. He then sent a Muni called Gaurmukha to Sringi to beg him to withdraw the curse.

Day and night, the brahmanas around Parikshita chanted powerful mantras to keep the serpent-king Takshaka away. Great war-elephants encircled that tower, so no one could get within a thousand yards of it. Why, they said that not even the air could find its way into Parikshita's tower.

The king sat within, counting the days, the very moments. With great composure, he conducted the affairs of state from his tower. It so happened, that at this time, a brahmana called Kashyapa heard about the curse. This Kashyapa had many powerful siddhis and he decided that if he saved Parikshita's life the Kuru king would reward him well. Kashyapa set out for Hastinapura.

It was the sixth day of the week that Parikshita had been given to live. Takshaka himself assumed the guise of an old brahmana, and accosted Kashyapa on the road to Hastinapura. The serpent said, 'Whence in such haste, Brahmana? You will tire yourself out if you run like this.'

Kashyapa replied, 'Parikshita of Hastinapura has been cursed. Takshaka will sting him tomorrow, and he will die. But I know the mantra that can quell even Takshaka's venom, and I mean to save the king's life.'

Takshaka gave a death-rattling laugh. His eyes flashed green, and the shadow of an immense hood glimmered over the elderly brahmana's face. The naga hissed, 'Friend, Brahmana, I am Takshaka. Do you think you can save Parikshita if I sting him?'

Kashyapa was proud of his powers, and said smugly, 'Indeed I shall. There is no venom in creation that I cannot cure with my mantra.'

'Prove it to me, Brahmana. I will sting this banyan tree, let me see you make it live again.'

'I will, easily!' said Kashyapa.

In a trice Takshaka became an awesome serpent, and darting at the banyan tree he fastened fangs like sharpened pillars in its bark. In less time than it takes to tell, the tree subsided with a sigh, burnt to ashes by Takshaka's venom. Kashyapa gathered those ashes and, setting them before him, said, 'Watch me now, O greatest among serpents.'

He drew a palmful of water from the nearby stream, and murmured his mantra of power over it. Then he sprinkled that water over the mound of ashes. There was a flash of light and, lo, the banyan tree stood green and alive as before, reaching for the sun with its branches.

Takshaka was shaken. He said to Kashyapa, 'Most magnificent of Munis, tell me why you mean to save Parikshita's life.'

'If I give him back his life, Parikshita will reward me.'

Takshaka promised, 'I will give you any wealth you want, if you promise not to go to Hastinapura.'

Kashyapa fell to thinking, 'If I accept the serpent's offer the king will die and I will gain no punyam from saving his life. Moreover, my fame shall not be known in the world. If I save Parikshita, all his people will rejoice. That is the nobler way.'

But as he stood deliberating, Kashyapa had a divine insight. He knew beyond doubt that Parikshita's time to die had come, and Takshaka was only the instrument of destiny. That brahmana accepted the naga's offer and went home with the gold that Takshaka gave him.

When Takshaka arrived in Hastinapura on the seventh day, he saw the tower of seven storeys the king had built for himself, and heard that Parikshita was on the seventh level, surrounded by magical herbs and protected by powerful brahmanas, chanting mantras. Moreover, war-elephants and legions of the finest soldiers guarded that lofty sanctuary.

The serpent wondered how he would reach the king he must kill. But he had no doubt he would, for he knew Brahma had ordained that Parikshita would die today, and nothing could save him. Takshaka had not come alone to Hastinapura, but with a complement of his followers. Now his serpents turned themselves into a group of brahmanas, wearing the sacred thread and with ashes smeared on their lofty brows. They had ostensibly brought holy roots and fruit for Parikshita. Takshaka himself became a tiny, worm-sized serpent and hid in one of the fruits.

The brahmanas came to the guards of the tower and were stopped by the hefty fellows. The false Munis said, 'We have come to save the king from Takshaka. We will chant the recondite Atharva, so the serpent will not dare come near. We have often come to the city of the sons of Bharata, but armed guards have never barred our way before.'

The sentinels said, 'Come tomorrow, Munis, and you shall have free access to the king. Today, no one may go up.'

The brahmanas said, 'Then take these roots and fruits to Parikshita, and give him our blessing.'

They gave the salver on which they had brought the fruit and roots to the guards, and went away. The guards brought the salver to the seventh storey of the tower, and Parikshita ordered the fruit and roots to be given to his ministers who sat with him on the vigil.

The king selected just one bright fruit for himself. But as he was about to bite into it, he saw the strangest copper-coloured, black-eyed worm crawl out of its flesh. Before he could fling the fruit out of the window, the worm became ten-hooded Takshaka and, quick as a streak of lightning, held Parikshita fast.

Seeing Takshaka, the ministers fled down the tower, some even leapt off the seventh level in fright. But Parikshita lay helpless in the monstrous serpent's coils. Slowly Takshaka fastened fangs themselves like towers into the Kuru king's throat, and killed him in a moment," says Suta serenely in the Naimisa vana.

One of Saunaka's Munis asks, "And the Devi's Purana, when was than told?"

"When Parikshita died, his ministers took his venom-blackened body to the banks of the Ganga and burned it. But no mantras were chanted because of the manner in which he had died. Later, an effigy of Parikshita was made of kusa grass, and this was cremated on a pyre of sandalwood, and Vedic hymns were intoned, and food, clothing, cows and gold were given as alms to brahmanas. Shock lay over the ancient city of Hastinapura. Parikshita's son was still a stripling when his father died, but fortunately, there were able ministers in the land who administered the kingdom until the prince Janamejaya came of age. When he was eleven his family priest taught him the blessed Gayatri mantra, the seed of all wisdom. Later, the

Acharya Kripa taught him the use of weapons. There were other wise Munis who taught him the Vedas and dharma Shastras, and Janamejaya grew into a sovereign well nigh as accomplished and just as his granduncle Yudhishtira, who was Dharma Deva's own son.

A few years later, the king of Kasi gave his daughter Vapustama to Janamejaya to be his queen, as had been the custom between the two noble houses since time immemorial. The young couple lost themselves in tender love, while ministers still ruled the kingdom.

It happened that a Rishi called Uttanka wanted to be rid of Takshaka, who infested the forest where he had his asrama, and was the bane of his life. Uttanka arrived in Hastinapura and Janamejaya received him cordially. When they sat together in the audience chamber, the Rishi suddenly said, 'My lord, have you so lost yourself in pleasure that you have forgotten to take revenge on your father's killer? Do you mean to remain a child all your life?'

The startled Janamejaya wanted to know what he meant. Uttanka said, 'You don't even know who your enemy is, and the great wrong done to the royal house of Kuru, the wrong that has yet to be redressed. Janamejaya, it was the snake Takshaka who killed your father, didn't you know?'

Janamejaya had been just a child at the time, and no one had told him. Now he turned to his ministers, who said, 'It is true, lord, your father died of snakebite, and the serpent that bit him was Takshaka.'

The young man cried, 'But I thought my father had died of a brahmana's curse. What does Takshaka have to do with it?'

Uttanka said fervently, 'King of kings, it was Takshaka who fulfilled the brahmana's curse; it was he who burned your father high in the air. Haven't you heard that Parikshita's body was so charred with venom that the proper rituals could not be performed for him? Surely, your father's spirit cannot be free but wanders between heaven and earth in torment.'

Janamejaya had tears in his eyes, as he asked, 'Blessed Uttanka, how can I set my father's spirit free? I will do anything so that Parikshita finds peace. Ah, I have lived in such delusion, but I will make amends. Muni, only tell me what I must do.'

Uttanka replied, 'You must perform a sarpa yagna, and let all the serpents of the earth be your sacrificial beasts. Let Takshaka himself be offered in your yagna fire, and your father's spirit will find peace.'

Janamejaya ordered a yagnashala erected on the banks of the Ganga, a hall of a hundred pillars. The agnikunda, the fire-pit at the heart of that yagnashala was as large as the crater of a volcano. When the preparations were complete, the king and his brahmanas arrived there, and the sacred fire was lit while sonorous mantras were being chanted. Uttanka was, of course, the chief priest. Oblations of sanctified butter and ghee were poured on to the lofty blaze, and the powerful incantations swelled loudly from a thousand brahmanas' throats.

Far away, Takshaka felt the potent mantras snaking out to seize him in subtle coils. He fled in terror to Indra, and cried, 'Lord of Devas, save my life!'

Indra saw how the great naga trembled. The Deva made Takshaka sit on his own throne, and said gently, 'Have no fear.'

But Uttanka's mantras reached inexorably into Amravati, where Indra rules, and sought to seize Takshaka and draw him down into Janamejaya's sacrificial fire. Takshaka fled to the only person left who might save his life. The serpent flew to the feet of Astika, the son of the Muni Jaratkaru.

The youth Astika arrived at Janamejaya's sarpa yagna, and eulogised the Kuru king in exquisite verse. Moved both by the praise and that boy's beauty, Janamejaya said, 'Tell me what you have come for and it shall be yours, whatever it is you want, if it is in my power you shall have it.'

Astika stood radiant before the king and said, 'Then, stop this yagna.'

Janamejaya could hardly believe his ears. But Astika said again, 'What I want is that you stop this sarpa yagna!'

Janamejaya had no choice but to call off the sacrifice, and he sat stricken in the yagnashala of a hundred pillars that he had erected on the banks of the Ganga. It was there, to console that monarch who grieved for his father's unappeased spirit, that Vyasa's disciple Vaisampayana related the profound Mahabharata in full. Still Janamejaya was disconsolate, and turned for solace to Vyasa himself, who was present there.

The young kshatriya moaned, 'Alas, that my father died without honour, died of snakebite, seven storeys in the air! Ah, Vyasa Muni, tell me how will Parikshita's soul rise into heaven, and how my own distraught spirit can find some peace,'" Romaharshana pauses his tale to moisten his lips with some water the Munis have set before him.

ELEVEN

THE SUTA TAKES UP HIS PURANA AGAIN, "KING JANAMEJAYA SAID TO VYASA Muni, 'Who is this boy Astika, who appeared so suddenly and thwarted my yagna? Why did he save Takshaka's life?'

Dwaipayana replied, 'Once there was a Rishi called Jaratkaru, who was a celibate and a man of peace. As he roamed the forest, one day, he saw in a secret cave the spirits of his ancestors. They said to him, "Child, you must marry, and have a son. Only then will we your fathers find heaven for ourselves."

Jaratkaru replied, "If I find a young woman without searching high and low for her, and if she is implicitly obedient to me in all things, always, I will marry her."

And he went on an extensive tirtha yatra, to every sacred ford in the land. Some time before this, it happened that Kashyapa Muni's two wives, Kadru and Vinata, between whom there was always sharp envy, had a wager between them. Kadru saw Surya Deva's blazing steed in the sky, and thought of a base plan to deceive Vinata. She went to her before the sun rose the next day, and said, "Do you know what colour the Sun's horse is?"

Vinata said, "Of course, who doesn't know the Sun God's horse is white?"

But Kadru said, "Are you certain?"

And Vinata was. Kadru said, "If the Sun's horse is black, will you be my slave for ever?"

"And if the creature is white, will you be mine?"

"Agreed!" said Kadru, and Vinata thought she could not lose this wager; who didn't know that the Sun's horse was a pristine white, just like the Sun's light? But Kadru called her sons, the great serpents, and said to them,

"Children, cover the Sun's chariot-horse with your bodies so it seems black tomorrow."

Some of the snakes demurred and their mother cursed them, "May you fall into Janamejaya's fire!"

The others did as Kadru asked; they entwined themselves around the Sun's white horse and that beast seemed night-black when Kadru and Vinata saw it. Vinata ran to a lonely place and began to sob heartbrokenly. Her son Garuda saw her with eagle's eyes, and flew down to comfort his mother.

Garuda said to Vinata, "Mother, why are you crying? Tell me what ails you."

Vinata sobbed, "Ah, I have become Kadru's slave!"

Garuda went to Kadru and offered to show her and her sons the world. He took them on his back and flew across the awesome sea. On the other side, the man-bodied, eagle-headed Garuda asked Kadru, "Is there any way in which my mother can escape being your slave?"

Thinking for a moment, Kadru replied, "Fetch some amrita from heaven for my serpent children to drink and your mother shall be a free woman."

Garuda flashed into Devaloka like a golden arrow and, beating Indra and his Devas back fiercely, made off with the chalice of amrita. He brought that chalice to Kadru, who cried, "Vinata is no more my slave!"

Her serpent sons went to purify themselves with a bath before they drank the nectar and Indra spirited the precious chalice away. When the snakes came back clean, ready to quaff the amrita and become immortal, they found the nectar gone. In despair they began to lick the sword-sharp kusa grass on which they had left the chalice. Which is why they and their children after them have forked tongues, for the blades of grass divided them.

The serpents whom their mother cursed to die in Janamejaya's yagna, when they refused to cover the Sun's horse to make it seem black, flew to Brahma for refuge. Among them was the majestic naga Vasuki, whom the Devas and Asuras had once coiled around golden Mandara when they churned the ocean of milk.

When he heard why they had come, Brahma said, "Vasuki has a sister called Jaratkaru. Let her be given in marriage to the Rishi of the same name, and they will have a son who will save you all from Janamejaya's sarpa yagna."

Thus, Vasuki and his serpents went to the Muni Jaratkaru and begged him to take their sister for his wife. The Rishi said, "I will. But let her be warned that if she disobeys me in the least thing, I will leave her."

Thus, the Muni Jaratkaru married the comely nagin Jaratkaru, and they lived happily in the vana in a white hut made of leaves and branches. Of course, the nagin assumed an enticing human form, and Jaratkaru was well satisfied with her. She came to love her husband, and never in the least thing did she cross him.

One afternoon, Jaratkaru felt drowsy, and decided to fall asleep. He said to his wife, "I am going to sleep now, don't wake me for anything."

She busied herself with the housework. The sun sank in the sky, and shadows lengthened. The Muni Jaratkaru slept on. His wife grew anxious that night was falling, and it was time for the twilight sandhya. She was afraid that darkness would set in without her husband having lit the evening lamps of worship. But her husband had said he must not be disturbed for anything, and she knew he had sworn to abandon her if she ever disobeyed him. Yet, if the sandhya worship were not observed, dharma itself would be breached.

Trembling, Jaratkaru the nagin shook her husband awake. The Muni opened his eyes, and roared, "Dare you disobey me! I told you I was not to be awakened for anything. Leave my house this instant, haughty woman, go back to your brother!"

Tears in her eyes, his wife whispered, "What of the cause for which my brother gave me to you?"

Her husband said, "That is already within your womb," and turned away from her forever.

The nagin Jaratkaru went home to her brother Vasuki, and told him the Rishi had turned her out, and what he had said at last. Vasuki was certain, "A Muni like him will never lie," and kept his sister with him. In time she gave birth, O King, to the brilliant Astika, who came to your sarpa yagna and saved the lives of Takshaka and his race,' said Vyasa to Janamejaya.

But the Kuru king was still distraught. 'My father's spirit has no peace, and never shall, for my sarpa yagna has been abandoned.'

Vyasa said, 'Build a temple to the Devi, and worship her with the Amba yagna. No family that does not worship the Devi has any peace, and those that do are given their hearts' every desire, and moksha thereafter.'

Janamejaya said, 'Blessed Vyasa, tell me more about the Devi. I would hear her sacred Purana from your lips.'

And then my guru Vyasa told that king the Devi Bhagavatam, to bring some repose to his anguished heart," says Suta.

TWELVE

SUTA SAYS, "JANAMEJAYA ASKED MY MASTER DWAIPAYANA, 'WHO IS THE Amba you ask me to worship? Where was she born? Who were her father and mother? Omniscient Vyasa, enlighten me about the Devi. I had thought that Brahma, Vishnu and Siva are the three Gods who create, preserve, and destroy the universe. Is there any other beyond these three? Aren't they eternal?'

Parasara's son Vyasa said, with a smile, 'Once, as I walked alone on the banks of the Ganga, I saw that Narada Muni sat plunged in dhyana beside the murmuring river. He sat in padmasana, the lotus posture, his eyes shut and his face utterly serene. I approached Brahma's son softly, and waited for him to emerge from his trance.

When Narada opened his eyes, I prostrated myself at his feet in the sand. He laid a hand on my head in blessing, then asked in his bright and friendly way, "Dwaipayana, your face is bursting with the questions in your heart. Tell me, what do you want to know?"

I said eagerly, "Master, who is the origin of this infinite universe? Where does this brahmanda come from? Some of the wise say Siva, others Vishnu, and yet others are certain that Brahma is the first Creator. Then there are those that will worship only Surya Deva, the splendid Sun, and others only Indra in Amravati. So, too, Varuna, Agni, Vayu, Soma, Yama and Kubera have their bhaktas. As do Ganapathy and Karttikeya.

Then, my lord, there are the bhaktas of the Devi, who insist that she is the pristine creatrix, the source from whom all the other Gods have come. These say that Devi Bhavani is saguna and nirguna, as well, of infinite forms and formless, too. They say she gives all that their hearts desire to her devotees, and even moksha if they want it.

Then, there are those who say the universe is too vast to have been created by any one God or Goddess. These maintain that all that is springs from Prakriti, and Nature is all there is. The Samkhyas, whose acharya is the Muni Kapila, say this.

My heart is roiled with confusion, Narada, and indeed this life is as full of darkness as it is of light. There is as much suffering and death on earth as there is joy and pleasure. I feel like a drowning man, whose head is plunged repeatedly under a sea of doubts. I beg you, enlightened one, save me."

Narada said to me, smiling, "Vyasa, once I too was tormented by this same confusion, and took my doubt to my father. I said to Brahma, 'Lord, what is the root of this cosmic plant, the universe? Are you its first creator, or is it Siva or Vishnu? Whom should I worship as the highest God? I have prayed at all the sacred tirthas, yet my heart finds no peace.'

Brahma said to me, 'Only the unattached know the answer to the ultimate mystery. Once, when the universe lay dissolved in the primal sea Ekarnava, Narayana lay plunged in sleep upon his serpent bed, which floated on those waters. A golden lotus sprouted from his navel, and I was born within it. I saw no land, no sun, moon or stars, no mountains or anything other than the single ubiquitous sea. And I wondered: who has created me? Who will protect and destroy me?

Whom shall I worship, I asked myself, and heard a voice speak out of sky, 'Tapasya is your way.'

So I sat in tapasya for a thousand years, in the lotus in which I was born. Then the voice spoke to me again. 'Create,' it said, simply. As I wondered what it was I must create, the Danavas Madhu and Kaitabha appeared, roaring at me, 'Come fight us, or be our slave!'

I clambered down the interminable stalk of the golden lotus, and saw the most wondrous Being lying on a coiled and infinite serpent upon the darkling sea. His complexion was deep blue like a rain-cloud, and he wore fulvous yellow silk. He was four-armed, a wild-flower garland around his throat, and his four hands bore a conch, a disc, a mace and a longbow. He was Lord of the universe, I knew, but he lay plunged in nidra, deepest slumber.

I remembered the Devi then, and began to laud her. Soon, she left Mahavishnu's body and he awoke. For five thousand years he battled the

Asuras Madhu and Kaitabha, until finally he slew them. It was then that Rudra joined us two. Suddenly, the sky above was lit with a blinding radiance and we saw the exquisite Devi had appeared within that light.

She said to us in her entirely lovely voice, 'Now create, sustain, and destroy the universe, until the next kalpa ends.'

But we asked, 'Mother, how shall we create when there are no elements to create from? No earth, fire, water or air, but only this endless sea?'

The Devi smiled, and a shimmering vimana flew down from heaven, a crystal ship. A jewelled stairway stretched down from that wondrous craft and, at the Devi's word, we three climbed into it. Without a whisper the vimana rose into the sky and flew at such speed that our very bodies turned into luminous vapour, until we slowed again and saw that we hovered above the earth, blessed bhumi. The earth that was not meant to exist, for Siva had destroyed it by calling down the sun, and then it had rained without pause until everything was absorbed into Ekarnava.

But here we were in a precious vimana, hanging over a familiar blue-green world that was certainly real. We landed softly on that earth, cloaked in maya so none saw us, but we saw them. There were rivers and forests there, mountains, continents and oceans. Men and women lived on that planet, as did plants, great and small, birds and beasts, and every manner of living creature. We were astounded. This was another Bhumi, exactly like the one we three created, preserved, and destroyed.

As if in response to a doubt that sprang up in our hearts, the vimana rose away from that world, silently, and flashed into the sky at breathtaking speed. The azure firmament parted for us like another sea, and we flew into a marvellous realm—Devaloka, the heaven of that earth! There we saw Indra and his Devas dwelling in Amravati, as magnificent and rather like the one we ourselves had known, which now lay plunged in Ekarnava. Devaloka was full of unearthly, splendorous beings, eleven Gandharvas, centaurian Kimpurushas, Kinnara fauns, Vidyadharas and Yakshas.

We saw the Lord Satakratu there, with his Sachi. We saw Varuna, Soma, Agni, Kubera, Surya, Yama and all the Devas. We heard the Devi's soft laugh, and again the mystic vimana flew up higher still and, in the twinkling of an eye, we had arrived in Brahmaloka, that is heaven for the Devas.

We were amazed, Narada, to see another Brahma in that luculent realm, ensconced in his marvellous palace. In his sabha were all the Vedas and their angas, the nagas, the mountains, the oceans and rivers. Narayana turned to me and breathed, 'Pitama, who is this four-faced one?'

And I had to reply, 'I do not know, Vishnu. Why, I am uncertain who I myself am now!'

Next, our vimana flitted in a wink down to icy Kailasa, austere, auspicious mountain. We heard koyals warbling among its foothills, we saw delightful Yakshas at play. And in a cave on that mountain we saw the three-eyed Lord Siva, wearing tiger-skin and elephant-hide, seated serenely in a yogasana, meditating. At the mouth of the deep cavern stood hillocky Nandiswara, and at hand we saw resplendent Ganapathy with an elephant's head, and six-faced Karttikeya. The Lord's ganas thronged that mountain.

We were speechless with amazement, most of all our own Rudra. The vimana rose softly away from that Kailasa and now we flew in moments to another wonderful aquamarine city, and here of course we saw another Narayana, four-armed, his skin the hue of the atasi flower, wearing xanthic raiment and a ruby around his neck that shone like blood. We saw the exquisite Lakshmi sitting languorously at that Vishnu's side; and our Narayana trembled, he had broken out in a fine sweat!

We sat in that vimana, and stared mutely at each other. All that we had taken for granted, always, was the dust of illusion. Again the sky-ship flashed away, and brought us to a sea of nectar, and upon it a magical island that sparkled like a jewel under the noonday sun. We knew that isle of legend at once; it was the Mani dvipa. As we alighted, soft as flowers, we saw the lambent, mythic trees that grew there, mandara and parijata, asoka, bakula, ketaki, champaka, kuravaka, that were the ancestors of all other trees in time. From their branches hung great jewels as their fruit.

All kinds of sweet bird-song trilled from all around, and the very air was fragrant with music. A panel on the crystal vimana slid open, and we descended. When we had wandered a brief way, marvelling at the beauty of the ocean isle, we were arrested by a dazzling brightness that shone from a glade some way ahead. We approached cautiously, and for a moment stood spellbound by the sight that met our eyes.

We saw a splendid pavilion, and within it the mystic throne that is called Sivaakara, whose four legs are Brahma, Vishnu, Siva and Dharma. It was brilliant as a rainbow. A glimmering cover lay over it, encrusted with gemstones of incredible radiance. But these paled before she who reclined languidly upon that couch, bright as a streak of lightning. Her dark body was perfect, and anointed with fragrant sandalwood paste. She wore a crimson garment and a scarlet garland around her throat. Her eyes were reddish as well, and so entirely enticing that we stood staring at her unabashedly, for we were under her spell.

The Devi Bhuvaneswari sat there, a smile on her lips; two of her four hands held a noose and a goad, and the others were raised in mudras of protection and blessing. We three, Brahma, Vishnu and Maheswara, who create, nourish and destroy the universe, had never seen, or even dreamt of such beauty as hers. Why, we realised that the birds in that blessed place sang the occult mantra, Hrim, which belongs to the Lady whose skin is the colour of the rising sun, in her youth's lush bloom, and who is merciful past understanding.

She wore earrings shaped in the Sri Yantra, that is the arcane symbol of Tripura Sundari. Delectable Deva women surrounded her—Hrillekha and the others. Ananga Kusuma and the other Devis were with her, as well.

Vishnu, Rudra and I had never seen the Devi Bhagavati before, and we stood transfixed by her beauty, wondering who she was, and what she was called. Ah, even as we gazed at her, suddenly she was transformed—the ineffable young woman stood before us with infinite eyes and infinite limbs!

Then Narayana whispered, 'It is the Devi Bhagavati, the Mother of us all, the Mula Prakriti. She is the Satchitananda. Look, the shaktis and vibhutis surround her. I saw her upon the Ekarnava, as I floated there on the banyan leaf as a child, when the kalpa began. She sang softly to me, I remember, like a mother to her child; it was the song of the universe. Let us approach the Mother; she wants us to, else we would not be here.'

We went nearer and then the Devi smiled at us through an arch of her cloister. Instantly, we found ourselves transformed. Brahma, Vishnu and Siva had become three women; we had become our own shaktis! We were young, and we were beautiful, and now we were allowed to approach the Devi. Saying AUM, we entered her pavilion. From outside it had seemed small enough, but when we stepped in we realised it was infinite, as was she who sat upon her splendorous throne and shone with the brilliance of a million suns.

We bowed at her feet, and heard her laugh softly. We soon realised why. In her crimson toenails we saw the universe, Narada! And that was just the beginning of all the visions we saw in the Devi's presence. We were lost in wonder for a hundred years, for we saw not just this universe, but countless others.

Then, we hymned the Devi, and Rudra said, 'Bhavani, we have forgotten the mula mantra we once had from you. If we are to create, nurture and destroy the universe in this kalpa as well, give us that mantra again.'

And she gave it to us once more, from her own lips. She said gently, 'Shakti enlivens the Purusha. You will have need of your shaktis before you begin the universe again.'

And from her own body, she created the three Devis who are the consorts of Brahma, Vishnu and Siva through the manvantaras. She came to us herself, as Saraswati, Lakshmi and Uma. And when we saw those three Goddesses we felt inspired: we knew we could begin our universe again. The Devi and her mantapa vanished around us; just her mantra echoed softly everywhere, like the very air of Mani dvipa. And we three Gods were male again.

Saraswati, Lakshmi and Uma were with us now, and we climbed back into the crystal vimana. It lifted away from the jewel isle, with a sigh, and, swift as thinking, we were back upon the Ekarnava, the endless sea where Vishnu had slain Madhu and Kaitabha. And we were ready to begin our great tasks, for we now knew who the origin of all things was, whom we must worship,' my father Brahma said to me,"

Narada said to me,' said Vyasa Muni to the Kuru king Janamejaya," says Suta to the Rishis in the Naimisa vana, hanging on his every word.

THIRTEEN

SUTA SAYS, "JANAMEJAYA ASKED VYASA EAGERLY, 'WHAT HAPPENED WHEN the Trimurti returned to the sea of dissolution, Muni? How did Vishnu perform the Devi yagna?'

Vyasa said to the king, 'Free of their womanhood, and their Shaktis with them now, the three Gods flew back in the vimana to the Ekarnava. When they saw that single, infinite sea, they raised the world out of it, and the earth was made in part of the marrow of the Asuras Madhu and Kaitabha, and was called Medini.

The earth supports all things, and is called Dhara for that. She is vast, and for her vastness, she is known as Prithvi and Mahi as well. Ananta naga, the interminable serpent, supports her on his thousand hoods like a jewel.

Brahma created the mountain Meru, of countless golden peaks. From pristine Meru, the continents would unfurl like petals from a calyx.

Then, Brahma made the first Munis from his divine thought, Marichi, Narada, Atri, Pulastya, Pulaha, Kratu, Daksha and Vasishta.

Marichi's son was Kashyapa, and Daksha had thirteen daughters, among them Aditi, Diti, Danu, Kadru and Vinata. From the union of these women with Muni Kashyapa, the Devas, the Daityas and Danavas, the Kinnaras and Gandharvas, the nagas, men, and all the other living beings were born.

Then, Svayambhuva Manu issued from the lower part of Brahma's body, and Satarupa from his left side, and he hardly knew how they were created. Manu and Satarupa's sons were called Priyavrata and Uttanapada, and they had three daughters of incomparable beauty.

Brahma created ineffable Brahmaloka, high above the golden mountain, Meru. Vishnu created Vaikuntha, above all the other worlds, and dwelt there with Sri Lakshmi. And Siva, the greatest God, made white Kailasa, the solitary mountain that was like a full moon risen on the earth, and he lived there with his bhutas and ganas.

Between Meru and Brahmaloka, Brahma created Devaloka for Indra and his Devas. The parijata, tree of wishes, the nectar amrita, Indra's four-tusked elephant Airavata, Surya's steed Ucchaisravas, the peerless and seductive Apsaras, Soma the Moon and Dhanvantari the first physician, were churned out of the ocean of milk, the Kshirasagara.

The wheel of kaala began to turn slowly, by the will of the three great Gods, Brahma, Vishnu and Maheswara.

Then Vishnu in Vaikuntha had a vision of the jewel-isle, Mani dvipa, and he saw the Devi Bhagavati in her temple, and heard her mula mantra again, resounding from everywhere, the seed of all things. Narayana remembered who it was that had enabled Brahma, himself, and Siva to create the worlds, and he decided he would perform a yagna to worship the Devi, and give thanks to her.

Vishnu found an auspicious place on the earth, and created an immense yagnashala. He appointed twenty-seven Brahmanas to conduct the yagna, and invited Brahma, Rudra, the Devas and Rishis to attend. When that solemn, elaborate and original homa was complete, a voice spoke out of the sky, saying, "Vishnu, from now you will be the first of all the Gods. You shall be the saviour of the universe, and have first worship everywhere. When dharma decays in the world, you will incarnate yourself to restore it, and your avataras shall be worshipped for ever."

The voice faded, but all that heard it were filled with fervent bhakti for she who had spoken, the Devi Bhagavati, wonderful past describing.'

Janamejaya asks, 'Immaculate Vyasa, tell me more of the blessed Devi Purana. I feel wondrous peace steal over my spirit as I listen to you.'

Vyasa said, 'Once, in Kosala, in the city of Ayodhya, there ruled the noble Ikshvaku king Dhruvasandhi of the Suryavamsa. Dhruvasandhi was a king of dharma, and Kosala flourished during his reign.

The king had two beautiful young wives, Manorama and Lilavati, who were the delight of his days and nights. In due course, they both became pregnant. Manorama gave birth first to a fine prince, and he was named Sudarshana. A month later Lilavati delivered a radiant child, and they called him Shatrujita.

As the two children grew, it turned out that Shatrujita was by far the handsomer of the two, and he was the one with a gifted tongue. Soon, there was no doubt which of them was the favourite of the people, the ministers and the king himself. They all openly preferred Shatrujita to his less charismatic older brother. Sadly, even Dhruvasandhi was partial to his younger prince.

The king was a keen hunter, and one day in the jungle he and his party wounded a lion with their arrows. Roaring, the beast escaped into the thicker forest. Though there was hardly any more dangerous sport than this, Dhruvasandhi insisted that they follow the lion and kill him. Typically, the king led the hunters himself. The wounded lion left a trail of blood that was easy to follow, and the king and his party went after him.

Suddenly, in a small clearing, with a shattering roar, the lion charged. Dhruvasandhi drew his sword in a flash and stood his ground, like a lion himself; his hunters shot a hundred arrows at the animal in a flurry. But the king of the jungle leapt at the king of men, and they fought like ancient enemies. Dhruvasandhi struck the lion deeply with his blade, and the lion raked him with claws like daggers. The others could not shoot at the lion any more, for fear of striking their king. Man and beast rolled on the ground together, both roaring, until the king plunged his sword deep into the lion's heart, and the lion tore out the king's throat. Then both lay dead, their bodies fallen across each other.

Word flew back to the palace in Ayodhya, and the city was plunged in mourning. Vasishta, who was the kulaguru of the Ikshvakus, arrived in the vana and performed the last rites for the dead Dhruvasandhi. His body was cremated in the jungle's heart, as though on a field of war where he had fought his final battle.

Though Shatrujita was a great favourite with the people and even with the king's ministers, there was no question that the older prince, the quieter Sudarshana, would now be king. Being just five years old, the princes were not yet of age, but the kingdom must have a sovereign, at least in name. Vasishta said that the coronation should not be delayed, because the people were anxious for their future.

But now, there arrived in that noble city king Yudhajita of Ujjain, Lilavati's father, and he began to say that his grandson Shatrujita was only a month younger than the introverted Sudarshana, and was far better suited, by both gifts and temperament, to be king.

Meanwhile, Manorama's father Virasena, king of Kalinga, arrived in Ayodhya as well, and he, of course, was adamant that Sudarshana be made king. An acrimonious debate ensued in the royal sabha of that city. Both Yudhajita and Virasena had brought their armies with them, and these were camped outside the city-gates in case the dispute had to be settled by force.

The arguments grew louder, and more provocative. Yudhajita shouted, "Shall only the older prince become king, even if his brother is a hundred times more worthy to sit on the throne? And then, Sudarshana is only older by a month, and that is no difference at all."

Virasena cried stubbornly, "The eldest prince is the heir to the throne. It has always been so, and it always shall."

Yudhajita turned angrily on the ministers of Ayodhya, "All of you always preferred my grandson to the pathetic Sudarshana! Why do you hold your craven tongues now? You know Shatrujita is the one fit to be a king. How much wealth has Sudarshana promised you to take his side?"

Virasena yelled, "How is your grandson more worthy to be king? Because he has a pretty face and a koyal's voice? Are these the qualities a king most needs?"

By now, Yudhajita was beside himself. He roared, "I care a whit for your arguments. Let us see if Sudarshana sits on this throne as long as I am alive! I will tear you all apart, why I will cleave the earth in two if my grandson is not made king!"

The unseemly debate lasted not some moments, or even hours, but days and weeks; and it seemed there would never be a solution, for neither Yudhajita nor Virasena would give in. In time, word of their tussle flew through all the kingdoms, and other kings arrived at the gates of Ayodhya with their armies, and took one side or the other.

Hearing that there might be war, some tribals and gypsies also gathered in the woods that fringed Ayodhya, and these had come to loot and plunder if the opportunity presented itself.

And indeed war did break out between Yudhajita and Virasena; the two armies fell on each other, and let flow a tide of blood. The sky was dark with a million arrows; it rang with a million dreadful roars and screams. It was also thick with wheeling kites, vultures and other carrion birds arriving in black swarms to feast on the dead.

The blood of men, and of elephants and horses that bore them into battle, stained the earth. And those that still lived trembled to see the rill of blood that flowed on that field outside Ayodhya; just as sinners plunging down to naraka shudder when their eyes behold the sinister Vaitarani that flows down into the bowels of Yama's domain.

Grisly human heads, dissevered, floated upon that scarlet tide, plentiful as coconut-shells that float down the Yamuna, which young boys use for their games. Vultures hung over the dead like the warriors' own dark spirits trying to plunge back into the bodies from which they had been expelled with killing.

One warrior slain in battle rose at once into heaven in a subtle vimana. An Apsara was already in his arms, and between kisses he said to her, "Look at my body lying headless on the field!" and laughed in delight at her caresses, each one a sweet life.

Another dead warrior, also with an Apsara in his lap and looking down, was rudely surprised when his wife on earth climbed onto his funeral pyre and committed sati. Next moment, she was beside him and dragging him away from the nymph's embrace!

Two other kshatriyas who slew each other began to fight in heaven as well, over the same Apsara. Another grew so smitten by the nymph who received him that he began to describe his valour to her, and to praise her past all reason, so he would never lose her. As if the Apsaras of heaven could ever be attached to one man!

The dust of that battle rose in clouds and covered the sun's face, so that night seemed to have set in betimes, or a blood-red twilight where the dust-cloud reflected the lake of gore below. The battle lasted until Yudhajita cut Virasena's head from his neck in a scarlet fountain. The legions of Kalinga fled screaming.

Manorama heard the news, and was terrified. She was certain that Yudhajita would kill her and her Sudarshana, as well. Desperately she called her husband's loyal minister Vidalla, who was the most intelligent man in the kingdom.

The queen said, "My husband is dead, Yudhajita has killed my father. My son is still a child and I have no one to turn to. When Yudhajita rides into Ayodhya again, both my son and I will be at his mercy. His daughter Lilavati has always been envious of me. Tell me what I should do, Vidalla, and quickly!"

It seemed Vidalla had already thought of every eventuality. He didn't hesitate a moment before he said, "You must not stay here, and neither must

I. We must flee before Yudhajita returns. I have an uncle Subahu, who lives in the forest around Varanasi. He has an army, and will protect us."

On the pretext of seeing Yudhajita outside the city-gates, Manorama came out of Ayodhya in a chariot, with Sudarshana, a maid, and Vidalla. Yudhajita allowed her to perform the last rites for Virasena, and then, at twilight, she said she would return to Ayodhya. In fact, she slipped away and rode hard for two nights and days and reached the banks of the Ganga.

But it seemed that her time of misfortune was upon her. Manorama, her sakhi, Vidalla and young Sudarshana were waylaid by some bandits, who took all the jewels and gold they had, and even their chariot and horses. Her whole world destroyed in a few days, the queen crossed the Ganga by raft at night. Vidalla feared for her life if they remained on this side of the river.

After another day's hard journey they arrived, ragged, in Bharadvaja's asrama on Chitrakuta, little Sudarshana grave and clinging to his mother's hand.

Bharadvaja saw the beautiful young queen, and said to her in some amazement, "Devi, why are you here in this jungle, and your young son with you?"

Now all her grief burst from her. She began to sob uncontrollably, and could not answer the august Muni. Bharadvaja turned to Vidalla, who said quietly, "My lord, this is Manorama who was king Dhruvasandhi of Kosala's first queen."

Vidalla told the Rishi all that had transpired in Ayodhya after the king's death. Because the man spoke the truth, Bharadvaja said, "Stay with us in our asrama. You have nothing to fear here and I promise you that one day Sudarshana shall be king in Ayodhya."

And so the Muni gave Manorama and Sudarshana a kutila to live in, and they remained there in peace with the queen's sakhi. Vidalla also stayed on in the asrama, for he could not go back to Ayodhya.'

Thus, Dwaipayana began his tale of Manorama and Sudarshana of the House of Ikshvaku, and Janamejaya listened absorbed,"

Suta tells Saunaka's Munis.

FOURTEEN

SUTA CONTINUES, "MY GURU VYASA SAID AT KING JANAMEJAYA'S SATTRA, 'Yudhajita went back into Ayodhya in triumph, and he asked for Manorama and Sudarshana. He thought they were deceived by his allowing them to cremate Virasena on the battlefield, and now he intended to put them both to the sword. But that queen and her son had fled.

Kosala must have a king, so on an auspicious day, Yudhajita had his grandson Shatrujita crowned in Ayodhya. Vasishta was the chief priest, and all the Munis and ministers chanted the Atharva Veda during the solemn ceremony, while outside the palace a thousand conches blared in unison, bheris and turiyas resounded and singing and dancing broke out in the streets.

Yet there were those in Ayodhya who were not carried away by the festivities. Such quiet men remembered Manorama and Sudarshana, and agonised about where they were. When Yudhajita had made certain the throne of Ayodhya was secure, he went home to Ujjaina.

But it was not long before Yudhajita heard that Manorama and her son were in Muni Bharadvaja's asrama on Chitrakuta. He gathered an army, and set out for the Ganga and that mountain beyond her. He took with him Bala, a nishada chieftain, and came to meet Durdarsa, the king of the tribals of Sringaverapura.

On Chitrakuta, Manorama heard that Yudhajita was coming, and she went in tears to Bharadvaja, and cried, "Muni, what will I do? Yudhajita means to come here and kill my child, so his grandson is secure on the throne of Ayodhya. Save me, holy one, my life and my son's are in your hands."

When Yudhajita arrived in that asrama, Bharadvaja met him and said, "Manorama and her son are in my care. You cannot see them."

Yudhajita replied, "I will not leave without taking them with me. You are a man of peace, Muni. Give them to me peaceably, or I will take them by force."

Bharadvaja's eyes glittered. He said in a soft voice, "You know what happened to Kausika, when he tried to take Vasishta's cow from that Rishi's asrama with force. I beg you, leave us before I grow angry."

The king called his minister aside, and said, "I mustn't leave Manorama and Sudarshana alive. Even the weakest enemy can grow strong in time, and become a threat. I have killed Virasena. If I spare Manorama and her son, one day they will surely come for my head, and my Shatrujita's.

I must take these two from here and kill them. There are no soldiers in this old hermit's asrama to prevent me."

But his minister said in alarm, "My lord! Never be so rash. Bharadvaja needs no soldiers to fight us. He can reduce our army to ashes with a look from his eye. If the Muni protects Manorama and her son, we can do them no harm. Moreover, my lord, Manorama has no wealth of any kind. Her son can never be a threat to us.

All this world spins round on the wheel of fate. Be merciful today, and politic as well. Ask for the Muni's blessing, and let us leave here in peace."

Yudhajita struggled a moment with his kshatriya nature, then fell at Bharadvaja's feet and asked his pardon and blessing, which that kindly Rishi gave. The Ujjaina king went back to his kingdom.

Manorama wept in relief and she also prostrated herself before Bharadvaja in gratitude. Sudarshana grew in that sanctuary like the moon waxing. His inseparable companions were the Rishis' sons and it was a joy to see those children at play together.

Once, the Munis' sons saw Vidalla in the asrama while they were at a game with Sudarshana, and called out playfully to the minister, "Klib! Klib!"

Sudarshana, who was a little way off, repeated what they said, but leaving out the last consonant. "Kli!" he called in his lisping voice, and felt the most delicious stirring in his body. Again and again, the child repeated that syllable, never knowing it was the mula-mantra of Kama Deva, who is the God of love. Each time he felt a soft ecstasy within his body.

So, without being initiated by any guru other than destiny, the little prince Sudarshana acquired a mystic mantra. He would repeat it in his mind whenever he was alone and just before he fell asleep, and that mantra transformed his very nature. Day by day, he grew more brilliant.

When Sudarshana was eleven, the Rishis began to teach him the Vedas. They were astonished at how quickly he mastered the dharma-Shastras. No one knew about the secret power he had gained from repeating Kama Deva's mula-mantra. The once reticent prince became a magnificent archer and scholar, he knew all he needed to about politics and the moral sciences. He brimmed with quiet assurance.

Then, one day, while young Sudarshana sat chanting his mantra, the Devi appeared before him in a vision. Ah, she was crimson-hued like a kimsuka flower; she wore scarlet raiment, and great blood-red rubies. He saw her as Devi Sri Lakshmi, mounted on Garuda with her Vaishnavi shaktis around her.

The Devi called Sudarshana softly to follow her through the forest, to the banks of the Ganga. The prince went without an instant's hesitation and, after he had bathed in the great river, the Devi gave him a splendid bow, two magic quivers of arrows, and an unearthly coat of mail. Then, she raised her hand over him in benediction and vanished.

After this, Sudarshana became a fierce Devi-bhakta and worshipped the Goddess whenever he could, often wandering down alone to the banks of the Ganga where she had once called him. Now, it happened that the king of Kasi had a lovely daughter called Shashikala. One day the princess sat with her sakhi under a flowering champaka in her garden, when she saw a brahmana hurrying along into her father's palace.

Shashikala stopped the man for fun and cried, "Whither from in such haste, Muni?"

"Why, from the Rishi Bharadvaja's asrama, Princess," replied the cheerful mendicant.

Playfully Shashikala asked, "Tell me of an exceptional thing in the asrama, Muni, the most beautiful thing of all."

Without hesitation the Muni said, "Why, the prince Sudarshana, Princess! Ah, he is handsome past describing, that son of Dhruvasandhi of Ayodhya. I would even say," the brahmana went on breathlessly, "that if you haven't seen our prince, your eyes have been given you in vain. And besides, he is a great archer and a deep scholar too. Well, let me put it thus, lovely Shashikala, our Sudarshana is fit to be your husband!"

And, smiling broadly, the Muni breezed away on his errand, leaving Shashikala flushed, a little short of breath, her heart beating faster than ever before in her life. The Rishi's description captured the princess' imagination and she fell in love with Sudarshana without ever having seen him.

One night, perhaps a month after she first heard of the prince in the jungle, Shashikala dreamt of the Devi. The Goddess appeared brilliantly in her dream, and said, "Child, the prince in the forest is my bhakta. Ask me for a boon, and he shall be yours."

Shashikala felt she was drowning in a sea of rapture. The next morning, she was so radiant that her mother, the queen, began to press her to divulge the cause of her joy. But Shashikala was bashful, and would say nothing. Only to her sakhi, the one who had been with her when she first heard of Sudarshana, did she confess the truth, giggling and blushing wildly all the while.

Then suddenly, the princess had tears in her eyes as she whispered, "Ah, sakhi, what shall I do now? I have never seen the prince, yet I am in love with him." They sat beneath the champaka again and the princess looked around to see if they were overheard. When she saw there was not another soul around, she confided, "I see him in my dreams, sweet sakhi, and he is as handsome as Kama Deva!"

Then she sat plunged in silence for a while, before continuing anxiously, "Whatever will I do, when my own mind turns against me? When I look at the sandalwood paste you rubbed on my body, it seems like pale venom. The garland around my throat slithers like a serpent, and, falling through my window at night, the rays of the moon seem like fire! I have no peace anywhere, doing any of the old things that once gave me such simple joy. I can never be happy again until I have the prince Sudarshana in my arms."

The sakhi laughed throatily, "Such wild day-dreams you must be having, Princess!"

Shashikala blushed, then confessed softly, "But they don't leave marks on my lips and breasts, or stain my sheets with virgin blood! Ah, why couldn't I have fallen in love with any of the princes or kings my father knows? How easy everything would be then."

"What is gained easily is seldom worthwhile, and hardly lasts a brief season," said her sakhi, who appeared to know about these things.

So, prince Sudarshana, who had lost his kingdom when he was barely five, who had grown up on wild roots, fruit and berries, in a Rishi's asrama in the heart of the forest, with no wealth or army, and no power, found a kingdom to rule over which he never dreamt of. Never knowing it, he became the king of a beautiful princess' heart.

Shashikala had learnt the Saraswati mantra when she was just a child, and now she began to chant it every day, and to pray to the Devi to make Sudarshana, prince of her dreams, with whom she made shameless love in her fantasies, the lord of her life.

One day, when he was meditating on the Kama mantra, Sudarshana had another vision of the Devi. The next morning it happened that the hunter king of Sringaverapura brought a gift for Sudarshana, who was his friend. He arrived in the forest with a splendid chariot with four white horses yoked!

When the nishada had gone, the prescient hermits of the asrama said to Sudarshana, "The Devi has blessed you, all the omens cry out that you will soon be a king of the world."

Sudarshana redoubled his worship, and anywhere he rode in his chariot it would seem that an army rode with him, of countless foot soldiers, horses, chariots and elephants. It was the magic of the mula-mantra. That prince felt as if he was already monarch of a great kingdom, for the wind whispered that he was, the birds called him rajan, and the animals of the forest honoured him. He worshipped the Devi at every sandhya, and was perhaps happier than any king with a real kingdom.

But Shashikala pined for him, the lover she had never set eyes on, and took to her bed, with only her favourite sakhi to care for her needs. The princess was pale as a lodhra flower, and never came out of her bedchamber. Her father, king Subahu of Kasi, decided that only a husband could cure his daughter's ailment, and hastily decided to hold a swayamvara for her, at which she could choose any prince she cared to.

Subaha had an opulent pavilion built for his daughter's swayamvara. But even while the construction was underway, his child said stubbornly to her sakhi, "I love Dhruvasandhi's son Sudarshana, and I shan't marry any other prince!"

The sakhi went to the queen Vaidarbhi, and told her what Shashikala said, and the queen in turn told her husband Subahu. The king listened to this in astonishment, and then he began to laugh as if he had never heard anything so absurd. He said to his wife, "Sudarshana is a pauper, hiding in a Rishi's asrama. He has no kingdom, no wealth, no army, no power; what kind of prince is he? Tell Shashikala to remove this foolishness from her head. She will see a hundred fine princes at the swayamvara, she can chose any one she likes."

Vaidarbhi called for her lovely daughter, and set her on her lap as she used to when the princess was a child. The queen stroked Shashikala's hair, kissed her again and again, and then said, "My child, you must forget this fantasy you have woven around Sudarshana. It is time to begin your real life. Your father has heard what you have been saying, and it has made him very anxious.

Do you know that Sudarshana is the most unfortunate prince in all Bharatavarsha? How can you even think of marrying him? He has no kingdom, no friends except the hermits of the forest, no wealth or power. He lives on roots and fruit, like a vetala. And you, my precious child, there is no princess in all of Bharatavarsha as beautiful, as accomplished, and as fortunate as you are.

Forget this childish fancy, Shashikala. You will see a hundred magnificent princes at your swayamvara, and you can choose any of them to be your husband. Why, Sudarshana himself has a brilliant brother, Shatrujita who is king of Kosala. You could have him, if you want."

The queen lowered her voice then and, her eyes full of warning, said, "Shatrujita's grandfather, Yudhajita of Ujjaina, is determined to kill Sudarshana at the first chance he gets. So his grandson's throne is secure. The prince has escaped with his life so far only because Bharadvaja protected him, saying that he was just a child, and should not be harmed. But the prince is a young man now, and how long will the Rishi save him from Yudhajita? Yudhajita already killed Virasena of Kalinga, Sudarshana's grandfather."

But her daughter replied, "The Devi herself appeared to me in my dream, and told me that Sudarshana is destined to be my husband. How can I marry any other man?"

The day before the swayamvara, Shashikala was feverish with anxiety. She sent a secret messenger, a brahmana, to Bharadvaja's asrama. The message the man bore for prince Sudarshana was, "The Devi Bhagavati has ordained that you and I be married. Tomorrow is my swayamvara. O Prince, make sure you are in my father's city tomorrow, or I will kill myself before I become any other man's wife."

When Sudarshana heard the message he prepared to set out at once, for an irresistible sense of destiny stirred in him, too. Bharadvaja gave him his blessing. But when his mother Manorama heard what he meant to do, she wailed, "You mustn't go! Yudhajita will kill you if he sees you there. My son, you are all I have, the support of my old age. Don't abandon me!"

But her son said serenely, "Mother, what is written must come to pass, and not you nor I can prevent it. But it is the Devi Bhagavati who commands me to attend the swayamvara, and I must go."

Seeing he was determined, his mother began to shower blessings on him, "Ah, my son, let Ambika protect your face, and Padmalochana your back! Let Parvati watch over your sides, Sivaa look all around you! May Varahi, Durga, Kalika, Paramesvari, Bhavani, Girija, Uma, Chamunda, the amsas of the Devi Mahamaya Bhuvaneswari protect you everywhere and at all times!"

Then she cried, "I will also go with you, my child. You cannot ride alone into danger."

Manorama, who was once a queen, climbed into her son's chariot and they set out for Kasi. In that city, its king Subahu received them with honour. When he saw how splendid was the prince who had grown in the forest, he housed Sudarshana and his mother in a large mansion, and had his own servants wait on them.

Kings and princes from all over Bharatavarsha had gathered in Varanasi for Shashikala's swayamvara, for word of her beauty had traveled everywhere. The city teemed with a hundred strapping kshatriyas. The Karusa king was here, and the kings of Madra, Sindhu, Mahismati, Panchala, the Vindhyas, Karnataka, Kamarupa, Chola, and powerful Vidarbha, all with their great legions. Yudhajita had come to Kasi, as well, bringing his grandson Shatrujita, who was king in Kosala.

When Yudhajita heard that Sudarshana had arrived in his chariot, and the princess preferred the prince who had nothing, the king of Ujjaina roared, "I will kill the upstart! Shashikala will marry my Shatrujita."

But the king of Kerala, who was famed for his knowledge of dharma, said, "This is an ichchaswayamvara. The princess' choice shall be binding. There is no place here for arms or a show of strength. Why are you so anxious, when Shatrujita is such a brilliant prince? Moreover, he is king in Ayodhya. Why shouldn't Shashikala choose him, or indeed any of the other kshatriyas here? Calm yourself, Yudhajita, your hands are already tainted with Virasena's blood."

But the king of Ujjaina growled, "The jackal doesn't dare eye the lion's prey. Why is Sudarshana here at all? The kshatriya doesn't live by fine words, but the sword!"

And he stalked away from the other kings. Seeing Yudhajita was intent on killing Sudarshana, the other kings went to Subahu, their host. They asked the lord of Kasi, "Why is Sudarshana here? Do you make a mockery of this swayamvara? Yudhajita means to kill him."

The king of Kasi said, "My daughter has set her heart on him. How many times I begged her to forget the pauper, but she does not listen. I am helpless, my lords. Shashikala called Sudarshana here, not I."

The king of Kerala said, "Let Sudarshana be fetched here, we will ask him what he intends to do."

Sudarshana was sent for, and came before that glittering throng of the rulers of the earth. He stood quietly there, not speaking until one king said to him, "This is a swayamvara for royal kshatriyas. The most powerful princes on earth have come here to vie for the princess' hand. We have all come with our armies, and some of us are ready to do battle for Shashikala. How have you come here unattended, bringing only your mother with you?"

Another said, "You have no kingdom, army or wealth. You don't belong in this company."

"You are a hermit, tell us how you dared come to Kasi."

Sudarshana had a smile on his face. In a soft voice, he said, "My lords, all that you say is true. I have no kingdom, legions, friends or wealth. I heard of the swayamvara and came to watch it, with no special purpose. But, my lords, I did not come of my own will, but because the Devi Bhagavati told me to.

The Devi, who is my Goddess, is all of yours as well. I have no enmity with any of you. But if you decide to make an enemy of me, She who is the cause of all causes, the mother of the universe, will protect me. I only do what she asks of me; my life is in the hands of the one who spins the wheel of fate."

But the kings said, "What you say is true, but Yudhajita of Ujjaina means to have your head."

Sudarshana laughed. He said, "A man is born into this world by his karma, and by fate alone does he leave it, when his time has come. Not a moment before his time comes can any man be killed, by any king or even by the Devas. It is only kaala, time, who creates and destroys a man. I am a bhakta of the Devi from whose hands time flows. She protects me, and I fear neither Yudhajita nor any other man."

The kings saw how determined he was, and the best of them were secretly pleased,' says Vyasa Muni to Janamejaya the Kuru king, whose sarpa yagna had been ruined," says Suta.

FIFTEEN

"VYASA MUNI WENT ON, 'THE NEXT MORNING, SUBAHU USHERED HIS ROYAL guests into the sabha he had built for the swayamvara. Such a resplendent assembly of kings and princes took their places in that sabha. Silks and jewels past compare shone in the shafts of sunlight that fell through lofty windows.

Then, a thousand conches sounded at once, so it seemed the very earth trembled at their bass. The auspicious muhurta had arrived. In some excitement himself, King Subahu made his way through the passages of his great palace, and knocked on his daughter's door.

Shashikala opened that door, and ah, she was more beautiful than her father had ever seen her. She had just bathed and put on the resonant silks and ornaments that were heirlooms handed down from the ancient mothers of her family. She looked like a Goddess stepped down briefly into the world of mortal men. Her father stood before her, breath-taken to see how exquisite his child was.

Subahu said, "Come, child, take up the garland you will set around your husband's neck. All the princes and kings are waiting for you."

But his princess said, "I will not go to the swayamvara. The Shastras say that only a dissolute woman parades herself before the eyes of so many men, for all men have lust in their hearts. Even as I walk into the sabha, they will strip me naked with their gazes and my chastity will be forfeit.

Am I a whore that so many men must cast their eyes over me, and think how desirable I am? I do not care for this swayamvara, father. I have already given my heart to the prince I will marry. This garland is only for Sudarshana. If you love me at all, choose an auspicious day and lagna, and give me to the prince I love."

Subahu saw the tears in his child's eyes, and he knew that her heart was true and it was made up. He clasped her in his arms to comfort her, but then, he thought, "What will I do now? The kings have come with their armies, and I cannot face them all by myself. As for Sudarshana, he has not one soldier to fight for him!"

Anxiously, the king made his way back to the sabha where all the kshatriyas waited. As bravely as he could, Subahu said, "My lords, though I begged my daughter, and her mother implored her as well, she will not come to the swayamvara. I don't know what to do, and throw myself upon your mercy. I am prepared to give you all such gold and jewels as will satisfy you, in return for the trouble you have been put to.

My lords, my Shashikala is still a child, as you see by what she does. If I punish her or force her to come out here, I fear she may kill herself. I beg you, think of her as if she were your own daughter, and forgive us both."

Perfect silence fell on the sabha, and it was a sympathetic quiet; for, the kings had been moved by what Sudarshana said to them earlier. But Yudhajita's eyes burned crimson, and he roared, "Subahu, you fool! Is this the time to tell us this? Are you an idiot, as well, that you couldn't anticipate this? And I suppose you mean to give your daughter to that penniless Sudarshana, after making fools of the rest of us.

But I will not stand for it. I will kill you first, witless king, then Sudarshana, and my grandson Shatrujita shall marry your Shashikala, over her father's dead body if need be!

Listen to me, Subahu, a man must think of family, honour, wealth and equality, when he gives his daughter in marriage. Marriage is not a matter of a young girl's whim of a day; we both know that, and so do all these kings here. You and I have been friends for many years. Let reason prevail on you, Subahu. Fetch your daughter here, and let her choose any kshatriya for her husband, and I am content. Any, except Sudarshana, whose life I will not spare today."

And it seemed that Yudhajita had swayed most of the other kings, because they began to murmur among themselves that Subahu had indeed made fools of them. Subahu bowed his head, and said, "I will ask my wife to speak to Shashikala."

He went and told Vaidarbhi what had happened. The queen saw how distraught her husband was. They went to Shashikala and her mother said,

"If you insist on being stubborn, Yudhajita means to kill your father and Sudarshana. You are still young, my child, you don't understand the ways of the world. I beg you, give up your obstinacy, and marry any other prince but Sudarshana. Save your father's life."

And Vaidarbhi wept before her daughter. But Shashikala said, "Father, marry me to Sudarshana at once, and then turn us both out of your city. At least you will be safe then, and fate's purpose will be fulfilled, whatever she intends. I can never give up Sudarshana, any more than I can pluck my heart from my body, and then hope to live on. Go now, gentle father, tell the kings the swayamvara has been postponed until tomorrow. And tomorrow, let them be guests at my wedding to Sudarshana."

The father looked at his daughter, and she spoke with such quiet determination that he saw that nothing would change her mind. She was a grown woman suddenly, who would die if need be to fulfil what she believed to be her destiny. She was a woman of substance, and the king could say nothing to her.

Shashikala took her father's hand, and said, "My lord, it is the Devi who has decided that I will belong to Sudarshana and no one else. She will protect us from all these kings, their power is as nothing before hers." Her voice was low as she added, "And, if Bhagavati so decides I will die at Sudarshana's side rather than betray my love."

Suddenly, Subahu also felt inexplicably calm, as if someone unseen had plucked his anxiety from him. He embraced his daughter, then went back to the swayamvara sabha and announced, "There will be no swayamvara today. I have decided my daughter shall be married tomorrow, instead. My friends, bear with me until then. Return to your camps now, and we shall meet again tomorrow.

Perhaps I will devise a trial of strength or skill for the princes in the night, and let the one who succeeds win my daughter's hand. Until tomorrow, then, my lords."

And Subahu swept out from that sabha. He sounded so confident, that Yudhajita and the others felt sure that he had persuaded his daughter to change her mind. They left the city for their royal tents, pitched outside Kasi, each one surrounded by his own legions. Meanwhile, in a sequestered apartment in the very heart of the king's palace, frenzied preparations were underway for a secret wedding. Sudarshana and his mother had been fetched, and the prince from the forest was being clothed in the finest silks. Not far from that apartment, a delighted princess was also being adorned to be a ravishing young bride.

The brahmanas in Subahu's palace had hastily found an auspicious muhurta. When the time arrived, Sudarshana was led in to the wedding chamber and made to sit on the vedi. He was given achamana, and sweets to eat, arghya, two pieces of silk, and two golden ear-studs set with jewels.

The sacred agni was kindled, and Shashikala was fetched in by the older women of the court. When Manorama saw the princess, tears of joy filled her eyes. Shashikala was as lovely as Kubera's daughter. The bride and groom sat before the fire, side by side. The laja homa was performed and the young couple circumambulated the agni.

Then it was the hour for gifts, and Subahu gave Sudarshana two thousand horses from the Sindhu lands, two hundred chariots, all fully armed, a hundred and twenty-five caparisoned bull-elephants, all decked in golden ornaments, a hundred cow-elephants, a hundred maids to be his daughters companions, a thousand soldiers, and much wealth besides, as Shashikala's dowry.

The lord of Kasi came to Manorama and, bowing deeply to her, said, "O Queen, I am your servant now, tell me what I can do for you."

The tears escaping her soft eyes, Manorama said, "I have no words with which to thank you, but I see that there is no king in all Bharatavarsha as noble as you are, Subahu of the great heart."

Smiling, Subahu said, "Rule my kingdom from now, Manorama, and I will be your Senapati. Or stay on in Kasi with your son, and let him have half my kingdom." Then, a shadow crossed his face, and he said grimly, "But, I must try and appease the others now, and if they will not be pacified, we must fight them. But I have no fear. Victory will belong to the side that has dharma with it, and the Devi's blessing!"

Manorama said softly, "Let fear have no hold over your heart, noble king. I have seen a miracle today, and faith fills my heart. I am certain now that, with the Devi's grace, my son will have Ayodhya back one day, Ayodhya that is rightfully his."

Thus, Subahu and Manorama sat talking until dawn broke, and the kings camped outside Kasi heard the news that Shashikala and Sudarshana had been married in the night.

"Subahu deceived us. We will kill him, and Sudarshana as well!"

"And take Kasi for ourselves!"

"And Shashikala!"

Even as they spoke, a serene Subahu arrived in their midst with his guards and ministers. Silence fell over the other kings; they stood glowering at their host. Subahu folded his hands to them, bowed, and said, "My lords, be kind enough to join us for a banquet to celebrate my daughter's wedding. Friends, she was obdurate, and nothing I said could change her mind. I had to give her to Sudarshana. The thing is done now, and I beg you all to forgive me if I have caused offence, and to come to my palace and bless the young couple, and eat with us."

But the angry kings said, "We have already eaten. There are other matters we must attend to now."

They spoke with such menace, that fear gripped Subahu and he went back quickly into his city. Some of the other kings, led by Yudhajita, decided that they would blockade Kasi, and, when Sudarshana emerged with his bride, they would kill him and take Shashikala for themselves. Some of them decided they would stay to watch what happened,' my master Vyasa told the Kuru king on the banks of the Ganga," says Suta in the sacred forest.

SIXTEEN

SAUNAKA AND HIS RISHIS NEVER INTERRUPT SUTA'S PURANA FOR A MOMENT, but sit spellbound, as if their lives depended on what he said.

Suta goes on, "Satyavati's son Dwaipayana said to Janamejaya,

'His soldiers brought word to Subahu that the kings outside his city had blockaded the gates of Kasi. Sudarshana came to his father-in-law and said, "You must let us leave now. We shall go to Muni Bharadvaja's asrama first, and then decide where to go from there.

Fear nothing, my lord, the Devi Bhagavati, who is the Mother of the universe, protects us. What can these kings do against her power?"

Subahu said, "I will come with you, at least for a way."

They came to the city-gates, Sudarshana riding his white chariot, with Shashikala beside him, and they saw the enemy host confronting them. Sudarshana began to intone his mantra, the Kamabija, and thought fervently of the Devi. All around that chariot, there rose the bass of conches, the blare of trumpets, and the roll of a thousand drummers beating up a storm. Sudarshana stood absorbed, his eyes shut.

Subahu saw that Yudhajita led the blockading army, with his grandson Shatrujita beside him. Roaring, the enemy flew at Sudarshana in his chariot, his half-brother before all the others. Arrows darkened the sky, and Subahu plunged his ratha forward, his soldiers around him, to meet the enemy's charge. Suddenly, a hush fell on that field and both armies froze in their ranks.

Yudhajita and Shatrujita froze as their horses reared in alarm, whinnying at the strange apparition which had materialised between the two forces: an immense lion, and upon the golden beast's back rode a shimmering Goddess, her lustre like another sun risen on the earth. She rode her lion between the two armies, daring anyone to approach her.

Sudarshana opened his eyes, and murmured, "Look, Shashikala, the Devi has come to protect us."

Subahu stood entranced. Yudhajita roared, "Who is this woman who rides a lion? What does she want here?"

At that moment, the lion gave a roar that drowned every other sound on that field. Horses and elephants bolted, and, in a moment, there was a channel cleared through Yudhajita's legions, a way along which Sudarshana now fearlessly drove his chariot.

Yudhajita roared, "Shall we let a mere woman and one lion frighten us? Kill them, and kill the upstart Sudarshana!"

And he plunged at Sudarshana, his bow flaring arrows and Shatrujita beside him. Sudarshana held them both off for a time. Then, suddenly, the Devi was at his side on her beast. Yudhajita shot his arrows at her as well, and Shatrujita too. The crimson Devi smiled, she raised her own bow in one of eight hands. With another hand, she loosed a volley at the enemy. In a blur, both Yudhajita and Shatrujita were dead; their heads struck off by the Goddess' crescent-tipped shafts.

Suddenly it seemed a thousand Devis stalked that field of war, in a thousand dreadful guises, riding a thousand dreadful beasts. The enemy perished in a scarlet tide before Durga's legion of her own selves, and those that did not fled screaming.

Subahu leapt down from his chariot and prostrated himself before Bhagavati. Again and again, he lifted his head, then set it down in the dust at her holy feet.

"Mother, Jagaddhari, I have no words with which to praise you! Bhavani, unworthy as I am, today I have seen you with my very own eyes. I see how you protect your bhaktas, O Devi. You have come yourself to save Sudarshana's life, O Apara, transcendent one! I lay my head at your feet. Mother, bless me."

The Devi smiled tenderly, and said to Subahu, "King of dharma, name your boon."

"What more could any man want, than seeing you like this with his mortal eyes? Not the kingdom of the Devas is more precious than what I have seen today. I beg you, Devi, for the boon of bhakti. Let my faith in you never waver, and let your grace be upon my city forever. Bless me, Sri Durga, that I be your bhakta for ever."

The Devi said, "I will remain here in this Kasi, always, good Subahu. For as long as Kasi stands upon the face of the earth."

Sudarshana arrived, and fell at the Goddess' feet. Tears of ecstasy flowing down his face, he worshipped her, "Mother of the sky, mother of mercy, you have saved me today, though I have such scant faith. Let me be your servant from this day, Devi. Command me, what shall I do with my life now? Where shall I go?"

Smiling, Bhagavati said, "Have you forgotten Ayodhya, your father's city, Sudarshana? Go to Ayodhya now, and rule as king of the Kosalas. For, that is who you are. Worship me always, Sudarshana, and I will care for you and yours. Keep an idol of me in your kingdom, pray to it at the three sandhyas, and I will be with you. Celebrate the Navaratri puja in autumn, for it is mine. Fear nothing, Sudarshana; you are my bhakta and I love you."

With that, her hand raised in benediction over her kneeling devotee, the Devi and her pristine mount vanished. Like the Devas to Indra, the stunned kings of the earth who remained alive ran to Sudarshana. They fell at his feet, as if he were their lord and master. Even Subahu bowed deeply before his son-in-law, for there was no doubt that he was the Devi's chosen one, and he was lord of Ayodhya now, king of the ancient Ikshvakus.

Those kings cried, "We are your servants from this day, Sudarshana. By your grace, we have seen the Devi with our eyes. But tell us, O King, how did the mother of the stars come to save your life?"

Sudarshana said, "When I was a child in Muni Bharadvaja's asrama, I was given the Kamabija. And every day I would chant it silently, as often as I could. In time, my bhakti grew and the Devi would appear to me in dreams and visions and tell me what to do. I came to Kasi at her behest, and she has protected me, why, she has returned my kingdom to me."

Word flew to Ayodhya of the happenings in Kasi, and by the time Sudarshana rode into his father's city, bringing his mother and his bride Shashikala with him, a grand welcome awaited him. The city was festive with arches and banners; the streets had been washed and scented with attar and other exquisite perfumes. Garlands of jasmine, lotuses, and every bloom of the season, festooned the whole place and the smoke of incense swathed Ayodhya.

Riding his white chariot through bright lines of soldiers turned out to receive their new king, Sudarshana arrived at the royal palace at the heart of the city. There, Shatrujita's mother Lilavati waited for him, having heard the news of the deaths of her son and father. Like a supplicant Sudarshana came before that queen, who stood at her door, tense as lightning. He was surrounded by his supporters, yet he was humble.

He bowed to her, touched her feet and said, "Mother, I did not kill either your son or your father. The Devi Bhagavati took their lives. As for me, I say to you that you shall have the same honour in Ayodhya as does my mother Manorama. You were both my father's queens and I make no difference between you.

Mother, the wise say that sorrow and joy come in life according to one's karma, and one should not be moved too much by either. As a puppeteer makes his puppets dance, so too the soul leads us through the mazes of time, through grief and delight, which are only the fruits of our karma. I had to flee into the jungle as a mere boy, an innocent. I lived in an asrama and learnt precious lessons in the wilderness that I would not forsake for any kingdom.

All this was surely because of the karma of lives past, and I learned that the Munis of the forest who live on roots and fruit are happier than kings who live in palaces."

Lilavati listened silently, as he went on, "The human birth in the sacred land of Bharata is a rare one. It is a birth by which a soul can tread the way of dharma, which leads to moksha. To me, the quest for moksha is more vital than the one for wealth. Indeed, mother, this great kingdom the Devi has blessed me with today is only another asrama on my way. I beg you, O Queen, don't be disconsolate."

Then Lilavati took Sudarshana's hands, pressed them against her lips and began to sob loudly. "Ah, my child, I am guilty! I am so guilty, and fate punishes me now, just as I deserve. My father sinned when he took your kingdom by force. My son sinned when he sat on the throne that was not his by right. They cared nothing for the suffering they caused Manorama and you, and now retribution has caught up with them, and they have paid with their lives for what they did.

Sudarshana, you will scarcely believe me when I tell you that I was always unhappy at what my father did. Yet, I was just a woman and could not oppose him. Often I would try to tell him, or, later, my son Shatrujita, to fetch you back from the forest, and have you crowned in Ayodhya. But they would brush aside what I said, calling me a foolish woman who knew nothing of the ways of the world.

And now, dharma has been done by the Devi herself. Who am I to complain when I know that my father and son were to blame? Sudarshana, I have been unhappy at what my son grew into. Yes, he was handsome and clever, but I saw that he was also greedy and ruthless. There was no more dharma in Shatrujita than there was in Yudhajita, and I hardly feel the grief a daughter and a mother ought to at their deaths. Instead, I feel the joy a sister does at Manorama having returned home, and I feel the joy of a mother to see you again; and grown into a man, and bringing your lovely bride home to Ayodhya!"

She clasped him to her and wept. Soon, Sudarshana was brought into his own palace, from where he would rule the kingdom of Kosala. The first thing he did was call his court astrologers, and ask them to name an auspicious day on which he could install a sacred image of Devi Durga on a golden throne, for him to worship. For, he said, he would rule Ayodhya in her name.

So it came to pass, the grace of the Devi was upon the entire kingdom, and the rule of Sudarshana was as blessed as Ramarajya. His people knew how the Goddess transformed their prince's life, how she came herself to save her bhakta, and there was no home in Kosala which did not have an idol of the Devi, no town or village that did not have a Bhagavati temple, and no man, woman or child in that kingdom who did not worship her. It was a time of dharma, and darkness was banished from the land. Kosala prospered as it had done during the golden reigns of Dilipa, Raghu and Sri Rama.

In Kasi, Subahu also worshipped the Devi with the fervor of a convert. He, too, installed a great idol of her in his palace, and had a hundred shrines for her built all over his kingdom. It was in Kasi that Durga had appeared on her beast, and the people of that city, many of whom had seen the miracle with their own eyes, worshipped her as ardently as they did Siva in the Viswanatha temple.

From Kasi and Ayodhya the Devi's fame spread like light through Bharatavarsha, and it seemed all the sacred continent was suffused with her grace,' said Vyasa Muni to the Kuru king," the blessed Suta unfolds his timeless Purana for the Rishis of the Naimisa vana.

SEVENTEEN

SPRING AND AUTUMN ARE THE MONTHS OF SICKNESS AND DEATH; THEY are even called Yama's teeth. They are the thresholds of Uttarayana and Dakshinayana, when the sun turns north and south, and these are the seasons when the world is unstable. It is at these times that men have a special need for grace, and so the Devi's Navaratri, the first nine nights of the bright halves of the months of Chaitra in spring, and Asvina in autumn, are observed as times for special prayer.

Spring is a cruel time, but autumn is dangerous. It is in autumnal Asvina mainly that the Devi's Navaratri puja is undertaken. On the day of the new moon, amavasya, the bhakta collects what he needs for his vrata of nine days, which begins the following morning.

*

"Janamejaya said, 'Muni, tell me some of the deeds of the Bhagavati herself.'

Vyasa began, 'Once, when Mahishasura ruled the world, there was a war between the Devas and the Asuras. Would you hear of it?'

'I am agog for it, Swami.'

'It was a time when the great were so much greater than you can begin to imagine O King, and when the evil were so fearful that to even conceive of them is beyond the comprehension of any man of this shrunken time. But the battle was the same eternal one, between dharma and adharma, the forces of light and darkness.

Mahisha, the awesome Asura, climbed sacred Sumeru, golden mountain from where continents unfurl like petals from a lotus, the blessed mountain that is perhaps the holiest place on earth. There, he sat for ten thousand years in a searing tapasya, worshipping his Creator, four-faced Brahma, Sire of the worlds. One day, irradiant Brahma appeared on his swan and said to the Asura, "I am pleased with you Danava. Ask me for any boon, and it shall be yours."

Without a moment's hesitation, Mahisha said, "Lord, make me immortal, so I need never fear death."

But his Creator demurred. "Death is certain for he who is born, even as birth is certain for he who dies. Why, all these immense mountains, and the deep ocean, the sky and the very earth, the void and the galaxies, will die, when their time comes. Ask me for any boon other than immortality, and I will give it to you."

A moment's pause, then the Asura said, "Pitama, grant then that no man of any of the races of Swarga, Bhumi or Patala causes my death. That will do as well for me, for surely, no woman born can kill Mahisha! So, if I die, let it be only at a woman's hands."

Smiling, Brahma said, "So be it, Danava. Only a woman will take your life."

And Brahma went back to Brahmaloka, whence he had come, and Mahisha back to his kingdom, jubilant.'

Janamejaya wanted to know, 'Muni, who was this Asura Mahisha?'

Dwaipayana said, 'Danu of old had two sons, Rambha and Karambha, and they were the greatest, most renowned Danavas of the race of darkness. Though they were demons of great power, they had no sons. The two Asuras arrived on the banks of the sacred lake, Panchanada, and began a tapasya.

Karambha entered the lake and sat in penance in its water, often submerging himself for days on end, for he was a master of pranayama. Rambha found a pipal tree on the shore, haunted by Yakshas and Yakshinis, lit four fires around him and sat worshiping Agni Deva. Indra heard of this, and was furious. He arrived at Panchanada as a crocodile and devoured Karambha in the water, so the Asura did not even have time to cry out but a scarlet stain floated on the lake, covering it from end to end.

Rambha knew his brother had died and, in savage grief, decided to offer his own head to the agni he worshipped. He seized his long jata in his left hand, took up a short, sharp axe in his right, laid his head on a flat rock before the sacred fire, and was about to behead himself, when Agni appeared before him, incandescent.

The Fire-God's eyes were flames, his flowing locks, and his very body cold flames of different hues. He said to the Asura, his bhakta, "Fool! What are you doing? Don't you know there is no greater sin than to kill oneself? For there is no redemption for this sin. Ask me for any boon instead, and it shall be yours!"

Rambha put down his axe and rose. "Lord of the Devas, bless me with a son who will destroy my enemies and be sovereign of the three worlds. Let him be a master of maya, of shape-changing, and let him be stronger than anyone and invincible to all the races of Swarga, Bhumi and Patala."

Agni said, "So be it. Never think of killing yourself again. Take any woman to yourself, instead, and the son you have will be greater than you are."

With that, the Fire-God vanished. Rambha's roar of joy echoed across the Panchanada, and the lake-waters rose in hilly waves and dashed against her shores. With the tree-spirits, his friends the Yakshas, around him, Rambha rejoiced. But the Danava had been continent for a thousand years, and now that his tapasya's purpose was fulfilled, a raging lust burned like fire through his immense body, intensified since Agni Deva had promised him a great son with any woman he chose.

Then the strangest thing happened. As if by fate, a she-buffalo wandered into that place, and she was strangely luminous. The Asura Rambha took one look at her, and he was smitten! With a hundred endearments he approached her, quivering with desire. He stroked her smooth flanks, he kissed her face, and when he saw that she too bent her head in compliance and lowed sweetly, Rambha mounted that beast, and, roaring in delight, coupled with her!

It was the most unusual sight, and the invisible tree-sprites, the Yakshas and Yakshis, watched the exceptional lovers in awe. It was the strangest thing, but the Danava fell deeply in love with his she-buffalo, and she with him. When he had slaked his wild lust on her many times, he grew more immense still and lifted her onto his shoulders to take her down to patala, which was his home. Just then, they heard a fiery bellowing.

On the banks of the sacred lake they saw another mighty buffalo, but this one was a bull who stood pawing the ground and snorting, his great horns lowered. Even as Rambha set down his she-buffalo and turned to face the bull, the beast charged and gored him through his chest, impaling him with both sword-sharp horns, then tossing him high into the air and catching him on his horns again. Five times that terrible bull buffalo did this, as if in outrage, and life fled the Asura Rambha's body.

Now plainly aroused, the bull buffalo turned in triumph on the she-buffalo, which he considered his fair prize won in battle. But, with tears flowing down her face to see her Asura lover slain, she ran to the Yakshas of the pipal tree for protection. The bull chased after her, lowing like thunder. Suddenly a hundred magical beings, some beautiful, many grotesque—some with their feet pointing backwards and others with gaping holes in their backs, some with two and three heads and others with none, some many-eyed, others with just one—materialised at the foot of the tree in a motley throng around the she-buffalo. They all had glittering bows in their hands, and the bull buffalo hardly knew what slew him, but slumped to his knees in a moment, struck through every marma by a hundred arrows.

The Yakshas set up a cheer at their victory, then, on feet light as wishes, they came crowding round their precious friend, the Asura Rambha who had lived among them for a thousand years and now lay with his chest slashed to ribbons, his heart cloven, and his blood leaking copiously on to the ground. Those tree-spirits wept and set up a loud lament, and finally, saying a hundred dark and secret prayers for the dead Danava, the Yakshas built a pyre of dry, fragrant wood and hauled Rambha's torn body onto it.

Just as they were about to set him alight, the she-buffalo, his love, who was with child by the Asura, came wailing that she meant to immolate herself on her dead lover's pyre. The kindly Yakshas did all they could to dissuade her, but she was adamant. The Yakshas lit Rambha's funeral pyre by magic, and it blazed up in spectral hues. Bowing to those loyal friends, the she-buffalo walked calmly into the blaze.

Then, a miracle! As the tongues of flame leapt high, easily consuming the strange lovers, suddenly a shaft of blinding light shot up into the twilight sky from the heart of that burning pyre. Within it stood a newborn and enormous Asura—it was Mahisha, born from his dying mother's womb! His body was half human, and half that of a great bull buffalo, his head bore huge curved horns and a black tail flicked restlessly behind him. His roar shook the earth and the sky, and even the Yakshas cowered from him. Next moment a second light appeared at the heart of the consuming fire, and another dreadful Asura, his skin and eyes crimson as blood, and his face both ghastly and familiar, stood forth. He was Rambha, reborn from love for his son Mahisha! And now he was called Raktabija, born from a bloody seed,' said my guru Vyasa to the king," says Suta in the forest.

EIGHTEEN

FOR THE NAVARATRI PUJA, THE BHAKTA CHOOSES SOME AUSPICIOUS LEVEL ground, and erects an open mantapa, twenty-four feet square. He makes a proper roof and an arched gateway to lead into the mantapa. He then creates a vedi at its heart to be his altar: six feet square and a foot and a half high, made of packed earth. Now, he comes to seek the blessings of learned brahmanas versed in the worship of the Devi, and to ask them to conduct his Navaratra puja.

The next morning, the pratipada tithi, the first day of the waxing moon, the worshipper comes early to a river, lake or tank, or to the well in his village or home, and bathes, performing the everyday sandhya vandana. Now he brings the brahmanas, either nine, five, or at least one of them, into the mantapa, with all reverence, and they begin the puja after the bhakta has rewarded them according to his means.

Vital portions of the Chandi Stotra and the Devi Bhagavatam are read to appease the Devi Bhagavati. The nine-syllabled Durga mantra is chanted, AUM Hrim Srim Dum Durgayai Namah! by a brahmana who has kept a fast the previous night. The Svasti vachana from the Veda is chanted, Svasti na Indro vriddhasrava.

Only when the puja has formally begun is the vedi adorned with two silken cloths, and then on that sacred throne the bhakta installs an image of the Devi, the Mother. She must have either four or eighteen arms, be adorned with jewels, wear strings of precious stones around her neck, bear all her ayudhas in her many hands, as well as her sankha, chakra, gadha and kamala. She must of course be mounted on her beast, a splendid lion.

If the bhakta does not own an idol of the Devi, he can set an earthen water-pot on the vedi, filled with gold and jewels such as he has, and with holy water from a tirtha, and five green shoots, their young leaves immersed. Beside the idol or water-pot should be a mystic yantra, the Sri-chakra, with the Devi's mantra inscribed: AUM Hrim Srim Chandikayai namah.

Music should be heard in the sacred mantapa.

*

"Dwaipayana resumes his Purana, with the Kuru king listening avidly, 'When Mahishasura had his boon from Brahma, his roar of joy sent avalanches hurtling down a hundred peaks. The Asura came down the mountain, and lost no time in setting about the conquest of the earth. He was stronger than any other being in creation, and no king of the world could stand against him at all. Moreover, he had such savage demons as his commanders that he swept all before him, and was Lord of this bhumi in no time.

Mahisha was undisputed sovereign of the sea-girt earth, all the kings of men were his slaves, and paid him homage. Mahisha's Senapati was Chikasura, whose very appearance on a field of war was enough to put an enemy to flight, so dreadful was he, and so strong as well. Chikasura was also a loathsome Asura of fiendish ways, and his vanity was legend. He would tear the head off any friend or foe, for the least provocation and often for none at all.

Tamra was in charge of Mahisha's treasury, to rival which there was no other. And his ministers and generals, each one more horrific and violent than the others, were Asiloma, Vidala, Udarka, Vaskala, Trinetra, Kala, Bandhaka and a hundred more. When Mahisha had quelled the earth, and enjoyed it for a hundred years, he turned his eyes skywards to Devaloka and sought to subdue that heaven.

He sent a fierce messenger to Indra in Amravati, saying, "O thousand-eyed, seek refuge in Mahisha, Lord of the worlds. Be my vassal, Indra, or prepare to fight me."

Indra heard this message from the Danava in surprise. Then, he began to laugh softly. The king of the Devas said, "It is not dharma to execute a messenger, whatever be the message he brings. Otherwise, rude fellow, I would have sent you back headless to your master. Tell Mahisha he has gone mad with arrogance; but I have the cure for him. Tell him Indra said,

'Son of a buffalo, I am eager to meet you in battle! You are so rapacious that you have lost your reason. I mean to make myself a fine longbow with one of your horns.'"

The messenger came quailing before his master Mahisha. He said in a low voice, "My lord, Indra is smug in heaven, with his Devas around him. He wasn't moved by your message, but sent you such a reply that I dare not speak it."

In a moment, Mahisha's eyes turned crimson. He quivered, his black buffalo's tail flicked behind him. He pawed the earth in his sabha, and truly like a great wild beast enraged, passed a stream of steaming urine. Then a bellow erupted from him that threatened to dislodge the earth from her orbit.

Mahishasura cried, "The king of the Devas wants battle. Gather your armies, my brave Asuras, we must crush that devil in the sky! He is a seducer of other men's wives, a liar and a traitor. It is by his friend Vishnu's power that Indra is still king of Devaloka. But I am Mahishasura, and I fear neither Vishnu nor Indra. Why, let all the Devas fight me at once, and I will kill them all. Let Varuna, Yama, Kubera, Vayu, Surya, Soma, and all the rest come to battle. My Asuras shall triumph against them all!

My friends, soon we will rule Amravati, and have the havis of every yagna in heaven and earth. We will drink the Soma rasa in Devaloka, and lie with Deva women in Nandana, the enchanted garden. The eleven Gandharvas will play heaven's music for us, and Urvashi, Menaka, Rambha, Ghritachi, Tillottama and all the Apsaras will dance for us.

I am Mahisha of the great boon; no Deva, no Asura, no man of any of the races of heaven or earth can kill me. Why, by myself I can smash the hosts of Swarga with my horns and hooves. But we must show them how great the race of Asura is. We must go majestically to heaven. So, send word to the corners of the earth; tell all my generals to come with their legions. Fetch our Guru Sukracharya here. He must perform the rituals for our victory, and we must worship him before we set out." Thus, spoke the mighty Mahisha.

Meanwhile, when the Danava messenger left the luminous Sudharma in Devaloka, Indra hastily called a council of his Devas. He said to them, "Rambha's son Mahishasura is lord of the Danavas. He is a great sorcerer and master of a hundred mayas. The Asura has subdued the earth and is demented with pride. He just sent me a messenger, saying, 'Indra, pay me homage, accept me as your master, or be ready to fight me.'

My lords, not even the weakest enemy is to be trifled with, and this Danava, I have heard, has a powerful boon from Brahma. Ponder deeply, my friends, and tell me what we should do. I am not for attacking the demon before we know how strong he is. Rather, let us send spies to assess the strength of his army and discover who his generals are. The Asuras are not to be divided with discord. They are fiercely loyal to their king, and he looks after them well."

When Indra's spies returned to Amravati, the Devas were astounded to hear how powerful Mahishasura, the buffalo's son, had become. In some panic, Indra called another conclave of his lustrous ones, and to that council he summoned his guru, the wise Brihaspati.

"The Asura Mahisha means to have war with us, Guru. Tell us what we should do."

Brihaspati thought about this for a moment in silence, then, said, "First of all compose yourself, my lord. What is written in the book of fate must happen, and agitation will not help you. All creation turns on the wheel of time, and we see wise men begging for food while fools live in opulence. No armies can turn fate away, O Indra, what is written must happen. All that we can control to some degree is our own minds. So if you are serene and patient when suffering inevitably comes, it will not seem as long or as sharp as it does to the impatient, anxious man."

Brihaspati spoke in a low, soothing voice. There was a hypnotic quality to what he said, and Indra felt somewhat calmed as he listened.

The Devaguru went on, "Distress and joy are only the fruits of one's own karma. If one is beyond attachment, the root of every misery, one is free from pain and pleasure, joy and grief. A deed once done must bear fruit, and the one who does it must enjoy or suffer those consequences, even if it takes a thousand ages. Fate is ineluctable, therefore, O Indra, be dispassionate. If danger threatens, do your best to avert it; but, then, be indifferent to success or failure in what you do. Contentment is the wealth you should seek for yourself, my lord. It is a kingdom which never perishes, and which no one can take from you."

The thousand-eyed Lord of the Devas listened in some absorption to his guru, and knew the truth of what he was saying. The panic had left his heart, and he said again with some composure, "Guru, what you say is true for Rishis. But kingdoms are neither won nor kept without effort. No man who waited for fate to make him a king as he sat in dhyana, ever became one. Why, no man ever became famous, wealthy or happy without breaking his back. Only the weak extol quiescence, master. Knowledge is an ornament that hermits wear, and contentment is for brahmanas. But for those who would rule, prowess is their most precious treasure."

There was fire now in the thousand eyes of the Deva king. He said, "I will kill this Mahisha as I did Vritra, Namuchi and Balasura of old! I have my Vajra, master, and I have you. Siva and Narayana will support me. I beg you Guru, start chanting the mantras that will remove every obstacle from my path. Let victory be mine!"

Brihaspati smiled to listen to his sishya. He said, "I see you are determined to fight, and I will neither encourage nor dissuade you from your purpose. But, as for victory and defeat, these things are not in my hands or yours, but already written in the book of fate. I am afraid that book remains closed to me, and the future is obscure."

Indra decided the first thing to do was to visit Brahma. He said to his father, the four-faced Creator, "Pitama, the Danava Mahisha has collected an immense army and means to attack me in Amravati. I am afraid, O Brahma, I need your help."

Brahma, who had granted Mahisha his boon, thought for just a moment before he said, "Let us go to Kailasa, take Rudra with us, and then seek out Vishnu. Let there be a council in Vaikunta, to decide what can be done about Mahisha."

So, Brahma, Indra, and all the Devas and Lokapalas with them, arrived on pearly Kailasa, lone, most sacred mountain, and found Siva at dhyana in his cave hung with breathtaking stalactites like peerless works of art. They hymned Siva with his thousand auspicious names, then, told him why they had come. Siva seemed pleased to go with them to Vaikunta.

In Vaikunta they worshipped blue Narayana, Lakshmi's Lord, and Indra told him about the threat from the Demon with the boon. "Even as we speak, Mahisha's monstrous legions flow in a tidal wave towards Amravati."

Vishnu said, "We must take our own army to meet him. Have no fear, we shall crush them easily."

And the hosts of heaven gathered in glory under the banners of the great Gods that led them. Every soldier of light rode his own wondrous mount. At the head of heaven's army were Brahma on his shimmering swan, Vishnu on his golden eagle, Siva on his snorting bull that trod air, Indra on his great white elephant, Ganapathy on his magnificent mouse, Karttikeya on his resplendent peacock, Yama on his black buffalo; and a thousand Devas and Gandharvas, Kinnaras and Kimpurushas, Yakshas and Guhyakas, and all manner of Rudra ganas. Every bright race of the three realms also rode in flashing vimanas and on other extraordinary mounts to the great war. Each warrior of that brilliant army bore the most marvellous weapons, too, of every sort.

The legions of darkness and the hosts of light soon met, and a dreadful battle broke out. The sky was obscured by arrows, astras, axes, parasus, musalas, gadas, pattisas, bhusundis, chakras, shaktis, tomaras, mudgaras, naracahas, bhindipalas, langalas, and a thousand other ayudhas, all deadly, many sorcerous, howling and wailing fearfully, and letting flow rivers of blood between heaven and earth, and upon both.

The horrific Chikasura was Mahisha's Senapti, and he thundered about everywhere on a black elephant's back. He struck Indra with five scorching shafts that drew five roars from the Deva king. Next moment, Indra cut Chikasura's head off with a crescent-tipped arrow like silver lightning. His severed head roaring as if to rend the sky, Chikasura toppled from his beast. In a trice, Indra cast his adamantine Vajra at the black mastodon, cutting its trunk open, and the animal fled trumpeting shrilly, deep into the Danava ranks.

Mahishasura, who was still at the rear of his oceanic forces, saw this. He growled to another terrible general of his, "Vidala, go and cut haughty Indra's handsome head from his throat and drink his blood. Kill Varuna; kill all the arrogant Devas. Bring their heads back to me."

Mounted on another dark elephant, the stupendous Vidala lumbered into battle, and the Asura was as big as an elephant himself. His fangs were like small trees, his breath was fire, and he charged the Deva army like a black cloud with lightning in it. Indra shot him with deadly narachas like serpents, but the demon cut them down easily and replied with a luciferous volley of his own. The Deva king shredded the Danava's sizzling shafts, then, cast his gada at Vidala's elephant, taking the beast in the trunk and drawing blood.

Trumpeting in agony, the leviathan turned tail and blundered back through the ranks of the Asura army, trampling hundreds of Mahisha's own soldiers. When the animal was calm again, Vidala scrambled off its back, mounted a chariot, and came roaring back into battle. Again Indra and he faced each other, again the stream of fire flowed between them and Indra was crimson-eyed with rage that an Asura could dare to defy him like this.

Indra set his son Jayanta before him on Airavata, and charged the Danava again. Jayanta bent his bow in a circle, and shot five whistling arrows deep into Vidala's chest while his father drew the demon's fire. Vidala's roar made the planets wobble, and he fell onto the floor of his chariot in a swoon. The Devas celebrated with echoing rolls on a sea of dundubhis, like the thunder before the pralaya.

A huge roar of 'Jaya, Indra!' could be heard from numberless blithe throats, as Gandharvas sang and Apsaras danced their delight.

Fuming, Mahisha ordered the fell Tamra to take the field against the enemy, and to take no prisoners. Tamra rode to battle and a swath of silver arrows went before him, streaming from his bow like thoughts from a mind. Tamra's fighting Asuras were hardly less valiant than their general, and a fulgurous battle erupted on that field perched between heaven and earth.

Varuna joined the fray with his terrible pasa, the fluid noose. That was the most uncanny weapon, for it seemed to remain always in the Sea-God's hands, yet it also flew everywhere and choked life from a thousand Danavas each moment, so that their ghastly tongues lolled from their lips and their eyeballs fell out of their sockets.

Beside Varuna rode the dark and dreadful Yama, the Lord of death, mounted on his water buffalo, his danda in his hand. That glowing staff was hardly less wonderful than Varuna's paasa. With one sweep of that ayudha, which elongated itself limitlessly at his will, Yama would brush away a thousand enemy warriors in a moment. They would just vanish from the field, into his dark halls of death.

The air between the armies was roiling with the roars and screams, with arrows, axes, musalas, shaktis and parasus. Yama struck Tamra in his face with the terrific danda. But the Asura neither vanished into death, nor seemed moved at all by the blow. He stood his ground, a horrible demon, covering Indra and his army in a bank after bank of occult arrows, drawing blood in geysers from the ones of light.

Enraged, Indra summoned his shakti, and it shone like a star in his hands. With a long roar, the Lord of the Devas cast that shakti at Tamra, and that ayudha took the demon in his chest with a blinding explosion. He fell unconscious and was carried off the field. At Tamra's fall his Asuras panicked, and fled in all directions, howling weirdly,' said Krishna Dwaipayana to the Kuru king at his sattra," says Suta Romaharshana, most excellent pauranika, to the avid Munis of the Naimisa vana.

NINETEEN

"VYASA MUNI CONTINUED, 'WHEN TAMRA WAS STRUCK UNCONSCIOUS, Mahisha's roar threatened to rive the very fabric of time. He struck the earth with his mace, and the sun and moon shuddered. Bellowing like a thousand wild-buffaloes, that Asura emperor rushed at the king of the Devas.

He struck Indra a blow on the arm with his gada, so the Deva nearly fell off Airavata's back. But in a flash, the thousand-eyed one smashed that mace into dust with his thunderbolt of adamant. Roaring, Mahisha drew his scimitar, shining like a shard of the sun, and rushed at Indra again. Such a battle they fought, the king of heaven and the master of darkness, their roars shaking the firmament.

Then the Danava began to fight with sorcery. He cast the samvari maya to spread an illusion over the battlefield. In a trice a hundred thousand white buffalo-warriors appeared and fell on the host of light from every side. Indra trembled; he hardly knew what to do. Varuna, Kubera, Yama, Agni, Soma, Surya and all the rest fled.

Stilling the terror that plunged through his blood with dhyana, Indra prayed fervently to the blessed Trimurti, to Brahma, Vishnu and Siva. In a moment, the darkness the buffalo-legions brought to the field was dispelled in luminescence, as the three great Gods appeared, mounted on a swan, an eagle and a mountainous bull, their weapons blinding in their hands.

As he flew into battle, blue Vishnu cast the Sudarshana chakra at Mahisha's mayic legion, and the army of buffaloes vanished in a wink. But Mahisha was not in the least perturbed. Lowing louder than ever, he rushed at Brahma, Vishnu and Siva, with a massive, occult parigha in his hand, the head of the mace glinting like an iron planet. Around that immense Danava, grown big as a mountain, swarmed his generals, hardly less terrible than him: Chikasura, Ugrasya, Ugravirya, Asiloma, Trinetra, Vaskala, Andhaka and many more.

Some were lean and sinister, others immense and brawny; some had two and three heads, and were horribly misshapen, others had just one glaring eye in their faces, and still others three and four eyes; some had no eye at all, yet they were not blind. Some of these monstrous warriors had flown to Mahisha from the ends of the earth, others from worlds deep in the sky, and others from the seventh and eighth, deepest patalas.

As a hunt of tigers may set upon a herd of cows, so the Asuras attacked the Devas. The sky was a darkness of arrows, some plain, and others wizardly, of light and fire. The air was a hoarseness of roars and screams. Devilish Andhaka, perhaps the most fell of all Mahisha's commanders, shot Hari Narayana with five sizzling shafts, their points dipped in serpent-venom. But, with transcendent archery, Vishnu sliced them into slivers even as they flew at him. Then these two assailed each other with a barrage of the most exceptional ayudhas, arrows and swords, humming chakras, whining musalas, black gadas, scintillating shaktis, and many more. For fifty days, they fought without pausing, and neither could subdue his adversary.

Meanwhile, Indra and the loathsome Vaskala fought, and that demon's breath was fire. Yama, who is death, fought three-eyed Trinetra, who battled him with a spate of weapons he loosed from six hands. Maha Hanu, a most beautiful demon, duelled with Kubera; and every now and then the Asura would seize some common soldier, a Yaksha or a Gandharva elf from Kubera's army, strike off his head, and then swill all the blood from his body in a long draught from the gaping throat. Varuna fought pale, quicksilver Asiloma with marine sorceries. And Mahisha himself battled Rudra, often locking interminable horns with Siva's frothing mount Nandiswara.

Suddenly, Mahisha cast his gleaming mace at Garuda, taking him in the chest so that blood suffused his eagle's eyes at the ferocity of the blow. Keening in agony, Garuda flew down to the ground, and sat with his feathers quivering. Vishnu consoled him, stroking his golden plumage, whispering tender comfort in his ear. Then the Blue God rose again in fury and loosed a clutch of blazing arrows at Andhaka. But in the space of a wish Andhaka raised a veil of maya before him, that Vishnu's shafts could not pierce.

His rage mounting, Narayana cast the Sudarshana chakra once more, flaming like a thousand suns at the demon. But Andhaka spun his own chakra at it, a wheel of abysmal darkness, deep as the void, and the Sudarshana was tamed! Andhaka's triumphant roar shook earth and sky. The Devas were deafened and fled in all directions. Beside himself now, Hari seized up his mace of power, the Kaumodaki, and flew at the Asura. He fetched Andhaka a blow like a thunderclap of the apocalypse, and that Danava fell unconscious.

Seeing his warrior fall, fulminant Mahisha sprang at Vishnu. Narayana pulled on his bowstring so the planets quivered in their orbits; he covered the great Demon in a golden cloud of arrows from the Saringa. But the invincible Mahisha erupted from that deadly mantle, and struck the Blue God on his blessed head with his iron parigha. Vishnu fell like a great tree struck by lightning. In a wink Garuda flashed up, set the fallen God on his back and flew out of battle quicker than sight.

Indra and his Devas were panic-stricken and their cries filled the air. Siva flew at Mahisha and struck him in his chest wide as a city with three fires from his relucent trisula. But Mahisha only laughed as if the triune infernos, that could swallow galaxies, only tickled him. He materialised a dark shakti in his hand, like a dreadful curse, and cast it at Rudra. A black thunderbolt, the sorcerous ayudha, struck the bull-mounted God. It would have incinerated the moon, but it fell away in a shower of sparks against Siva's fair chest.

Now, Vishnu recovered and flew back into battle. When he saw those two great Gods standing side by side, Mahisha's roar eclipsed every sound yet heard on that tremendous field. In a moment, he had become a black bull-buffalo, his horns long as streaks of lightning, his body big as a continent. He stood pawing the ground, tossing his horns, his coarse tail flicking from side to side behind him. The earth trembled under his hooves, and quaked when he raised his black face and bellowed. Then that incredible Beast tore up some mountains with his horns curved like sides of suns, and cast them down on Siva and Vishnu.

Hari and Hara were blurs. With empyreal archery, they smashed the peaks the Buffalo-demon cast at them into dust. That dust drifted out on spinning winds, deep into cosmic space and, in time, formed itself into whorled nebulae. Siva and Narayana covered the snorting Beast in clouds of fire. But he tossed his head, and was proof against their fiercest volleys. In despair, Vishnu hurled the Sudarshana at him again. In his buffalo-shape, Mahisha was not quick enough to stop the nitid chakra with his own wheel of night. Vishnu's ayudha felled the Danava.

But in a moment he sprang up again, now in a human form once more, his body glowing like a black sun, his cudgel luminous in his hand, and his growls like the rumbling of avartaka and pushkara, the stormclouds of the end of time. Hearing him, Vishnu raised his sea-conch, the splendid Panchajanya, to his lips, and blew a blast that made the Asura army quail, and the Devas and the Rishis of heaven, the Charanas, Kinnaras and Gandharvas, and all the hosts of light cried out in exhilaration.

When Mahisha saw his macabre legions struck with fear, he turned himself into a gigantic lion, big as a hill. The roars of that beast drowned every other sound that had been heard before on that field; now the tide of fear was turned back and the Devas shivered. With the loudest roar of all, Mahisha the lion sprang at Garuda, and raked him with claws long as an elephant's tusks, and he was covered in blood. Next moment, as Garuda floundered, Mahisha lacerated Vishnu's arm with a blow of his talons.

Hari cast the Sudarshana again at the monstrous lion in an eruption of light; at once, the Asura was a buffalo again, and gored Narayana deep in his chest with interminable horns. Twin fountains of blood sprayed from Vishnu's breast, and, stanching them as best he could, dazed at the Danava's primeval ferocity, Garuda and Vishnu flew blindly from the battle to Vaikuntha.

Seeing Vishnu flee, and seeing that Mahisha was indomitable, Siva flew back to pearly Kailasa. Brahma, who had blessed the Asura with the strange boon, fled before both of them. But the Devas remained steadfast, and still faced the Demon's ominous army. Indra, Varuna, Kubera, Surya, Soma, Agni, Vayu and their legions stood firm, powerful weapons gleaming in their hands.

When the three great Gods fled, the Asuras charged wildly at the Deva host, roaring like ten forests full of lions. As they came, in eerie spate, they covered the army of light with screaming narachas, like serpents spitting fire. A terrific conflict ensued, and at the heart of it all, killing a thousand Deva soldiers every moment, was Mahisha himself, Lord of darkness, the great, black bull buffalo.

Mahisha ruled that ancient field of war. Growing big as clouds, he would rip the peaks off more mountains and crush whole legions of Gandharvas under them. And then the jubilant roaring of the Danava army was like the thunderstorm at the end of time. At other times, Mahisha would lash a thousand Deva archers with his sweeping tail, and strike their heads off, for that tail could be sharp as swords when the Danava willed. Then he would explode on Indra's hapless army in a thunder of razor-like hooves, and only shreds of soldiers remained in steaming piles to show that glorious fighting-men and elves had stood before the savage Demon.

A hundred years the great war lasted, and Mahisha shone like a black sun on time. Now, seeing him like that, invincible to every weapon they cast at him, panic seized the Devas and Gandharvas and all the warriors of heaven. Indra leapt off four-tusked, flying Airavata's back in terror, and bolted from battle. Surya Deva leapt off his luminous steed Ucchaisravas, who goes swift as thought, and ran. Quick as light, Mahisha seized the two superb beasts, both once churned up from the Kshirasagara, for himself. And then there was no stopping the Devas any more; Varuna, Yama, Soma, Kubera, Agni, Vayu, and all the rest, fled in every direction, their wails of terror drowning the Asuras' celebratory roars.

Their roars and crude songs echoing in heaven and on earth, their matchless Lord at their head, Mahisha's army flowed like a bloody river into the city of Amravati, which the routed Devas had abandoned. But the delectable Deva women waited there, trembling, for the inexorable demons. For now, great Mahishasura would sit upon Indra's crystal throne in the Sudharma, his dreadful generals would sit around him, and wield power over the three worlds. And the beautiful Deva women, the gandharvis and all the rest, would lie in the coarse and insatiable demons' beds.

The vanquished Devas and their people hid in the wilderness, in the hearts of impenetrable forests, in lofty caves on unclimbable mountains, like beggars in the world. The Asura ruled the three realms for an age, and darkness was his way. At last, in despair, the Devas arrived in Brahmaloka, and prostrated themselves before the four-faced Creator on his Lotus-throne, surrounded by the Munis of heaven, Mrihi, Pulaha, Narada, Kashyapa and the rest, and by all manner of Gandharvas, Siddhas, Charanas, Kinnaras, Nagas and Pannagas.

Indra and his people eulogised the Pitama handsomely, then Indra said, "Merciful Lord, don't you see us in our evil time, the Devas of light going like filthy beggars? Mahisha sits upon my throne in Amravati, and the three worlds suffer his dreadful rule. Time itself is corrupted, and yet Pitama you are indifferent to our anguish. The Asura enjoys all that is ours; why, our women lie in his bed. Help us, Brahma, we beg you, do something to save us!"

Brahma's faces softened in compassion, he sighed and said, "Suras, what can I do? My heart is with you, for you have lost all that is rightfully yours, and indeed, creation is plunged in sin. But Mahisha is invincible, Indra. He has my boon that no man can kill him. Perhaps, we should go to Rudra upon Kailasa, and seek his help, and then, to Vishnu in Vaikuntha as well."

So, the Devas in their vimanas and Brahma on his hamsa, they flew to the lonely mountain that stood north of the Himalaya, risen like a full moon upon the earth. Siva had divined their arrival, and came out of his lofty cave to meet them, with Uma at his side. There was such grace upon all creation when Brahma and Rudra embraced each other at the mouth of that legendary cavern. Then, the Devas bowed to the eternal Ascetic, the Mahayogin, and took the subtle padadhuli from his feet.

When they sat inside, Siva asked, "Pitama, how have you graced Kailasa today with your presence, and you, O Devas?"

Brahma said, "Devadeva, Mahisha has scattered these Lords of light like straws in a gale. They roam the worlds, homeless and hunted. The offerings from every yagna on earth go now to the Asuras, and evil holds creation in the grip of its claw. Bhuta Bhavana, we have come to you for your help. How can the Devas be rid of Mahishasura?"

Siva smiled at this, and said, "Vibhu! It was you who gave Mahisha his boon, indeed, you are the root of all that has happened. He can only be killed by a woman. But where shall we find a woman to vanquish this Danava, who crushed us all in battle? Can Uma or Saraswati go to war? I think not. And even if they do, will they prevail, who have never fought a battle in their lives, or will Mahisha drink their blood? Indra's Sachi, too, is no warrior."

He saw the despair on the Devas' faces, and fell silent. Then he said softly, "Vishnu is the intelligent one, the saviour. Let us go to Vaikuntha, and ask him what we should do now."

As soon as Siva spoke, a strange surge of hope coursed through that opalescent mountain, through the Devas and Brahma. Eagerly, Indra and his people cried, "Let us go to Narayana, he will find a way!"

All around them, they saw auspicious omens. A fragrant wind swept sacred Kailasa, laden with exquisite scents of heaven. The sky was clear and all the quarters bright, and birds broke out into song everywhere in fine augury,' said Vyasa."

TWENTY

"VYASA MUNI CONTINUES, 'BRAHMA, RUDRA AND THE HOST OF DEVAS arrived in Vaikuntha, city of visions. O King, who can describe the beauty of Vishnu's city? It is beyond words. Yet, one can say that there are lustrous palaces and mansions here, great gardens full of enchantment, some with lotus-pools set in them like precious mirrors. These pools are overgrown with supernal kalaharas, whose stems have tiny jewels like dewdrops encrusted in them. Their colours defy the rainbow.

Charmed rivers flow through Narayana's realm, murmuring in ecstasy at where they are. There are lakes here, like small inland seas, on which water birds out of vivid dreams swim and set up a wild symphony of sweet song. The parks of Vaikuntha have champaka, asoka, mandara, bakula, amrataka, kuruvaka, mallika, and a thousand exotic and unknown trees besides these growing in them. They seem like trees of the earth, but only at first glance. Then, one notices they are strangely, wonderfully alive; why, you can hear them speak if you listen.

Bright deer and peacocks amble through the shady groves, some of the birds with shimmering fans unfurled, and more incandescent than any displayed by their cousins of the earth.

Koyals warble in soft bliss in the trees, bees hang in shining swarms over the fluorescent kalaharas. At the heart of the magical city stood a crystal palace, and this was where Vishnu lived. In the sabha of that mythic palace was a throne wrought entirely from precious jewels, mined on worlds scattered across the vaults of space. Upon that throne Vishnu sat, the dark blue and entirely beautiful God. His parisadas, Sunanda, Nandana and the others, were around him, so absorbed in his grace that they saw him everywhere, and in all things, him and nothing else.

When Brahma, Rudra and the Devas arrived with their train of Gandharvas, Siddhas, Kinnaras and the others, they were met at the lofty gates of Narayana's palace by his dwarapalakas Jaya and Vijaya, legends in their own right with golden staffs in their hands.

Indra said to those splendid gatekeepers, "Friends, tell your Lord that Rudra, Brahma, and the Devas have come to see him."

Vijaya went in to his master, and said, "Lord, Brahma and Siva have come to Vaikuntha with Indra and his host."

Hari rose at once, and came out to receive his illustrious visitors. They stood careworn at his gates; but the very sight of him seemed to restore them, as he, the blue saviour, moved affectionately amongst them, taking their hands and embracing them fondly. The Devas praised him fervently, for he was their protector through the deep ages, the God who saved them time and again from one great Asura or the other.

Vishnu led them into his sabha, and there were two thrones set there for Siva and Brahma, where only they ever sat. There were also lesser thrones for Indra and his Devas, many times more magnificent than any throne of the earth.

When they were comfortably settled, Indra said, "Jagannatha, you are our last refuge, and we come to you in despair."

Vishnu said, smiling, "What grieves you, Devas, that you have brought Brahma and Rudra to Vaikuntha?"

Indra moaned, "Mahishasura rules heaven and earth, my Lord, and he torments us. We are like beasts in the world, hiding from the Danava's hunters; while he enjoys the havis from every yagna in all the worlds. He tyrannises creation and time flows darkly for his power. No man can kill the Asura, for that is Brahma's boon to him. We beg you, Hari, deliver us from Mahisha: find us a woman strong enough to slay him."

Vishnu said musingly, "We all fought him together, but he was invincible. It is true, only a Devi can kill Mahisha. But who shall it be? Perhaps, if all of us combine our Shaktis to create such a Devi, she will be equal to the task."

He had hardly finished saying this, when the strangest thing happened. From Brahma's frontal face, from his brow, there issued a fiery light, pulsating. In a moment it had flowed out in a great flame, and stood burning before them, ruddy as rubies, a little hot and a little cool. A brilliant aura surrounded Brahma's Shakti, embodied feminine fire.

As soon as this manifestation was complete, Siva's Shakti issued from his brow and, ah, she was silvery, dazzling and so fierce that none of the Devas could even look at her. When that candescent Shakti was fully extruded, Vishnu's sublime Shakti flowed from him, blue as the hearts of rainbows. This luminous flame was iridescent with spectral colours, as she stood glowing in that sabha. The three Shaktis, of Rajas, Tamas and Sattva, stood waiting before the council of Gods.

Then, one by one, all the Devas emitted their Shaktis there, all brilliant, all fierce; and soon, eighteen pristine spirit-flames burned in that sabha. As the Devas and the Trimurti watched, even they awed, those Shaktis flowed together at the heart of that august and ancient chamber, into a single, ineffable flame, whose tongues licked the lofty ceiling. Why, the very sabha and Vaikuntha itself seemed to vanish for the brightness of that great female fire. It was mountainous, Himalayan, with a thousand peaks dancing.

Shading their eyes, the Gods gazed at that fire, which, once it had fused into a single blaze, began to lick together into a wondrous form. In awe, the Devas saw that a brilliant Goddess was being born from it, and she was so beautiful that she defined beauty anew. It was the Devi Maha Maya herself, and she stepped from that agni, tall as the sky, with eighteen arms in this manifestation, though it is told she has a thousand arms in her other, cosmic Form.

Her face was white, her eyes black, her lips were scarlet, and the palms of her soft hands were coppery. She wore ornaments that took even those Gods' breath away, and in each of her eighteen hands she carried a different dreadful ayudha, given her by the Gods,' said Vyasa, in some ecstasy. The Muni told his tale so well, that king Janamejaya could almost feel the heat of that Shakti-fire, and reach out and touch that apparition, her presence was so real.

When Dwaipayana paused, the Kuru king cried, 'Ah, do not stop, holy one. Your tale is amrita to me. I beg you, go on!'

Vyasa resumed solemnly, 'The Devi is Nirguna, O king, she is formless, ubiquitous, eternal. Yet, even as an actor assumes different roles to please his audience, the Devi assumes different forms in time, to see dharma done.

When she stepped out from that Shakti-fire of the Gods, her face was white as a lotus, and fierce; this part of her was from Siva's Shakti. Her hair was black as the night of space where no sun burns, yet it was luminous; her hair was formed of Yama, the Lord of death's, Shakti.

Her three eyes were of Agni-shakti, fierce and reddish, like burning coals. Her brows were black and arched like Kama's bow; they were born of the spirits of dawn and dusk, and seemed to cast coolness down on the burning eyes. Her perfect ears were from the flame of Vayu of the air; her slim nose was fashioned from the femininity of Kubera, the Lord of wealth; it was fine as the til flower carved in crystal. Her teeth were like kunda flowers, and were wrought from Daksha Prajapati's Shakti. Her lower lip was half a flame, made from the Shakti of Aruna, the Sun's sarathy; the upper half was from Karttikeya, Siva's son. Vishnu's tejas flowed into her eighteen weapon-bearing hands, and their eighteen scarlet nails were from the Shakti of the Vasus.

And her breasts, my lord, that one cannot begin to describe, were made of Soma the Moon's beauty, and her waist and her navel from Indra's femaleness. Her fluid thighs, glimmering legs and perfect feet were of Varuna of the Sea, and Bhumi, the Earth, was her womanhood, her yoni.

She transformed the fire of all the Devas' Shaktis for her body, and stood dazzling before the Gods in Vaikuntha. Vishnu was the first to regain enough composure to speak. He said softly, "Devas, give all your ayudhas to the Devi. She will have use for them against Mahisha."

Like Gods in a dream, the Devas went numbly to her who stood in that sabha like another sun risen in their midst, a sun like no other in all the heavens. Kshirasagara, the milky sea, gave her a diamond necklace, and a scarlet silken garment that would never wear or fade. Viswakarman gave her a crest-jewel for her crown, and it shone like a hundred moons; he gave her blinding white diamond earrings, bracelets for her wrists and arms, and anklets like star-clusters. Her gave her numberless rings, each one brilliant, for her long fingers on eighteen crimson hands.

Varuna brought the Goddess a crown of ocean-lotuses that never fade, and their scent was divine. He brought her a Vaijayanti, a wildflower garland for her breast. Himavan, the lord of mountains, brought her a golden lion from his caves to be her mount.

Regally, that Devi climbed astride her beast, and the creature's roar of joy reverberated throughout creation. Now, Vishnu extruded a second calescent chakra from his Sudarshana, a wheel of fusive fires that could slough off any Asura's grisly head, and brought it to the Devi. She took it from him, with one of her hands.

From Siva's trisula sprang another glittering trident, that would spew triune star-fire a thousand yojanas long at an enemy, and the Mahayogin brought it to the terrific Devi. Smiling, she took it from him, with another hand.

Varuna wrought another deep conch from his primeval ocean-sankha, as old as himself, and offered it to the Devi, and she took that as well. Agni brought her his incendiary weapon, the Shatagni of a thousand fires. Vayu the Wind's offering was a shining bow, more powerful than any other, and a silver quiver full of arrows straight as sunbeams. Every time that bow's string was drawn back, it made a noise like ten tempests.

Indra himself caused another thousand-jointed Vajra to appear from his own thunderbolt, and gave it worshipfully, hopefully, into another of the Devi's hands. He also gave her the golden bell from around his white elephant, Airavata's, neck, to fasten around the throat of her golden lion. Yama made another staff from his mrityu-danda, that reaps the lives of all beings when their time is over, and she received it in a perfect hand, so her very touch made the Lord of death tremble.

Varuna brought her a fluid pasa, a noose of water, as deadly as any ayudha she had yet been given, for it could choke life from an aksauhini in a moment. Brahma gave her a kamandalu, filled with holy water from the Ganga. Kaala, Time's, offering was an axe that glinted like a mirror of the soul; and Viswakarman's, a parasu so exquisitely wrought that she smiled to receive it. It was such a work of art that one might hesitate to put it to the savage use for which it was meant.

Kubera brought her a jewel-encrusted cup to drink from, and it was a thing of deep beauty; again, Varuna came before her with another lotus of a thousand glowing petals. Viswakarman wrought an impenetrable coat of golden mail for her, light as air. Vishnu gave her a feminine version of the mace Kaumodaki, on which a thousand little bells tinkled in the breeze, and it was an irresistible weapon.

Surya the Sun gave a gift of his own light to that Devi, and she shone brighter than ever. And when she now stood before them, armed and bearing all their offerings in her many hands, they were overwhelmed and began a panegyric to her; for, she was, indeed, Maha Maya, the Great Enchantress of the universe. They chanted many of her endless names.

"Salutations, O Sivaa, most auspicious Devi! Thou art peace and nurture, gentle Bhagavati, and thou art Rudrani, terrible one. We worship you, O Kalaratri, night of the end of the world, O Un-born Mother of all things, great and small.

Jagatmata, the Asura Mahisha torments us, and only you can kill him. We beg you, Mahamaye, deliver us from the Danava!"

And they fell at her feet in tears. She laughed gently, and that sound sent a thrill of bliss coursing through them. The Devi spoke for the first time since she had appeared from the Shakti-flames.

"This is amazing! That Brahma, Vishnu and Mahesa, Indra and all the Devas stand before me, trembling for fear of a mere Danava. Surely, Time is the only true God; for he brings sorrow and terror to the great, and lifts the miserable to the loftiest thrones in creation."

She paused to consider what she had said, and it seemed to amuse her, for she began to laugh. It was the strangest, most dreadful laughter; it was like roaring, and when the Devi threw back her head and laughed like that, the earth shook, the mountains trembled, the sky quaked, and the seas rose in tidal waves and lashed their shores. Even golden Meru, at the heart of the world, shuddered.

But the Devas were delighted! They fell at the roaring Devi's feet, and cried, "Jaya vijayi bhava! Be victorious."

In Amravati in Devaloka, Mahishasura heard the Goddess laughing and was angry. Who dared make such a noise, when he, Mahisha, ruled heaven and earth? He sent his scouts abroad to discover what the weird thunder was. "Bring me the devil who dares make such a noise. I will drink his blood! But, then, who can this be? The Devas I have crushed, and they and their kind hide in the wilderness in terror of me. No Asura would dare make such a terrible noise, for every demon in creation serves me. Go! Find out who roars like this, and bring the villain to me."

His scouts flew from Devaloka, and it was not hard for them to trace the macabre laughter to its source. Soon, Mahisha's men stood before the Devi Bhagavati, mounted on her fulvous beast, and, oh, she was completely beautiful! And entirely terrible, as well. They saw her carrying unearthly ayudhas in her many hands, and quaffing wine repeatedly from Kubera's golden cup, until the scarlet stuff dribbled down her chin. Mahisha's Danavas took one look at the lucific Devi, they couldn't bear the splendour and the fear of her, and they fled howling.

They flew back to their master of darkness and cried, "Lord, it is a woman who makes the strange sound. She is neither human, nor an Asuri but ah, she is exceptional and so beautiful that her beauty is a thing of terror. She is radiant, O Mahisha; she has many arms and carries a different weapon in each one. She sits astride a golden lion, wears ornaments such as we have not dreamt of, and swills crimson wine from a precious goblet. She drinks endlessly, and then she laughs! The sound we hear is her laughter.

O King, the Devas lie on their faces worshipping her, and they sing her praises devoutly. But she is so refulgent that we could not look at her for more than a moment, and we were seized with a dread worse than that of death. We fled back to you. We don't know who the strange woman is, nor what she intends."

Mahisha rose from his throne and stalked Indra's crystal sabha, the Sudharma, and he was both a great beast and an evil king. Some feverish passion seemed to have gripped him, some vast excitement. He gave a short bellow, and his deep eyes glowing and a smile on his face, said, "Fetch her to me! At first try to coax her here with soft words and priceless gifts. But if these gentler means fail, then bring her by force. But be careful, I do not want her harmed. Oh no, I want her for myself, I mean to make her my queen. For, by her very laughter I can tell that she is fit for me, and for no one else. Fly, my friends, I cannot wait to see her, to hold her in my arms!"

And at his great buffalo's black loin, they saw the moist, scarlet evidence of his lust. At once, Mahisha's commanders mustered a legion of the boldest fighting Asuras, and went to fetch the strange woman to their Lord. They went with elephant and horse, chariot and flitting vimana. By now, the Devi had left Vaikuntha, and they found her in a secluded tapovana.

Mahisha's generals saw her, and were awestruck again. They could not bear to look at her for the mantle of brilliance that covered her; it was like gazing at a star from too near. From a safe distance, their leader spoke to her with utmost courtesy.

"My master asks to you come to him, lovely lady, whoever you are. My master Mahisha is the Lord of the three worlds. He is invincible, no man can kill him, no Deva or Gandharva, Kinnara or Kimpurusha, Asura or Rakshasa: for he has a boon from Brahma. My Lord heard you laugh across the firmament, and was enthralled. We described you to him, and he lost his heart to you. Devi, come with us to our master; he can be man or beast, as he pleases, whatever you want him to be. O Mrigakshi, fawn-eyed one, come with us to our king."

And Mahisha's general fell silent,' Vyasa Muni said."

TWENTY-ONE

"IN A MOMENT, VYASA RESUMED, 'WHEN THE CORUSCATE DEVI HEARD Mahisha's message to her, she threw back her head in a most fetching way and gave another great laugh. Then she said in her voice deep as the rumbling of thunderclouds, "You don't know me, Asura. I am the Devi Maha Lakshmi, and I have come to kill little Danavas like you. The Devas live in terror of your master, they have been deprived of their share in the yagnas of the worlds. The earth has become a sinister place, since your lord rules it.

Yet, O Danava, you speak honeyed words to me and I am pleased by them. Otherwise, I would have made you a heap of ashes by now, with fire from my eye that can burn up the very stars. Go back to your master, and tell him this from me:

Evil One, leave Devaloka at once and burrow down into Patala where you belong. Or I will cut you into shreds with my arrows and send you to Yama's halls, as I have done with countless Asuras like you before. Listen to me, foolish Danava, for I am showing you mercy. I am no man, that Brahma's boon will save you from me. I am the Devi, and I have come just to kill you."

When Mahisha's general heard the terrible Goddess, he said, still mildly, and smiling, "Devi, you are only a woman, and our master Mahisha is the greatest warrior in the three worlds. How can you kill him? You have no army, and just look at you: how delicate you are, ah, how beautiful. But my Lord Mahisha is immense; he is half a man and half a great black beast! His legions are savage and endless, Devi. Mahisha will crush you as easily as an elephant disposes of a garland of mallika flowers.

What you say is true, that our king is an enemy of the Devas; but you, Devi, he already worships! Which is why I speak sweet words to you instead of killing you. You are young, you are delectable; my master offers you his entire kingdom, he offers himself as your servant. Forsake this reasonless anger, Devi, the only field upon which you should engage with our master is a bed of swan's-down. And then you will know perfect bliss!"

But she said, "You are a fool's general, Danava. And only a fool would choose to seek his death at a woman's hands, for only a fool would fail to remember how humiliating it is for a warrior to be killed by a woman. Asura, remember that when fate turns against one, a blade of grass becomes a thunderbolt. Fate has turned against your king now for his long villainy. Not his great body and his immense strength, nor the vast army that he commands, and not all his fierce commanders shall save him from me. His most impregnable fortress will not keep me out.

When any jiva is born into this world, all his pleasures and pains, his loves and sorrows, are already written and come with him; and so, too, does the moment of his death and he will not live a moment past that time. Go; tell your master what I said, say to him his death is nearer than he knows. If he wants to live let him take his army and his people and fly down into Patala, at once. There is no third way."

That Asura general, who was also Mahisha's chief minister, fell to thinking, should he kill the woman on the lion for what she dared say? But then his king had professed his desire for her; he wanted to marry the strange woman. The sage Asura decided he must not be rash. For if he killed the woman, Mahisha would be angry as he would be if she killed him.

The Asura went back to Mahisha, and said, "The beautiful Devi sits upon her golden lion with weapons in all her eighteen hands. I said to her, 'My master Mahisha, Lord of the worlds, wants you for his queen, lovely one. Marry him and you shall be a queen of queens, and mistress of all the wealth in Swarga, Bhumi and Patala.'

But, my Lord, she laughed in my face. She roared, "Your master is the son of a buffalo, and I mean to sacrifice him to the Devas, as should happen to beasts like him. Which woman in any world will have that monster for her husband? Tell him to find another buffalo like his mother, with whom he can lock horns. As for me, tell him I said, 'Flee Devaloka, at once. Plunge down to Patala, where you belong, Rakshasa, or I will tear you limb from limb!'

My Lord, I would have killed her at once, but you told me she was not to be harmed because you love her. It is a dilemma, O King; I cannot tell whether you should woo her or fight her. You must do as you choose, and the future is hidden from us."

Mahisha called a full sabha of his ministers, and said, "Wise ones, who is this Devi who rides a lion and roars like the thunder at the end of time? Is she really who she says she is? I want to know what counsel you have for me, my friends."

The ministers said, "Lord, a great emperor's court teems with sycophants and flatterers."

"To give lofty advice is easy, when one isn't sincerely concerned for the welfare of he who seeks counsel."

"But, the truth is, no man can see the future, and which man who cannot see the future can advise you on this thing? Who can tell who the woman is, and what she will do?"

They spoke in consort, non-committally, and their Lord growled, "I would hear what each of you thinks, one by one."

Virupaksha stood forth, a lean and ominous Asura. He said confidently, "The woman spoke in arrogance, my Lord! Empty words, hoping to frighten you." He laughed evilly, "We all know how strong many women hope to be, and this one dares to threaten you, Mahishasura, sovereign of the three worlds! If you are nervous that no boon protects you against her, then send me to fight the woman. I will bring her to you bound in a coil of serpents. And when I throw her at your feet, oh master, she will forsake her arrogance and submit to you. She will be yours, to do with as you please, and that will end this great debate over nothing."

Virupaksha sat down and Durdhara rose, an Asura so ugly that some enemies had swooned on the battlefield just to look at him. He said, "Peerless king of worlds, Virupaksha speaks wisely, but I have something to add to his wisdom. She desires you, master! Her fierce words are meant to stoke your lust. Women are never direct my Lord, but always say the opposite of what they truly feel. The harsh message she sent also means the opposite of what it says.

She says, 'I will pierce you with my arrows.' But who does not know that a woman's weapons are not arrows, but her sidelong glances. Yet, she speaks of arrows. So what she means, O Mahisha, is that she would be pierced by your shaft, my Lord. She says, 'I will lay you low on the field of battle.' Ah, my king, if once you begin to know what she is really saying, it can mean only one thing."

"And what is that, Durdhara?"

"That she means to ride my lord, after laying you down softly on your back," said Durdhara to an appreciative murmur from the sabha. But he hadn't finished his unusual analysis, "She says she will have your life, and surely Master, she means the seed from your loins! There is no mistake my Lord; she is mad for you and means to have you. The rest is only sweet provocation to excite you.

I have no doubt she means to give in to you soon; sama and dana are the ways to win her swiftly. Send her a loving message, and some gifts through me, O Mahisha, and I swear she shall be your love-slave in no time."

Thus, spoke the hideous Durdhara, but his comrade, the ancient Asura Tamra rose at once and said, "My Lord, I disagree with Durdhara. I saw evil dreams all of last night. Whenever I awoke trembling, I heard the birds of day singing dismally in the trees of night. In a final dream near dawn, a frail woman wearing a black gown that covered her from head to foot, stood in an inner courtyard of this palace and wept piteously and unceasingly. And this morning we have all seen the bats and owls that wheel through this city as if to foretell calamity, and they all cried out in fell voices. All the omens portend some terrible danger.

Then, just think of it, O King, who is this woman with no known mother or father who has appeared suddenly out of nowhere, riding a golden lion? Mahisha, who has ever heard of a woman having eighteen arms? And a deadly weapon in every hand! It must be as she says, that the Devas have summoned her from their Shaktis to kill you, since only a woman can. I say don't believe she means to make love to you. She has come to fight, and I would take an army out to meet her."

Mahishasura stalked through his great sabha on cloven hooves, pondering the conflicting counsel. Then he brightened, and said, "Well, then, take an army with you and go to meet her. Speak to her gently at first; offer her ornaments and gold. If she is amenable to persuasion, bring her thus to my bed. Only if she resists you and strikes the first blow, must you attack her with weapons. She is exceptional, Tamra, and even if you are forced to fight her do so with honour, and don't be barbarous when she is vanquished."

Suddenly, Tamra felt a sinking sensation in the pit of his stomach, as if Yama had stroked him. But that Asura bowed to his king and, taking an immense legion with him, went to confront the woman who rode a lion. As he went, the invincible Tamra saw all sorts of evil omens around him, and he shivered within himself though he showed nothing of what he felt to his warriors.

Since they went by swift vimanas, or mounted on uncanny beasts that flew as quickly as the sky-ships, Tamra and his legion arrived where the Devi stood between heaven and earth, her lion treading air. All around her there echoed the hymns of the Devas, praising her, and Tamra saw she wore wonderful wildflower garlands around her throat, and also radiant ornaments with gem-stones that sparkled like coloured stars.

The Asura approached her, humbly, as his king had instructed, and said, "Devi, my Lord Mahisha has heard of your unequalled beauty, and wants you to become his queen. My master has vanquished the Devas, and now he rules heaven and earth. He wants to share his boundless kingdom with you; he would make love with you in the fragrant Nandana in Amravati, and set you beside him on the throne of the worlds, above which there is no other.

Ah, Devi, look at you, how lovely you are, surely destined to be the queen of all creation. Look at your arms like lotus-stalks, and your hands like the flowers themselves. Tell me, why do your perfect hands all bear such savage weapons? What need have you of arrows when your eyes serve the same purpose? One glance from them is enough to pierce anyone's heart.

Then, just think, if you become my Lord Mahisha's queen, what magnificent sons both of you will have to rule the universe one day. Devi, what higher satisfaction does a woman have than becoming a mother? How else does she fulfil her womanhood? I beg you, come with me to my Lord, who waits eagerly for you."

But she laughed in Tamra's face, and said, "Fool, go and tell your master, who has obviously lost his wits for lust, that I say to him: I am not a she-buffalo like his mother, with horns on my head, and chewing grass, with a black tail and a great belly! I have no need for a husband, for I already have one—He who is truly Lord of everything, the witness of the ages, who is beyond desire. Tell him that Siva, the Auspicious One, is my husband; and would any woman abandon such an immaculate Purusha for a dull-witted, insignificant Asura?

Tell Mahisha, O Tamra, that I repeat what I said earlier to him. Let him take all his Asuras and fly down into Patala where he belongs."

Suddenly her eyes blazed crimson, and she was truly terrible before Tamra. She threw back her head and gave such a howl that galaxies shivered on their great peregrinations. Earth and sky trembled, and pregnant Danava women across the worlds miscarried in terror. Tamra, who was nearest the Devi, thought the end of the universe had come. He turned and fled from her.

Tamra arrived before his king, and his eyes were wide with fear. In a quavering voice, he said, "She deafened us with her howl, and then her golden beast roared so loudly, that we fled before our bodies were shattered by the sounds."

Mahisha called another sabha of his foremost Danavas. He said to them, "What shall we do now, my friends? Wise ones, our race's future depends on this council, and how secret what we decide here remains. We still know hardly anything about the woman who rides the lion, except what she herself says. We know she carries potent weapons, and that her roar and her howl are dreadful and exciting! My lords, those who say that it is only fate who decides all things are weaklings and cowards. Who has ever seen this fate? I say that what we achieve by our strength and our wisdom is fate. So, give me your counsel now, what shall we do next?"

Vidalaka, who was taller than any other demon there except Mahisha himself, rose, and said in his voice deep as an abyss, "First of all, let us discover whose wife she is who comes so brazenly to seek battle with us. For myself, I feel the Devas have created her out of their own Shaktis. When war breaks out, I have no doubt they will set her before them and then Vishnu, Rudra, Indra and the others will kill the rest of us. While she, the Devi, will seek you out on the field, my Lord, and fulfil the reason for her birth: to kill you.

I beg you Mahisha, to take care. As for us, our dharma is to serve you and die for you if need be; for, everything we have today is because of you. But as for victory or defeat, it is impossible to tell which one we shall have against the Devi."

Durmukha said, "Even if we are to be vanquished by her, we cannot but face her in battle. Why, great Mahishasura's army fought against the Devas of heaven and prevailed. All the power and wealth we enjoy today is because of our heroism, my Lord. And can we now fly down to Patala, because a woman with eighteen arms tells us to? No, that would bring eternal shame upon our heads, shame worse than death.

So, if she must have battle with us, let us fight; for, there is no shame in dying in war."

Vaskala, whose voice was so mellifluous that he could seduce any woman by just speaking to her, now rose and said, "Have no fear, Lord. I by myself will kill this Chandika on her beast, whose eyes already roll in her head from a surfeit of wine. Her courage is only the bravado of the purple grape. I fear no enemy, great King. Why, for you I will kill Indra, Yama, Kubera, Vayu and Agni, Vishnu, Rudra, Surya and Soma! What then is this drunken, arrogant woman? She is mad with wine, just send me to fight her and I will bring her pretty head back to you."

Durmukha seemed to agree with Vaskala's sentiment. He put in, "Surely the Devas have created this woman of illusion just to put fear in your heart; for, they can do nothing else to you. Let her come not with eighteen, but a hundred hands, and I will cut them all off, and her head, for an encore!"

All the Asuras roared their approval of what Vaskala and Durmukha said, and Mahishasura was emboldened,' said my master Dwaipayana to Parikshita's son, whose yagna had been prevented," says the Suta in the emerald Naimisa, forest of wonder.

TWENTY-TWO

"VYASA RESUMED, 'THE TWO DANAVAS, VASKALA AND DURMUKHA, HUGE as hills, went with their vile legions to confront the Devi. In voices like rolling thunder they said to her, "Beautiful One, we ask you to tread the high path of wisdom. No one in the universe except our Lord Mahishasura is fit to be your husband. Our master will come to you in a splendid human form, and in his embrace, you will know the bliss for which you were born. You will be queen of the worlds, as you are destined to be, and every other woman in creation will envy you. Only, say that you will submit to our emperor and worship him."

But the Devi laughed in their monstrous faces again, and said, "Do you think I am moved by greed and passion, that I will stoop to worship an Asura? Marriage, witless fools, is between equals. How can a Goddess, then, marry the lowest of all animals, the beast Mahisha? Go tell your master, whose body is as gross as an elephant's, who wears two horns on his head, that I say he should fly down into Patala, or prepare to die. I have not come to marry your king, but to kill him!"

At which the Danavas grew crimson-eyed with wrath. They seized up their bows and, their breath fiery, were ready to fight. But the serene Devi stood unmoved before them, a drunken smile curving her lips. She still swilled freely from the flagon of wine, that could never be drained, and the Danavas had never seen such contempt in an enemy's eyes before.

Vaskala and Durmukha roared like ten thunderclouds, and loosed a tempest of arrows at the Devi. Their shafts were of potent sorcery, and blazed with dark fires fierce enough to consume armies. But she began to make the sweetest, strangest, sounds of delight at their attack, and answered their fire with five arrows of her own for each one of theirs.

Arrogant Vaskala decided to challenge her more closely, and, growing twice as large as he had been before, he flew his open vimana nearer. The wiser Durmukha remained behind, a spectator now. Such a battle erupted between the Asura and the Devi; the very sky seemed to be a livid stream of arrows, which extinguished themselves against one another. Both Vaskala's archery and the Devi's were transcendent. Time and again, the Goddess' laughter would ring across the firmament, and Asura soldiers would cower in fear.

Vaskala's vimana was swift as thought through the air, but the golden lion was quicker, easily frustrating the demon's blinding manoeuvers. Growing impatient, Vaskala leapt out of his vimana onto solid ground, and charged the Devi with his mace in his hand. But, ah, she was quicker than thinking and smashed him down disdainfully with her own gada, with a stroke like lightning from one of eighteen hands. Vaskala fell with a sigh, spitting blood.

But he was a great Asura of his ancient race, and sprang up almost at once; seizing up another iron club he rushed howling at the Devi once more. But, with a beautiful smile, she impaled him on her trident with another hand, and Vaskala died with her face filling his final moment, and his heart bursting with the realisation of who she truly was.

When Durmukha saw Vaskala slain, his anxiety turned to fury. He raised his conch and blew an earth-shaking blast on it. At once, his legions swarmed around him, thousands and thousands of hideous and magnificent demons. Some of them had three and five heads, some had no heads at all, some had just one glaring eye on their faces, and others glowered dementedly from ten and even twenty eyes. Some were tall as trees, others squat and thick, but naked, with monstrous phalluses dangling. There were Asuras in that bizarre army who were neither man nor woman, and others who were both and coupled lewdly with themselves, while they came into battle, carrying the most macabre weapons to be found anywhere in creation.

That Asura legion teemed around its general, Durmukha the Ugliest, and it rode in sleek vimanas or was mounted on the backs of the most bizarre beasts: flying rat and boar, serpent and unknown rodent, black elephant and bison, panther and wolf, hyena and jackal, crow, kite and dog, vulture and huge, crimson-faced squamous lizards, and other strange creatures, some of which were Asuras themselves that had changed their shapes to be mounts for their comrades.

At its terrible general's command, that legion of the night swept from every direction at the lustrous Devi, who sat serenely upon her glowing beast. Like thunderclouds scudding from everywhere to eclipse the sun in the sky, the Asuras flew at Mahamaya from four sides. Then, her lion threw back his black-maned head, and gave a roar that silenced the screeching and roaring and howling of the demons and beasts that rushed at them in a tide.

As if her lion's roar was a signal to her, the Goddess on its back erupted into movement. Her eighteen hands were eighteen livid blurs around her, and it seemed that eighteen armies of light fell upon the dark host that attacked her. In an incredible moment, long as lives, an array of awesome weapons flashed at the charging demons. In less time than it takes to tell, as if in another mandala of event, the Asura legion was desiccated by luminous ayudhas of every sort. They died with relucent arrow, shining mace, splendid spear, calescent trisula, nitid astra, whirling chakra, incandescent danda, aqueous paasa, blazing naracha, screaming Shakti, explosive musala and tomara, and other weapons too profound to describe.

One moment she stood facing the dreadful army rushing at her from every side; the next, she had loosed a flash flood of scarlet gore across that field, a river on which severed heads floated like gourds that children first learn to swim with, and headless bodies like weird fish, while some were more like whales in those eerie schools. In no time, the fleet of scavengers that had served the Asuras as mounts, the wolves and jackals, the vultures, crows, kites, dogs and hyenas, turned in glee on their slain riders, and fed avidly on their corpses, standing knee-deep in the river of blood. The great lizards quenched their thirst at that river. The stench of corpses hung heavily on the air, and the piteous cries of the dying mingled with this pall.

Perhaps, in shock more than anything else, Durmukha roared at the Devi, "I say to you, foolish woman, take great Mahisha for your husband, or I will send you to your death!"

The Devi laughed horribly. "Your own death is so near you, foolish Demon, that she drives you mad and you rave at me. I mean to kill you first, and then the she-buffalo's son!"

Durmukha immediately covered her in a mantle of flaming astras. The Devi tore that veil of darkness to shreds. Then she shattered the Asura's chariot that flew on land and air with equal facility. Durmukha hefted a glittering mace of immense power, and ran at her. He struck her lion a blow like an earthquake, but that beast only roared even louder and was not hurt.

The lion's roar had hardly subsided, when one of the Devi's exquisite arms made an arc in the sun that her demon adversary hardly saw. It was a left hand that bore a battle-axe, and it cut Durmukha's hoary head from his neck so cleanly that it took him a long moment to realise that she had killed him. Why, it was only after his head lay on the ground, that the Danava gave his last, astonished roar. Then, his body big as a hill swayed and toppled before the triumphant Goddess, and a smile lit her beautiful face. The Asura's dark blood flowed in a rivulet around her chariot-wheels.

Heaven and earth resounded with the supernal music of Gandharvas. The Devas poured down fragrant, barely tangible petal-rain on her out of their subtle realms, and Apsaras danced above her in the clouds, and a thousands Rishis, Siddhas, Kinnaras and Vidyadharas cried her name in joy, and hailed her with 'Jaya!'

What was left of the Danava army fled back to their sovereign who sat on Indra's throne. When Mahishasura heard that Vaskala and Durmukha were slain, his bellow reverberated through the three worlds. Froth on his black lips, his tail twitching in frenzy behind him, his eyes crimson and rolling dementedly, he roared, "How can this be? They were awesome warriors, yet a mere woman has killed them. A hundred thousand of my fiercest Asuras have perished. Now what shall I do?"

Chikasura and Tamra cried together, "Never fear, Lord. We will bring you her delectable head."

They went with a horrible army to kill the lovely Devi. When they had surrounded her like a sea of all the malignant beasts in creation, she raised her conch to her lips and blew an echoing blast on it, and at the same time pulled on her bowstring with another petal-soft hand, and it seemed the sky would crack in two at those sounds. Her face shone so brightly that the Danava warriors ran in all directions.

But Chikasura roared at them, "Cowards! What fear overcomes you? Stand and fight, craven Danavas, and watch me cut this woman's head from her fine throat!"

And when he threatened them with weapons, they swarmed around that Asura general again, though they kept their eyes turned away from the terribly splendid Devi. Then Chikasura came nearer, and when he saw how beautiful she was, he was moved to say, "O, Lotus-eyes, why do you roar so dreadfully? Ah, look at you, how delicate your limbs are, how entirely desirable. Devi, how I hate the thought of having to kill you. I have never heard of a woman taking the field of war before. Why, your skin is so soft that even the petals of a mallika flower would injure it. What, then, of the barbs of war?

Ah, this Kshatriya dharma is such a cruel law, that decrees I have to face you in battle today, Devi, fragile one. I have heard you slew a hundred thousand Asuras. I had thought the weapons of a woman are her full breasts, with black nipples, and the damp softness between her thighs. Any man would gladly lay his life down before those weapons! Why, a look from your eyes would be enough to vanquish the bravest warrior. Yet, here you are, riding your lion, with other ayudhas in your hands. Your place is in a bed of down, lady, with your legs garlanded around the back of a fortunate man, perhaps my master, while he buries his weapon of love in you, again and again!

Lovely one, what great goodness have you discovered in war, that you have come armed before us? Do the roars and screams of warriors attract you, or is it the sight of weapons flashing in the sun, and the scarlet springs they draw when they find their mark? Surely, the sight of men with their limbs and heads hewn off, and hyenas and jackals, kites and vultures tearing greedily at their flesh, lapping their blood, isn't the sight that excites you, Devi? Only cunning poets are enamoured of these spectacles, and always from a safe distance; only they say that those who die in battle find heaven for themselves. But who knows what is the truth about death or war, beyond their brutality, and the anguish they bring? And poets, as we know, are in the employ of kings whom they must flatter.

Therefore beautiful one, I beg you to forsake this war. Come away with me to my Lord Mahisha's palace, or, indeed, go anywhere you please, but abandon the idea of fighting. You are a woman, you do not belong on the field of battle."

She said, "Danava, you know nothing of dharma. But that is only to be expected, for who else would serve a buffalo's son? I mean to make a lake of your master's blood, and yours as well, Demon. And my fame will live forever, for what I do. So, prepare either to flee to Patala, where you and your master belong; or prepare to die."

Chikasura's face was a mask when he heard her; his eyes glinted in rage. He bent his bow in a circle and loosed a flurry of arrows at her. But, amazingly, she cut those shafts in two, perfectly along their length, with her own wizardly volley. Roaring, the demon charged her in his chariot to drag her off her beast. Suddenly she struck him fifty blows with her mace in less than a moment, her hand swifter than time, and the colossal Asura fell out of his chariot in a faint.

Tamra saw Chikasura fall, and rushed at the Devi. She crooned to him, "Come, Danava, come, your death is waiting for you. But then, you Asuras are all such weaklings that fighting you is like fighting small children. Where is your master, the idiot, now? Plotting how to save his worthless hide? Danava, I have no desire to kill you; it is your master I have come to kill. So, save yourself, go back to the buffalo's son and send him to me."

With a roar, Tamra unleashed a gale of fire at her. He was a quicksilver archer, and he and the Devi fought a keen duel, her laughter rocking the field. Then Chikasura woke from his faint, and came howling back into battle. The two Asuras fought her at once, but she held them off effortlessly, still drinking from her flagon of wine whenever she cared to.

But soon, she tired of this battle. She was after Mahisha; it was him she had come for. In a moment, her archery was a supernatural thing; Chikasura and Tamra had the fine armour they wore shredded on their backs. Those Demons sprouted crimson kimsuka flowers of spring all over their huge bodies. But the wounds only served to rouse them to greater valour, and the battle grew more heated than before.

Roaring so the earth trembled under him, Tamra rushed at the Devi's lion and smote the beast on its head with his gada, a blow like thunder. Briefly, the lion staggered where he stood. Tamra's triumphant laughter rocked the earth. But it was the last sound he ever made. In a flash, the Devi cast her battle-axe at him and took his slim head off his swollen body in a scarlet blast.

Seeing his precious friend perish, Chikasura abandoned caution and flew at the Devi with his own battle-axe in his hand. But she met his onrush coolly, with three arrows: the first shaft smashed his axe in shards, the next cut his hand off at the wrist, so he screamed, the third struck his head off in a red geyser. The two Asuras' blood flowed in a brook, and their legions fled back to Amravati, where Mahishasura waited impatiently for some news.

Again, petal rain fell from heaven on the victorious Devi, and Gandharvas sang her praises in unearthly tongues,' my master Vyasa said to the king of the Kurus," says the sublime Suta in the jungle.

TWENTY-THREE

"'THE NEWS THAT CHIKASURA AND TAMRA WERE SLAIN STRUCK MAHISHA like an astra. Tears welled in his eyes, and he sat plunged in silence on his throne. Then he sent Asiloma and Vidalakhya, two of his wisest Asuras, laden with all sorts of treasures, to the Devi.

Asiloma was a monstrous Danava, but blessed with a serene manner. He said pacifically to the Goddess, "Devi, tell us why you want war with Mahisha. He means you no harm; indeed, he sends you a treasure of precious gifts to show his sincerity. We have come to make peace with you, lovely one.

Ah, life is full of pleasure, if only you learn how to enjoy it. Beautiful, powerful one, I beg you, see the folly of the path you have chosen for yourself. Why are you killing these Danavas without any reason? They have done you no harm, yet you have made widows of their wives, and their children fatherless."

She said, "Demon, I am only a witness in the world. I have no desire, and I am eternally free. I have no enmity with anyone, but when great evil rears its head I must crush it or the worlds would be plunged in darkness, and where will the good find refuge then? I have come to restore dharma, Daitya, for your evil master means to extinguish it forever.

The Devas and the Trimurti preserve the worlds, and they too are born again and again to keep dharma alive. But your king has a boon that only a woman can kill him, and who else shall that woman be, but me? Your king is an enemy of dharma, Asura, and I mean to have his head. He sits upon a lofty throne, far from his proper station in life, and darkness sweeps the three realms. He abuses the boon he has. If you truly want peace, I will give Mahisha another chance. Let him abandon Devaloka and return to Patala where he belongs, where the noble Prahlada dwells."

Asiloma, who was a wise demon, turned to his comrade Vidalakhya, "Danava, you have heard what she says. What shall we do now?"

Vidalakhya, who was a scholar of the Shastras, said, "Our Lord Mahisha knows that he will die if he meets this Devi in battle. Yet, he is so full of arrogance that he prefers death to doing what she asks, which, after all, is only just. Our king saw how Durmukha, Vaskala, Chikasura and Tamra perished, and their legions with them. He heard how easily she slew those Danavas, who have by themselves put armies to rout. Still, he did not hesitate to send us to confront the terrible Devi, to send us to our deaths.

We are like puppets, my friend, and the puppet-master holds our lives in his hands. Mahisha has already heard the Devi's message to him three times. If he meant to do as she says, he would already have abandoned Devaloka and gone down into Patala, which my blood longs for! But he does not mean to strike peace with her, Asiloma. I fear our master has chosen to die, as if death were a bewitching woman in whose arms he means to lie forever.

Mahisha will not be pleased to hear the same message from the Devi again. It is best we fight her, and even die ourselves, rather than return to him with her haughty words."

Asiloma could not argue with what his friend said, so both those Asuras donned their kavachas and mounted their chariots in readiness for battle. Though they were learned and refined demons, they were ferocious warriors as well. Vidalakhya gave a blood-chilling roar, and shot seven arrows as swiftly as one at the Goddess on her lion. Asiloma stood at a slight remove, watching. He did not stand long thus, for some of the Devi's hands moved in a blur. She annihilated Vidalakhya's volley in the air, and then struck his arms and his head off with three luminous shafts of her own.

Nothing else for it, Asiloma came to battle, though his heart shrank in fear at what he had seen. The wise Danava said humbly to the Devi, "My master Mahisha could never tell what was true from what was pleasant. But I dare not tell him this; why, I would rather give up my life to you, Devi. So, fight!"

And he covered her in a cloak of arrows, humming with occult power. She cut them down and struck him with a score of shafts, so that he bled all over his body, and was indeed like a kimsuka tree in bloom. He saw he would die and wanted to be done with it. Seizing up an iron mace, he sprang out of his chariot and ran at her. He, too, struck the lion a terrific blow on its head. The golden beast lashed out with its claws, and Asiloma's left arm hung limp from its shoulder.

But, roaring, and braver with pain, he leapt straight up onto the lion's broad shoulder and swung his gada at the Devi's lovely face. But the blow never landed, for quick as a flash she had struck off his head with her axe. Seeing their generals slain so quickly, the Danava army began to flee. Growling fearfully, the lion hunted them, and killed a good number before the rest escaped.

When Mahisha heard the news, he decided it was time to take the field himself. That Demon's heart fluttered at the very thought of seeing the Devi face to face. Strangely, he did not care that she was his enemy and that she had killed so many of his bravest, most loyal Asuras. No, she obsessed him night and day, and he must have her for his bed, he must hear her cries as he thrust his immense manhood in her body soft as lotus-petals. She must become his love slave. Nothing else would do, thought Mahisha, who had always had what he wanted.

But then, she may be repulsed by the sight of him as he usually was: half a black, shaggy beast with a tail and two horns on his head. So with his powerful maya, he easily assumed a resplendent human form; so, wearing lustrous silks and shimmering ornaments, he was as handsome as Kamadeva. The women in his own palace felt faint to see him like that, and he set out with an endless wave of soldiers to conquer the Devi Bhagavati.

When she saw him marching towards her, she raised her conch to her lips and blew a bass note on it, deep as the first sound from which time and place were made. Mahisha came on serenely.

He said to the Devi, "It is sweet delight that all the world hankers after. Lovely, lovely one, delight is never found in isolation but in the company of a lover."

He stopped to stare at her, he could hardly believe that anyone so beautiful could exist. His heart pounding, he went on, "I am your slave from this moment, that my eyes have been fortunate enough to see you. For you are far, far lovelier than I had heard. Your beauty exceeds my wildest dreams. Ah, look at you, Devi: your face, your neck, your breasts, your waist like a sigh, your flaring hips, your thighs, your exquisite legs, your crimson feet.

Yes, my mind is made up, my life has changed forever from this moment: I mean to spend the rest of my days serving you as your slave. I will give up my enmity with Indra's people; you only have to ask it of me. I will do anything for you, why, I think I would gladly give up my very life for your sake. Now, come to me; you belong at my side, you are meant to be my queen. Come to me, and let my life begin anew."

But she threw back her perfect head, and laughed. "Gross Danava, I have not the faintest interest in pleasure. For I have eternal bliss, and what pleasure can compare with that? As for a man, the supreme Purusha is my Lord, how can I want any other, let alone you? Mahisha, seek your peace, for only peace will give you the joy you are seeking. Woman is bondage; she can only bring torment to your life.

Listen to me, Asura. Take yourself down to Patala, which is your natural home. Or else, prepare to die. Seven times you and I have exchanged these same words, you importuning me and me telling you to fly down to Patala or die. The wise say that when even enemies exchange words seven times, friendship is struck up between them. So, as you and I are now friends, I tell you as a friend, go down to Patala if you want to stay alive. But if it is death you are after, come, fight me and I will gladly kill you."

But Mahishasura replied like a man in a dream, "Ah, your body is as soft as lotuses. How can I think of piercing this body with any shaft other than the one of love, in its proper place? Devi, I am Mahishasura who vanquished Hari, Hara and the Lokapalas. Think again before you decide to fight me. I beg you, instead, be my queen; or else, go back to where you came from in peace. Ah, you are beauty incarnate, the loveliest woman in creation. Devi, what fame shall I gain for myself if I kill you? What happiness?

Contrary to what you say, no man on earth can be happy without a woman, and no woman without a man. The greatest joy is a perfect union between a man and woman. For all your beauty, I see you are lacking in wisdom. Who has put the foolish thought into your head that pleasure is not worth pursuing? Look, my lady, at how happy Vishnu is with Lakshmi, Brahma with Saraswati, Rudra with Uma, and Indra with Sachi. You and I together shall be happier than any of these; we shall be master and mistress of the universe.

Devi, I think Kamadeva sees how delicate is your skin and is afraid to pierce you with even his flowery shafts of love. For, the man who wants you to be his wife stands before you and you turn your face from him. Or, perhaps, my enemies the Devas have told Kama to look askance at our love. Be that as it may, say that you will be mine now, lovely one, or you will regret it later, when passion strikes your heart. You will regret it as much as Mandodari did her initial pride."

"Who is this Mandodari? Whom did she spurn, that she regretted it later?"

"She was the daughter of Chandrasena, lord of the kingdom of Simhala. When his child came of age, the king began to look for a husband for her. The brahmanas in his court told him there was a prince called Kambugriva, of Madra, who would make the princess a perfect groom. But, spoilt as she was, being a king's eldest daughter and his favourite, Mandodari refused even to consider marriage. Not knowing life or the world, at all, she said to her mother, 'Never! I will never marry. I mean to be a virgin the rest of my life, and take vows of sannyasa. There is nothing as abject in the world as being dependent on a man, and I prefer a life of tapasya for myself. I mean to seek liberation, not bondage, and the wise all say that marriage is an impediment to moksha.

Mother, when a girl marries, she swears by sacred Agni that she will serve her husband in every way. Then, in her father-in-law's house, she is a servant to her husband's mother and his brothers and sisters. All the time she must think of her husband's happiness and not her own. Frequently, her reward is to have her husband marry another, younger woman. Then, even if she is neglected she may never turn her eyes to another man, for that is a grievous sin.

Finally, after a life of suffering, when her husband dies at last, his wife's lot as a widow is dreadful. Where is there any joy at all in marriage? Not a moment of it, if one is honest, mother, and I will never marry!"

Her mother told the king Chandrasena about his daughter's decision. He sighed and accepted it, thinking that perhaps she was indeed sincere about remaining a virgin, and becoming a sannyasini in time. Puberty was upon Mandodari, but she would listen to no entreaty from her mother or her sakhis, even when they described the pleasures of marriage to her in some detail.

One day, the princess went into the nearby vana, with some of her sakhis. It happened that king Virasena of Kosala, of the Ikshvaku line, came hunting in that very forest. Virasena saw the dark and lissom Mandodari from a way off. The handsome young king brought his chariot near, and asked one of of the sakhis, 'Who is your beautiful friend? Tell me who her father is, for I mean to ask him for her hand.'

Seeing how splendid he was, the sakhi asked shyly, 'Tell us who you are first, stranger. What are you doing here in the Simhala kingdom?'

Virasena said, 'I am king of the northern kingdom of Kosala. I have been out hunting, and I think I have lost my way. But, perhaps, fate brought me here just to find your friend, she has captured my heart.'

Hope for her mistress surged in the sakhi, for Virasena was irresistible; moreover, she saw he had an open, honest face. She said, 'My lotus-eyed princess is Mandodari, the daughter of king Chandrasena of this kingdom. She lives yonder in her father's palace.'

Virasena stood trembling, his eyes had never for a moment left Mandodari, who had not so much as looked at him yet. The young king said to the sakhi, 'I see you are a most intelligent girl. Go, tell your princess Mandodari who I am, and tell her I beg her to marry me at once by Gandharva vivaha, so we need waste no time asking her father or my mother. Ah, I have never felt like this about any woman, I can't wait for her to be mine! Tell her I have no other wife, and never shall, if she will be my queen. If she wants to ask her father first, I will wait.' And he stood fairly devouring the princess with his eyes.

The sakhi, who was Mandodari's sairandhri, her bright-eyed flower girl, took the king's message to the princess. And the sprightly girl added her own wisdom, 'Women find heaven for themselves only by serving their husbands, every great Rishi has said so. And then he is so handsome you will be lucky to have him in your bed!'

But Mandodari hardly looked at Virasena, but cried, 'Tell the shameless man to stop staring at me with his lustful eyes. Tell him I am a sannyasin, and to go away.'

Tears in her eyes, the sakhi cried, 'You are spurning fate that brings you such a dashing husband, and he seems so honest as well. Love is powerful, Mandodari, it can strike you down at any time. I beg you take this king to be your husband, before fate grows annoyed with you.'

But the princess would not listen. 'Let fate do as it likes, but for now, I don't mean to marry! Tell the king to leave us alone.'

The sakhi came sadly to Virasena and said, 'It seems my mistress isn't destined to have a handsome husband. Forgive her if you can and be on your way, noble king.' And she showed him his way home.

Broken-hearted, Virasena took his army and made his way back to Kosala, and his capital Ayodhya. His heart burned, for he felt fate had cheated him by showing him the alluring Mandodari, who made him feel what no other woman ever had, and then having her spurn him," said the dreadful Asura Mahisha to the resplendent Devi,' my guru Vyasa said to the Kuru king, Arjuna's great-grandson."

TWENTY-FOUR

"THE DARK DWAIPAYANA, YUDHISHTIRA'S GRANDFATHER, CONTINUED, 'Mahishasura went on, as the Devi listened to him with no emotion on her face, "Mandodari had a sister called Indumati, a pretty girl just two years younger than the elder princess. Soon, Indumati also came of age, and her father arranged a fine swayamvara for her, to which all the eligible princes and kings of Bharatavarsha were invited. Indumati, who was altogether a more sensible girl than her sister, quickly chose a fine-looking young Kshatriya who touched her heart to be her husband.

But that was not all that happened at the swayamvara. By cunning fate, Mandodari too was struck by love's subtle lightning. She saw the lord of Madra, a slim, dark youth with lank hair and a loose-limbed, insouciant manner, and it seemed Kama chose that moment to strike her with all his five flower-shafts. She was pierced, she was helpless, she was raging with love for the young king Charudesna, who had a nose much too large for his face, and rather shifty eyes.

Mandodari was not a princess to wait for what she wanted. In that very sabha, she strode up to her father and announced, 'I have lost my heart to the king of Madra, let us also be married right away.'

Charudesna did not have a savoury reputation, but Mandodari was as adamant about marrying him, immediately, as she had been before about never marrying at all. Her poor father Chandrasena was quite helpless, and Charudesna seemed perfectly willing to have the elusive Mandodari for his wife, especially since she was truly beautiful while her sister Indumati could only be described as being pretty. So, both sisters were given away in marriage to different princes, who, when the ceremonies and rituals were concluded, took their brides back to their kingdoms.

Mandodari was blissful in her husband's home for the first month after she was married. He was an expert lover, and she was too innocent to wonder how this was so, but imagined he was a virgin like herself when they married. As was the custom, Mandodari's father had sent some of her sakhis with his daughter, to be her companions in her new home in Madra. It was the same bright sairandhri who had urged her mistress to marry Virasena in the forest, who came in to the young queen's room one day with her face dark.

'What is the matter, Chitra? You look as if you have seen a pisacha?'

'I would rather not tell, mistress,' replied the girl.

But Mandodari, so used to having her way in everything, would not let her be until she told her what it was that had upset her. At last, the sakhi, who had been the queen's playmate since they were children, blurted, 'I saw your husband just now in the passage, when I was on my way to you.'

'And so?'

'Well, he had that new young maid Shalini with him.'

'What are you trying to say, Chitra?'

'You know the small table that rests against the wall at the far end of the passage, in the dark corner? Well, she was on that table, her back against the wall, and she had her legs draped round your husband's shoulders, while her stood before her and thrust at her as if for his very life.'

Mandodari gasped, she turned red. The next day, Chitra was sent back home to Simhala. In the night, the queen asked her husband about what her sakhi had said, and he laughed, saying the girl had tried to seduce him a week ago, but he had refused her advances and she was angry. She had made up this lie. Chitra was forgotten, and Mandodari spent another contented month with her husband.

But truth will out, and one evening at the time of her sandhya prayers, when she was usually in the puja chamber, Mandodari happened to come into her bedroom to fetch some incense she had left beside her bed. She walked into the room, and stood rooted at the door, her world crumbling around her. For, there on her very bed lay her husband, quite naked on his back; and, in the raw herself, astride him piquantly, so her head was at his groin, and his face buried in hers, was yet another maid-servant, one of her own sakhis.

Mandodari ran sobbing from that room, and before the idols in her room of worship she vowed she would never lie with her husband again, nor even speak to him, but would pursue a spiritual life once more and avidly seek moksha. Now that rash princess remembered how haughtily she had spurned Virasena, how she had indeed broken his heart without a thought. Now, she knew the same anguish that noble prince had felt, when she callously sent him away.

She thought of taking her own life, for she was in torment, that proud woman. But then, the sin of taking one's own life clings to one for many lives. She could not very well go back to her father's house; she would be the laughing-stock ever after. Caught by fate like a rat in a trap, Mandodari bitterly rued having refused the king of Kosala. Every night she saw Virasena's gentle face before her eyes, he haunted her dreams. But, of course, it was now too late for her, and so she must endure the rest of her life as best she could, in misery and prayer.

Devi, like Virasena, I too lay my love at your feet. Don't spurn me, lovely one, and then live to regret it some day, when you find yourself shackled to a man who does not love you, and betrays you at his whim. Come away with me, we were meant to be together. Take me for your husband and we shall rule the worlds, side by side."

But she was unmoved. With the strangest smile, she said, "Go down into Patala, or prepare to fight me. I see that you are a greater fool than I thought that you dare compare me with this Mandodari. Do you even know who I am, Danava? I am the mother of heaven and earth; I am the formless Parashakti. You see me like this because I have come to establish dharma in the worlds, the dharma that you seek to destroy, Demon. I have come to kill you Mahisha, you son of a buffalo. Let us have done with words. Come, fight me now!"

She spoke with scorn sharper than arrows, and at last, it dawned on Mahishasura, Lord of worlds, that she had indeed come to kill him and not to make love. His chest heaved and his eyes burned scarlet when he thought of her arrogance, and how she spurned him again and again, calling him a buffalo's son. That dreadful Asura's breath turned to fire, when he thought of how many of his soldiers she had slain. Before her eyes, he was half a great beast again, big as a hill, with horns long as trees, his body covered in black fur, his long tail flicking from side to side. He stood before the Devi, pawing the earth and bellowing from time to time: awesome Mahishasura, conqueror of the Devas!

But she only laughed to see him like that, as if he was the most comical creature imaginable. In fury, Mahisha covered her with a thousand searing arrows. But she swept them aside with thought-like volleys of her own. Bellowing louder than ever, the Danava shot incendiary astras of dire sorcery at her, but she cut these down contemptuously as well and broke the bow in his hands.

Seeing his Lord held up by the blazing Devi, Durdhara came flying into battle. He struck the Goddess with a poison-tipped shaft that stung like a serpent, plunging brief agony through her blood. With a roar to match Mahisha's bellowing, she struck Durdhara with an explosive astra, blowing him to crimson shreds. Three-eyed, horrific Trinetra shot seven arrows at her, and they found their mark on her perfect body. But she drew them out with a magic spell, and cast her trisula at the demon, piercing him through all three eyes, killing him at once.

Great, wild Andhaka flew blindly into battle and smote the Goddess' lion on its head with an iron club. But the beast reared on its hind legs and brought that Danava down on his back. The lion tore open his chest with claws like whale-hooks and began to feed on his heart. Mahisha still kept up his scathing archery and the Devi contained his fire. Then he pierced her with two elliptical arrows, and she cast a gada heavy as a mountain at him. That club struck Mahisha squarely in the chest and felled him.

When he rose again, the Asura charged his beautiful adversary with his mace in his hand. The Devi's lion loomed in the Danava's path, and Mahisha fetched the beast a stupendous blow. The lion staggered briefly, then leapt at the Demon and raked his chest with claws of iron. Blood flowed down Mahishasura's black chest in four streams, and the lion still rushed at him, again and again, talons flailing.

Suddenly, with maya, Mahisha turned himself into an enormous lion as well, and the two beasts fought, tooth and nail, their roars shaking the holy ground upon which they fought, their blood flowing free under the sun. Slowly, the Asura began to prevail over the Devi's beast. In rage, she struck Mahisha with two narachas like serpents so that his head turned blue and he had to abandon his feline form.

In a flash, the Danava had become an immense bull-elephant, his trumpeting shook the sky to its foundations and the juice of musth flowed copiously from his temples, for, he was maddened by the nearness of the Devi and by battle, too. This behemoth plucked the peaks off nearby mountains and cast them at his lovely enemy like thunder and lightning. But she was imperturbable; she smashed those crags into dust with thaumaturgic astras.

Suddenly the Devi's lion sprang onto the Demon-elephant's head, and mauled him with claws longer than Garuda's talons. In a flash, the elephant vanished and a great and terrible bird, a Sarabha, appeared in its place. Its feathers were streaks of lightning, its beak was a scimitar, its talons were daggers, and it flew at the Devi and her beast with a shrill cry. But she hewed off one of its wings with her battle-axe, and, in a blink, Mahisha was a steaming bull-buffalo again, and charged the Devi with lowered curved horns that seemed as long as time.

Mahisha the buffalo tore up vast hills by their roots and hurled them at the Devi. But she smashed them with stunning volleys from her fluent bow. She still swilled thirstily from her flagon of wine, and her clear and terrible laughter rang out across that endless battlefield and Mahisha thought he would go mad just listening to her.

Then he also threw back his horned head, and bellowed with laughter. He roared at her, "Prepare to die now. lovely one. Let Yama enjoy your youth and beauty. I see now that you are mad, that you came to kill me, Mahisha, Lord of the worlds. I will have your head first, and then the heads of the Deva cowards who sent you here. Stand and fight, woman, I will drink your blood today!"

She roared back, "I mean to end the Devas' fear today. I will part your foolish head from your ugly body. Ah, a little more wine for me, then the earth shall drink your blood!"

She drank again deeply from her golden cup, and her eyes rolled now. Then she set her beast at Mahisha, and for the first time she became the aggressor: she flew at the Asura. The sky was full of divine voices crying encouragement to the Devi; dundubhis, bheris and turiyas echoed all around. Bright petal rain fell around the avenging Goddess, and all that field was steeped in the scents of heaven.

"Jaya!" they cried to her, the Rishis, Gandharvas, Devas, Pisachas, Uragas and Kinnaras, Siddhas, Charanas, Apsaras, and all the other races that suffered Mahisha's tyranny. Meanwhile, Mahisha changed forms swifter than time, becoming one dreadful creature after another, and attacked the Devi with weapons, claws, talons, beaks, fists and his horns and hooves.

Once he struck her squarely through her dark breast with a twin-headed arrow like two serpents. Her eyes turned the colour of the setting sun, and she cast her trisula like lightning at the Demon. The trident struck the Asura through his chest, drawing three fountains of blood from him, as he fell unconscious. But he was up in a moment, and rushing at the Devi as a bull buffalo again, he kicked her in the face with flying hooves so she almost fell off her lion's back.

Seizing his advantage, he gored her and kicked her repeatedly, until she was bathed in her own blood. Then, her eyes glittered like cold blue stars. A spinning chakra, which was the inner Shakti of the Sudarshana, appeared over one of her fingers, flaring like a wheel of the sun. She held it aloft so that the Danava had to shut his eyes.

In a final voice she said to him, "Look Asura, this is your death I have at my finger."

She flicked her wrist forward, and the blinding chakra flashed at Mahishasura. The roar, which erupted from his dark belly, was cut short in his throat. The chakra struck his head from his neck in a blast of blood, which covered all that battlefield red as the kimsukas of spring. Like a mountain stream frothing from a cleft in the rocks, Mahisha's blood gushed from his severed throat, bubbling and warm. His huge body swayed for a moment, its hands still raised to seize the Devi's throat, then it fell with a report that shook the three worlds, and bright Nagas, with jewels in their heads, came slithering up from Patala to see whether time was ending.

When great Mahishasura fell, panic seized his Danavas and that army of thousands fled howling in every direction. The Devi's golden lion chased them and gorged itself on demon-flesh. Glowing now that her task was accomplished, the Goddess took herself off the field of war and waited for the Devas in an auspicious grove of trees.

The Devas appeared there, fell at her feet, and began to eulogise the triumphant Devi. "Oh, it is by your power that Brahma creates, Vishnu preserves and Siva destroys the universe! The Trimurti are helpless without you, Devi, Cause of all causes. Only cunning Pauranikas seduce foolish men away from your feet to worship Vishnu and Siva. They are nothing without you, Devi. You are the primal power from which Hari and Hara were born!

Mother, we thank you, you have freed us of the terrible Mahishasura. The worlds are liberated from evil's yoke. We, the Devas, breathe in peace once more."

The Devi raised her hand over them in blessing, and said, "Is there anything else I can do for you, Devas?"

They replied, "Devi, all our purposes were achieved when you killed Mahisha. Let all the worlds worship you from now. Let your fame be like the very air that men breathe."

She smiled at them radiantly, and then vanished before their eyes,' Muni Vyasa told the Kuru king," says Suta in the blessed forest.

The Rishis of the forest sit agog; surely, the Purana is not over yet. Slowly, rhythmically, Romaharshana continues, "My guru said to king Janamejaya, 'When the Devi vanished, the Devas took up the task of establishing dharma on earth again. Indeed, by the Goddess' grace, and after the death of Mahisha, their mission was not hard. For, dharma is natural to creation and it subsides only when some great evil obscures it.

Compassion and goodness welled naturally, once more, in men's hearts, and in the hearts of all the created. Indra resumed his throne in heaven, and his Lokapalas were again the Lords of the elements and of time. On Mahisha's earthly throne, the Devas set Shatrughna, the king of Ayodhya, of the House of Ikshvaku. Dharma returned to the three worlds.

The clouds gathered again, in season, and fragrant rains fell. The world was blessed with a springtime of plenitude, and her fields were rich with rice and wheat, her trees festive with flowers and fruit. Cows yielded sweet milk now, while their udders had shrivelled and dried during the years of Mahishasura's tyranny.

The forests were full of rapturous bird-song, and the subtle arteries of the earth surged in undiluted joy: that the Gods were in their heaven, and all was well again above and below. The rivers and streams of the earth ran sparkling and crystalline; why, their very waters seemed to sing of the world's deliverance from evil. Charmed lakes were heavy with brilliant lotuses; those mystic flowers had never bloomed when Mahisha lived.

And all men lived in dharma, in harmony with the world and themselves and fulfilling their natural tasks. Most of all, the Godlessness that had raised its head darkly in men's hearts vanished, as if it had been a nightmare from which humankind had now awoken. The Vedas were sung, the Shastras studied, and fires of yagnas lit homes and asramas. Worship was the way once more and it rendered life ambrosial.

It was again a time when it was more natural, and easier, to love your fellow man than hate him. There were no more wars in the world; men were honest and satisfied with what they had. Envy and covetousness left their hearts, as if they had never dwelt there at all. Women were chaste, and their husbands faithful. Children revered their parents, and the tradition of guru and sishya was stronger than ever.

The Brahmanas of the world were exemplary priests, the Kshatriyas were just rulers, the Vaishyas excellent tradesmen, and the Sudras immaculate servitors and artists. No man exploited or abused his fellow, and fine harmony dwelt in all things. The rule of heaven was in the world, and peace and goodness dwelt in men's hearts.

More than anything else, after Mahishasura's death, the worship of the Devi Bhagavati was established on earth. Her temples were everywhere, and her grace. Sickness of spirit and body left the world; men lived fruitful lives, and died only in the fullness of time, when they had achieved all they had been born for. It was a blessed time, and the earth bloomed, and there was harmony in Swarga, Bhumi, and Patala below, by the blessing of the Devi,' Vyasa Muni told the king," the knowing Suta told the Munis of the Naimisa.

TWENTY-FIVE

"THEN, JANAMEJAYA WANTED TO KNOW ABOUT THE TWO OTHER invincible Asuras, Sumbha and Nisumbha, who had also tyrannised the worlds once, and whom the Devi slew. 'Who were they, Muni, that dreadful twain?'

Vyasa said, 'Kalpas passed after Mahishasura's death. The wheel of time spun around and at times the Devas and dharma would rule the three worlds, and at others some great Asura with a boon would usurp Indra's throne in Devaloka, and establish a reign of darkness over the triloka. Usually, an incarnation of Vishnu or Siva would kill the Demon, and peace and truth would return to creation.

But after many manvantaras, two Asuras were born called Sumbha and Nisumbha. They were brothers and awesome Demons. Once, when they were still youths, they came out of Patala, their home, and arrived at Pushkara, Brahma's lake that is perhaps the most sacred place on earth. They sat there in flinchless tapasya, without eating or drinking, locked unmoving in yogasanas, their breath so controlled that they breathed barely five times a day.

It is told they sat for an ajuta, ten thousand years, in dhyana. Their Pitamaha, the Lord Brahma, was pleased with them. He flew down from Brahmaloka on his swan, and stood before those two Danavas. Softly, Brahma the Creator called those two Demons out of their dhyana. When they opened their eyes after so long, they saw him, the resplendent One.

He said to them, "Daityas, I am pleased with your tapasya. Tell me what boon you want, and it shall be yours."

The emaciated Asuras' faces and bodies were covered by ten thousand years' jata, yet they shone. They rose painfully, and walked around their lustrous Grandsire in pradakshina, heads bowed and hands folded. They came before him again, and they were so frail and weak that they collapsed at his feet, panting from the effort of just one circumambulation.

Their voices choked, they said to him, "O Brahman! Pitamaha! Lord of Gods, there is nothing more terrible in the world than death. Ocean of mercy, if you are truly pleased with us, grant us immortality."

"No one in the three worlds can give you that boon. All that live must die; it is the law of the universe. Why, even I, Brahma, will know death, when the time comes for the stars to be extinguished. Ask me for anything else, Daityas, and I will give it to you. Immortality is not in my power to bestow."

The Asuras conferred among themselves, and the time had come after so many ages for someone else to ask for ancient Mahishasura's boon. Sumbha and Nisumbha had perhaps never even heard of that ancestor of theirs, who once asked Brahma for the very boon they now asked for.

Sumbha said, "Lord, grant us that no male of any race or species of Swarga, Bhumi or Patala can kill us. No Deva or Gandharva, or any of the celestials; no Daityas, Danava, Asura, Rakshasa, Gana, Bhuta, Yaksha, Pisacha; no man, bird, fish or beast. There is no woman anywhere that can harm us, so we won't ask for a boon against women."

Brahma, who remembered Mahisha of old, smiled. The thought flitted across his mind that perhaps it was time again for the Devi to incarnate herself. The Pitamaha said, "I grant your boon, Asuras."

When Brahma had vanished before their eyes, Sumbha and Nisumbha went back to their home in Patala. Now, they called great Bhrigu, best of Munis, and told him about their tapasya and the boon they had from Brahma. He saw that the future belonged to those Daityas, and agreed to be their priest. He wrought an auspicious golden throne, and on an auspicious day Sumbha, who was the older, was crowned king of his people.

Word went out like wildfire that once more a great sovereign sat on a throne in Patala, and Asuras from the three worlds, who had lived in an abject condition for a yuga, toiling under the Deva yoke, swarmed to Sumbha. Millions of fierce and bitter Daityas came, wanting to have power again, and honour. Among the greatest demons that arrived to serve Sumbha, the new emperor of darkness, were the feral brothers Chanda and Munda of untold strength, and their legions that had repulsed Deva armies across the galaxies. Dreadful Dhumralochana arrived with his sinister forces to discover for himself whether the new Daitya emperor was indeed worth serving. When he saw Sumbha, and felt that Demon's immense power, Dhumralochana stayed and became one of Sumbha's chief commanders.

Sumbha and Nisumbha's army swelled, and with it their power. A thousand great Asuras and Rakshasas, who had resisted the Devas on far-flung worlds, heard about the new king with the boon who now sat upon the throne of Patala, and they came streaming to him in chariots and vimanas, on elephant-back, or riding great birds, tigers, serpents, and other stranger mounts.

The renowned and terrible Raktabija, a Danava with a great boon himself, arrived with two fearful aksauhinis. This monstrous Asura was indestructible, for, if one drop of his blood fell on the ground in battle at once a thousand identical demons sprang from it, each once as savage as Raktabija himself, each one armed to the fangs and bloodthirsty. The learned Raktabija, who had also once been a tapasvin, was welcomed warmly and made a prominent general of Sumbha's army.

The renown of the new Demon sovereign in Patala, and his vast army, spread across the worlds, and the Devas were disconcerted in heaven. But the canny Sumbha made sure that he was truly prepared for war with the Lords of light, before he sent his macabre legions out to battle. They spewed from the nether world like some plague, millions and millions of ferocious Asuras, interminable legions, with just one purpose in their hearts: to conquer all the created worlds. Every demon of that endless army was prepared to die for his cause.

They swept over the kingdoms of the earth in a tide, and no human king could resist them. Many nations of the earth joined the Asura army, or became their agents, thinking that surely the future belonged to the mighty king in Patala and his brother, who were said to be immortal. These nations and their people, who sold their souls to evil, were given great wealth and power in the world. Their kings wielded subtle sorcery over other nations, and had weapons and armies that could not be resisted by those lesser nations, which still served dharma.

When the earth was subdued, and the law of evil established more or less across its face, Nisumbha took a huge army of men and demons and invaded Devaloka. Indra met the Daitya legions at the gates of Amravati, and battle broke out. Thousands fell on both sides, fell Asura and Rakshasa, and blithe Gandharva and Kinnara. Finally, Indra himself rode into battle, mounted on white Airavata. Nisumbha had been waiting just for him, and they fought.

When a day went by, and neither the Deva nor the Asura seemed to gain any advantage, Indra cast his Vajra, a diamond thunderbolt, at Nisumbha. That weapon of a thousand jagged joints struck the Demon squarely in his chest with an explosion like a star bursting asunder, and the Daitya fell unconscious. Yet, even that ayudha, which could have razed an army, did not kill the Daitya with Brahma's boon.

Word flew down to Sumbha on earth, and he arrived at once in Devaloka in a thought-swift vimana, and flew at the Deva hosts. His archery was matchless, and thousands perished before the tide of arrows with which he swept the legions of Swarga. Gandharva blood, Kinnara and Deva blood flowed in rivers. The Lokapalas, Yama, Varuna, Kubera and Indra himself were beaten back by that Asura. Agni, Vayu, Surya, Soma, Kama, the Vasus and Aswins, the Adityas and Maruts, and all the rest, he routed. They fled in terror of him, for they saw that all their starry weapons were of no avail against Sumbha.

Sumbha marched into Amravati with his legions, and everything in heaven was now his to enjoy: the Parijata, tree of wishes, Kamadhenu, the cow of plenty, all the untold wealth and power of Devaloka, and the Apsaras as well. Sumbha set his Daityas, Raktabija and the rest on exalted thrones, and they ruled the three lokas in place of the Devas. Sumbha himself ruled the realms of Indra, Kubera, Soma, Surya and Yama; he received the worship of every sacrifice on Swarga, Bhumi and Patala. His power was unrivalled.

Nisumbha held sway over the domains of Varuna, Agni, Vayu, and Akasa. When the Devas fled celestial Amravati, it is said that the Daitya brothers sported with the gorgeous Apsaras in the charmed Nandana, and that they drank amrita there from the hands of the nymphs who were not past enjoying the company of the virile and darkly elegant demons.

The Devas fled into the wilderness, and lived in desolation in mountain-caves and in the hearts of deep jungles and trackless deserts. They, the Lords of heaven and earth, lived like beggars, in shameful exile. Fortune had deserted them, and their lives were as inglorious now as they had been majestic when Indra sat in the Sudharma on the throne to which the three worlds pay homage.

Darkness fell on creation, for an Asura was sovereign in Amravati and his Daityas were masters of the elements, of time and destiny. Evil kings, loyal to Sumbha and Nisumbha, creatures of night that served their eerie Lords' purposes, ruled the tenebrous earth. Men fell to greed and lust, to thieving and murder; rapacity of every sort held sway. Ignorance and sorrow shrouded every heart, and anarchy was the order of the day. Thus a thousand years passed, and evil held all the races and kingdoms firmly in its clasp, while the terrible Sumbha was Lord of heaven and earth.

The Devas were all but forgotten; they roamed the outer wastes like lunatics, often in disguise, for the Asuras would kill them if they were discovered. Yet, Indra and his people hardly needed to disguise themselves anymore, for the lustre of their bodies had faded in a thousand years, and they looked like common beggars.

One day, when their old arrogance was quite crushed and abject despair seized them, the Devas came to their guru Brihaspati in a pitiable throng, and Indra said, "Master, save us, we are in hell. Perform some potent yagna that we may vanquish the Daityas."

Their wise Guru said, with a smile, "Yagnas and mantras are helpless against destiny. Ah, you are the very Devas whom the mantras and yagnas invoke! And look at you, now, that fate has turned against you."

Brihaspati was thoughtful for a moment, then, he said slowly, "My Lord, in ancient times, that have all but vanished from memory, there was another great Asura with a boon exactly like the one that Sumbha and Nisumbha have. So many ages have passed since then that I think you have forgotten even the name of Mahishasura."

So many yugas had passed that the immortal Devas had indeed forgotten Mahisha. But Indra remembered something, "Wasn't he the Danava who was a buffalo's son?"

"Yes! And he too couldn't be killed by any man of any of the races."

"Then how did we kill him?"

"You worshipped the Devi Bhagavati, and she appeared on her golden beast and killed the Asura for you."

The Devas remembered now. Brihaspati went on, "Only the Devi can help us, you must worship her. I can feel it in my blood, it is time again for her to incarnate herself, for I fear men have forgotten her. I have heard that ever since she was born as Uma to be Rudra's wife, the Devi dwells on the Himalaya, for he is Parvati's earthly father."

The Devas bowed to their sage master and took themselves to the white Himalaya where they sat in dhyana at the cave-mouth within which, they had been told by some Munis, the Devi dwelt. Without pause, they chanted her bijamantra, the blessed Hrim. They became immersed in that pristine syllable that is verily the Devi herself. The Devas forgot themselves in their worship; at times, spontaneously, praise of the Devi would flow from one or the other's lips, while he who spoke was unaware that he had spoken.

Suddenly Indra would exclaim in rapture, "Oh, Devi, mercy and forgiveness are but thy manifestations!"

Or, some weeks later, Agni would cry, "Thou art the seed of the universe, the beginning and end of all things!"

Or Varuna would whisper a vision he had, "Mother of galaxies! Mother of the three fathers of time!"

Vayu would breathe, "The worlds have forgotten you, Bhagavati, come among us again."

And one day, when an age had passed, the Devas felt a blinding light enfold all the mountain where they sat in dhyana. They opened their eyes, and saw the Goddess before them. Ah, she was young! Hers was the loveliness that defined beauty; hers was the light from which all others lights flowed! She smiled at them so their hearts were swept with bliss, and said in a voice like a rumbling cloud, "Whom are you calling to so desperately, Suras, upon this icy mountain of the earth? Why are you here, and not in your heaven?"

The ones of light were all aquiver at her presence of grace, at her stunning beauty, at her salvational voice. They said to her in awe, in huge love, "Devi, Bhagavati, Sumbha and Nisumbha torment the worlds. They have cast the Devas out of Devaloka and rule the three worlds in our place. Evil stalks creation and demons like Raktabija, Chanda and Munda hold sway over time and the elements. Like Mahishasura of old, Sumbha and his brother cannot be slain by any man. You are our only refuge, Mahamaya. Merciful Mother, save us!"

And the Devas wept before the Goddess,' said Vyasa of matchless intellect and wisdom to the Kuru king."

TWENTY-SIX

"AFTER A BRIEF PAUSE TO RECALL THE PURANA MORE CLEARLY, VYASA Muni took up his auspicious narration once more.

'When the Mother of the universe saw the abject condition of the Devas, she also had tears in her fathomless eyes. Suddenly a great rage seized her. Delicate Parvati began to tremble in wrath before the supplicant Devas, ah, her body shook so violently that the mountain quaked beneath her feet, and it seemed that the sky would fall and time end. Her roars echoed across the earth, and then the strangest thing began to happen to her as the Devas watched.

At her shaking and roaring, from that exquisite Goddess' tender body sprang another female form. This was the fair Ambika, whose name would be a legend across the three worlds throughout eternity. She was beautiful past imagining, and fearsome too, and she sat astride her golden beast, a great lion. When this white Devi had sprung from her, and stood apart, the Goddess Parvati herself was perfectly dark, she was black as the cosmic void where no lamp of any star burns.

That black Devi, whom Parvati became when she had extruded Ambika, was called Kalika, and Kalaratri: the night of destruction who is Durga, the Goddess who is well nigh impossible to attain, and who fulfils every desire. They stood there, the two Devis, one dark and one fair, both beautiful and dreadful, wearing resplendent silks and ornaments, and bearing fearsome weapons in their fine hands.

The Devi Ambika said to the Devas, "Never fear, your enemies shall perish and you will rule again from Devaloka."

Then she set black Kalika behind her on her lion, and they vanished. The Devis flew up into Indra's Amravati, lambent city of heaven, where now the terrible Sumbha ruled. They flew straight into the immortal garden, the Nandana, and stood under the white parijata. There the Devi Ambika began to sing softly to Kalika in such a sweet voice that all the wonderful birds and beasts of that garden were enchanted.

The birds in the living trees began to sing the Goddess' song, for they knew that this is where their own songs came from. The deathless beasts of that garden crowded around the Devis, and laid their heads in their hands. Why, that song pervaded all creation, and far away the Devas thrilled to hear it and quivered in hope.

At this time, it happened that the Asuras Chanda and Munda were out strolling in that charmed garden. They, too, heard the Devi's song and were entranced by it. They came to discover which Apsara warbled so delightfully in the Nandana, and, very likely, to enjoy her beneath the flame-like trees. They saw fair Ambika and black Kalika, the one singing to the other, both incredibly beautiful, and enfolded in such light that it blinded the Daityas even to look at them. Chanda and Munda were seized with wonder and fear.

Those Asuras ran into the crystal Sudharma where their sovereign, the matchless Sumbha, sat surrounded by the most evil, most powerful Daityas in creation. They bowed low to him, and Chanda said, "Lord, a woman from the Himalaya has arrived in your garden. She is mounted on a golden lion, and she is so beautiful that even Kamadeva, the God of love, would fall in love with her."

Munda took up the story now, "Not on any of the lokas will you find a woman as lovely as her. Why, fortune shines from her, as though fortune began with her. My Lord, she is singing in such a sweet voice that the deer in your garden stand enraptured. They come and lay their heads in her hands. The birds have all fallen silent in the trees, and listen avidly to her song."

Chanda said, "Lord of the worlds, she is fit to be your queen. First discover whose daughter she is, and why she has come here. Then take her for your wife, and spend your days in bliss."

"You are master of heaven and earth, you sit on Indra's throne in Amravati. The parijata tree belongs to you, as do four-tusked Airavata, seven-faced Ucchaisravas, Kamadhenu, and all the treasures of the three worlds. Kubera's treasure, worth a Padma, is yours. Varuna's white parasol is unfurled over your throne. Your brother Nisumbha wields Samudra's pasa. Why, you vanquished Yama himself when he came for your life, and now you have his danda in your hand.

The pushpaka vimana stands in your courtyard, great Daitya, and so, too, this most priceless jewel amongst women has made her way to you, to become yours. Only when you have her beside you as your queen, will all the other treasures that are yours find their true lustre and significance."

There was another Asura, Sugriva, a trusted man of his king's, in that sabha. Sumbha said to that Daitya, "Go, my friend, speak sweetly to the lovely one and fetch her to me. Flatter her profusely, for there is no woman on any world that can resist listening to her own praises."

Sugriva came to the Devi on her lion, and said, "My lord Sumbha, the enemy of the Devas, and master of the universe, has heard of your beauty and your grace. He sent a message to you through me. My lord Sumbha says to you:

'I have vanquished all the Devas and their hosts and now I am Lord of the Triloka. I have a share in every yagna on heaven and earth; my power pervades all creation. All the treasures in the universe belong to me; why, there is nothing that is not mine. All the races are my subjects, and I am their king.

Delicate, flawless, perfect one, the moment I heard of you, my heart was struck by love's lightning. I, Sumbha, Lord of the universe, am now your slave, and will remain so until I die. I am immortal, bewitching one; no man, Deva, Gandharva, Asura, Kinnara, Rakshasa, or any of the others can kill me. I beg you, be my queen. Rule the worlds at my side!'

Thus said my Lord Sumbha to you, sweet lady. May I take your reply back to him?"

The Devi Ambika smiled inscrutably at Sugriva. She said, "I know all about your master Sumbha, and his brother Nisumbha as well. I know that Sumbha destroyed the Devas in battle, and cast them into the wilderness like beggars. I know he is a highborn and noble Daitya, a home of all the qualities, and the thirty-two auspicious signs. He is brave and generous, handsome as Kamadeva, and invincible in battle against any man. I know he is wealthier than any other king, and that, indeed, heaven and earth are his to rule.

I have been on earth, and saw how all the Devas, Gandharvas, Kinnaras, Charanas and Siddhas tremble at the very mention of Sumbha's name. I have come here to seek a husband for myself, messenger. So go and say to your master that I said:

'O Sumbha, I have heard you are the most beautiful, powerful, learned, generous, fearless, intelligent, wealthy, noble Daitya in the universe. And I am keen to be your queen, Asura. Yet there is one condition I must make before I wed. The man I marry must first vanquish me in battle. For I am strong, O Lord of the worlds, and I could never respect a husband who is not stronger than I am.'

Tell your master I am impatient to be his queen. So let him come at once, defeat me at arms, and make me his wife."

The Daitya Sugriva was dumbfounded at what he heard. He began to laugh softly, and said, "Most beautiful one, it seems you speak in jest at my expense. How could you even think of facing my Lord Sumbha in battle? He is the conqueror of Indra and the Devas; there is no one in the three worlds that can match him at arms.

Think again, of what you are saying. I beg of you, come with me now and be married to my lord, lest he grow annoyed at your fanciful message to him and send his Asuras to seize you by force. I am only a humble messenger, Devi, but Sumbha has terrible demons at his command that will drag you before him by your hair. Delicate one, come peacefully with me, the battle you are best suited to is the sweet one you and my lord will have between the soft sheets of his bed of down. Ah, perhaps, that is the battle you mean?"

But she was adamant, "No doubt you speak the truth, good messenger. But I have already committed myself to be won only after a fight, and I cannot go back on what I have said. Put it down to my childish nature if you like, but I will never marry a man just for his beauty or his wealth. He must fight me before he can have me for his wife, and the first battle must be with arms on a battlefield, and then we shall have the other campaign in a bed!"

Sugriva looked at her again, and saw that she was truly determined. He was afraid, and, only after much careful thought, came back to Sumbha on his throne that the worlds worshipped. Hesitantly, that Asura began, "My lord, a minister should always speak both truly and sweetly to his king. But, often, this is hard to do. When the message that a messenger brings to his master is not sweet, for no fault of his own but only of the one who sent the message, the messenger trembles to deliver it."

He paused, and Sumbha said, "Go on, Sugriva, don't be afraid."

Nothing else for it, Sugriva went on, "My Lord, before I could ask her where she came from, or whose daughter she is, the lovely one said to me,

'I know your master Sumbha is Lord of the three worlds and that there is no one like him in heaven or on earth. I have come here looking for a husband. Tell Sumbha that, when I was a girl and playing with my friends, I swore a childish oath that only the man who can defeat me in battle shall have me for his wife. Tell your master that he must first vanquish me on the field, if he wants me for his queen.'

My Lord, she is haughty and waits there on her golden beast with weapons in her hands, for you to come and fight her."

Sugriva fell silent, quivering with fear. Sumbha turned to his brother Nisumbha, who sat beside him in his sabha. He said, "Intelligent one, say what I should do now."

Nisumbha replied promptly, "It isn't right that you or I go to battle against her. Send Dhumralochana. He will bring her to us trussed up, and you can make her your queen."

Sumbha called for the savage Dhumralochana, and said, "Take a legion with you, go into the garden and fetch the arrogant woman to me. But be careful you don't injure her, or even break her delicate skin. But if there are any others who fight for her, kill them. First, kill the black Kali who is her companion. Go now and bring her to me safely, for I mean to marry her."

Dhumralochana took sixty thousand Daityas with him, and went into the Nandana. He decided to speak sweet words of persuasion to her first. That demon said, "Ah, you are even more beautiful than Sugriva said! My lady, my master Sumbha pines for you. Ever since he heard you had come here to his garden, he is not himself but yearns for you to be his queen.

Devi, my master is not perhaps as bright as he may be that he sent me here with these warriors. But I know very well the battle you meant when you challenged him to fight you first. You meant the delicious battle of the bed with its sweet sharpness. I assure you, you will find my master Sumbha as great a warrior between sheets, as he is on the field of war. I swear you will hardly be able to bear his shaft of love, any more than the Devas did his shafts of battle. You will swoon for joy, again and again, just as you yearn to, lovely one!

Truly, you are beautiful and noble enough to be my master's queen, as is no other woman in all the universe. So come and embrace your destiny, and bring this dark Kali with you, to serve you."

At which, black Kalika began to laugh in the most wild and fetching manner, her fierce head thrown back. She said, "Flatterer! Have you any thought for what you are saying? Ah, fool, the Devi means to kill you! She means to raze your army, and kill Sumbha and Nisumbha too. And here you are, trying to seduce her into your dim-witted master's bed with sweet talk.

Don't you know who the Devi is? That you try to match-make her with your puny king? Will the lioness marry the jackal, Asura, just because she feels aroused? Will the she-elephant marry a donkey, or a kamadhenu a buffalo? Go, tell your masters that we have come to fight, and we mean to kill them before we leave this place."

She spoke so rudely, that Dhumralochana's eyes turned crimson. He cried, "Hideous one, I will cut your ugly head from your body, strike this lion dead, and carry your lovely companion back to my Lord Sumbha!"

Kalika mocked him, "I thought you were a warrior when I saw you, Asura. But you must be Sumbha's court jester, that all you deal in are words."

With a roar, the Daitya loosed a tide of arrows at the black Goddess. They were fell shafts, swift as light, but Kalika cut them down in a wink. The Devas arrived in their subtle vimanas above the enchanted battlefield and cried out the Devi's name, and Kali's and 'Jaya!', which means victory. Kalika slew the sorcerous mules that drew the Daitya's chariot, she smashed the chariot itself, and then her wild laughter rang out again across that sylvan field.

Another chariot arrived for Dhumralochana, and, climbing into it, he covered her in a cloud of all sorts of bizarre and deadly weapons: mudgaras, narachas, astras, shaktis, musalas, pattisas, and others that were nameless, but flew at Kalika in light and fire. The black Devi hardly seemed to make an effort, but cut down all the Asura's missiles with a stream of arrows that flared from her bow like thoughts from a mind.

The Devi's conch resounded above the battle in deep thunder. Ambika didn't sit idle either, and all around Dhumralochana his demons perished in waves, and soon his chariot waded through a small lake of Asura's blood at Kali's unearthly archery.

Roaring louder than ever, the Daitya general seized up his strangest, most powerful weapon, the parigha. It was an ayudha of a thousand flames. It howled in his hands, as the Asura raised them to cast his parigha at the dark Devi, crying, "Ugly Kali, meet your death!"

But at that moment Kali bared her fangs and gave a roar. Heaven shook, and the earth far below, and at that sound, Dhumralochana was turned into a mound of ashes that the winds of Devaloka blew away in the four directions.

When the Asura's soldiers saw their general killed so easily, panic took them and they fled from the Devis, howling, "Save us! Save us!" But by then the sprawling garden in which that battle had been fought was as sanguinary a sight as any battlefield in heaven or earth. Asuras' corpses lay everywhere, limbless, headless, their horses and elephants had also fallen around them. Only now could the Goddesses themselves see how many thousands they had slaughtered, in so short a time.

The Devas showered fragrant petals of light down on the triumphant Devis, and already another army stalked that field, an army of scavengers. The legions of carrion-eaters had arrived, as if out of thin air, the hyenas, jackals, wild-dogs, vultures, crows, kites and the batabarapha pisachas, who also eat the dead.

Now fair Ambika raised her sankha to her cherry lips, and blew such a blast on that conch that Sumbha heard her in his sabha, deep inside his great palace, that had once belonged to Indra.

The Lord of the Asuras rose from his splendid throne, which was a single ruby carved into a round seat, and crossed to his wide window. He saw the remains of his army of sixty thousand fighting Daityas fly screaming back to him. There were scarcely ten thousand of them left alive, and not a warrior among them did not bear some mark of the Devis upon him; some had no hands, others no legs, while still others had one eye put out in their bestial faces. All of them were covered in shiny blood, either their own, or their comrades' who had perished on the field.

Sumbha and Nisumbha cried in one voice, "Why are you running from battle, cowards? Where is Dhumralochana? And where is she whom he went to fetch?"

When he found his voice, the soldiers' commander said, "Lord, the black Devi Kalika killed Dhumralochana. And the fair Ambika, whose conch you hear shaking Swarga and Bhumi, slew fifty thousand of our bravest men, in a wink."

Another soldier breathed, "You would hardly believe how our lord Dhumra died, O King. Kali turned him into ashes with a roar!"

And another said, "Lord, this is the Mother of the universe who sits upon her lion in your garden. She has no army with her, only her dark Kali, who is her own self. O Sumbha, the Devas and Hari and Hara, all the Kinnaras and Gandharvas, will join forces with her if she only asks them to. But she stands alone, and I fear she is equal to the rest of us. Why, I think she could put out all the suns in the sky!"

Sumbha drew his brother Nisumbha aside. He said, "What shall we do now? She has killed Dhumra, whom no Deva could face in battle. You are younger than me, Nisumbha, but in a crisis you have the older head. Do we persist with our plan to enjoy her in bed, do we flee Amravati, or do we continue to fight? Decide, my brother, my heart is clouded with doubt and strange fear."

Nisumbha answered him at once, "Don't think of fleeing, my Lord. Let me take some Daityas into battle against her, and I will bring her to you, fit to enjoy."

But his brother said, "Why should you go into battle yet? Let Chanda and Munda go and fetch her to us, so we can share her as we do the kingdom."

The Daitya emperor turned to Chanda and Munda, "Take an army with you, my friends. Kill the black Kali, and bring the fair Ambika to us for our pleasure. But if you can't take her alive, if she won't come at any price, then kill her as well, O heroes; for, she has killed fifty thousand of our people."

And Chanda and Munda set out at once, not really fearing this battle against two women,' said Vyasa to the king of the Kurus on the banks of the sacred river," says Suta in the vana.

TWENTY-SEVEN

"VYASA WENT ON, 'CHANDA AND MUNDA ARRIVED IN THE FRAGRANT garden despoiled by a battle, its lily-pools tainted with demons' gore. All its birds and gentle beasts had fled, but the Devis still sat astride their lion and sang softly to each other, and their golden laughter tinkled there.

The two Asuras saw the devastation around them, and decided to first coax the Goddesses with sweet talk. Chanda said, "Ah, perfect one! How sad it is to see such beauty wasted in savage war. The cowardly Devas have sent you alone to your death. Such a pity, such treachery."

Munda put in, "You have come to battle Sumbha of the Daityas with just a dark sakhi and a lion to fight for you! Don't you know who Sumbha and Nisumbha are? Don't you know that the hosts of Swarga fled before their might? Why should you sacrifice beauty like yours for the sake of the Devas, who are not ashamed to send a woman to fight their battle for them? No, seek your delight in our lord Sumbha's bed. Be his queen, be queen of all the worlds. If you would only come with us and let your eyes see how magnificent is our king, you would not hesitate to be his wife."

But the Devis laughed in their faces and Ambika said, "Fools! Shall I then leave Hari and Hara and the Devas, and marry an idiot Asura? And for what? To be mistress of the worlds that are already mine, and have been since long before there was a Sumbha or a Nisumbha! Do you even begin to know what you are prating about, witless demons? A thousand Sumbhas and Nisumbhas have I known in the course of time, and killed them all; as I mean to kill you both today, and then Raktabija, Nisumbha and Sumbha too!

Why waste time on empty words, Asuras, when you are meant to be warriors? Pick up your weapons, and prepare to die like heroes, and find mukti for yourselves."

Chanda and Munda quivered with rage when they heard her. They raised their bows over their heads and pulled on their bowstrings so the ground shook under their feet. But the Devi Ambika raised her sankha to her lips once more, and blew such a note there that the ten quarters of the sky trembled with the sound. Screeching, Chanda attacked the Devi with a flare of fire-arrows. But she cut them all down in a wink, with archery like the demons had never seen.

The Devi answered the Daitya's fire with an arrow storm of her own, and it seemed the sun was blotted out with a swarm of locusts, while the sound those shafts made was deafening. Now, Munda began to fight as well, and his valour was no less than his brother's. The sky seemed to take fire. Suddenly, there was a clap of thunder over that field and the Asuras saw the fair Ambika grow black as Kali. Next moment she emitted a third and hideous Goddess from between her eyes, and lo, she was fair again! The new dark Devi grew before their eyes. She grew immense and became truly dreadful; she was Bhadrakali.

Her eyes were red as kadali flowers, her skin black as moonless nights; she wore elephant- and tiger-skin, her fangs were like sharp ivory pillars, a garland of skulls was around her neck. Her breasts were huge, her lips hung loose and her tongue lolled out a yojana from her crimson mouth, her belly was grotesque like a deep, dry well. Her hair hung wild and loose, and she was four-armed and bore an axe, a noose and a trisula in her hands black as pitch.

The demons quailed at the very sight of her; she was like the Night of the dissolution embodied. Quaffing thirstily from a vat of raw liquor that she carried, then licking her lips, she rushed at the Asura army, ululating weirdly. She launched herself at them like a hundred Yamashaktis. She picked up great war-elephants and their monstrous riders, thrust them into her yawning maw, and chomped on them in delight. Crooning, with rivulets of blood flowing down her jowls, she swept up whole legions, and chewed them up like dainties. Her fangs shone scarlet, as now and then she spat out the axle-rod of a chariot she had consumed, and used it for a toothpick.

In wrath, and terror, Chanda summoned a lucific chakra and cast it at Bhadrakali. The weapon spun at her wailing. But she caught the incendiary disk in her black hand and blew it out as if she was extinguishing a night-lamp. She cast her subtle noose at Chanda, and he was bound fast and helpless. Struggle as he would, with his gigantic strength, using every spell he knew, he could not free himself from that umbilical paasa.

Seeing his brother quelled, Munda flew at Kali. He summoned a feral shakti and hurled it at her. But Kali shattered that weapon of a hundred fires with an astra called the Isika, and the flames of the shakti were doused in the sky. Then, marvellously, the paasa that held Chanda fast divided itself in two, and Munda was also bound in coils of light, and could not move.

Meanwhile, Ambika and the lovely Kalika on their lion razed the rest of the demon army, with astras that blew phalanxes to shreds, or immolated columns of Asuras into white ashes. Laughing wildly now, Bhadrakali brought Chanda and Munda to Ambika, trussed up like wolves. She roared to the fair Goddess, "I have brought you two animals for your sacrifice. Accept them, O Devis."

"In the yagna, there is no envy, only purity. Let the Devas' work be done."

Kali smiled hideously, as the demons sullied themselves. She crooned, "Let this axe of mine be as the yupastamba. And here is the offering!"

With that she hewed off the two Asuras' heads with a single stroke of her glinting blade, and greedily drank the blood that spouted from their necks like mountain-springs. The delighted Ambika cried, "Be known as Chamunda from now, that you have killed Chanda and Munda!" And Kali would be known as Chandika and Chamundeswari, for the two Daityas were saved, that they died at her blessed hands.

Shocked to see their generals killed, the Asuras fled back to Sumbha on his throne. Those that Ambika and Kalika left alive came as piteously as had the men of Dhumralochana's men before them. They came howling, all of them wounded, many dismembered, and they stood shaking before their sovereign.

Those demons wailed like terrified children, "Hah! Save us! Save us Lord! Chandika means to consume the worlds today."

One vile Daitya cried, "She burns like the fire at the end of time, and no one can contain her. Chanda and Munda are dead. She cut off their heads with her axe, and drank their blood until there was not a drop left and their corpses were white as ghosts; then, she cast them aside like dolls she was tired of playing with. Ah, Lord, she picked up whole columns of our soldiers, elephants, chariots and all, and ate them! And Ambika and Kalika were hardly less terrible, their astras were the cracks of doom yawned before us, and our legions fell in and perished."

Another said, "There are three terrible Devis, where there were two! A river of blood flows in your garden, my lord. Your demons' flesh is the sludge of that river, their broken chariot-wheels are its whirlpools, their severed hands and feet are its fish, their heads struck off like floating tumbi fruit, their arms and legs the sharks. And the golden lion stalks the banks of this river, his jowls crimson, feeding on the dead as he wills, roaring with joy."

A third demon said, "Oh, Sumbha, the Devis mean to extinguish our very race. We beg you, while there is still life left in us, let us flee to Patala. Give the Devas back their dominions, and let us live in peace. Just think, my Lord, three women have decimated your invincible legions, more than a hundred thousand Asuras, whom the Devas could not withstand. This is the hand of Fate, a great warning; pay heed to it, O Emperor. For, when their time comes a blade of grass turns into a thunderbolt, and Indra's Vajra into a blade of grass."

Then, there was a wise ancient among them, who now reminded Sumbha and Nisumbha, "My lord, when you performed your great tapasya in the Pushkara kshetra, and the Lord Brahma appeared before you, you asked for invincibility against men of all the races. But you have no boon to protect you against women. Three women have come to kill you now. Why, this is the Devi Bhagavati, who devours time itself at the end of the kalpa, who has come to drink your blood!

She is Sandhya, the refuge of the Devas; she is Gayatri, the mother of the Vedas. She is the eternal One, who always was, before the three great Gods; she is the mother of the fathers of the universe! She is Saumya, gentle, and if you ask for sanctuary at her feet like lotuses, she will not refuse you, and you will be saved, and with you the race of Asuras.

I am an old man, my Lords, and I have seen a great deal of life. I beg you, listen to me now, for what I say is wisdom; she is the Truth who has come hunting in your garden. You cannot resist her, but only submit to whatever she wants."

Now Sumbha roared so that his palace shook. "Fools, hold your tongues! You have fled because you are cowards, and so attached to living. Fate rules the worlds, and who can change what is written in her book? I don't care at all if I live or die, and what is written must be.

Why, even Brahma, Vishnu and Siva are not beyond fate. All that are born must finally die, and not the time of their birth nor of their dying do they choose themselves. So, when I have accomplished everything I was born for, I too will perish. But I am not afraid of dying! And if you are, my Asuras, I pity you; for there is no cure for your illness. Indeed, take yourselves down to Patala and cower there for the rest of your miserable lives, if you want to let fear rule you. My dharma is to stay and fight the woman on the lion.

She and her black friends have killed so many of my Daityas; they have killed Dhumralochana, Chanda and Munda. My dharma is to have revenge on the women, or to die trying. And I am no coward that I will abandon my dharma for the sake of living some thousand years in fear and trembling."

He paused, and let his dark gaze wander over his ministers and generals. Finally he said, "Now tell me, Asuras, must I don mail and go out to fight the women myself, or is there any among you who will still go to battle for my sake?"

The fierce Raktabija had been straining as if at a leash. He sprang up, a head taller than any other Asura in that sabha. He was lean and sleek, an altogether sinister demon. He said in his low, hoarse, voice, "My lord Sumbha, let me go to war. I will bring you either the women's heads, or them alive, for the pleasure of your bed."

Sumbha clasped his general, and Raktabija set out with an aksauhini twice the size of the legion Chanda and Munda had taken to battle. He went with chariots and horses, elephants and interminable columns of foot soldiers. By now, the three Devis had left the garden where they had been, for the corpses that lay there had begun to decompose, and the stench of putrefaction filled the place. Chandika, Ambika and Kali had taken themselves off to a diamond mountain upon the Himalaya, and sat on its peak, still singing sweetly to each other.

When they saw Raktabija's army approaching, a sea of fighting demons, the Devis' laughter rang out under an azure sky. Ambika raised her conch to her lips, and blew a sky-shaking bass on it. Watching from the safety of invisible vimanas, the Devas exulted.

Raktabija also came humbly before the Devi Ambika, and said, "Your beauty is indeed past compare, Devi, and it is no wonder my master Sumbha desires you. I am his general Raktabija, and I have come to take you to my lord, dead or alive. I am no Dhumra, Chanda or Munda that you will ever vanquish me in battle. I am invincible, Devi, yet I will speak with you first and try to show you the path of wisdom, for one endowed with such beauty as you.

Yours is a rare gift, Devi, for there is no other woman as lovely as you are. Such beauty is wasted on the battlefield; it belongs in a soft bed where the most powerful emperor in creation can enjoy it, as it was created to be enjoyed. Ask any brahmana and he will tell you that sringara and shanti are the most desirable of the navarasas. Wrath and war are bestial and lowly, and only meant for those who are not born blessed with the qualities that enhance love and lovemaking. You have no such lack; indeed, one so exquisite as you is created just for loving. Why do you want to pervert your essential nature, your sweet dharma, and seek war instead?

Vishnu lives with Lakshmi, Brahma with Saraswati, and Siva with Uma. Indra is with his Sachi, Kama with Rati. The great trees of the earth have creepers twined around them; the stag is with his hind in the jungle, the tiger with the tigress. It is only those who are impotent or ugly who embrace a life of sannyasa in their youth, because they cannot enjoy love. You are young; you are enchanting. My lords Sumbha and Nisumbha are magnificent Daityas, handsome beyond describing, powerful and manly beyond telling. Choose either of them, and become his queen. This is the way of wisdom for you, Devi."

The Devi Ambika laughed in Raktabija's face. She said in a rumbling voice, "Dim-witted Danava! I have already told your master's previous messengers, I will only marry a man who is stronger than I am, one who vanquishes me in battle. Let either Sumbha or his brother quell me on the field, and I will be his wife. Why bandy words with me? I have heard you are a warrior, Raktabija; come, show me your valour."

She spoke so scornfully, that the formidable Daitya attacked her at once. He shot a thousand arrows at the Devi and her lion—serpentine shafts. But she cut them down with archery that defied seeing; Raktabija hardly saw the Devi's arms move, all he saw was his barbs being shredded in the air and falling harmlessly all around the radiant Goddess. He gazed in awe at this, and next moment, was struck unconscious by a clutch of blunt arrows that struck his head and knocked him down. None of them drew blood, for it seemed the Devi knew what would happen if this demon's blood was spilt.

Raktabija lay in a deep swoon while his soldiers panicked around him, their cries echoed against that mountain's glassy sides, as they fled everywhere crying, "Boomba! Boomba!" which is the call for extreme danger. Sumbha heard the desperate cry as far as his palace, and rising from his throne, said, "Let the Kambojas and Kalakeyas march against the woman. She must be tamed today!"

These were two of the fiercest tribes of fighting Asuras that Sumbha commanded. They were the elite warriors of his kingdom, personally chosen and trained by the king and his brother. Mounted in chariots, and on horses and elephants, they streamed into battle against the Devis. Ambika saw them coming. She raised her bow and pulled on its string, and the ground shook at that sound. When she blew on her conch as well, the Kambojas and Kalakeyas slowed their mad rush at her.

Chandika opened her black mouth wide as a cavern, and gave a roar that echoed above Ambika's sankha, and the lion roared louder still. Kalika pursed her dark lips, and whistled piercingly, and that sound ruptured the ear-drums of a thousand Asuras, and blood trickled from their ears.

But Sumbha's fighting demons paused only for a moment. Then they roared back their defiance and swarmed up the mountain again, crack troops, armed to the teeth, so highly trained that they would die without a thought, for their king. They swept up the mountain in a wave, and loosed another tide of arrows in the sky, blotting out the sun, mantling the air in darkness. The Devis managed to dissipate this first shroud of shafts. But they saw that the Daityas who had come to battle now were exceptional warriors, and they would be hard-pressed to contain them, once they gained the higher mountain.

When the first Kamboja and Kalakeya legions clambered over the rim of the peak on which the Devis were, the battle grew more intense than it had yet been. Rivers of deadly arrows occluded the sky, and other streams rose on high to drown them. Thousands of demons died, but now the Devis sighed and moaned, and even shrieked with the effort they were forced to make to keep the Asuras at bay. The mountain rang with the fierce yells and roars of the Daityas; even when they died they seemed to roar in exultation, as if they enjoyed dying as much as they did war!

Suddenly, a blinding lustre lit that mountain like another sun risen from the very rocks. In it, there materialised yet another Devi, dazzling even beside the brightness of Ambika and the hunting Kali. She was the Lord Brahma's own Shakti come to fight at the Goddess' side. In moments, a hundred such lights shone on the Himalaya, as the Kambojas and Kalakeyas stood gaping.

Out of those refulgences stepped a hundred Devis, the Shaktis of a hundred Gods, all armed, all riding immaculate vahanas and vimanas. Brahma's Shakti, Brahmani, came mounted on her white swan; she bore a string of beads and her kamandalu, besides her ayudhas. Vishnu's Shakti was called Vaishnavi, and she flew on Garuda's back, and carried the sankha, the gada, the kamala and the chakra Sudarshana in her hands.

The Devi Sankari arrived on her black bull, Nandiswara, who is hardly less than a God himself. She bore the crescent-moon on her brow, a king cobra coiled around her body, amulet on her arm, and the trisula of three fires in her right hand. She also held a dumaru in her left hand, and made it chatter rhythmically whenever she wished.

Karttikeya's resplendent Shakti, Kaumari Devi, who was his spitting image, arrived on a shimmering peacock. She held Agni Deva's spear in her hands. Indra's Shakti, the fair Indrani, arrived on a four-tusked white elephant, Airavata, who trod air. She wore the brilliant ornaments of Devaloka and carried the thousand-jointed thunderbolt of the Lord of the Devas, the glittering Vajra.

The Shaktis of some of Vishnu's avataras came as well. The Varahai was a great female boar, big as a hill, her tusks like trees; she rode on the backs of some Pretas, who are souls of the dead. The Narasimhi was as awesome as the Narasimha himself. She was half-lion, half dark woman; her weapons were her fangs like swords and her talons like scimitars.

Yama's Shakti arrived, riding on the back of a black buffalo, her staff of retribution in her black hands, and she was both lovely and terrible. That mountain teemed with an army of Shaktis, all delighted at this chance they had to fight a great war: the Shaktis of Kubera, Surya, Soma, Vayu, the Adityas and Vasus, Agni, Varuna, Ganesa, and all the others appeared on that mountain, alight. They came armed, and eager for battle.

The Devi Ambika exulted, and Sumbha's demon army cowered at the refulgence of the Shaktis. Then, it is told, that Mahadeva Siva appeared before his Devi, Ambika, and said, "Now raze the race of Asura from creation, and let there be peace among the worlds. Let the Devas rule from Devaloka again, let brahmanas perform their yagnas, let dharma thrive, and all the created live in harmony."

When Siva spoke thus, another most dreadful female Shakti issued out of Chandika's body. She sprang forth as a light, but, soon, stood embodied before Sankara. She was entirely horrific, her hair wild, her face black and grimacing, her fangs protruding, her black breasts exposed. Hundreds of howling jackals surrounded her, and she said with an awful smile to Siva, "Sankara, be our messenger today. Go to Sumbha and tell him to leave Devaloka and fly down into Patala where he belongs. Tell the Daitya brothers to save themselves and their race from death. Otherwise, let them come to the field, and die!"

Siva Sulapani flew to Sumbha who sat arrogantly in the Sudharma, on the throne that the worlds worship, Indra's throne that is a single immense ruby. Siva materialised in a form of light, and said, "I am Hara, destroyer of the Tripura, and I have come to save your life. Sumbha, leave Amravati, relinquish your power over Swarga and Bhumi. Fly down to Patala, where you belong. Bali and Prahlada rule vast kingdoms there; you shall also be a king in the nether realm. If you do not listen to me, Sumbha, you will find death for yourself at the Devi Ambika's hands."

Siva vanished, a bright mist before the Asura's eyes. But, Sumbha roared his anger that anyone dared challenge him, and he sent another ten legions out to battle against the Devis on the mountain. A million demons, their weapons and armour glinting in the soft sun, came swarming up that massif. The Devis crooned in delight. Then they roared and screamed softly for joy, almost as though they were about to make love. Then they hunted the Daityas on that mountain, until Asura blood flowed in torrents down its pale slopes.

The Devi Ambika razed a whole aksauhini with archery such as the stars had never seen before. Typhoons of arrows, oceans of arrows, rose in the firmament at her will, and the sky resounded with demons' shrieks and howls and curses as their hands and arms, their legs and heads were struck off, before they even had time to raise their own weapons. Some had their chests shredded in slivers, and others were cut clean in two at the waist.

Chandika hunted even more fiercely. Grown vast again as the mountain itself, she swept down on the Asuras and fed on them. She stuffed legions of foot soldiers and whole sections of cavalry into her mouth without favour, and chewed on them, her eyes rolling, blood dribbling down her jowls. She seemed to favour the elephants most of all, and ate these with more relish than anything else. She carried a vat of harsh cane-liquor in her hands and swilled from it often. And Kalika was as terrible.

Brahma's Shakti, the Brahmani, killed the enemy in the strangest manner. She blessed them with holy water from the kamandalu she carried in her hands, and they were burnt to ashes at her purification, screaming. Siva's Devi, Maheswari, plunged her great bull at the enemy, and the beast trampled thousands of demons with flying hooves, and gored twice as many with horns sharp as swords. That Shakti herself then incinerated tens of thousands of Asuras with the three fires from her trisula which she swung everywhere, and it seemed three blinding rivers of coloured light flowed all over that white mountain.

Vaishnavi swung her mace, the Kaumodaki, and felled legions. But she was not content and loosed the Sudarshana at the enemy. The wheel of fire flew everywhere, and the demons in its path had no time even to scream before they were beheaded or carved in strips. Some, the chakra ashed whole. Indra's Shakti, Indrani, cast her Vajra at Sumbha's fighting demons, and it was no less final than the wheeling chakra. It erupted across the Himalaya, and a thousand jagged streaks of unearthly lightning consumed the Daityas.

Narasimhi stalked that uneven field; her talons were like Devastras and decimated the Danavas. The demons quailed at her growls, and she hunted them with dread, and tore their throats and their hearts out, and devoured them as they stood petrified before her. Ambika struck the Daityas down in waves, and Kalika and Chandika tore their flesh and devoured them.

Kaumari razed aksauhinis with arrows of light, and Varuni swept away phalanxes with her fluid flying paasa. Sumbha's army was being routed on every side, and the Asuras fled down that mountain, screaming in panic, slipping over the blood-slicks of their slain comrades. The Devas showered celestial blooms down on the army of Devis, and the lustre and fragrance of those flowers terrified the demons more than ever. All around, the peaks echoed with the desperate cry of "Boomba! Boomba!" '

Said Vyasa Muni to Janamejaya, by the murmuring river,"

Says Suta, the pauranika of genius.

TWENTY-EIGHT

"'WHEN RAKTABIJA HEARD THE CALLS OF DISTRESS, HE ROUSED HIMSELF, and came to fight the Devis again. He came mounted in his chariot that was as easy through the air as it was upon the ground. He flew up the Himalaya, his eyes red as kimsuka flowers, and his roars ringing above the terrified screams of his soldiers being slaughtered by the legion Goddesses.

Once, this Demon had sat in tapasya to Rudra, a penance of such rigour that not even the great Rishis could match it. Siva appeared before the Daitya and granted him a rare boon: that if a drop of his blood fell on the ground, a thousand Asuras would spring up from it, each one as powerful as himself. Now, blowing on a great horn, Raktabija came to war like Yama himself.

The first Devi he saw was Vaishnavi, hunting from golden Garuda's back. Raktabija cast a Shakti at her, howling like a tornado, bright as a sun-flare. But that meridian Goddess struck the weapon of fire aside disdainfully with the magical mace, the Kaumodaki. Almost at once, she loosed the Sudarshana chakra at the Daitya. It flew at him, spinning fire, and took him in the chest.

Raktabija's wild laughter rang out across that mountainous battleground. A spring of scarlet blood flowed from his breast where the chakra struck him, it flowed in a stream on that pale peak. For every drop of that Demon's blood that touched the earth, a thousand Daityas sprang up, each one as formidable as Rakta himself.

Indrani cast her Vajra, thousand-jointed thunderbolt, at Raktabija. The Demon's laughter rang louder than ever, as still more of his blood flowed on the mountain. Like awful spectres, thousands and thousands of Raktabijas sprang up from his blood. In anger, not knowing what was happening, the other Devis attacked Raktabija. Brahmani struck him with her danda, Maheswari excoriated him with her trisula, and Varahi gored him with silver tusks.

Ten thousand Raktabijas struck back at the army of Devis, with storms of arrows, tempests of clubs, gales of lances, raging infernos that were astras. The Goddesses fought back more majestically than ever. But for every drop of the enemy's blood they spilt, a thousand other implacable demon-warriors appeared. Heaven and earth teemed with Raktabijas, millions of them. The Devis were shocked; they were helpless, not even they could contend with an army of demons that multiplied itself endlessly, whenever it bled. The Shaktis dared not think what would happen if Sumbha and Nisumbha came to battle now.

The Devi Ambika turned to the black Chamunda. With anxiety in her voice for the first time, the fair Goddess said, "You must drink every drop of blood we spill before it falls on the earth, or the war is lost!"

The Devi Chamunda turned herself into a whirlwind upon that field, a great storm with thirsty lips that were everywhere. Bhadrakali began to quaff the jets of blood that sprang from the wounds the other Devis and Ambika opened on the million Raktabijas. The army of Goddesses cut the army of Raktabijas to shreds, and not a drop of their blood fell on the earth, but Chamunda swilled it all.

She went carolling across that mountain, she flew singing in the air and she was drunk on Asuras' blood and cried that it was sweeter than any wine she ever had. Why, she drained off the demons, leaving them pale as lotuses, while she bloated into a monstrous form, swollen with gore. She was a black and crimson cloud that engulfed the field of war, and every Asura on it. In as much time as it takes to tell, just Raktabija himself stood alive amidst the bloodless corpses of all the demons that had sprung from his blood.

The Devis Ambika and Chamunda closed in on him together. Ambika hewed his head off with her axe, and, in a wink, Chamunda seized both his head and his trunk, drained them at a gulp, and flung his bloodless carcass down among all the rest. Ambika raised her conch and blew a blast on it sending all the other Daityas scuttling from that mountain field.

Those demons fled to their king Sumbha on his ruby throne, and cried, "Raktabija is dead. Ambika cut his head from his neck, and Chamunda drank his blood."

"The army of Devis is invincible, Lord, it is better we abandon Devaloka, and fly down to Patala."

"Before they kill us all, O Sumbha!"

"Before the very race of Asuras is extinct, my Lord!"

But death stalked Sumbha close, and his wisdom had fled in alarm. He sprang up from his throne, his eyes were vermilion, and his dark lips throbbed in fury. In a low voice, the Lord of the Daityas said, "Cowards! You fly down to Patala if you want, or, better still, go fall at the Devis' feet, and beg for their protection. But I am Sumbha, master of the worlds, and I mean to kill the women, or to die fighting them."

His voice rolled like thunder through his splendid sabha. "Every man's death is already ordained when he is born into the world. I do not fear death, or want to prolong my life by being a coward. My honour is more important to me than my life. Nisumbha, my brother, I mean to face these evil women in battle. Will you come with me?"

But Nisumbha cried, "There is no need for you to go into battle, as long as I am alive. Stay here in your sabha, my Lord, and I will bring you Ambika shortly, alive and warm for your bed."

His brother blessed Nisumbha, when that warrior knelt before his king. The brahmanas and the singers of the Asuras' palace sang praises of Nisumbha, as he mounted his golden chariot, and went to war against the Devis. He went with a teeming army, legion upon legion of savage Daityas swarmed around him.

Sumbha also gathered his army and went with his younger brother. But, it is related that he honoured the dharma of war and remained behind Nisumbha's army, as just a spectator.

Indra and his Devas, the Yakshas, Gandharvas, Apsaras, Kinnaras, Charanas and all the other celestials gathered in the sky above, in subtle vimanas hidden in clouds. Even as he approached the Devi Ambika, Nisumbha loosed a storm of fire at her. Towering flames from the Daitya's astras licked at earth and sky. The snow on that white mountain melted and icy rivers flowed down its sides. Yet, not a shaft of that Demon's flight reached the Devi or Kali at her side.

The Devi Ambika's clear, beautiful, mocking, laughter rang there, like another crystal stream in the crisp air and she said to Kalika, "How powerful a thing is hope! These fools see the corpses of a millions demons all around them. They see jackals feeding at Raktabija's carcass, yet they come to war against us, still hoping to win." Her eyes shone like cold planets, "But I mean to kill Sumbha and his brother today, before all their legions."

She raised her bow, and covered the advancing Nisumbha in a cloak of arrows, sharp as serpents' fangs. That Demon smashed them into dust with brilliant volleys of his own. The Himalaya quaked with the sound of their bowstrings. Nisumbha had come into battle surrounded by an Asura host. These savage Daityas now flew at the Devis from every side. The pitch of battle rose to a crescendo, and the Devi was just a blur as she fought that army by herself, killing a thousand Asuras every moment, and turning the streams of melted ice that flowed down the mountain scarlet with demons' blood.

The mountain-air was a thickness of screams and roars, all cut off abruptly by the Devi's luminous archery. Now, she loosed her lion at the enemy, and the golden creature came to hunt the Danavas like a feline embodiment of Yama. Its mane quivering, its roars terrifying, it fell on Nisumbha's soldiers. The lion tore their throats out with fangs like daggers, it ripped their chests open and gouged out their innards with talons like swords. It drank their blood, and ate their burning flesh, an arm here, a leg there, and the screams of those that beast hunted rang above every other sound on the field.

Meanwhile, Sumbha grew impatient and came up the mountain with his legions, by another pass. Kali and Chamunda met him there, and a pitched battle broke out. The black Devis slew a hundred thousand of Sumbha's Asuras; Chamunda feasted on their flesh. Then, parting his army like a great hill standing in the course of a river, Sumbha, emperor of the Daityas, stood forth. His archery was such that even those two Devis could not resist him. He struck Kalika deep in her breast with an astra, so she swooned, and, next moment, he pierced Chamunda in her belly and she fell.

At once Ambika rode up on her lion, both she and her beast roaring stentoriously as she snatched Kali and Chamunda up from the ground. Her eyes were scarlet with fury, and, just seeing her for the first time, Sumbha stood transfixed, trembling as if she had struck him through his heart with a shaft of primeval desire. He had never seen anyone like her in all his life. He stood unmanned, weak with love, and the sign of it showed plainly at his groin.

Ambika saw that great Demon, the Lord of the three worlds, thus, and she threw back her head and laughed at him. She saw clearly in his eyes the tumult his heart felt. She saw desperate love and, then, the truth dawning ineluctably: that he would never possess her, but only die at her hands. And she saw, that, even in that certainty, Sumbha felt strange contentment. Just then, Nisumbha, who had climbed there by another trail, challenged her thunderously.

In his hand he held a gleaming sword, and a shield embossed with eight crescent moons. That towering Demon first fell on the Devi's lion and struck it several times, deeply in the neck and face, while the beast's roars shook the mountain, and its blood flowed copiously. In a wink, the Daitya whirled his blade above his head and flung it like lightning at the Devi Ambika. She struck it to powder with a languid blow of her mace, and then struck Nisumbha on his arm, drawing a screech of pain from him.

Nisumbha seized up a battle-axe now and swift as thought cut the Devi in her side. But, with a smile, she stanched the wound, and it healed miraculously before the Demon's eyes. Then she made the strangest sound from her throat, as of a thousand great temple bells ringing all together. A death-knell! Nisumbha saw she drank deeply from the flagon of wine in her hands, and her eyes glittered.

Meanwhile, the Devas had flown down to the mountain, where an encounter was underway between them and the Asuras. The ones of light hunted brutally on that field and a thousand Danavas died every moment by weapons of fire and light. The Himalaya was strewn with corpses, blood flowed in rillets and packs of dogs and jackals, wolves and hyenas, feasted there, as did great, bent vultures, kites and crows. The air was full of the screams of those cut down, or immolated. Indeed, the air was a single, long scream, for whole phalanxes of demons perished every moment, consumed by incendiary Devastras.

Nisumbha saw his Asuras dying all around him, and, with a fulminant yell, he flew at the Devi again, with another great mace. He smashed the lion on its head, such a blow that the beast sank to its knees for a moment. Nisumbha's triumphant laughter drowned every other noise on that field. He was truly a great Daitya now, a Demon from the deepest pit of hell. He had grown with mahima, and loomed over the mountain like another peak sprung up suddenly. The Asura bared fangs like streaks of lightning, and struck the Devi Ambika twice with his mace, blows like thunder.

The sun hid his face in fear; the sky grew black as midnight. Then Ambika shone like another sun risen on that mountain, her voice was the very voice of time, as she cried in anger, "Dare you strike me, fool? I will send you headless into heaven."

Next moment, it seemed a bright crescent-moon rose for a moment on that mountain, and then vanished. It was the arc the Devi's axe made as it struck Nisumbha's head from his neck and the grisly thing went bouncing down the mountainside, still roaring. Then, the strangest thing: the Demon's lips on his head that went hurtling down the sheer slope still swore at the Devi, crying how he, Nisumbha, would cut her in small pieces and have her for his evening meal! And here, above, the Asura's headless trunk still attacked the Devi, swinging the studded mace at her, at the Devas around her, at Kali and Chamunda. If any of his own demons came in the way of Nisumbha's wild mace-strokes, they died, because being headless, he had no eyes with which to see.

With a tinkling laugh to see this bizarre performance, the Devi Ambika severed the Demon's arms and legs, with four sickle-headed arrows. Nisumbha fell like one mountain falling on another and five rivers of his dark blood swept down five valleys in cascades.

When his Daityas saw Nisumbha fall like that, their cry of "Boomba!" resounded everywhere as they threw their weapons down and fled in disarray to Sumbha. Sumbha saw his demons running to him, and asked, "Where is my brother? Why are these men fleeing the battle like cowards?"

The Asura soldiers cried, "Lord, your brother lies dead on the field. The Devi cut off his head, his arms and legs, and his blood flows down the Himalaya in spate."

"O King, the Devi slew all his men, except just us, who fled in fear!"

"Sumbha, this is the great Devi, the origin of the stars and time, who has come to kill us. We beg you, Lord, don't face her in battle."

"She is no ordinary woman, she is the Parashakti come hunting us."

"She is like another night of the pralaya, and the Devas sing hymns to her from the sky."

"Time is more powerful than any king, even you, great, great Sumbha. Time has humbled Brahma, Vishnu and Siva. She has humbled Indra, and, today, we fear she comes to humble you, O King, and the very race of Asuras. Time is a wheel that spins round. When she favoured you, you drove Indra and his people out of Devaloka, and ruled the worlds. But now she shows us a different face, and a woman riding a lion razes the Daitya army as she pleases. Lord Sumbha, it isn't the Devi or the Devas who mow down our Asuras like stalks of corn in a field. It is Time herself, inexorable Kaala.

Fly down into Patala at once, Sumbha. Save yourself! Save us all! And when the wheel of time spins in our favour again, we shall return to rule Swarga and Bhumi once more."

"You are the lord of the Danavas and Daityas. You are the hope of our race. If the Devi kills you, we, your people, shall all be lost."

But then, those frightened demons shrank back from their king. They saw that his eyes had turned the colour of blood, and rolled in wrath. His mighty frame shook, and he said in a soft and deadly voice, "Fools, what are you saying? My people have perished fighting for me, my heroic generals have died; and you want me to run away from this war like a coward? What will my life be worth, if I save it thus?

Ah, what is this life of mine worth, anyway, when my brother Nisumbha, conqueror of the Devas, lies headless on the field, slain by a woman? As you say, Time is all-powerful. And, when it is time for any creature to be born, so he is. So, too, when the moment of his death comes, no one can save him. We cannot choose when we live or die, but we can decide whether we do so as heroes and warriors, whose fame will live forever, or as cowards on whose name posterity will spit.

Why, Brahma himself dies, when he has lived a hundred years of his life. Fourteen Indras live and die during each of Brahma's days. But, when his time comes, even the Creator of the worlds passes on. Vishnu's life is twice as long as Brahma's, and Siva's twice Vishnu's. But, when their time comes, the great Gods die, too, and all these worlds and heavens with them.

And just as all the living must die, all that die will live again. I care not a whit for death, my Asuras. But for honour, I will give up my life. Prepare my chariot, and those who will, ride with me into battle!"

He was so majestic, that noble Daitya, that his people were emboldened and not one fled the battle. They would rather die than abandon such a king. The Asura Sumbha, lord of the worlds, climbed to the pinnacle of the towering Himalaya, and saw the Devi Ambika on her lion. She was so completely beautiful; it seemed that all the enchantment in the three worlds was gathered within her.

She wore exquisite ornaments and silks, and the Devas, Yakshas and Kinnaras stood around, worshipping her with sacred stotras and parijata blossoms. From time to time, she blew on her conch to celebrate her victory, or made with her lips the fine and strange sound of temple bells ringing. Sumbha saw her for the second time, and was completely bewitched. He thought, "How lovely she is, lovelier than any other woman in all time. Yet, she is a peerless warrior too. Look at her, the flush of youth on her cheek, her limbs so delicate, so womanly. But she feels no passion! She belongs in a soft bed, her legs twined around a strong lover's back. But, here she is, killing Asuras for her pleasure instead.

Ah, she has killed my generals and my Nisumbha; but I cannot help still wanting her! Nothing else matters to me, but to have her in my arms. But she is not susceptible to the sweetest flattery and endearments, or even the most potent mantras. We have tried both, and failed to move her. Oh, how shall I subdue her, to make her a mark not for arrows in battle, but for the tumid shaft of love?"

Then, he quieted the fever that made his blood boil through his body. More calmly, he said to himself, "But her feminine appearance is deceptive, why, it is a death-snare that has claimed a million Asuras' lives. She is not in the least as she seems, neither soft nor vulnerable. She is stronger than a hundred, a thousand, great Danavas; she is a fell army by herself. She is terrible, death incarnate, and merciless. She divides herself in three and drinks our blood and eats our flesh. I must not let her appearance deceive me, as it did Dhumra, Chanda and Munda, and, even, Rakta and Nisumbha. She is a dreadful enemy and I must kill her!"

Sumbha approached the Devi and said, "Come, let us fight! But, O, this war between us is such a waste: of time, of lives, of your woman's nature. I was taught that the arena of love is a woman's battlefield, where she wins her soft victories. Her eyes are her arrows, the heart their target. The perfume she wears on her body is her armour, her modesty her ornament. How coarse it is, O Devi, to see a woman as lovely as you take the field of war. Won't your breasts get in the way when you draw your bowstring to your ear? Whither, then, your modesty, beautiful one?"

She sat on her wild beast, smiling coolly at him. The Danava went on, musingly, "Ah, exquisite one, you abound in such contradictions. Black Kalika and hideous, foolish Chamunda, with their fell voices, are your nearest companions. Instead of a golden chariot, you ride this fearful beast. I beg you, either abandon this weird life of yours, or take another form, ugly, black, fanged, clawed, and yellow-eyed, so you are suited to war. Otherwise, leave all this madness behind you, come away with me and be my queen. For you are much too beautiful and tender for me to fight!"

The Devi Ambika saw how aroused that Demon was, just looking at her. She laughed delightedly, and said, "Poor Danava! Passion distresses you so much, that you will not fight me. Here are Kalika and Chamunda. They are fierce enough for you to face in battle. Fight them." She turned to black Kali, and said in the sweetest voice, "This Sumbha likes only fierce women, Kalika. Kill him for me, please."

Her crimson tongue licking her lips, Kali picked up her mace and advanced on the lord of the Asuras. She was like Yama come to that mountain, except that she was a woman. A fervid battle began between Kali and Sumbha. She struck him first with a blow like a volcano erupting; then, he struck her back like spring thunder. When Sumbha struck Kali squarely across her face, she roared like Pushkara and Avartana, the stormclouds of the Pralaya, and it seemed that the mountain they fought upon would fall into the sea. She grew immense before Sumbha's eyes, raised her mace high over her head, and, with a single blow, shattered the Demon's golden chariot, and crushed his sarathy and his horses to a bloody pulp.

At the last moment the Daitya himself leapt out of his ratha, and was saved. He stormed at her, and fetched her a staggering blow across her dark breasts with his mace. It rocked Kali back on her heels; her tongue lolled like a streak of scarlet lightning from her mouth, and her howl shook the sky. Sumbha's fiendish laughter echoed there, shaking snow and ice off the pines that grew all around them.

Quick as thought, Kalika seized up her axe and hewed off Sumbha's left hand. His naked wrist sprang a geyser of blood, and his bellows rang across the Himalaya. As he tried to stanch the flow by holding his hand to his lips, his face and body were drenched in gore. Still howling, his valour undimmed, great Sumbha hewed again at Kali, with his right hand. The blow landed on her belly and drew a cry from her. But, quick as light, she cut off his right hand as well.

Roaring, and with blood cascading from his severed wrists, that Daitya leapt high into the air and fetched Kali a stupendous kick with both his feet and she fell over. Rising with a curse, now streaked herself with Sumbha's blood, she hewed at his legs with her curved sword, and struck them both off at the knees. Four streams of Sumbha's blood flowed down the Himalaya. Still, he roared as fiercely as ever, still he tried to hobble toward the black Devi, to attack her. His spirit was unvanquished.

Now, almost with admiration for the indomitable Asura, Kalika took his head off his neck, in a flash of blood, like a lotus from its stem. When the brilliant head of Sumbha, master of the three worlds, rolled down the Himalaya and fell into an icy mountain-stream that would bear it to the sea, the Devas broke into song. They lauded the three Devis on the mountain, Ambika, Chamunda, and Kalika.

A fresh malaya breeze sprang up there and rippled the streams of Sumbha's blood that gushed from his severed parts, until his huge body was drained. The breeze became a wind and covered the magnificent Daitya's corpse with snow, as if to embalm the memory of his courage. All the quarters were clear and auspicious, and a marvellous current of hope surged through the world again. Fires in every altar burned pure and smokeless, and the havis was untainted again throughout creation. For, no longer did Demons rule the three worlds, their yoke had been broken by the blessed Devi.'

"O King," said my master Vyasa to Janamejaya, "any man who hears the tale of how the Devi slew Sumbha and Nisumbha, especially he who hears it many times and realises its inner meaning, shall have his every desire fulfilled. The childless man will have sons, the impoverished man shall acquire wealth, and the sick shall be cured of their disease. And those who hear this story with true devotion, why, they even get moksha when they leave their bodies.'" says Romaharshana to the Munis of the Naimisa.

TWENTY-NINE

"JANAMEJAYA SAID IN A LOW, KEEN VOICE, 'MUNI, STRANGE DELIGHT FILLS me when I hear about the Devi's deeds. I feel I want to hear them over and over again. But, first, tell me how I can worship the Devi, and hope to have her grace.'

Vyasa said, 'Once, the good king Suratha of Kola was betrayed by his ministers to a marauding mleccha horde. They divided his own army against him, and routed, Suratha fled into a jungle. In one day that king lost everything. He plunged blindly through the jungle, tears streaming down his face, and arrived by fate in the asrama of the Rishi Sumedha.

That hermitage was built on the banks of a turquoise-blue river, and it was like a bit of heaven fallen into the world. Exotic fruit and flowering-trees grew around the little log-huts that served as shelters for the Muni and his disciples. Wild creatures came there, deer and tiger lay side by side, with no enmity between them. It was as if the lust of the hunt dare not enter Sumedha's asrama. The air was full of koyals' songs. Under the trees, sat the Muni's many sishyas and their chanting of the Vedas was like a sacrament upon the air.

Suratha stood for a moment at the edge of the glade and immediately fear and grief left his mind as the deep peace of the asrama swept over the vanquished king's spirit. He tethered his horse to a tree and walked into that hermitage like a man walking into a beautiful dream. He felt he would like to spend the rest of his ruined life there.

Suratha saw the Rishi Sumedha sitting under a large nyagrodha tree that stood at the very heart of the glade; indeed, the asrama had first been built around that patriarch of the forest. The Muni's body was attenuated by his long tapasya, and his slender form was perfectly quiescent, swathed in light. He was gently expounding the Veda to a knot of sishyas who hung on his every word.

Just to see that holy man filled Suratha with a joy past his understanding. Tears filled the king's eyes, and, without a word, he went and fell at the Muni's feet. Sumedha saw that this visitor was no ordinary man. He offered the king arghya, and a seat of darbha grass to sit on.

The Rishi asked, "Who are you, friend? Why do you weep? Is there anything we can do for you?"

"I am Suratha, and I was king of Kola. But I was vanquished in battle, and I have lost my kingdom, my wealth, my army, my queen and my children. I come seeking sanctuary. I will do whatever you say, for there is no one in the world that can help me but you. I fear my enemies are out hunting me. Save me, Muni, or I am lost."

The Rishi gazed into the king's eyes for a moment, and Suratha had the eerie feeling that the sage was gazing into his very destiny. Then Sumedha said, "Stay here in my asrama, O King. By the power of my tapasya, your enemies will never find this place. But as long as you are here, you may not kill any living creature. You will have to live on wild rice, fruit and roots, as the rest of us do."

Suratha agreed readily, and began living in relative peace in the asrama. One day, he went for a walk by himself in the jungle, and sat under a shady mango tree. The king thought, "The mlecchas have my kingdom, and they are savage men. I am sure that they persecute my people, and I am sure my poor elephants and horses don't get properly fed. My servants must either be in prison, or begging on the streets; and, as for my queen and the women of my harem, I dare not think of what they are subjected to."

As Suratha sat ruminating sadly under the tree, he saw a man approaching, who seemed to have been crying and looked sombre. Suratha beckoned to the stranger who seemed to be in trouble, and asked him to sit at his side under the mango tree. When the man sat, with a deep sigh, the king asked him, "Who are you, friend? Why are you so distressed? The wise say that two men who exchange seven words with each other become friends. Speak to me, tell me why you are so sad."

The man thought Suratha was a Muni, and said to him, "I am a Vaishya, and my name is Samadhi. I am a devout man, but my wife and my sons are not like me. They have always been greedy for money. Why, friend, they took everything I owned and threw me out of my own house, saying I am a miser." His eyes filled again, then, controlling himself, the Vaishya said, "But tell me who you are, stranger. From your face you seem to be a noble and fortunate man."

"I am king Suratha of Kola. My own ministers betrayed me to the mlechchas, and I was driven from my kingdom. Well met, Vaishya! We are both in distress, and we shall make good friends. Let us spend our time together here in the heart of the forest. Let us forget our troubles, and find our serenity."

But the Vaishya cried, "Ah, how can I be serene, my friend? O King, I yearn for my wife and sons, and to be with them in our home despite what they have done to me!"

Suratha was amazed. "How can you yearn for them when they have betrayed you, Vaishya? Even enemies are better than relatives who torment a man. Calm yourself, my friend. See where the truth lies, and remain here in the forest in peace."

But the Vaishya sighed, "Ah, my friend, I miss my wife and sons sorely, and I cannot help myself. Perhaps, they even miss me, and regret what they did. How shall I find peace when my mind is as restless as the wind?"

Suratha confessed, "To tell you the truth, I too am at poor peace. I worry constantly about my kingdom and the havoc the mlecchas must be wreaking in it."

"Ah, what shall we do, friend?"

The king said, "There is an enlightened Rishi's asrama nearby. It is there that I live now. Come, friend Samadhi, let us go to the wise one and ask him for a cure for our grief."

The Vaishya agreed and the two friends went to meet Sumedha. They found the holy one at dhyana under his nyagrodha tree, where he was perfectly tranquil, his face bright and a smile full of kindness on his lips. They prostrated themselves before him, and then Suratha said, "My lord, this is Samadhi the Vaishya. We met in the forest. He and I are both tormented by misfortune, O Muni; for, just as I have lost my kingdom, he has lost his home."

Sumedha said, "I thought you were at peace in my asrama, Suratha."

"I have surely found some peace, my lord. But my mind turns back repeatedly to dark thoughts of my kingdom. I think of my people suffering under the mlecchas' yoke, and of what indignities my queen and my children have to endure. I think of my servants, and how they must be persecuted by the invader. Ah, Rishi, I know this world is all maya, a dream. Yet, I have not found the detachment that lifts a man above joy and sorrow, and makes him calm. All night I dream of my horses and elephants, and how lean and starved they must be without their proper feed. What must they think, except that I have abandoned them?

I know that they are just beasts, and no kin of mine. But all night I see their sad eyes full of tears, and I hear them cry piteously in the dark. And, just like my friend Samadhi, my mind will not be still.

Great master, nothing is hidden from you. Tell us both how we can find some happiness again."

The Rishi Sumedha smiled. He said gently, "The Mulaprakriti, the Devi Maya, is the one who binds and frees all creatures in the universe. She is the cause of causes. If you worship her she will bring joy to your spirits."

Samadhi asked, "How do we worship the Devi, O Muni?"

"**Aim Hrim Klim Chamundayai Bichche**, is her mantra. But, listen also to the ritual of the Devi Bhagavati.

The bhakta must rise before the sun and bathe. Donning a white cloth, he performs the Vedic and Tantrik sandhya. He sips water for achamana and selects an auspicious place for his worship. There he sits facing the east on a kusasana. He sips holy water again, three times for achamana. Then he regulates his breathing in pranayama, and performs the bhuta shuddhi, by which the corporeal body is purified, and the subtle body invoked. Symbolically, he dissolves earth into water, water into fire, fire into air, air into ether, ether into ahamkara, ahamkara into mahat, and mahat into Prakriti, the final cause.

Next, he performs the jiva shuddhi by which the sadhaka becomes the Devatamaya. Next, the Matrika Nyasa. He identifies the six chakras mentally, in their correct places. He places his hand on the different parts of his own body, where the different letters of the alphabet reside on the body of the Devata.

Now the worshipper says aloud the time, date, and month of the year, and begins to meditate on the different parts of his body and the Planets and Devas who rule over them. He purifies the place of worship and the offerings he will make during his worship, by sprinkling them with water, and reciting the Astra or Phat mantras. Thus, he removes every obstacle from his path.

Now, on a copper plate, with white sandalwoodpaste, he draws the two triangles that intersect with the vertices facing in opposite directions, one over the other. Outside this hexagon, he draws an octagon, like a lotus of eight petals. Outside this, he draws the boundary, the Bhupura. On each of the eight petals of the octagon, he must inscribe one syllable of the nine-syllabled bija mantra, and the ninth syllable must be engraved at the heart of the yantra, at its corolla.

Having installed the yantra in an auspicious position, the bhakta must worship the Adhara Shakti with the Pitha mantra. He must invoke the Devi, by chanting the bija mantra towards an image of her, or a golden plate that represents eternal femininity. Then he worships the ganas in the six angles of the hexagon, Indra and the Devas in the octagon, Vajra and the ayudhas in the Bhupura.

Merged in deep dhyana, the worshipper immerses himself in the nine-syllable mantra of the Devi: **Krim Dakshine Kalike Svaha**. This is the nitya kriya for the worship of the Devi, but on the Navaratra, during the bright fortnight of Chaitra, and specially Asvina, the bhakta must observe a fast, keep the Navaratra vrata. The most auspicious days are the eighth, ninth and fourteenth days of the waxing moon. Regardless of who he is, the man who worships the Devi during the Navaratra, in Asvina, has his every desire granted."

Suratha asked, "Does the Navaratha homa differ from the nitya homa you have described?"

Rishi Sumedha said, "A square altar is built specially for the Navaratra, and a vessel of holy water placed on it, upon a yantra just like the one used in the nitya puja. Around the vessel, yava grains are heaped, and a pandal is erected above the altar. The altar is embellished with bel leaves, karavira, satapatra and champaka flowers, fruit, incense, and many lamps. The Devi is worshipped thrice daily, at the three sandhyas of each day, at dawn, noon and sunset.

A young virgin should be worshipped as an embodiment of the Devi herself, with sandal, ornaments, scented oils, and garlands of flowers. The poor and Brahmanas are fed, and the bhakta fasts for nine days, and eats his first meal on the tenth. The devotee who keeps the Navaratra vrata acquires unswerving bhakti for the Devi, and has his every wish fulfilled."

Sumedha smiled, and his face shone with kindliness. He said to Suratha the Kshatriya, and Samadhi the Vaishya, "The way out of your misery, my friends, is to worship the Devi Bhagavati. Keep the Navaratra vrata, and all your troubles will end. The suffering in a man's life is only the Devi subtly calling you. She calls you both. Worship her and she will save you from your distress, and bless you someday with moksha."

The king and the Vaishya were deeply comforted to hear what the Muni said to them. They felt hope spring up again in their desolate spirits. They prostrated themselves once more before the sage. When Sumedha blessed them, the Vaishya Samadhi said, "Holy one, we have surely been led to your feet by our punya of past lives. Your wisdom makes us pure, Muni, your peace calms our minds. We will worship the Devi Bhagavati with a fervent tapasya. We beg you, be our guru, give us an auspicious mantra."

Suratha also inclined his head, to echo what the Vaishya said. Sumedha then laid his hand on their heads, and gave them the bija mantra, **AUM Mahishamardinyai Svaha**. He also taught them the method of dhyana. They bowed to him, and with his leave, took themselves to the bank of the river that flowed nearby and began their worship. They spent a month sitting in padmasana, their eyes shut, chanting the bija mantra and the three legends of the Devi. Bhakti took root in their hearts and grew swiftly.

Suratha and Samadhi did nothing else but worship the Goddess. But, once a day they would come before the Muni Sumedha and prostrate themselves at his feet for his blessing. The bhaktas ate only fruit. A year went by and they grew stronger by their tapasya. Then they ate only the leaves of certain trees. Another year passed and both the king and the Vaishya dreamt of the Devi Bhagavati on the same night.

They saw her wearing scarlet robes and unearthly ornaments. During the third year, they were true tapasvins and subsisted only on water. But when three years passed, and the Devi had still not appeared before them, they grew desperate. The two bhaktas said to each other, "If we cannot have a vision of the Devi after three years of dhyana, we may as well not live any more."

Both agreed, and they dug a triangular kunda and lit a fire of yagna in it. They meant to make a final sacrifice to the Devi Ambika: of their lives. When the fire blazed up, Suratha took his sword and began to slice slivers of his own flesh from his body to feed the flames. Samadhi the Vaishya did the same. They found they felt no pain, but only great exultation at what they did. Their blood flowed, and they offered it in ecstasy to the Devi.

Suddenly, the fire in the pit of sacrifice burned bright as suns, and the tapasvins were blinded by white flames like massive columns of light. From those flames, the Devi Bhagavati stood forth before her devotees. In her voice deep as the sky, she said, "You are my favourite bhaktas. Ask me for anything, and it shall be yours."

Suratha's hair stood on end with rapture, and he said, "Devi, let me vanquish my enemies and have my kingdom back."

The crimson Devi said, smiling, "Your enemies are enfeebled. Return to your city, and rule for ten thousand years. After this life you will be born as Surya Deva's son, and be known as Savarni Manu."

She turned now to the Vaishya Samadhi who stood before her with folded hands. She said, "And what would you have of me, Samadhi?"

The long tapasya had made Samadhi a wise man. He said softly, "Devi, bless me with wisdom, that the bonds of samsara which bind my heart are loosened. I want enlightenment, Mother of worlds, I want to see the truth and to be free."

The brilliant Devi raised her hand over him. Next moment, she vanished before their eyes, and a common fire burned once more in the pit of sacrifice, and the wounds they had inflicted on themselves were all miraculously healed. Glowing with their experience, the two bhaktas came to the Muni Sumedha and told him what had happened.

Just then, they heard a great noise at the edge of the asrama. Sumedha smiled, and said to Suratha, "Look Kshatriya, your ministers who betrayed you have come to beg your forgiveness."

It was true. Not only his ministers, but most of his people as well had come to beg Suratha to return and to be their king once more. They had risen up themselves to kill many of the mlecchas, and had driven the rest out of the kingdom. They fell at his feet, and begged his forgiveness, and there was no doubt that the Devi Bhagavati had wrought this miracle. Suratha went home to his kingdom with his ministers and his people, and began to rule more wisely than ever. The Devi Ambika's grace was upon that king, and his was a just and prosperous reign.

But Suratha was not the only one whom the Devi blessed. As the king's ministers came to Sumedha's asrama, a strange thing happened to Samadhi the Vaishya. He sat some distance from the congregation in the hermitage. His wife and sons did not come to ask his pardon, or call him back home. Instead, the Devi visited Samadhi again, subtly, in his spirit. She loosed a tide of knowledge and joy into him, she set him free!

When he knew the Truth, all the Vaishya's old attachments fell away from him like a snake's old skin. A thousand-petalled lotus unfurled in his head, and he was one with the Parashakti, with eternal bliss. The illumined Samadhi spent the rest of his mortal days wandering from one sacred tirtha to the next, and, when death came for him, the Devi appeared and took him unto herself, and he had moksha,' said Vyasa Muni to Janamejaya," says the Suta to the Rishis of the Naimisa.

THIRTY

THE RISHIS SAY TO ROMAHARSHANA, "YOUR PURANA IS AMRITA TO US, sweet Suta. We have heard of Viswakarman's son Vritra, and how Indra slew him. We would hear that tale from you in detail, because we are confused by what we have heard so far. Why, what we have heard leads us to believe that Indra and Vishnu himself forsook dharma to kill Vritrasura, who was a Brahmana's son, and a Brahmana himself. Also, we heard you say the Devi Bhagavati killed Vritra, but common knowledge has it that Indra did."

The Suta says, "Janamejaya of the Kurus asked my master Vyasa the very same thing. He said, 'Muni, I have heard that both the Devi and Indra killed the Asura Vritra. How can this be, holy one?'

Vyasa replied with a smile, 'Your taste for the Purana grows day by day, O King. Listen, then, to the legend of the Asura Vritra. All that happens in the three worlds does so by the delusion of Maha Maya. Darkness and light, good and evil, are all her creations, her illusions, which she sends forth and destroys at her will. No creature in Swarga, Bhumi or Patala is free of the three gunas of Maya. The Devas and the Trimurti themselves are no exception; they also fall prey, from time to time, to an excess of one of the gunas, and thus, to selfishness. Why, when they are deluded, even Vishnu and Indra commit treachery and murder.

The Prajapati Viswakarman was the architect of the Gods. He was gifted, brilliant, and a great yogin and Brahmana. But, once, arrogant Indra slighted the Prajapati, and an enmity grew up between the two of them. To avenge himself on Indra, Viswakarman, the cosmic genius, created a wonderful son, and called him Trisiraska Viswarupa. The boy was handsome past imagining; he had three beautiful faces. He used each face for a different task: the first he used to read the Veda, the second to eat and drink with (especially amrita!), and with the third, he studied the universe around him.

When he had read the Veda, drunk amrita, and seen whatever he wanted to of creation, he decided to sit in tapasya. He renounced every pleasure he had enjoyed, and Trisira sat in padmasana, and began a fervent dhyana. His passions restrained, his mind turned inward, upon itself, he became an ascetic. In summer, he performed the searing panchagni-sadhana. He lit four fires around him, and the sun was the fifth above. Then he suspended himself by his feet from a tree. In winter he sat in icy streams, often entirely submerged. Soon, he did not eat anymore.

The subtle fire of Trisira's tapasya went scorching through the mandalas. Indra, in Devaloka, grew alarmed. He was afraid that, with such a penance, Trisira may even usurp his sovereignty over the three worlds. Moreover, Trisira was Viswakarman's boy, and Indra had no doubt, the moment he was powerful enough, he would come to kill the Deva king. Meanwhile, Trisira shone like a sun where he sat in meditation, his radiance streamed through the lokas.

There are many methods to distract any Muni from tapasya, and the king of the Devas is a master of them all. Through the ages, he had found that the swiftest and most effective means to sway any hermit from his rigor is seduction. Indra summoned the Apsaras Urvashi, Menaka, Rambha, Ghritachi, Tillottama, and some others, too. Each one was an unearthly beauty, of charms that not man or Deva had ever resisted.

The king of heaven said to those women, "I have a grave task for you, one upon which my very life depends. My fiercest enemy sits in a tapasya such as time has seldom seen. He grows more powerful every day, and soon he will come to kill me. Apsaras, you must seduce him out of his dhyana."

The Apsaras were willing enough, and went straight to the place where Trisira sat motionless, hardly breathing any more. The nymphs came in a bewitching throng, and were clad in such flimsy raiment, so none of their breathtaking beauty was hidden. They came singing in soft voices, and dancing, so even a corpse may have risen to savour their charms. Trisira did not seem to see or hear them. Those enchanters came near him, and he could surely smell their bodies' fragrance that could drive a man out of his mind. Still he did not stir, or open his eyes on any of his faces.

The Apsaras went back to Indra, in pique, and said, "Lord, this three-faced one is no ordinary tapasvin. We could not tempt him at all. He is like an incarnation of Agni; his body is like fire. We were afraid that he may burn us to ashes with a look, if he opened his eyes. His tapasya is profound, Indra. Beware of him."

Indra waved them away, and his alarm mounted. Something had to be done about Trisira, and quickly. Indra muttered to himself, "If he can't be seduced, then he must be killed."

He called for Airavata, his white elephant, and flew through the sky to where Trisira sat upon the mountain. Indra poised himself in the air above the Muni. He felt a pang of conscience, when he saw how serene and absorbed Trisira was. The three-faced tapasvin glowed like a full moon where he sat. Light flowed from his body in a stream and spumed through the mandalas. For a moment, the Deva was gripped by doubt: how could he kill a Rishi who sat in such quiescent contemplation?

Then he remembered that the hermit below him was Viswakarman's son, born to be his, Indra's, bane. Drawing a deep breath, Indra summoned his Vajra, the thunderbolt of a thousand joints. Murmuring a mantra, he cast that terrible weapon at Trisira. The Vajra struck Trisira squarely in his chest, and, never opening his eyes, the yogin keeled over where he sat, dead.

Indra exulted, but the other Rishis of Devaloka were aghast. They cried, "Indra has killed a brilliant and innocent Muni at his tapasya. He must pay for this sin."

Indra went back to Amravati, but Trisira still glowed brightly where he had fallen. Some days passed, and Indra returned to the scene of his crime. Trisira lay still, yet his body shone. Indra grew anxious that perhaps he was not dead. Just then, he saw a woodcutter called Taksha passing near. The Lord of the Devas hailed the man.

Indra said to Taksha, "I struck this enemy with my Vajra and he fell. But his body shines brightly still, and I fear he is not dead. Strike off his head with your axe, friend woodcutter, and then he surely shall not be alive. Do this for me, and I will reward you richly."

The woodcutter replied, "Lord, the Muni's neck has three heads upon it. It is too thick for my axe to sever. Moreover, I will not cut off a dead man's head. Can't you see, O Indra, the three-headed one is already dead? Why are you so afraid of him?"

"He is my enemy, and he is dangerous. I feel sure that life still lingers in his body."

"My Lord, he was a Brahmana. You have incurred the sin of Brahmahatya by killing him."

Indra said confidently, "I will do prayaschitta for my sin later. But just now, I must make sure he is dead. Haven't you heard, O Taksha, that enemies must be killed, one way or another?"

"I cannot do this vicious thing," said the woodcutter, "the Muni isn't my enemy."

"If you cut off his head, I will let you have the offering of the head of every beast from every sacrifice of men."

Now this was a tempting offer, for any sacrificial offering is auspicious. Taksha thought about it for a moment, then, smiling, he stepped up to Trisira's body, and with three strokes of his axe hewed off the dead Rishi's heads. Then the strangest thing happened. Thousands and thousand of birds flew out from those severed heads. From the head that used to chant the Vedas, bright kapinjala birds flew out in swarms; from the head that gazed upon the universe, as if to drink it down, there came twittering tittiris, and flocks of kalavinkas issued from the head that drank amrita. The birds covered the sky in dense, song brimming flights, for a time, then flew off in every direction.

Heaving a sigh of relief, Indra returned to Amravati. Quite pleased with himself, Taksha also went back to his home. Both of them thought only of what they had gained by killing Trisira, neither thought of the consequences of what they had done. But when Viswakarman heard of the murder of his son, he gnashed his teeth and wept. Roar after roar came from him, then he swore he would create another son to avenge his gentle Trisira. Why, he would have a son who would kill Indra.

Viswakarman lit a fire of yagna, and poured dark oblations onto it, all the while chanting mantras from the fourth Veda, the occult Atharva. For eight days, he sat before that fire, until the flames turned to great slabs of white light. On the eighth night, a splendid young man stood forth from the flames.

When Viswakarman saw that youth, his son, he cried, "My child, you shall be Indra's enemy. Now, grow!"

Like a fire fed with ghee, that youth grew immense. In moments, he was a towering figure before his father, his face shining in the sky like another sun. He was an Asura, resplendent and terrible as well. Why, he seemed like Yama himself, and in a voice like doom, he said to his sire, "Father, why are your eyes red with weeping? Tell me the cause of your grief, and I will remove it. What else is a son meant for? Shall I drain the ocean? Shall I crush the mountains into dust? Shall I keep the sun from rising? Shall I cast the earth deep into the sea of space, or shall I kill Indra, Yama, and the host of Devaloka for you?"

When Viswakarman heard the love in his stupendous son's voice, he said, "Truly, you are magnificent enough to end my sorrow, my vrijina."

His boy said, "Give me a name, father, and tell me how I can quell your grief."

"I name you Vritra, my child. You had a brother called Trisira, of three wise and blameless faces. Ah, how you would have loved him, if only you had the fortune to know him. He was the gentlest and sagest youth in all of creation. He sat in tapasya, and the three worlds glowed with his penance. But Indra was afraid of my pure son, and struck him down with his Vajra. Not content with that, he had a woodcutter hew off Trisira's heads with his axe."

Tears flowed down Viswakarman's face, when he spoke of his dead child. He said grimly, "Indra must die for his sin of Brahmahatya. Vritra, you must avenge your brother."

Vritra growled, and the world shook beneath his feet. Then, Viswakarman, artisan of genius, began to fashion great and fearsome weapons for his son, so he could kill the king of the Devas. He made a veritable armoury for his fiery boy: great axes, a bow and inexhaustible quiver, trisulas, gadas, shaktis, tomaras, parighas, pattisas, chakras. He taught him the mantras for all the astras and narachas. He made a coat of golden armour for him, light as the breeze, and impenetrable. Finally, he wrought a supernal vimana for Vritra, which was formed like a cloud, and flew quickly as thoughts.

Viswakarman performed the svastyayana over his warrior son, to protect him, and then he sent his powerful child to take revenge on Indra. In war, it is natural for an enemy's enemy to become a friend. So, the Asuras whom Indra and his Devas had vanquished and driven down into Patala came streaming to Vritrasura, to join him. Soon, Viswakarman's son had a fell and teeming army to command.

Indra's spies brought word swiftly to their king of light, about the Asura Vritra and his sinister legions. "Lord! Viswakarman has performed an abhichara to have revenge on you. He has created an Asura who is taller than Mount Meru. All the Danavas have flocked to this Vritra, and he comes to kill you, O Indra."

When Indra's Devas heard this in their gleaming Sudharma, they were terrified. For, they knew that their king had sinned. Dharma had been violated, and punishment would surely follow. Suddenly, other Devas came running to their Lord in alarm; evil omens had appeared everywhere in Devaloka. The rooftops of Amravati swarmed with birds of night and carrion, owls, crows, kites and vultures in great, dark flocks, at midday. Hyenas, wolves, and jackals came in packs, out of nowhere, and bayed the morning sun. At high noon, the howling of midnight's Rakshasas rang dismally through the city of light.

Strange, ugly women, clad in rough, black cloth, went from house to house crying dementedly to the Devas, "Leave your homes and flee! Doom is upon you!"

The fires of sacrifice burned low, and billowed with purulent smoke. Many were extinguished suddenly, though there was no breath of wind stirring where they were lit. The Apsaras and Devastris fell into torpid swoons, and dreamt of vile demonesses who shaved their heads and drank their blood. The Devas found themselves crying, for no reason, and could not stanch their tears. Huge, blood-headed lizards scuttled everywhere, nodding their heads in the most macabre way. Black comets with tails of fire fell out of the sky, and the sun and the moon were cloaked in ominous haloes.

In the Sudharma, Indra trembled. He called for Devaguru Brihaspati, and said, "Winds of death sweep our city, and the very stars fall out of the sky. Evil omens are everywhere. Perform a yagna, O Guru, for our safety."

But Brihaspati hung his head and replied, "Lord of the thousand eyes, you committed Brahmahatya when you killed Trisira. I fear retribution for your sin is at hand. Viswakarman's second son, Vritra, is a fire-born Asura, and he is invincible against all the Devas. The omens mean just one thing—that Vritra is on his way to kill you."

Just then, a clamour broke out in the streets, and they saw all the folk of Swarga—the Yakshas, Kinnaras, Gandharvas, Rishis, Charanas, Siddhas, Apsaras, and all the others fleeing in panic, in every direction.

Indra began to shout commands, "Summon the Vasus and Rudras, call the Aswins and the Adityas! Pusa, Bhaga, Vayu, Kubera, Varuna, Agni, Surya, all of you, arm yourselves! Mount your vimanas, the enemy is upon us!"

Indra mounted Airavata, and flew down to a lofty mountain, north of the Manasarovara, that is a portal between Bhumi and Devaloka. The Deva host followed him in their vimanas, and mounted on extraordinary beasts and birds.

It was not long before Vritra arrived there, as well, with his monstrous legions. A tumultuary battle broke out. That sacred mountain and the sky above it were lit up with astras, shaktis, and serpentine and luminous narachas. The armies of darkness and light hewed at each other with clubs and swords, parighas, pattisas, paasas like liquid fire, glinting parasus, and every other conceivable weapon. Arms and legs, heads and trunks, hewn off, fell everywhere, and the howls and screams of the dismembered and the slain echoed all around, starting avalanches that were tinted scarlet for the streams of blood that flowed.

The two armies, of millions of warriors, evil and blithe, were locked in a savage contention. It is told that war lasted a hundred human years, which are two months and a half by the time of the Devas. Vritrasura was invincible. He mowed down the Gandharvas and Kinnaras, the Yakshas and Charanas, the great Naga heroes, the Guhyakas and warlike Siddhas, with the coruscating weapons his father had given him. Though they also took heavy toll of the forces of darkness, the Devas grew afraid for their own lives.

Varuna was the first to flee, and then Vayu, Yama, Surya, Chandra, Indra himself and all the army of light turned tail before the terrible Vritra, and the war was lost. The triumphant Asura came to Viswakarman in his asrama, and prostrated himself at his feet. The son said to his father, "The Devas are vanquished, they have fled. I took Airavata, and Indra ran from me on foot. I have brought you the white elephant as my spoil of war. I did not kill Indra because I have heard one must never kill a man who is terrified, and running from battle."

Viswakarman's sad face lit up with a smile. He said softly, "I am proud of you, my heroic son! You have begun to fulfil the destiny for which you were born." He embraced his brilliant boy, "My child, you have lightened your father's grief, though you haven't removed it."

He paused, then said, "Now worship Brahma, Vritra, with a great tapasya. Get a boon of immortality from him, and then kill Indra. Vanquishing him in battle is not punishment enough. He is guilty of the vilest Brahmahatya; he must pay for it with his life. Nothing less will do, nothing else will make our revenge complete or remove my anguish."

The Asura Vritra went to mount Gandhamadana upon the earth. There, he bathed in the cold and sacred Mandakini, then made a seat of kusa grass for himself and sat upon it in padmasana. Slowly he yoked his body and mind, hardly eating, but quieting his breath with pranayama. Soon, he did not eat at all, but only drank water. And later, Vritra sat entirely absorbed by his tapasya, neither eating or drinking anything, and hardly breathing any more. The subtle fire of his tapasya spiralled through the three worlds, and he shone like a sliver of star upon the mountain.

When Indra knew about Vritra's tapasya, he sent all sorts of Gandharvas, Yakshas, Pannagas, Kinnaras and Apsaras, with various magical powers, to disturb the Asura. But Vritra sat on, unmoved,' said Vyasa to the king," says the inspired Suta in the jungle.

THIRTY-ONE

"THE ORIGINAL PAURANIKA, MY GURU KRISHNA DWAIPAYANA SAID, 'EVEN the Gandharvas and Apsaras, who took sweet song and seductive dance and scent to Vritra's mountain, returned to Indra without swerving the Asura from his penance. Vritra sat for a hundred years in dhyana, and one day four-faced Brahma appeared before him, riding a swan.

Brahma said, "Ask me for any boon, Vritra of the great tapasya, and it shall be yours."

Tears of joy in his eyes, the Asura prostrated himself before the resplendent Creator, and said humbly, "My Lord, I am so fortunate to see you with my eyes. You know my heart, knower of all things. You already know the one desire I have—to be immortal. So, grant me, Pitamaha, that I cannot be killed by any weapon that is solid or fluid, or with any of stone, metal or wood, or any astra of fire or light. Grant me this boon, Lord of worlds, and I will conquer the Devas and rule from Amravati."

Brahma said, "Child arise, the boon you want is yours," and vanished before Vritra's eyes.

Vritra went in joy to Viswakarman, and told him about the boon he had. The father embraced his son, and cried, "Now kill Indra, and rule the worlds! I still see your brother Trisira's gentle faces before my eyes and they cry out to me for revenge."

Vritrasura gathered an immense army, and set out to conquer the Devas. As they marched under the lead of their new emperor, the Danavas raised their voices and their shouts shook heaven and earth. Indra trembled to hear that sound. Quickly, he mustered his host of light again: the Lokapalas, the other Devas, and their legions. Soon a pitched battle was underway. Weapons of every sort flashed in the sun, and scarlet blood, as limbs and heads were hewn off, thousands each moment, and roars and screams were as common as the air the two forces breathed.

The battle swung one way and then the other. But, looming like a mountain over the Deva army, awesome Vritra was indomitable. The Devas' fiercest weapons glanced off him like bits of straw. He mowed down entire legions with weapons of fire, and, inexorably, the Danavas had the better of the Devas. Gandharvas and Kinnaras perished in thousands, their mellifluous death-cries ringing over the grisly battlefield at the gates of Indra's Amravati. Then, forging his bloody way through the thickest fray, Vritra was upon Indra himself.

In strange fear, Indra stood rooted and helpless before his enemy, as if his sin of killing Trisira paralyzed him. Viswakarman's stupendous son seized the Lord of Amravati. In a wink, he ripped off the Deva's golden armour and cast it from him. And, yawning open his great mouth, Vritrasura swallowed Indra whole!

The Devas saw this and fled in panic, crying out their king's name. They ran to Brihaspati, and cried, "Guru, rescue the thousand-eyed one from Vritrasura's belly. Use abhichara, use any sorcery, hurry! Indra may already be dead."

Brihaspati replied, "Indra still lives in Vritra's belly. We shall have him back alive."

With that, he began to intone some powerful mantras that came into his mind at that moment, mantras he had never known before. When Vritra heard that occult and potent chant, he yawned. It was the first time in creation that any creature yawned. Helplessly, the shining Asura yawned and yawned, hardly knowing what he did but unable to stop himself. In a flash Indra flew out from his belly, and fell on the ground before him. It is told that since then all creatures have begun to yawn, Gods and demons, men and animals.

They fought again, the Devas and the Danavas, Viswakarman's Asura son, big as a mountain, and Indra, Lord of the Devas. That battle lasted a long time, some say twenty thousand human years. But at last, Vritrasura prevailed. Indra and his Devas were vanquished and they fled from Devaloka, leaving the demons masters of the three worlds. In Amravati, in the glittering Sudharma, Viswakarman's son sat on Indra's ruby throne that the worlds worship. His chief Asuras were given the tasks and the powers of the Gods who had fled.

Every treasure that belonged to the Devas now fell into the hands of Vritrasura and his Danavas. Squadrons of fabulous pushpaka vimanas were theirs, untold gold and jewels, Airavata, Ucchaisravas, Kamadhenu and the Parijata. Best of all, the exquisite Apsaras were theirs to bed to their wild hearts' content, and lovely Naginas, Devastris, Gandharvis, Yakshis, Kinnaris, and all the delectable women of heaven. They also had a mystic share in every yagna across the three worlds, and became immeasurably powerful.

The shattered Devas fled into exile, and hid like beggars in remote wildernesses where the Danavas couldn't hunt them—in secret caves of mountains of the earth, in tiny oases in the hearts of deserts, and in forbidden forests: great Indra, Surya, Varuna, Agni, Yama, Vayu, Soma, and the rest. Vritrasura's power and majesty swelled day by day, and with it his arrogance. He kept his father beside him, and Viswakarman was richly consoled; grief hardly touched him any more.

After an age, centuries of roaming the outer wastes, one day the Devas gathered, the Rishis and Gandharvas, and the other dispossessed celestials. They decided to take their misery to Lord Siva, and seek redress from him. So they came to Kailasa, the lonely mountain that stands to the north of the Himalayas like a great pearl, or a full moon fallen onto the earth.

They climbed to the middle reaches of the white and precious mountain, and prostrated themselves at the feet of glorious Siva. The Mahayogin stood before them in his eternal hermit's guise, emerald cobras coiled around his ash-coated and emaciated body, like ornaments.

Abjectly Indra said, "Ocean of Mercy, Devadeva, Lord, what shall we do? Vritrasura has driven us out of Devaloka, and we wander the earth like beggars. The Asura is swollen with hubris, and the worlds fall swiftly into darkness and anarchy. It is time Vritra died, Mahadeva. We are shriven of our vanity, and I have paid for my sin. Restore us to our proper kingdom."

Siva said mildly, "Let us set Brahma before us, and invoke Narayana. The Blue one will find a remedy for you, a way to kill Vritra."

Siva summoned Brahma with just a thought. With the four-faced Creator as their chief priest, the Devas began to chant the Purusasukta slokas that invoke Hari Narayana, who is the saviour of the ones of light, throughout time.

In a while Vishnu stood before them, dazzling. He said sweetly, "Lords of the worlds, what makes you call out to me so fervently? You Mahadeva, and Brahma you, and you, Devas."

They did not answer, but stood silent. Vishnu said again, "Tell me what ails you, Devas, perhaps I can ease your sorrow."

Siva now said, "You know all things, Hari, so you know that Vritra has vanquished the Devas and seized Indra's throne in Amravati. Help the Suras now, they have no one but you to turn to."

Vishnu mused a moment, then, said, "Vritrasura was born from the fire, and he has Brahma's boon. He will be hard to kill without some deception. We must first pretend to make peace with him. Then, when he is lulled into a false safeness, kill him. Go to him now, and agree to any terms he wants. Make a friend of him, and, when he believes you are no longer the enemy but his willing subject, even his dearest friend, kill him. Devas, when the moment arrives I will enter Indra's Vajra myself, so Vritra can be killed. The Asura has become a tyrant, he must die."

The Devas agreed readily, but now the Blue God said, "Before anything else, you must worship the Devi Bhagavati. Only if she blesses you, can Vritrasura be killed."

The Devas took themselves to Mount Sumeru, the golden mountain at the heart of the world, and they worshipped the Devi fervidly. One day, she stood before them, entirely enchanting, full of love and light. Her skin was softly ruddy, like the blooms of the Parijata; she wore resonant silks and unworldly ornaments past compare. Hers was a presence of infinite grace and mercy, and she spoke to them in her voice that was the most beautiful one they had ever heard, "Why have you come to Meru, Devas? Why do you worship me like this? For what boon?"

Indra said humbly, with tears in his eyes, "Devi, Vritrasura tyrannizes the worlds. He has made a living hell of our lives. Bless us, that we may kill him."

She smiled, ah, bewitching them, and said simply, "Be it so." With that, she vanished like a bright mist.

Glowing with the Devi's blessing, the Devas, the Rishis, the Gandharvas and all the others with them, now went off to Amravati, to the Sudharma, where Vritra sat on Indra's throne. The Asura blazed like a white fire of yagna. He was so splendid it seemed he may consume the worlds and the Devas with his lustre.

The Rishis of heaven then said to Vritra, "Lord of worlds, greetings! Great, great Vritra, how radiant you are, how boundless is your majesty! Everything is perfect in your life, glorious one, except your enmity with

Indra. We Munis urge you to rid yourself of this final fear. Both of you have no peace of mind, for this enmity. Both of you sleep ill at ease, for anxiety of the other. The wise say that, when the time comes, a noble enemy makes the best friend a man can have in life.

Years have passed since your last battle. You, Vritra, are master of the worlds. Let there be peace between Indra and you, and thus let there be peace in all creation. Let the Rishis go back to their tapasya in serenity; let there be harmony once more in the three worlds, and among all living creatures.

Indra seeks refuge in your grace. He seeks an end to enmity. He swears to accept whatever terms you choose to impose, to have peace. It is the Truth for which the stars wheel round in the sky; and the sun, the moon, and the planets. The earth rests upon the Truth; the sun rises for its sake, the wind blows for it, for the Truth the oceans are contained by their shores.

In the name of that Truth, now, let there be peace and everlasting friendship between Indra and you. Great Vritra, share your dominions with him, on whatever terms you are pleased to dictate."

Having heard the divine Rishis out patiently, Vritrasura said, "You are Munis, and never speak falsely. You are serene, and investigate the hidden causes of all things, before you arrive at any conclusion. Yet, precious ones, the wise say that an intelligent man never makes friends with a shameless, licentious, and evil person. Especially, an enemy who is a murderer.

Indra, whose cause you have come to plead, is all these things. He is a scoundrel, a villain, and it is only because your hearts are so innocent that you speak on his behalf. But I say to you, Munis, the one you speak for is not worthy. He is treacherous, and a serpent."

The Rishis said, "Every being in creation must reap the fruits of his karma, good and evil. A treacherous man must, in time, suffer for his treachery. But, Vritra, what do you fear from Indra, that you will not make peace with him? We have told you that you may lay down any conditions you choose, and Indra will honour them. Speak your mind freely, tell us what you want from the Deva."

With no hesitation, Vritrasura said, "Let Indra and his Devas swear that none of them will kill me, by day or by night, or with any weapon that is solid or fluid, or with any astra of fire or light. Then, perhaps, we can speak of having peace between us."

The Rishis agreed at once, and fetched Indra. The Deva swore a solemn vow before the Munis, with Agni as his witness, that, neither he nor his people would try to kill Vritra by day or by night, or with any weapon that was solid or fluid, or with any astra of fire or light. Vritra was strangely moved to see Indra thus humbled. The noble Asura rose from his throne, and impulsively embraced his old enemy. He naively imagined that all would indeed be forgiven and forgotten between them from now.

On his part, Indra went out of his way to ingratiate himself with his newfound friend. Indeed, on a few occasions he offered excellent counsel to the Danava emperor, and won his trust, gradually and effectively. Like any good spy, Indra lived the role he was now playing; at times, he himself wondered whether he did not truly love Vritrasura, his master, as his dearest friend.

The strangest, most intimate, relationship grew up between the Deva and the Asura. Soon, Vritra could not do without Indra's company, and even Indra felt lost unless he was with his friend. They roamed the worlds together, and slowly all mistrust between them evaporated, and the simple-hearted Vritra would often say their first enmity had only been so that they would come together like this later, in perfect friendship.

They roamed the Nandana together. Together they made love, side by side, to women of every race, on heaven and on earth. There was no secret Vritra kept from Indra and, uncannily, Indra found himself telling Vritra the most intimate things about himself, that not even his wife Sachi or Brihaspati knew. They were inseparables, the Deva and the Asura, and everyone marvelled at how nature had been subverted by this strangest friendship ever.

Vritra forgot how long Indra had been Lord of the worlds, ages before he, the Asura, was born. And Indra watched his friend carefully for any sign of weakness; and, truly like a serpent, waited for a chance to kill him.

One day, Viswakarman called his son and said, "Don't trust Indra like this. It is unwise ever to trust a man who has been your enemy, one you have vanquished in battle. You don't know Indra as well as I do. He was treacherous enough to enter his own mother's womb, and cut up the child nestling there with his Vajra. Indra is only waiting his chance to kill you, and have his throne back. Ah, my simple-minded child, he is shrewder than you think. He fawns on you, and pretends to be a loyal friend and minister to you. But he is only biding his time."

But Vritrasura's time had drawn near, and he ignored his father's counsel. He kept Indra beside him, as his most trusted friend. He took the Deva with him everywhere he went. Then, one evening, as the two 'friends' stood out on a pristine and solitary beach of the earth, with only the wheeling, screeching, gulls above for company, Indra felt a powerful intuition that the moment had arrived to kill Vritra.

The Deva saw it was neither day nor night; but then, he must also find a weapon that was neither solid nor fluid, and not an astra of fire or light either. He looked out to the smoky sea, into which a scarlet sun had just sunk. Indra saw great blue-green waves roll ashore, one after the other. He saw the silver foam that crested them. Vritra stood some distance away, with his back turned to Indra, gazing out over the sullen tide.

In a moment, Indra invoked his adamantine thunderbolt. Silently he called out to Vishnu, and, swift as a thought, Vishnu entered the Vajra and transformed it into a weapon of foam! Indra worshipped the Devi, who blessed that ayudha, and infused it with her own Shakti. Indra raised the weapon of foam, neither fluid nor solid, nor one of light or fire, over his head. It was the twilight hour, neither day nor night. Earth and sky fell hushed, the very waves stood still. Sensing mortal peril, Vritra turned to face Indra. With a terrible smile, the Deva cast his weapon of foam at Viswakarman's son.

A jagged streak of lightning, thousand-jointed, crackled out, livid, from Indra's hands. A clap of thunder like the end of the world rang out. The foam Vajra struck Vritrasura squarely, and he fell like a mountain, a font of blood issuing from his chest. Great Vritra fell, half in and half out of the sea, and the waves turned scarlet as far as the horizon. Indra would never forget the last look in Vritra's eyes, one of disbelief, and also, such grief that Indra had betrayed their friendship.

When Vritra fell, the Rishis, the Kinnaras, Apsaras, and Gandharvas hymned Indra. Indra knew that, without the Devi entering the Vajra of foam, as Shakti, Vritra could never have been slain. Not even Vishnu's power would have quelled that most magnificent Demon. The Devas installed an image of the Devi Bhagavati, made from a single, enormous ruby, in the Nandana, and worshipped her thrice a day, from then, at every sandhya. The Devi was called Vritranihantri by the knowing, for Indra himself knows that, without her Shakti, Vritrasura would still rule heaven and earth,' said Vyasa Muni," the Suta tells.

THIRTY-TWO

UNDER SUN, MOON AND STARS, ROMAHARSHANA RECOUNTS HIS BLESSED Devi Bhagavatam in the Naimisa vana.

"Vyasa said to Janamejaya, 'The Devas and Rishis went back to Devaloka, but they were at poor peace with themselves. The sages knew that they hardly deserved to be called Munis any more. Noble Vritra had trusted them, and they had betrayed him cold-bloodedly to his death. Even Vishnu felt pangs of conscience in Vaikuntha.

The Rishis said among themselves, "If Vishnu himself could be party to this treachery, which man will hesitate to sin any more?"

Viswakarman went to the place where his son lay dead, his chest torn open by Indra's weapon of foam. He took Vritra's peaceful face on to his lap, and wept and wept. Then, standing waist-deep in the sea, he performed the last rites for Vritra, and offered tarpana to his spirit. A scarlet sun sank into waves that murmured on and on about the sin that had been committed on that shore, and about Indra's guilt.

Standing there, Viswakarman offered a prayer for his dead child, then, in anguish, he cursed Indra that he would pay in full for his treachery. That he would suffer even as he, Viswakarman, was suffering now. Then Viswakarman climbed Meru, and sat upon the golden mountain in a stern tapasya,' said the illustrious Vyasa.

King Janamejaya said, 'Did Indra suffer in any way for what he had done?'

'As soon as he killed Vritrasura, Indra felt a great weakness in all his limbs, as if his very prana leaked out of his body. Even his Devas said their king had done a dastardly thing, killing Vritra who had taken Indra to his heart as his closest friend. Moreover, Vritra was a Brahmana, and Indra was guilty of Brahmahatya, twice over now. He was a Brahmaghataka, a Brahmana-slayer.

Everywhere Indra's treachery was the talk, among Devas and Munis, among Gandharvas, Kinnaras and Apsaras. The Deva king was in disgrace, he suffered torments of shame; for, such is the way of karma. Yayati was cast down from heaven for his sin, and spent eighteen years as a crab. Why, Vishnu himself had to be born in mortal wombs, human and bestial, over and over again, to pay for the sin of beheading the Rishi Bhrigu's wife. Even precious Rama suffered by that curse. Indra, also, had been cursed by a Brahmana.

Terror seized Indra, and he had no peace. His body lost its lustre, so he was hardly a Deva, anymore, in appearance. He was wan and listless; often, tears sprang to his eyes for no reason. Screaming nightmares tore through his sleep, and by day, he sat anxiously on his throne, his thousand eyes red-rimmed.

Once, hearing her husband sigh piteously to himself, Indra's queen Sachi came near him and said "My lord, you have killed your worst enemy, and resumed power over the three worlds. Indra, the Danava army has been scattered, then why do you sigh like this, and cry from time to time? Why, at times, you seem to swoon on your very throne from some overwhelming grief?"

Could it be that, too late, Indra realised he had loved Vritrasura? Could it be that he mourned his enemy?

Indra sighed more deeply still, and said, "There is no pleasure left in my life. My sin clasps me close, choking all the joy from my heart. No Gandharva's song, no Apsara's embrace, can delight me any more. Darkness engulfs me, and grief and terror. Guilt stalks my every moment, waking and asleep. My heart seems to have forgotten what happiness is. What use is it living like this, my queen? It is better if I die. For my own Devas turn accusing eyes on me, and I can almost hear them cry in their hearts, 'Betrayer! Murderer!'"

And nothing Sachi did or said could console Indra. He was king in Devaloka, he lived in a palace, unrivalled in all the worlds. All the wealth in heaven and earth was his, the loveliest women were his to enjoy as he pleased; but Indra was in torment, he was in hell. And one day, when he could not bear the terror any more, he fled from Amravati, even like a madman, or one possessed by a demon, and he went down to the earth, without telling even his queen.

Indra arrived at the Manasarovara, the sacred lake in the north of the Himalaya. There, on a searing impulse, to escape his very life, the Lord of the Devas turned into a water-serpent, slid into the hollow stalk of a lotus, and hid there.

When Indra was found missing from Devaloka, the other Devas, Rishis, Gandharvas, Apsaras and the rest grew anxious. Why, anxiety swept all creation, in a subtle tide. The monsoon brought no rain, and fields, lakes, tanks, and rivers were dry. The worlds fell into anarchy, and disease and strife broke out among men and immortals. A century passed; still there was no sign of Indra.

In despair, the Devas crowned Nahusha Lord of the three worlds, and installed him on Indra's throne. Nahusha ruled wisely at first and order returned to creation, while the wretched Indra lived the life of a water snake in the Manasarovara.

But, with power and success, arrogance inevitably overtook Nahusha. He began to indulge himself excessively. Always he was to be found with the Apsaras, in the Nandana, and in his harem. Then, one day, the king saw Sachi, grieving by herself, and he lusted after her.

Nahusha sent for some Munis, and said to them, "You have crowned me king in Indra's place. Yet, his queen Indrani does not come to me. Go, speak to her, and say the king of the Devas commands her to come to his bed.

The Rishis went to Sachi, and said abjectly, "Nahusha is king of Devaloka now, and he sends us to say you must go to him in his harem. What shall we do, Devi?"

She went desperately to Brihaspati, the Devaguru, and cried, "Brahmana, Guru, I seek refuge!"

Guru said kindly, "Be at peace, child. I will not let Nahusha lay a hand on you. I give you my protection."

But when Nahusha heard this, he was livid. He called the Devas, and swore, "Angirasa's son hides Sachi in his home, though he knows I desire her. I will have Brihaspati's head."

The Rishis and Devas entreated him, "Lord, king of kings, forsake this sinful thought. Puloma's daughter is perfectly chaste. When Indra still lives, how can Sachi even think of taking another husband? You are king of the three worlds now, Nahusha, you are the guardian of dharma. If you commit such a sin, how will the rest of us remain pure?

Besides, all the Apsaras of heaven are yours to enjoy. Dharma is with Brihaspati, that he has given the Devi Sachi shelter. Don't let lust blind you to the truth."

But Nahusha scoffed at them. "Dare you speak to me of dharma! Devas, where was your precious dharma when Indra seduced Ahalya? Or when Soma took Tara from Brihaspati? No, I will not be satisfied until I have Sachi. She, too, will be happy when she comes to me. So, let her not delay, but come at once to my harem. Bring her to me any how, with soft words, or bring her by force."

And he glowered at them so fiercely, they were terrified. The Devas and Munis went to Brihaspati, and said, "Gurudeva, all of us together made Nahusha king of Devaloka. It is natural that he now wants the queen of heaven for himself. Hand her over to us, Guru, we mean to fetch her to Nahusha."

Brihaspati cried in rage, "The Devi Sachi is a chaste wife, who has sought shelter under my roof. I will never abandon her."

The Devas said, "Nahusha says he will kill you, if he doesn't have Sachi. What will you do, Guru?"

Brihaspati said, "Sachi must go to Nahusha and speak sweetly to him. She must tell him that she will become his queen, as soon as she knows that Indra is indeed dead. She will ask Nahusha to let her go abroad, seeking any trace of her husband or his death. Nahusha will give her leave, and she must somehow find Indra and bring him back. No one else is powerful enough to vanquish Nahusha now."

Brihaspati explained his plan to Sachi, who willingly agreed to collaborate. Guru and the Devas took Sachi to Nahusha. He rose, smiling, from his throne. His eyes were alight to see her. He said, "Ah, today I have truly become king of Devaloka, that I see you before me. I am the Lord of the Devas, and they worship me. You also worship me now as your lord and husband. Lovely Sachi, be my queen from now."

Sachi flushed; she quivered with shame to hear him. She said, "King of the Devas, I have a boon to ask of you. I cannot give myself to you, heart and soul, until I am certain my lord Indra is dead. Or guilt and doubt will torment me forever. I beg you, let me satisfy myself that Indra has truly perished. When I am content, I will be your queen."

Nahusha considered this for a moment. Then, he said, "Be it so. But hurry, my love, and come back to me."

She gave him a bewitching smile, and, in his great vanity, he never doubted that now she loved him, and was as eager to be his wife as he was to have her.

Sachi hurried back to the Devas, and told them of the short lease of time she had gained. But Nahusha would not wait for long, before he forced himself upon her. Sachi was desperate, and for her sake, the Devas flew to Vaikunta, to Vishnu. They said to Narayana, "Lord, Nahusha is king in Amravati, and he desires Indrani for his bed. She said to him that she will be his queen as soon as she learns that Indra is indeed dead. No one knows where Indra is. His sin of Brahmahatya consumes him, and he hides from us in strange fear. Nahusha is so powerful now that he sits on the throne of the three worlds, that none of us can resist him. Vishnu, Lord, help us."

Vishnu said serenely, "Let Sachi worship the Devi, who protects all women. As for Indra, he must perform an Asvamedha yagna to be free of his sin."

"But where is he, that we may tell him what to do?"

"Indra is a serpent hiding in the stalk of a crimson lotus upon the Manasa sarovara on earth. Go to him now, tell him that if he performs the Asvamedha his sin will be washed away, and terror will leave him. Nahusha has enjoyed Indra's throne for too long. He has grown arrogant and careless of dharma. It is time Indra resumes his power in Amravati."

Brihaspati and the Devas found Indra, the water snake in the lotus stalk in the Manasarovara. With their help, the anguished Deva king managed to perform the Asvamedha yagna. When a white stallion had flown through heaven, earth and the nether worlds, and a host of Devas with it, daring anyone to arrest its careen, the steed was sacrificed by Indra. It is told, with that Indra's sin of Brahmahatya, and all his other sins, fell on to the earth, and its mountains, rivers, trees, women, and Bhumidevi herself shared his savage burden.

Indra was light again, his shout of joy echoed against the white peaks that surround the precious lake. Yet, fear did not leave him entirely, and he knew the time had not yet arrived when he could oust Nahusha from Amravati. For, that king had been a great tapasvin once, and his store of punya was not yet exhausted.

Meanwhile, Sachi prayed fervently to the Devi Bhagavati that Indra may return to her. Brihaspati came to her, and told her of the Asvamedha that Indra had performed. But, still, there was no sign of her lord. In despair, Sachi put on a hermit's garb, deerskin and tree-bark, and began a fierce tapasya to the Devi Bhuvaneswari, Mother of heaven and earth, Mother of all creatures and all the Gods.

Sachi hardly ate, except to keep her soul in her body, and chanted the Devi mantra, which Guru taught her, without even sleeping. She offered flowers and incense to the Goddess, she sacrificed animals in the Devi's name. In a few weeks, Nahusha began to ask after Sachi again. But then, the Devi appeared one night, at the midnight hour, to Indra's queen. She came mounted on her swan, and serene as eternity.

She was absolutely beautiful; why, she defined beauty; for all beauty flowed from her body, luminous as a thousand soft moons. Her iridescence was like tender lightning around her, rays of grace filling Sachi's chamber of prayer. The four Vedas appeared there, personified, and began to hymn the Devi. She held the noose and goad of retribution in two of her hands, and her other two hands made the mudras of banishing fear, and granting boons.

The vaijayanti of stunning gemstones hung around her throat, down to her very feet. Her smile lit the three worlds, and the quality of mercy welled from her like a sea. Peace and grace streamed from her eyes, and she, the Mother of all the worlds, high and low, Mother of the universe, all the mandalas subtle and gross, said to Sachi in a voice deep as time, "Tell me what boon you want, Indrani."

Sachi knew how rare it was to have a vision of Durga. She knew that one must live thousands of lives before the Goddess would appear before one. Sachi fell at the Devi's feet in some ecstasy. "I was married to Indra after great suffering, and I have loved my lord, and been faithful to him always. Now he has gone missing, and Nahusha wants me for his bed. Ah Devi, I yearn to see my husband, my soul longs for him. Yet, he doesn't come to me, and not even the Devas will tell me where he is."

The Devi Bhagavati said gently, "Here is a duta of mine. He will take you to the Manasa sarovara, where your lord hides still. Tell him that it is almost time for Nahusha to lose his throne, and for Indra to rule the worlds again. I promise you this, child, you will have your husband back, and he shall be king of the worlds once more."

At the Devi's word a shimmering messenger stood, hands folded, before Sachi. The Devi herself vanished like a dream at waking. The duta took the queen Sachi's hand, and they flew, quick as wishing, to the Manasarovara,' said Vyasa to the absorbed king," says the Suta Romaharshana.

THIRTY-THREE

"VYASA WENT ON, 'THE MANASAROVARA RIPPLED ACROSS THE EARTH LIKE a blessing. Bounded by steep mountains, violet water stretched away as far as Sachi could see. Everything here was pure, truly like a dream of Brahma's. As soon as he set her down beside the sacred lake, the duta vanished from her side. A malaya breeze wafted the scent of lotuses at her, ruffling her hair. Sachi stood hesitant on the banks of the lake, then, a voice spoke to her from the very water, a familiar, beloved voice.

Through his lotus-stalk, Indra said, "My love, what has happened to you? You are wan and thin, as if you have been wasting from some disease. Sachi, terror gripped me for my sin, and I came and hid here as a snake, away from the eyes of all the living. Yet, the very water scalded me, until I performed the Asvamedha yagna. Now I feel lighter, and I think that, soon, I will return to Amravati and to you, and rule Devaloka again."

Tears flowed down her lovely face, and she sobbed, "You may not find me alive when you do, Indra! The Devas crowned Nahusha king in Amravati, and he says my place is in his bed. Guru hid me until now, but Nahusha threatened to kill him. The others all fear him, for he sits upon your throne, and they even suggest to me that there is no harm in my becoming Nahusha's queen.

No one would tell me where you were. But I worshipped the Devi Bhagavati. She came to me, and sent me here with her duta."

Sachi wept piteously, and Indra now appeared before her, in his own form, and took her in his arms. Wiping her tears with shining fingers, he said, "Sachi, I have been waiting for my time to come. Every day I feel stronger. It won't be long now, I swear to you. I will return and be king in Amravati again. But if we are hasty, all will be lost. You must be patient, Sachi, you must learn to wait. And now you must go back before I am discovered."

She wailed, "Go back? Nahusha will force himself on me, if I return! Who will save me from him? I may as well die if I am not chaste anymore."

Indra, who was no novice at adultery, laughed. He said, "Ah, my pure Sachi, you are my saviour. My love, the purity of your heart is better protection that a legion of Devas guarding you. For, lust finds its way past legions, and creeps in through the midnight door. I will tell you how to be rid of Nahusha. Listen."

Indra had a plan that could not fail, and when she heard it, Sachi was persuaded to return to Devaloka. She went to Nahusha and said, "My lord, I have sought my husband Indra everywhere, and could not find him. I will be your queen now. Yet, there is one desire I have, so our marriage may be blessed for ever."

Nahusha trembled with excitement. He cried, "I am king of the Devas. There is no desire of yours I cannot fulfil. Ask me for anything, and it shall be yours."

Sachi said, "First swear to me that you will grant what I ask, that not even Indra could give me."

"I swear on everything that is holy, on all the tapasya I have performed, that I will give you whatever you want."

"My lord, Indra rides on Airavata, Vishnu on Garuda. Rudra's mount is Nandi, the bull; Karttikeya goes on his peacock and Ganapathy upon his mouse. Yama has his buffalo and Brahma his swan. It is only fit, that, when you come to take me for your bride, you come on a mount never seen before, one loftier than any of the others, a vehicle that the Lord of heaven deserves."

Nahusha looked perplexed. "What might such a mount be, Devi? Is it something Viswakarman can fashion for me?"

"There is no need to trouble Viswakarman. I want you to come to me in a palanquin borne by the Rishis of Devaloka. No king of any of the three worlds has ever ridden in such a litter. But then, you, my lord, are a greater king than any other in all time."

It is told the Devi Bhagavati sat on Sachi's sweet tongue and beguiled king Nahusha with vanity, though he was one of the wisest kings ever. Puffed up with pride and delicious anticipation of having this peerless woman in his bed, Nahusha cried, "The Saptarishi and all the other Devarishis shall bear my litter when I come to marry you. I am their master; I am master of the worlds. How will they refuse me? Go now, my love, and prepare yourself to become my queen. I will come to you soon, and I will come as you want me to."

When Sachi left his presence, Nahusha called the Rishis of heaven to him. When they came, he said, "Munis, I am Lord of Devaloka now, yet Indrani does not sit at my side. She wants me, holy ones, to come to fetch her on a litter borne by you Munis. I beg you, have mercy on me and carry me to her on your shoulders. I am on fire for Indra's wife. I have no sleep at night and no peace by day either. Don't refuse me, Rishis, or I will lose my mind."

Out of compassion, the sages agreed. On the eve of the appointed day, word was sent to Sachi to be ready, for Nahusha was coming to marry her in the morning. The Rishis were far from happy about the task given them, but they came to Nahusha's palace at the proper muhurta, and hoisted his golden palanquin, with the king riding in it, on to their shoulders. Never had a stranger sight been sight before, and all the Devas, Gandharvas, Kinnaras, Apsaras, Siddhas and the other brilliant folk of Devaloka crowded the streets of Amravati to watch the progress of that wedding party.

Deluded by Mahamaya, and Indra's cunning, Nahusha felt a great surge of pride. Which king had ever been borne by the Saptarishi on their backs? Surely, there was no other man like him in all eternity. And then, he was gripped by tumultuous excitement, as well; in a brief hour the perfect Sachi would be his, naked in his bed. The very thought made him dizzy, for he had spent months dreaming of her.

"Sarpa! Sarpa!" shouted Nahusha to the Munis, staggering along under his considerable weight. Which meant, "Hurry! Hurry!" But, then, 'Sarpa' also meant serpent. When they came within sight of Sachi's palace, Nahusha could not contain himself. He seized a whip that lay in his litter, and began to flick it at the Rishis who bore the front of the palanquin!

Awesome Agastya was one of those Munis; Agastya, who had devoured the Rakshasa Vatapi, Agastya who had drained the very ocean at a gulp, once. Blinded with lust and vanity, Nahusha dare to strike that greatest of Rishis with his whip, crying "Sarpa! Sarpa!" to him. Nahusha had seen Sachi at a window of her palace, and the very sight of her drove him mad. He was determined to impress her, to show her he was a greater king than Indra had ever been.

But when Agastya felt three strokes of Nahusha's whip on his back, the Muni's eyes blazed like fire. The king cried again, "Sarpa!"

Whirling round in wrath, Agastya cursed Nahusha. "Arrogant king, be born a sarpa! Fall down into the earth below, and be a serpent for an age. Slither like a worm on your belly, and live on the flesh of wild creatures in the forest."

Terror seized Nahusha. He begged the Muni, "Forgive me, lord! I meant no harm. Withdraw your curse."

But Agastya said, "A Rishi's curse can never be withdrawn. But one day, after an age, when you hold the strongest man on earth in your coils, and mean to devour him, his brother Yudhishtira will answer your riddles on dharma, and you will be free again and return to Devaloka. From Yudhishtira, you will learn the lesson of humility, vain Nahusha. Until then, be a snake!"

Nahusha felt an eerie transformation come over him. He felt a serpent's emerald scales glisten on his skin. Fervently, he began to hymn Agastya Muni, but, as he did, his voice turned strange, it was a serpent's hiss. Then, as Sachi and all the Devas watched, astonished, Nahusha fell out of his golden palanquin and down through the sky. As he fell, he became a great python, a hundred feet long, his head as big as an elephant's. Down he fell, still hissing Agastya's name, onto a nyagrodha tree in a forest of the earth. He lay there stunned for some days, coiled in the branches of the tree. When he awoke, he remembered nothing of how he came to be here, or of who he had been before. All he knew was that he was a huge constrictor, and the lust of the hunt stirred powerfully in his belly.

When Nahusha fell out of heaven, Brihaspati flew to the Manasarovara, bringing word of what had happened to Indra. Soon, all the Devas arrived on the banks of the sacred lake, and asked Indra to return with them to Amravati, and be king of the three realms again. Indra abandoned his snake's form, and went back to Devaloka. A grand investiture was performed in the crystal Sudharma, and, having paid in most part for his crime of Brahmahatya, of killing Viswakarman's two sons, Indra assumed the ruby throne of heaven again, with the chaste and lovely Sachi beside him.

From then, it is told, both the Deva king and his queen were fervent bhaktas of the Devi Bhagavati. For, they had no doubt that, in their darkest hour, the great Goddess, the Mother, had not deserted them; though Indra had paid in full, with terror and exile, for his crime,' Vyasa Muni said.

Janamejaya wanted to know, 'O Muni, even Indra was cast down from heaven by terror, when he sinned. What is this karma, that is more powerful than the Lord of the Devas is? How does karma work, is no one above it?'

'The knowing say that karma is of three kinds, Sanchita, Vartamana, and Prarabdha. Sanchita karma is what a soul has accumulated over many births; Prarabdha karma is Sanchita karma that has begun to take effect in a life; and Vartamana karma is present karma, and has nothing to do with the past, or with other lives. Every life is a combination of these three kinds of karma, and even the Gods, why, some say even Brahma, Vishnu and Siva, can hardly unravel karma, but are subject to it.

O King, the fruits of any karma, once done, must be endured, whether pleasant or painful. Not in a hundred million kalpas, is the slightest karma lost. In each life, when a soul incarnates in a new body, it takes up a certain amount of Sanchita karma from past lives, to exhaust in the present one. Be it a man, a Deva, a Gandharva, and Apsara, or any living creature, an animal or bird, they shall all pay, eventually, for what they have done in other lives. It is Sanchita karma, and nothing else, that determines who one is born as, and where.

Why, even Dharma's sons, Nara and Narayana, were born into the world more than once, to reap the fruits of Sanchita karma. All embodied souls derive their bodies from Gods and from Demons, too, depending on what their karma is. If you study any great man carefully you can begin to tell which Deva's amsa he is born of. Many kings have Indra's amsa sharira, men of great energy are amsas of Agni, men of wrath are born of Yama, and those of uncanny strength are amsas of Vishnu himself.

The pain and joy a jiva will experience in any lifetime is already encoded in his body, and in the earth and the stars, at the time of his birth. Fate is an intricate, inscrutable and profound thing, O Janamejaya. Not the Gods have eyes that can penetrate fate, not the Trimurti are impervious to karma. Why, Dharma's son, Nara, performed tapasya on Badarikasrama. Yet, when Nara was born as Arjuna, he reaped none of the fruits of the Sanchita karma of that awesome penance. Instead, like any common man, he suffered exile and humiliation. Why, he was forced to wander across Bharatavarsha alone, for twelve years, while his brothers and Panchali lived in majesty and comfort in Indraprastha. He had to suffer by himself in the wilderness, for his was a greater destiny than any of theirs.

It is karma, O King, which takes each man down his separate path in life. Every man is alone, for the way he walks is just his alone, and each man wonders at some time why he is so different from the rest of his fellows. But then, each man's karma differs from the karma of all other men. The more lives a man lives, the more unique his karma is; those the world calls great men are merely souls who have lived more lives than others, and have learnt through their long experience that the way of dharma is the only path to liberation.'

Janamejaya asked, 'What is yuga dharma, O Muni?'

Vyasa said, 'The people born in each yuga differ from those of the others. Every man born into this world is subject to the nature of the age he is born into. Perfectly devout men are born into the Krita yuga; men fond of both wealth and religion, into the Treta; those fond of wealth, worship, and sensual pleasure, into the Dwapara; and men born in the Kali yuga are hardly devout or spiritual at all, but only sensual, and believe exclusively in wealth and pleasure.'

The king said, 'Where are the free spirits of the Krita, the Munis of the Treta and Dwapara? All around me, I see the worlds falling into darkness, and the men of our times have grown bestial in their natures.'

Vyasa said, 'The world is peopled by ignorant men, men of darkness, in the Kali yuga. Yet, the pure spirits of the men of the other ages still dwell in Devaloka, and the realms of the Rishis of heaven. When the sinister Kali ends, these souls will be born again into the world, and then the spirits of evil born into the Kali yuga will remain in some naraka, until another Kali dawns upon the world. This is the age of evil, when the dharma will all but vanish from the world, and good souls will hardly be born at all.

Yet, any man who does some good in the evil age will not be born into it again, but will find birth for himself in the next Dwapara yuga; just as, good men of the Dwapara will be born in the Treta, and so on. At times, for complex purposes of destiny, good souls are born into the Kali yuga, and evil ones incarnate even in the pristine Krita yuga. Sinners of the purer ages are born into the dark, tormented times of the earth. Even a good man born into the Kali yuga turns helplessly to evil, for the spirit of the age will force him to. Why, the very earth turns into a living hell, in the feral Kali.

The castes are mixed so thoroughly, no man knows what he is. The Brahmanas of this age are Rakshasas of the Dwapara Yuga; what to say, then, of the Kshatriyas, Vaishyas and Sudras? All dharma dies out in the Kali, until men have no true religion at all, but are atheists, or worship strange creeds and cults, that have no basis in the sanatana dharma, the eternal truth. Arrogance, wealth, and viciousness are prized as virtues in the Kali yuga. Gentleness and truth are seen as signs of weakness, and are mocked.'

Janamejaya asked in some alarm, 'Then, how do men find mukti in this fearful time? How do they find peace of mind?'

'There is no peace to be found in the Kali yuga, but the wise say that moksha is easier to have in the Kali than in any other yuga. And the only way to mukti in the age of evil is bhakti. Men and women have grown so petty, and their hearts are filled with such evil that worship is the only path to salvation. Indeed, no one in the Kali yuga can find mukti for himself, but only by a God's intervention. It is told that the Gods are easily pleased in the sinister yuga, in which even the smallest lamp of devotion shines so brightly in the night of the spirit that engulfs the world,' said Vyasa Muni to the king."

THIRTY-FOUR

"JANAMEJAYA NOW ASKED, 'TELL ME ABOUT THE TIRTHAS, MUNI, WHICH are they? What does it profit a man to bathe in them?'

'Among rivers, the Ganga, Yamuna, Saraswati, Narmada, Gandaki, Sindhu, Tamasa, Gomati, Kaveri, Chandrabhaga, Vetravati, Charmanwati, Sarayu, Tapi and Savramati. Indeed, any river that flows into the ocean is sacred, for she is an amsa of the Devi Bhagavati. In all the months except Sravana and Bhadra, the rivers of the earth wash away a man's sins. In those two months, the rivers are like a woman with her period; for, they bear the waters of the monsoon upon them, in tide.

The other great tirthas of Bharatavarsha, O King, are Pushkara, Kurukshetra, Dharmavana, Prabhasa, Prayaga, Naimisavana, and Arbudavana. Then, there are the mountains: Srisaila, Sumera and Gandhamadana are the holiest of them, though every mountain is said to be permeate with the Brahman, and the Devi's grace. Of lakes, the Manasarovara, Bindusaras and Aksoda are the most sacred, though, again, every precious mountain lake has its blessings to bestow.

All these tirthas, O King, are considered sacred by the Rishis of the earth. But the tirtha they all agree is more holy than any other is Badarikasrama, where Nara and Narayana sat in tapasya, in ancient times. All the tirthas purify a tirtha-yatri to some extent. But true Chitta Shuddhi, the final purification, can only be had if a man bathes in the gyana Ganga, the river of the spirit that flows within his own heart. In the Kali yuga, a bhakta can realise that most sacred river only by grace, by worshipping the Devi Bhagavati, or his chosen ishta Devata. Grace is the only path to salvation in the Kali."

Janamejaya was thoughtful for a while, then he said, "Muni, I have heard of the enmity between the ancient king Nimi and the Rishi Vasishta, who was Brahma's own son, born of the Creator's pristine thought. I have also heard that Vasishta was, once, Nimi's guru. What happened between them?"

"Nimi was a sage and just kshatriya, a son of king Ikshvaku of old. One day, he conceived the ambitious plan to build a great city called Jayantapura, quite near the Muni Gautama's asrama, and to conduct a deep yagna there. His father Ikshvaku approved of his son's grandiose plan, and soon Nimi set about collecting all he needed for his sacrifice.

He gathered many wise and prominent Rishis around him: Bhrigu, Angiras, Vamadeva, Gautama, Vasishta, Pulastya, Richaka, Pulaha, Kratu and many more, knowers of the Veda all, and incalculably holy men.

Now, Vasishta was his own guru, and Nimi said to him, "I want to perform a yagna such as the earth has never seen before. I want to perform a yagna of five thousand years. Guru, you must be my Ritvik."

Vasishta said, "Indra has called me to be his priest, at a five hundred year yagna he plans. I have already given my word to the king of the Devas. When I finish with Indra's sacrifice, I will gladly attend to yours."

But Nimi said, "I have already gathered the other Munis, I have collected everything I need for my yagna, the rice, and ghee, the wood and the golden vessels. We have decided upon the place where the yagna will be held, and even the muhurta for us to begin. How can I wait five hundred years for you, Vasishta? You are the Kulaguru of our royal House. How can you go elsewhere for another yagna, when we have need of you here?"

Vasishta did not answer the prince, at once, but said he needed some time to think the matter over. Yet, the next day, without telling Nimi, the Rishi went away to Devaloka, to sit over Indra's sacrifice. It was not an honour he would miss, and he had given the Deva his word. He believed Nimi would change his mind, and wait for him to return.

But Nimi had set his heart on his yagna. When he found Vasishta had left, he asked Gautama to be his chief priest. Nimi had himself crowned king and sacrificer in the new city, and, then, began his yagna beside the ocean, in a vast yagnashala. Nimi gave generous gold and jewels as dakshina to the Munis who sat at his sacrifice, and the holy ones were well satisfied. Those were, of course, times when kings of the earth were long-lived, and altogether Godlike. Five hundred years, of the five thousand Nimi planned for his yagna, passed. One day Vasishta returned to the earth, after performing Indra's yagna in heaven.

Nimi was asleep, when Vasishta came to see him. The king's servants would not rouse their lord, and the Rishi was kept waiting for an hour. Meanwhile, he also heard that Nimi had begun his sacrifice with Gautama as his priest. Trembling with rage, Vasishta cursed Nimi, "You have turned your back on me, your Kulaguru. You have bought yourself a priest with wealth. I curse you, Nimi, be Videha from now. You will lose your body, for what you have done."

When Nimi's servants heard the curse, they ran to their king, and woke him. Panic-stricken, they babbled that Vasishta had returned, and cursed him. But Nimi heard them out serenely. With no sign of being alarmed, he clothed himself and came out to where Vasishta still waited in wrath.

Nimi folded his hands to Vasishta humbly, and said without rancor, "Guru, I am your yajamana. I asked you, repeatedly, to be the chief priest at my yagna. You are the Kulaguru of the House of Ikshvaku. Yet, you chose to desert me, and sit over Indra's yagna instead.

Now, my lord, you seek to curse me, for doing what I could not help. All the other Munis had already gathered for my yagna, how could I turn them away without their cursing me? You are my guru, you should have understood my predicament. But now, that you have cursed me for no fault of mine, I, too, curse you, O son of Brahma." Anger flashed in Nimi's eyes, "This form of yours, Vasishta, is full of rage that you can hardly control. Wrath is your master, not reason. I curse you that this body of yours fall away from you!"

Nimi had great power, in those days, from his long yagna and from his lordship over the earth. Vasishta knew the king's curse would not fail to have effect. In some panic, the Muni fled to his father, Brahma, for sanctuary. Even before he arrived in the sacred mandala where the Pitamaha of the worlds dwelt, Vasishta felt his body fall away from him into chasmal space.

He arrived disembodied in Brahmaloka, and cried to his sire, "Now what shall I do, Father? Nimi's curse has taken my body from me. How shall I have another body, and still keep the knowledge that is mine? If I am born of a woman's womb, I will forget all that I know. Yet, if I don't have a body, how will I live among men and be of some use to the world?"

Brahma seemed to consider his son's predicament for a moment, then, said, "Take yourself to Varuna's abode. Enter his very seed, subtly, and remain there quiet, without his knowing you dwell in him. You shall indeed have a body again, and keep your store of gyana as well. Go now, all will be well again. But learn a lesson from this, my son."

The chastened Vasishta said, "Anger will not rule me again, Pitamaha."

Vasishta flew down the world, and into Varuna's realm below the waves. Subtly, the disembodied Muni went, and so entered Varuna's body and his seed. He remained there in dhyana, for a long time. An age passed, and one day, the Apsara Urvashi came with some sakhis to the world to bathe in the sea. She shed her fine garments on a silvery beach under a streaming moon, and laughing in delight, entered the water with her companions. At once, Varuna, Lord of the sea, grew sensible of her in his palace below the waves; for that Deva is aware of all things that touch his waters.

He caressed the naked Apsara with a gentle swell, and tumultuous excitement gripped him. Delectable Urvashi also felt a tidal desire take hold of her. Soon, Varuna was past all control, and, in his wondrous submarine palace, he ejaculated helplessly into a crystal jar he found. His seed spurted from him, golden and luminous, and with it, out flew the Muni Vasishta! In a moment, as Varuna watched in astonishment, two brilliant Rishis stood forth from his semen. The crystal jar fell in silvery dust around them. The first of those Munis was the great Agastya, and the other was Vasishta, returned with a new body after Nimi's curse.

Agastya Muni went directly to the Himalaya, to sit in tapasya for an age. Vasishta went back to Ikshvaku, and became Kulaguru to that royal House again. It is thus that both those Rishis are called Maitra-Varunis, Varuna's sons."

Janamejaya wanted to know, "What happened then to king Nimi? Did he also get his body back?"

"No, only Vasishta did. When the priests at Nimi's yagna heard about Vasishta's curse, they contrived to keep life in Nimi's body with the most arcane and powerful mantras. So the great sacrifice could be completed.

It is told that, when Nimi's yagna was fulfilled, in five thousand years, the Devas came to the chamber where that king now lay in exhaustion bordering on death. They said to Nimi, "Lord of the yagna, we are pleased with your sacrifice. Name any boon you want, and it shall be yours. Tell us what manner of body you wish to have from now, a human one, or a Deva's."

Nimi managed to smile, and he spoke softly to the Devas, "I have no desire to have another body, which can die at any time. No, let me live as spirit, above the eyes of all living creatures."

The Devas said, "The Devi Bhagavati is pleased with your yagna. Ask her for this boon, for only she can grant it."

Nimi thought of the Devi, and she appeared before him, even as it drew on time for his body to fall away from him. Bhagavati shone like a thousand suns, and she was the embodiment of beauty, and cast bliss all around her, as if it were her shadow.

In ecstasy, Nimi said, "Mother of worlds, give me the final knowledge, pure and simple, by which I may be free. Also, let me live above the eyes of every living being, and help show them the way to moksha."

The Devi smiled, and said, "So be it, O Kshatriya. When your Prarabdha karma is fulfilled, you shall have moksha. Then on, be as Vayu, and dwell above every living creature's eyes, and shine as the light of knowledge in them. Let all the living take thought from now, and when they do let their eyes blink, as they have not done so far. But only the beings of the earth shall blink. The Devas shall still not blink, but gaze steadily on all things."

The Goddess seemed to grow thoughtful for a moment. Then, she said, "But you must have a son, Nimi, to sit upon your throne when you are gone."

With that, she vanished. The king couldn't for the life of him imagine how he could have a son now, when his spirit was leaving his body. The Brahmanas laid king Nimi out in state, to die, and they covered him with fragrant logs of wood. The king did not breathe any more. They began to churn his body with an arani branch, chanting occult mantras all the while. Suddenly a resplendent youth sprang forth from Nimi's body. He resembled Nimi in every feature, and was as bright as that great king had been. And when he appeared, Nimi's body vanished as if it had never existed, melting away before the Brahmanas' eyes, by Vasishta's curse.

That prince was called Mithi. In time, he built a splendid city on the banks of the Ganga, and it was called Mithila. Nimi's spirit, it is told, pervaded all the land. He had lost his body and was known as Videha, and so were his kingdom, and every king who sat on the throne of Mithila, from then on. They were also known as Janaka, and were all realised souls, Rajarishis.

Then on, great king Nimi, of the unrivalled yagna, resides between the eyebrows of every living creature on earth, as a subtle guru.'

Janamejaya said, 'My lord, Vasishta was Brahma's own son, and he was Nimi's Kulaguru. Nimi performed such a profound yagna. Still, they were both prey to anger, and could not forgive each other. One cursed his yajamana, and the other his guru.'

Vyasa said, smiling, 'Who in all the three worlds has conquered anger? I tell you, O King, not Brahma, Vishnu or Siva is a perfect master of wrath. The gunas sway all beings, from the Gods down to the lowest beasts. Only the Nirguna Brahman, the eternal, unmanifest spirit, is truly above the passions. So, also, the Parashakti. Only the man who realises that primal Truth shall find liberation. He shall be set free from the cycle of births and deaths, the realm of samsara.

Janamejaya, knowledge is of two kinds. The first kind of gyana is known by the intellect, and perishes with the intellect. The second, however, is the gyana born of intuition, and of feeling deep in the heart and brain. This aparoksha gyana is awakened when a man meets a Sadguru. O Kshatriya, merely speaking of a lamp cannot dispel darkness. So, too, mere intellectual wisdom cannot dispel the darkness in our souls, nor set us free from the bondage of the human condition. Karma, that does some good to others, that is selfless work of mercy, is the brightest fruit of the tree of knowledge.

The hearts and minds of all the living are restless, uncontrolled. Men live like slaves to their wild hearts, their desires, their anger, and their greed. Depending on the mixture of the gunas in their natures, sattva, rajas and tamas, they are good, average, or evil men. Lust, rage and greed spring from the mind. When the mind itself is brought under control, these no longer torment a man, and he becomes contented within himself, and seeks his peace in his own heart.

But then, reality is complex and mysterious, and not the Gods can fathom it. Some men are naturally serene, while others are quick to rage. Thus, Yayati did not curse his guru Sukra, when Sukracharya cursed him to old age. But Nimi did not have such restraint. So, too, in olden times, the Haihayas destroyed the Bhargavas of Bhrigu's clan entirely in wrath.'

Eagerly, Janamejaya asked, 'Who were the Haihayas, Muni? What did they do to the sons of Maharishi Bhrigu? How could noble Kshatriyas kill Brahmana priests? There must surely have been some reason for it.'

Vyasa began his next tale, slowly, 'In the most ancient times, in the Haihaya clan, there was a king called Kartaviryarjuna. It was told he was Vishnu's amsavatara, and he was a mighty king, thousand-armed, and powerful even by the norms of that time, when all men were Godlike. Kartaviryarjuna was a devout king, and given to performing all kinds of yagnas. The Brahmanas of the Bhargava clan were his priests, and he lavished gifts and wealth on them.

The Bhargavas grew wealthy by the king's munificence. Indeed, they became the richest men in all the land, for Kartaviryarjuna gave away most of his possessions to them. When Kartaviryarjuna died, his heirs were reduced to near penury, while the Bhargavas were as rich as kings of the earth. Now, there came a time when the Haihayas needed to perform a sacrifice to restore them to their former glory. But they had no gold to give out, no jewels to gift the priests who sat over their yagna.

The Kshatriyas decided to ask the Bhargavas for some wealth. They sent a messenger to their father Kartaviryarjuna's former priests, begging for some gold and jewels with which they could conduct their yagna. The Bhargavas heard the messenger out, and then sent him back, saying they would bring the wealth themselves to their yajamans. By now, the once austere and devout Bhargavas had become blinded with wealth, and its lust. They feared the warlike Haihayas, and felt the Kshatriyas would plunder all the gold they owned.

In some panic those sons of Bhrigu dug deep pits under their homes and hid their gold there. But they had so much that not all of it could be buried. There were thousands of common Brahmanas, who were the Bhargavas' dependants. The frenzied Bhargavas now gave their treasures to these, for safekeeping until danger had passed, and fled to their mountains with their families.

At first, the Haihayas waited patiently for their father's priests to arrive with the gold they needed. But when months passed and there was no sign of the Bhargavas, the Haihayas went themselves to where the sons of Bhrigu lived, thinking that perhaps they had been haughty by sending a messenger. They found the Bhargavas' opulent settlement deserted.

The truth dawning on them, the Haihayas heard the Bhargavas had buried some of their wealth under the ground. The Kshatriyas engaged a force of men, and dug up the agrahara. They unearthed such a treasure-trove they were astounded. The Kshatriyas began to realise none of the wealth their fathers and grandfathers had given these Bhargavas had ever been used for the yagnas they were meant for. Instead, the sons of Bhrigu had hoarded all of it, kept it for themselves.

Those Haihayas were enraged that the Bhargavas had deceived them, and their sires before them, for generations. After all, the gold the sons of Bhrigu now enjoyed once belonged to great Kartaviryarjuna, who was lord of the earth.

The Haihayas rounded on the Brahmanas who lived nearby, as dependants of the Bhargavas. With them, they uncovered more wealth, incredible amounts of it. In fury, they slaughtered those Brahmanas, letting a river of blood. Now, those Kshatriyas hardly cared any more for the wealth they needed, or the yagna they meant to perform. They were blind with anger. They wanted dark revenge on the sons of Bhrigu, who had played them so false.

The Haihayas hunted the Bhargavas across the earth. They found them on remote mountains, and in the hearts of deep jungles, and, wherever they found them, they killed them without mercy. Why, they violated the Bhargava women, and cut their wombs from their bodies with knives. If any of those women were pregnant, the Haihayas would slice up the unborn fetus within its mother's body, and bring it out as a mess of gore.

When the Munis of the asramas, in which some of those Bhargava women hid, saw this savagery, they cried, "Stop this crime! You will pay for this dreadful sin someday, Kshatriyas."

But the Haihayas, who stood panting and bloody from head to foot, replied, "Munis, you have pure hearts, and don't know the half of why we are doing this. These Bhargavas are cheats, and thieves. They are treacherous, and their clan must be extinguished, for it is a curse upon the earth."

The Munis said in wonder, "What terrible thing have they done that you kill their children in their women's wombs?"

"Their fathers deceived our fathers for generations, bleeding them of all the Haihayas' wealth. They took from us without mercy, and, instead of using all our gold to perform yagnas, they hoarded it. Until, the Kshatriyas of our royal House were left impoverished and these wretches and their sons were richer than kings. We needed desperately to perform a yagna, and begged the sons of Bhrigu for some gold. We only wanted to borrow it, and even said we would pay a fourth as interest, to use the gold that was our fathers' once!

But these would not part with a coin. They buried their treasure under their homes, gave away much of it to their own Brahmanas, and fled. The Bhargavas are meant to be holy men, above being attached to wealth, but they have become common usurers. They have betrayed our trust, deceived our fathers for generations. It is wealth's very nature that she leaves those that hoard her. The Bhargavas deserve killing, O Rishis, their women deserve to be made barren, so the very line of the sons of Bhrigu is extinguished."

So saying, the fierce Haihayas hunted the Bhargava women again. In terror, those women climbed the Himalaya, and hid in secret caves, trembling, sobbing. Ah, my lord, it is the lust for gold that makes men murderers. Why, they kill their own fathers, mothers, wives and sons for the sake of wealth. When greed takes a man's heart, he will do anything to get what he wants. Men abandon their lives, their very souls, for the sake of greed. And the wise know that greed is a more deadly enemy that even pride, lust or anger.

What happened between your own ancestors, the Pandavas and Kauravas, happened only because of the greed for kingdom and wealth. And they fought a war between them, that destroyed the power of the race of Kshatriyas forever, and ended an age.'

The king asked, 'How did the Bhargava wives overcome their fear. Did they escape the hunting Bhargavas?'

'On the sacred Himalaya, the Bhargava wives fashioned an earthen image of the Devi Gauri, and worshipped her. They were determined they would die with the Devi's name on their lips, before the Haihayas found them, and put them to the sword. Those women ate nothing, but starved themselves so they could die.

One day, soon, the Devi Jagadambika appeared to them in their dreams, and said, "A son of mine shall be born to one of you, from my subtle amsa. He will save you from fear."

With that, the Goddess disappeared. When the women awoke from their sleep, they felt deeply refreshed. Fear had left them, magically, and a great faith arose in their hearts that they would be saved. Then, one of the Bhargava women confessed she was pregnant. She glowed in her conception. Day by day, her pregnancy advanced upon the mountain. But one day, some of the other Bhargava women ran screaming into the cave they had sheltered in.

"The Haihayas have found us! They are coming to kill us!"

"Devi, save me!" cried the pregnant woman, and ran out of the cave. But it was too late. The Kshatriyas had arrived, their swords drawn. They saw the woman trying to escape, and roared, "After her! She is with child!"

As the woman ran from one corner of the cave to another, panting, her eyes like a hunted deer's, she felt a great disturbance in her belly. It is told the child within felt his mother's anguish and came bursting out of her body, from her thigh, bright as another sun! And with just a glimpse of that brilliant child, the Haihayas became blind. Their screams rang through the crisp mountain air, and all their power fell away from them in a moment.

I have heard that the darkness fell from those proud Kshatriyas' hearts, who had made themselves such brutal avengers. Their swords fell out of their hands, and they began to call out to the Bhargava woman piteously. "Mother, save us! We shall be your slaves from now on. Ah, forgive us, Devi. We were blinded by arrogance. We did not realise what we did. Forgive us Mother, give us back our sight. For, to be blind is worse than dying.

Give us back our sight, and live in peace with your son. The enmity between us ends here. Never shall we sin again."

The Bhargava woman said to those Kshatriyas, "It is not I who cursed you, Haihayas. And it is not in my power to revoke the curse. My son spent a hundred years in my womb, hidden, while you hunted our clan savagely. He is no common child, but born by the Devi Bhagavati's grace. He knew all the Vedas and Shastras even while he was inside me. My Aurava is the one who can restore your sight. Ask him humbly, and he may forgive you your genocide against our people."

The Haihayas prostrated themselves on the rocky ground before the bright Muni Aurava. They begged him, "Have mercy on us, great one. Give us back our sight, for our hearts see clearly again."

That wonderful Bhargava studied those supine warriors for a moment. He saw that they did not lie, but were truly contrite. He said gently to them, "Go back to your homes, Kshatriyas, and let your eyes have back their sight. Your blindness has served its purpose. In terror, your hearts have learned to see the truth."

The Haihayas went home to their kingdom again, and, it is told, they were given some gold by the Muni Aurava to conduct their yagna. Peace was restored to the sacred land once more. Heinous murdering no longer stalked its days and nights,' said Vyasa."

THIRTY-FIVE

AFTER THEY PAUSE FOR A SIMPLE MEAL, THE SUTA RESUMES HIS TALE IN the forest, "Janamejaya considered the story for a moment, then, he asked, 'Muni, why were those Kshatriyas called Haihayas? Did they have an ancestor called Haihaya?'

Vyasa said, 'Once, Revanta, Surya's son and himself a splendid Deva, was riding on Ucchaisravas, the Sun's own mount. He was riding to Vaikuntha to see the Lord Vishnu. It happened that the Devi Mahalakshmi saw that youth flying through the sky. She stood entranced by the luminous spectacle, for, of course, she too had once been churned alive from the Kshirasagara, and Ucchaisravas was her brother! Her heart went out to her equine sibling.

Vishnu also saw the bright youth that rode towards them, and said, "Devi, who is the magnificent boy?"

But she was so absorbed by the sight in the sky outside, that she did not seem to hear him. Vishnu repeated his question, a little more loudly, "My love, who is the youth on the horse of light?"

Still, she did not answer, but stood gazing raptly at Ucchaisravas. It seems Vishnu repeated himself thrice, and then, grew annoyed. He came up behind her, laid his hand on her shoulder, and cried sharply, "What is it that enchants you so much, that you won't answer me? Does the sight of that horse bewitch you that you refuse to speak to me? Is your heart not content here with me, perhaps, that you gaze so raptly at the sky? Well, be born in the restless world then, Lakshmi. Be born as a mare, since you are so attracted by horses!"

Now she trembled with fear. Soft cries came from her, again and again. She fell at her Lord's feet, and said, "O Devadeva! I have never seen you angry with me before. You have cursed me to a dreadful fate. Where is your deep love for me now, Hari? Ucchaisravas is my brother, and so I gazed at him. How will I live without you, for even a moment? No, I would rather end my life at once, than be apart from you."

He said sadly, "The curse may not be withdrawn. But when you have a son in the world, who resembles me in all his parts, it shall end. And you will return to Vaikuntha, and to my side."

When Revanta heard Narayana curse Lakshmi Devi, he was terrified. Turning Ucchaisravas round in a blur, he flew back to his father Surya Deva, and told him what had happened. Tears in her perfect eyes, Sri Lakshmi knelt at her Blue Lord's feet, to say farewell to him from whom she had never been parted for even a day, since he first took her for his own beside the sea of foam, the very hour she was born.

The next moment, the curse took effect. The Goddess of fortune turned into a shimmering mare, and she fell down into the world, into the place where the Sun's wife Chchaya once sat in tapasya, at the confluence of the Kalindi and the Tamasa. Deep, emerald forests loomed all around her, and she found herself north of the blessed Suparnaksha vana.

Sri Lakshmi sat under a spreading nyagrodha tree, and meditated upon the Lord Siva, the auspicious one, who fulfils all desires. She imagined him with his trisula in his hand. The cool-rayed crescent moon peeped out from his jata. He had five fair faces, each one with three eyes. His throat was vivid blue where he had once quaffed smoking poison. He had ten arms; his skin was white as camphor. He wore a tiger-skin round his waist, and elephant-hide across his chest, and bright cobras twined themselves around him like ornaments. He wore a garland of human skulls around his throat. Half his body was female, where Gauri was part of him. He was Ardhanariswara.

Thus, Lakshmi Devi pictured the Lord Sankara before her mind's eye, as she stood in tapasya, motionless. A thousand years she, the mare, stood thus in intense dhyana, and one day Mahadeva Siva appeared before her, mounted on huge Nandiswara, and he was more glorious than she had ever imagined him to be. The Devi Parvati sat before him on the great bull's back and, ah, she was entirely beautiful. Siva came surrounded by his wild ganas.

He said to Lakshmi, "Devi, you are the mother of all the stars. Your Lord Hari is master of the universe. How are you here, thus, as a mare, and worshipping me? A woman's dharma lies with her own husband, O Devi. Yet, you have turned all your thought to me, in fervor. Why, O daughter of the sea?"

Lakshmi, the mare, said to him, "Mahadeva! Most auspicious one, my husband has cursed me. Only you, O Sambhu, can save me from his curse. Narayana said to me, 'When you have a son in the world, like me in all his parts, my curse shall end and you will return to me in Vaikuntha.'

But, Siva, how can I have a son, when my husband is not with me? I committed no crime, my lord, but only gazed at my brother Ucchaisravas, as he flew across the sky. Lord, you and Vishnu are not apart from each other. You are the same person, the same eternal essence of all things. Thus, when I worshipped you, I only worshipped my Hari, no other. And I did not sin by doing this."

Siva smiled. He said, "Tell me how you know that Hari and I are the same. Why, the Devas and the greatest Rishis always make a difference between us. But you say we are the same person. Who told you this, O Sri? Are you sure it is true?"

The mare said, "O Siva, once I saw my Lord Vishnu sat in padmasana upon the ground, and he was sunk in dhyana. When he rose from his contemplation, I asked him, 'Hari, you are the greatest God, Brahma and the other Devas worship you. But, today, I see you sitting in dhyana yourself. On whom do you meditate?'

He said to me, 'I meditate in the lotus of my heart upon Mahadeva Siva, the highest Deva, who sometimes meditates upon me, and I, at times, upon him. For, our hearts are one bloom, in the most secret way. And there is, in truth, no difference between him and me.'

So indeed, Sankara, do I turn my heart to you in dhyana, for you are my Narayana, as well. So, I beg you to find a way for my Lord to come to me, that I may have a child by him, and return to his side in Vaikuntha," said Lakshmi, the shining mare.

Siva thought for just a moment, then, said, "I will send your Hari to you. And you shall have a son by him. I swear it."

With that, he vanished. Siva went back to sacred Kailasa. He had a gana called Chitrarupa who was an expert in such embassy. Siva sent this Chitrarupa to Vaikuntha. This gana could assume any form he chose, with just a wish, and it was told on Kailasa that he had never looked the same on any two days in all time. Indeed, the other ganas said that Chitrarupa's infinite appearances mimicked all the men born on earth through all the ages, and he had no form that was truly his own.

But, today, he went as a most resplendent being to meet Narayana. Arriving swiftly in a vimana, Chitrarupa saw the gates of Vishnu's palace which stood at the heart of an unearthly garden, dotted with fine pools and lakes, and pristine trees of wishes, kalpa vrikshas in profusion. Magical birds sang from their branches, and the very air here seemed laden with soft music.

Vishnu's dwarapalakas, Jaya and Vijaya, greeted Chitrarupa. When he told them whom he had come from, they hurried away to tell their Blue Master of his arrival. Soon, Siva's duta was shown into the presence of Mahavishnu. It is told, when that extraordinary gana stood before Vishnu, he assumed several forms in a few moments, in the ecstasy of seeing the Lord, and finally prostrated himself before Narayana as a stick of fragrant sandalwood!

Hari laughed in delight, and asked, "Tell me, wonderful messenger, what word do you bring from Sankara?"

Chitrarupa said, and his voice was his Lord Siva's, "Your Devi, Sri Lakshmi, Mother of the worlds, whom the Yakshas, Kinnaras, Nagas and Devas worship, is now a mare upon the earth. She dwells at the confluence of the Yamuna and the Tamasa, in tapasya. The three worlds are plunged in despair that the Goddess of fortune no longer smiles upon them.

O Hari, your enemies say to her, 'Now your Lord has abandoned you, Lakshmi, come and spend your time with us!' And they rejoice, seeing her misery.

I know what torment you must feel yourself; for, I remember what I endured when Sati committed agneyi at her father Daksha's yagna. It is not something I would wish on my worst enemy, let alone on you. I beg you, go down to her at once. Go as a fine stallion, and give her a child. Let the curse end, and both of you return to Vaikuntha."

Chitrarupa's voice was his own again, or one of his countless voices, and he said, "Thus, my Lord Sambhu asked me to say to you. And yes, my Devi Uma as well."

Vishnu had indeed been in torment, after he cursed Lakshmi. He quickly found that he could bear their separation far less than she could. But, then, he could not very well follow her down to the earth, without some pretext. That would have meant a terrible loss of face, and after all, he was Narayana, who lies upon the infinite Ananta, he was the Lord of the worlds. But now,

Siva had asked him to do what his heart had cried out to since the moment Sri had left him.

When Chitrarupa left Vaikuntha, it did not take Vishnu an instant, before he had turned himself into a great stallion, blue as rainclouds. He flew down to the sangama of the two rivers on earth. When Devi Lakshmi, the mare, saw that rampant stallion, she gave a whinny of joy. She knew him at once. Flanks steaming, eyes wild with desire, it is told, Vishnu the stallion mounted the white mare beside those rivers, one midnight-blue and the other golden.

A long time their blissful mating lasted, and then she was pregnant with his child. It took only moments, and Hari's grace, and Lakshmi gave birth to a fine infant, his skin blue as the night-lotus. Now, Vishnu turned to her, smiling, and said, "Now the curse ends, my love. Come, let us return to Vaikuntha."

The sky was full of wondrous light, as if someone had drawn back a veil that hid heaven's splendour. Legion pushpaka vimanas appeared, with Devas riding in them. The largest of them flew down with hardly a whisper beside Vishnu and Sri, and waited for them to climb into it. The Devi and her Lord were mare and stallion no more, but had back their Godly forms.

But now, Lakshmi cried, "Ah, my Lord, how can I leave our son here? He is dearer to me than my life."

Vishnu said, "He must remain here, upon the earth. Have no fear for him; he will be safe. He has a great destiny to fulfil in the world, which is why you and I had to come down from Vaikuntha. Listen, my love. The king Yayati has a son named Turvasu, whom his father calls Hari Varman. Even now, Hari Varman sits in tapasya at a sacred tirtha. What he wants is a son. This child of ours is for him."

Lakshmi was full of grief; but wisely, she did not try to impede destiny. She climbed into the vimana beside Vishnu, and it flashed away back to Vaikuntha. By Hari's grace, Lakshmi forgot all about what had happened. She remembered nothing of how he cursed her, and she became a mare; nor of how he joined her below on earth as a smoky stallion. She remembered nothing of the infant he begot on her.

Soon after his natural parents left the world, the little child was playing by himself beside the rivers, when a Vidyadhara called Champaka and his exotic woman, Madanalasa, flew past that place in their marvellous craft. They saw the beautiful child, bright as a bit of the sun. Champaka the

Vidyadhara flew down, picked up that child, and gave him to Madanalasa.

She was ecstatic; never had she seen such a lovely child. Why, he was as handsome a small Kamadeva, handsomer. She kissed him and cuddled him in delight, then, asked Champaka, "Whose child is he, that he is so beautiful? Who abandoned him in the forest. Ah, I think Siva knew how much I wanted a son, and gave this baby to me."

Champaka replied, "I will go to Indra, and ask him whose this child is, whether he is a Deva's, a Gandharva's, or a Danava's baby. If our Lord Indra agrees, we will say the Veda mantras over the little one, and take him for our own. But first, we must know who he is."

Champaka and Madanalasa flew, quick as thoughts, to Amravati. They took the wonderful child with them, and said to Indra, "Lord, we found this child on earth, where the Yamuna and the Tamasa meet. Whom does he belong to, O Indra? My Madanalasa has lost her heart to him. We want to make him our own. If you allow us, we will say the mantras of adoption over him."

But Indra said in alarm, "What have you done, Champaka? This child is Vishnu and Lakshmi's son. He was born for Yayati's son Turvasu, to fulfil a purpose of destiny. Even today, Turvasu will come to the place where the rivers meet. Fly back with the infant, Vidyadhara, and leave him there again. This is no common child. Why, the world shall know him as Ekavira one day, for there shall be no other hero on earth like him."

In some terror, Champaka flew back at once to the rivers of the earth, and left the shining child where he had found him. Meanwhile, the childless king Turvasu sat in fierce tapasya in a deep forest. He had sat thus, unmoving, for a hundred years. Suddenly, the darkness behind his eyes, and the inner spaces he was absorbed in were lit up brilliantly. Turvasu opened his eyes, and saw Vishnu and Lakshmi had appeared before him.

Yayati's son prostrated himself at the Lord's feet. Hari said gently, in his voice that was the soft swell of ages, "Arise, my child. Let sorrow leave your heart, for I will give you whatever boon you want."

"Lords of worlds, infinite One, how am I blessed to see you today? Only those that are free of all desire have a vision of you. But I am tangled in a million cares and wants, and yet here you are before me, O Mahavishnu. Bless me, Lord, for I don't deserve to see you."

Narayana said, smiling, "Humble king, I am pleased with your bhakti. Now say what boon you want from me."

"Lord, I have one desire that is greater than all the others. O Hari, give me a son who is like my very soul!"

The wise say the bhakta never knows to what lengths his God will go to please him. The devotee seldom realises that it is the One he worships who puts some of his desires into his heart. Now, Vishnu said to Turvasu, "Go to the place where the Yamuna and the Tamasa flow together. You will find a child there, like whom there is no other in any of the three worlds. That child is born from Sri's own womb, and he will be all that you want him to be. Indeed, he will be like your very atman to you!"

With that, the Blue One and his Devi vanished before the king's eyes. Turvasu fetched his chariot, which a Deva had given his father Yayati once. He flew through the air to the place Vishnu told him to go to. There he saw a wonderful child playing quietly by himself on the ground. The lustre of his body lit the woods around for a league, and reached for the very sky. Turvasu went up to that friendly child, and picked it up in his arms. He felt he had drowned in a sea of bliss. The rapture of his deepest soul coursed through king Turvasu, it seemed to him that he held sweet eternity in his arms.

Tears welled in Turvasu's eyes, and rolled down his face. He took the brilliant infant back to his city in his vimana. As he neared home, his people and ministers all came out to welcome him, after a hundred years. Sutas and singers went before Turvasu on his triumphal homecoming. Lovely women threw bright petals and fried rice grains over him and the child; they sang and danced all the way to the palace before his ratha.

Glowing, Turvasu climbed down from his chariot, and mounted the marble steps to his palace. Not for a moment did he let the dazzling child down from his arms. He went straight in to his queen, and placed that child in her arms. She was amazed, she was delighted, and cried, "Where did you get him from? He is such a perfect child! Whose is he, my lord? He enchants me, ah, I feel such delight when I hold him."

Turvasu told her who that child was, and declared a celebration in his kingdom. They called that boy Ekavira and it seemed, with his coming, heaven came down to the earth,' says the great Vyasa."

THIRTY-SIX

"VYASA WENT ON, 'LIKE THE FACE OF THE WAXING MOON, THAT BOY grew in his adoptive father's palace. Turvasu had the jatakarma performed for him, as soon as he brought him home. In his sixth month the king had the annaprasna ritual done, in which Ekavira was fed boiled rice. In the prince's third year, the chooda karana was performed; the child's head was shaved. During all these ceremonies, gold and jewels, cattle and grains, were given generously to the deserving.

When Ekavira was a prince of eleven, Turvasu held his upanayana, the ceremony of the sacred thread; from then on, the boy was among the twice born. When the thread made of a triple string of munja grass was tied crosswise around Ekavira, he was sent to study his dharma as a future king, archery and the Vedas with the most learned gurus. Ekavira proved a brilliant prince, and astonished the Brahmanas who were his masters by the swiftness with which he imbibed everything they had to teach him.

When his son's tutelage was complete, Turvasu called his Brahmanas to pick an auspicious day for the prince to be crowned king. They chose a day when the Arka yoga and Pusya nakshatram combined, and with great love and ceremony, Turvasu crowned Ekavira in his ancient sabha. Then, as all great kings did in those times, Turvasu went away to the forest to perform tapasya, in preparation to leave the world. He went with his queen to the Mainaka mountain, and lived on fruit from trees and roots of the earth, and stern dhyana. Their prarabdha karma for this life fulfilled, king Turvasu and his wife rose into Devaloka.

When Ekavira heard his father and mother had gained Swarga, he performed the funeral rites for them and offered tarpana and pinda for the safe passage of their souls. Then he set himself to the task of ruling his kingdom, with dharma as his sceptre.

The years rolled by, and deep blessedness was upon the kingdom, for Ekavira was a peerless king, and heaven's blessings seemed to be with him always, in abundance. It was a time of peace and plenty. One day, Ekavira went with a young minister of his, a friend, to the banks of the Ganga. It was spring; the trees were heavy with fruit and fantasies of flowers in every hue. Koyals and karandavas sang. The air was crisp and pure with the scents of the flowers of spring. Molten sunbirds hung over the open blooms, and carried golden pollen across the jungle.

All around in that sacred forest were the asramas of Munis, who lived in ceaseless prayer to call heaven's grace down upon the earth. The bright spring air was laden with incense, too, that rose from a thousand Rishis' vedis. Piyala, kadamba, champaka, mango, panasa, bakula, tilaka, sal, tamala, chakka, and mandara trees grew on the banks of the fragrant river, and on her golden water floated a treasure of lotuses, which opened and shut to rhythms of stars deep in the sky. Gentle deer cropped lush forest grasses, and raised their fine heads and gazed out of huge, soft eyes at the king and his companion.

Suddenly, on the banks of the river, sitting beside some fine crimson lotuses, the king saw a young girl. She must have been some thirteen summers old, and she was delectable; not yet a woman, but no longer a child. Budding breasts had begun to push their way out of her slender chest. Long, wavy tresses hung down her golden back, and she sobbed and sobbed, as if her heart was broken.

Ekavira approached her, and said, "Why are you crying? And who are you, lovely child? I am Ekavira, king of this land. Tell me what makes you cry like this, and I swear I will find a cure for it."

The girl turned her face up to him, and, drying her eyes, said, "Then, listen to my sorrow, O Ekavira. I am not from this kingdom of yours, but from the neighbouring kingdom where the just king Rabhya rules. Rabhya is a devout man, and his queen is the beautiful and chaste Rukmarekha. She had every quality a man could want in his wife, but she was barren. Rabhya and his queen were desperate to have a child. No homa did they not perform, but still the queen did not conceive.

One day, she cried to her husband, 'My lord, what use is it my living when I can't give you an heir? It will be best if I kill myself, and you take another wife.'

Rabhya was so dismayed that, at once, he had the holiest Rishis fetched to his court from the deepest jungles. Those Munis performed a putrakama yagna for the king, and from a sacred fire they lit in the palace, there arose a figure of white flames. It was a girl, ah, such an exquisite girl-child.

She was golden, like the flames from which she had emerged. Her face was like a full moon, her lips like bimba flowers, her hands and face softly ruddy, her eyes like lotuses. She rose from the fire even like the celestial garland, the Ekavali; and by that name, she would be known through the world.

King Rabhya received that child, who was a gift of the Gods, and he was beside himself with joy. He took her straight to his queen, and Rukmarekha was as delighted as he was. They performed the child's jatakarma, and every other ritual, even as if she was a son. The princess grew into a beautiful young girl, loved by all. Of course, she was like the very vision of their eyes to her parents. She was like prana to them; she was more precious than life.

She was a loving girl, warm-hearted, compassionate and friendly. But she was also very spirited, and drawn irresistibly to wild places and things. I, O King, am Rabhya's chief minister's daughter. My name is Yasovati, and I am Ekavali's sakhi. Most of all, my princess loved places where lotuses grew. The flowers were like her very life and she was only happy where she could be near wild lotuses, stroking their petals, breathing their scents.

Dragging me along, Ekavali would run off every other day into the forest, and come to the banks of the river. She would sit for hours near the lotuses that bloomed on the Ganga. She would watch them unfurl, to their own secret rhythms, and laugh in joy. The forest to which the princess went was an untamed and forbidding place. But she herself knew no fear. One day, I grew afraid for her safety, and for ours, who went with her, and I told her father the king that, when we were meant to be playing in the palace garden, the princess actually took us to the jungle, to the lotus pool on the river.

The king was so alarmed he had a lotus pool dug in his own garden. For a few days, Ekavali was happy with the new pool, but soon she missed the wild places of which she was so fond. Her father could not restrain her, so he took to sending a force of soldiers to guard her when she went out into the jungle. Of course, we, her sakhis, had no choice but to go with her.

One day the princess awoke very early, and set out even as the sun was rising for her favourite spot on the banks of the Ganga. What no one knew was that some wood nymphs lived on the river, near the lotus banks, and it was with them that Ekavali went to play. We, her companions, often thought that she was slightly touched in the head; for, she would spend hours on her own, talking to herself. But, in fact, she was speaking to the Apsaras, who came to play with her.

I was the only one Ekavali trusted with her secret, and, in time, the shy wood-apsaras would appear before me, as well. They were small as lotus buds, and actually stood within one of the unfurled flowers. That morning, as well, we sat with her beside the river, when suddenly our friends the Apsaras cried out in fear, and vanished before our eyes.

When we turned, we saw that a terrible Danava, whose name was Kalaketu, had arrived there with his legion of jungle Rakshasas. The demons were armed with swords and clubs, parighas, tomaras, bow and arrows, and all sorts of weapons. We saw that the Danava gazed at Ekavali with such lust in his eyes. She was in the flush of her youth, and which man could resist her? Especially in the jungle, where every desire is magnified.

Without a word, Kalaketu stepped forward and seized Ekavali. He draped her over his shoulder and began to walk away, when I cried to him, "Danava, take me in her place! I will come willingly."

But he hardly seemed to hear me. However, our guards who were waiting some way off, heard Ekavali's scream, and my cry, and came running. A battle broke out between our men and the Rakshasas, and their master, the Asura. Our soldiers had no hope of vanquishing the demons, who were terrifying to behold, and fought with weapons of light and fire. In moments, all our guards were dead, their heads hacked off with axes, or their hearts pierced with swords and arrows. Their blood flowed onto the earth and the river; it sprayed over the lotuses the princess loved so well.

Once more, Kalaketu hefted Ekavali onto his shoulders, kicking and screaming but helpless against his great strength. The Asura and his bizarre army set out for their own kingdom, in the heart of a forest that grows on the very lip of Patala. I ran after them, calling out my princess' name now and then. The Rakshasas laughed at me, but I think Ekavali was somewhat consoled by what I did. She howled, she wept, and in pity, I ran right up to her, flung my arms round her and kissed her face repeatedly. She also clasped me, and sobbed.

Then Kalaketu set her down, and said to me, not unkindly, "Your friend is terrified. I mean her no harm, but to make her my wife. Comfort her. Tell her that my city is like a city of the Devas. She will lack for nothing there, and be a great queen of our people. You must also come with us. You shall stay at your friend's side always."

We saw a strange chariot waited some way off. And now, that Demon set us both in that ratha, on either side of himself. It was a magic chariot, and, in moments, we arrived at his city and his great palace, with white walls smooth as glass, set with thousands of precious jewels. A hundred Rakshasas had charge to watch over us in that palace.

On our second day there, Kalaketu called me privately. He said, 'I have watched you through my white walls. I see your princess still weeps to be away from her father and mother. But tell her I want her to be my wife, to share my kingdom with me. Tell her I love her, and will be as her slave.'

I said to that Asura, 'My lord, I shan't be able to say these words to Ekavali. I beg you, tell her yourself.'

Kalaketu went to her and said, 'Lovely one, I am mad for love of you. Be my wife now, come to my bed, and let your beauty be fulfilled. My love, youth is a brief season in life, and one should not waste a moment of it.'

But my princess replied, 'Asura, my father said to me that I was to marry a prince called Haihaya. He described that prince to me, and I gave my heart to him, vowing to myself I would be his wife and no other's. How can I betray my vow?'

But Kalaketu was adamant. He said she would be his prisoner until she gave in to him willingly. Now, it seems that fortune smiles on me, at last, that she has brought you to me here in the heart of this forest. O Prince, my Ekavali languishes in Kalaketu's city, on the edge of Patala. The Asura's palace is surrounded by a moat and guarded by a thousand fierce Rakshasas. Ah, where is the Haihaya to whom she has given her heart? How will he rescue her?"

Ekavira said, in amazement, "I am the Haihaya your princess spoke of, for there is no other Haihaya in the world. But tell me, Yasovati, how did you escape from the Asura's city, when it is guarded by all those Rakshasas and by a deep moat? Didn't you tell Ekavali's father that his daughter has been abducted? Hasn't he set out to rescue her yet?"

The girl said, "Since my childhood, I have been a bhakta of the Devi Bhagavati. So, when we were prisoners in the Asura's palace, I began to worship my Devi, asking her to show us a way out of our predicament. One night, she appeared in my dream. Ah, she was glorious! She wore crimson silk and her eyes and hands were the hue of the kimsuka flower. She was exquisite, she was awesome, and she said to me,

'Child, Yasovati, you are asleep now. I give you the power to go out into the world in a subtle body. Fly to the banks of the Ganga in your dream, to the place where your princess used to play with the Apsaras of the lotuses. A prince called Ekavira will find you there. The great Rishi Dattatreya has given Ekavira the Mahavidya mantra, and he is my bhakta as well. Ekavira is Lakshmi's son, and he is the one who will set your princess free.'

Suddenly, I found myself outside Kalaketu's palace, his very city. I could indeed fly through the air, in my dream body, and I arrived swiftly in this place. And hardly had I sat down on the riverbank when you appeared, O Prince. I beg you, Ekavira, save my Ekavali. If you are the Haihaya, it is to you she has given her heart."

Ekavira gazed at her for a moment, then, said, "Destiny stirs in me. I feel an uncanny love for a princess I have never seen with my eyes. Come, Yasovati, take me to the Asura's city, for I mean to kill Kalaketu. Then I will take Ekavali back to her father, and ask him for her hand."

Yasovati said, "My lord, I beg you, first learn the Bhagavati mantra from me, or you will never find your way to the Asura's city. Bring your army with you, for you will have to vanquish Kalaketu's legion Rakshasas."

It is told Dattatreya himself appeared on the banks of the Ganga then, and the Muni initiated Ekavira into the Yogeswari mantra: **Hrim Gauri Rudrayite Yogeswari Svari Hum Phat Svaha.** Ekavira was a blessed prince, and the mantra conferred such power on him in a moment that tapasvin Rishis gain from it after a lifetime of dhyana. He took his army with him, and followed Yasovati the dreamer to Kalaketu's city. When the prince saw the city's ramparts thrusting up into the sky, ahead of him, Yasovati vanished before his eyes like a woman of mist.

From their lofty watchtowers, Kalaketu's Rakshasas saw the army camped some three yojanas outside their dark and charmed city. They saw how great that force was. Their spies who ranged the forest ran back to their king and cried, "Lord, an immense army of men has laid siege to us. Their king is a young man who looks like a Deva's son. He is brilliant, O Kalaketu, and dangerous. Prepare yourself for war."

Kalaketu gave orders for a force of his fiercest Rakshasas, armed with every kind of sorcerous weapon, to prepare for battle. Then, he said to Ekavali, "Who is he that comes to fight me? Surely, he has come for your sake. If it is your father, my love, I will never fight him. Why, I will bring him into my city and set him upon my own throne. I will give him wealth he has not dreamt of.

But if he is not your father who dares come to my gates, he shall find his death more quickly that he imagines."

He took Ekavali up to a tall tower in his palace, and made her gaze out at Ekavira's army, through a glass that made distant things appear so near you felt you could reach out and touch them. Ekavali gazed through that glass, and said, "It isn't my father or my brother who has come to your gates. Even the army he brings is strange to me."

"My Rakshasas tell me they saw your sakhi Yasovati with the king of men."

Ekavali laughed, "How could they when she has been asleep in her room all this while?"

Kalaketu said grimly, "Whatever be the truth, the king of men should know I am invincible. No warrior in the three worlds can stand against me in battle. I go now to fight him, whoever he is. I will bring his head back to you as my prize."

Ekavali could not tell why, but her heart gave a lurch when the Asura said that. The Lord of the Rakshasas mounted a silver chariot yoked to horses black as night, and rode out of his gates at the head of a fell army to fight the Haihaya king. A great battle broke out between the legions of men and those of the demons. Soon, the forest around Kalaketu's secret city was strewn with corpses, and blood ran freely over the ground. At last, the king of men, Lakshmi's son, and the Lord of demons came face to face. The rest of the battle paused around them, for they fought with devastras that lit up the quarters.

For a month, they fought, and finally Ekavira cast a gleaming mace at the Asura, a bolt of lightning, and it smashed Kalaketu's head like a ripe melon. Dribbling blood and brains, that Demon fell like a mountain. The earth quaked at his fall, and his Rakshasas fled in every direction, gibbering in terror.

Within the darkling city, Yasovati said to her princess, "The Haihaya king has come to save you, Ekavali. He has slain the Asura, and waits to see you. Come to him now."

Ekavali trembled, with an equal measure of shyness and desire. After Kalaketu had abducted her, she had become afraid of men. She was terrified that Ekavira would force himself on her. She was even more afraid that when she saw that king she may not love him. So, she wore some old clothes she got from Kalaketu's maids, and came out unwashed and dishevelled to the Haihaya. But, Ekavira did not seem to notice her garments or her hair, which was uncombed and hung loose behind her. He stood gazing at her as if it was the first time his eyes had seen anything. He stood riveted, his heart lost.

Ekavali, too, took just a look at Vishnu's son, and was in love. A wan smile touched her lips and her wise maid Yasovati knew that all would be well. But Yasovati also knew what must be done now, in propriety, and she said to Ekavira, "Come, O Kshatriya, take us both back to the princess' father. He has already said he will give her to you to be your queen. But you must go and ask him for her hand, formally."

And so Ekavira did. Rabhya was overjoyed to have his daughter back. He seemed to have aged a hundred years in the few days since Ekavali had disappeared. He had sent his soldiers north and south, east and west, to seek her out. But nowhere had they found trace of either her or the Asura who had taken her. But now, that king clasped his precious child to him, sobbing in great relief. And when he knew who the splendid king was who had rescued his princess, his joy was boundless.

The Brahmanas of king Rabhya's court were summoned, at once, and they decided on an auspicious date for their princess to marry the Haihaya. But then, Ekavali was not the only young woman to marry on that day. Ekavira's companion, who was out hunting with him, when he first saw Yasovati beside the Ganga, had lost his heart to that sakhi. He was his king's minister, and Yasovati and he were married on the same day as Ekavira and Ekavali.

In time, Ekavali bore her husband a fine son, and they called that prince Kritavirya. Kritavirya's son was the great Kartavirya. And thus, was the noble House of Haihaya founded in the world,' said Muni Vyasa to the Kuru king," says the Suta in the forest.

THIRTY-SEVEN

"JANAMEJAYA SAID, 'AH, MUNI, MY HEART YEARNS FOR MORE OF YOUR sweet Purana. I am amazed to hear how Narayana himself, who is above karma, was born into the world as a horse, and the Devi Lakshmi as a mare. Indeed, how is it that karma ensnares us all, O Vyasa? Why is life so full of grief?'

Vyasa said, 'Brahma's mind-born son, the great Narada, is an eternal wanderer. Once, his brother Daksha's sons, who wanted to be the first creators of the races of men, came to their uncle Narada. Narada said to them, "How can you be creators unless you know all there is to be known? Do you know the ends of universe?" They replied that they did not. Narada said, "First, go and discover the ends of the universe, then come back and become creators." And those children went off on the quest from which they would never return.

When Daksha heard of this, he cursed Narada, "Be you also a wanderer for ever, for the eternal wandering you have sent my children on."

So it was. By his father Brahma's power, Narada can go where he pleases, with just a thought. And, by his brother Daksha's curse, he has no permanent dwelling, but is an itinerant always. Once, Narada Muni arrived in my asrama. He played effortlessly, beautifully, on his vina, and was full of ecstatic songs. He sang hymns from the Sama Veda, and he sang the Gayatri, sweet as amrita.

When I had welcomed him with padya, water to wash his feet, and arghya, milk and honey, flowers and incense, which are the proper ways to receive such a holy Muni, we sat together under a nyagrodha tree that grew near my asrama. I was unhappy, then, and he asked me, "Vyasa, knower of the Veda, what grief clouds your heart?"

I sighed and said to him, "Great Narada, what joy is there in this world? I have lived long enough, but sorrow stalks all my days, and nowhere on earth is true happiness to be found, or peace of mind. Yet, souls incarnate repeatedly into this Bhumi, as if in helpless enchantment. Take my own life, Muni.

I was born on an island in the river. My father left before I ever knew him. My mother abandoned me for shame, and I grew by myself in the jungle, among wild beasts. Then, I took myself to sacred Meru and sat in tapasya to Mahadeva Siva. He blessed me with what my heart desired, with my son Suka. Ah, he was a brilliant child, and learned all I had to teach him, the Vedas and Vedangas, the Puranas and every Shastra I knew myself. And I was delighted. Then my son became your sishya for a time, and he was obsessed with moksha. He attained mukti, O Muni; he left me forever.

I was demented with grief. I abandoned my asrama on golden Meru, and wandered down into Bharatavarsha again. Ranging the earth like a madman for the sorrow that tore at me, I suddenly thought of my mother Satyavati. I came down to the Kuru kingdom, and sought the fisherman's hut beside the Yamuna, near the island where I had been born. I thought I would find my mother, and perhaps she could console me. Instead, I learnt she had married king Santanu of the Kurus, and gone to live in the palace in Hastinapura.

I built an asrama on the banks of the Saraswati, and began living there. In a few years, Santanu died, and my mother was left with two sons, Chitrangada and Vichitraveerya. Santanu's first son, by the Devi Ganga, looked after them. Bheeshma, of course, had sworn an oath of celibacy himself. In time, Bheeshma crowned Chitrangada king of the Kurus. But, Chitrangada did not live long. A Gandharva killed him because he had the same name as the Elf.

My mother Satyavati mourned. Bheeshma had renounced his right to the throne when my mother married Santanu. It was the condition on which Satyavati's father gave his daughter to the old king: that her sons would rule after him. Bheeshma crowned Vichitraveerya king. And, one day, he abducted three daughters of the king of Kasi from their very swayamvara, to be Vichitraveerya's queens. The eldest, Amba, never married my brother, but her sisters Ambika and Ambalika did.

But before they could have any children, Vichitraveerya caught a virulent consumption, and he died. Ambika and Ambalika wanted to commit sati on their husband's funeral pyre, but my mother Satyavati forbade them. For, if they did not have sons, how would the Kuru throne have an heir? Satyavati begged Bheeshma to take his brother's widows to be his wives. But he would not break the oath he had sworn in the names of his father, and all the Gods. My mother was desperate, for a time. Then Bheeshma himself told her, some sages of the forest said to him that in such a crisis a Rishi may be asked to father sons on the young widows.

When I was born on the river, my father gave my mother Satyavati a mantra she could summon me with, if she ever wanted to see me. Now she remembered that she herself had a son, who was also a Rishi. I was as much Vichitraveerya's brother as Bheeshma was. And, my mother called me to her, subtly, with the mantra. I appeared in Hastinapura, and Satyavati told me why she had thought of me, after so long. She wanted me to sire the heirs to the Kuru throne on Ambika and Ambalika.

And so I did. The first night, I went in to make love to Ambika. But she was so afraid when she saw me, wild as I was, dark, and with my beard and tangled jata, that she shut her eyes tightly as we made love. I cursed her, 'Let your son be born blind!'

The next night, I went to her sister Ambalika's bedchamber. She, too, was frightened of me. But my mother had warned her about shutting her eyes; she had told the young queen that I cursed her sister. Ambalika kept her eyes open, somehow, but she turned white as a sheet when she saw me. I cursed her as well, but more gently, 'Let your son be born as pale as you were when we were together.'

I went away from Hastinapura. In their time, Ambika and Ambalika gave birth to two strapping sons. Ambika's boy was born blind, and we named him Dhritarashtra. Ambalika's prince was born an albino, and he was called Pandu. Now, when I returned to Hastinapura to bless those children, Satyavati begged me to visit Ambika once more in the night. She said that, if she herself had another son, she would not have to trouble me like this. Moreover, she wanted a grandchild who was whole in all his parts.

I agreed, and went again to Ambika's room that night. The chamber was dark, no lamp burned within. A young woman waited for me in the darkness. She was young and beautiful, and surprised me with her ardour. It seemed the young queen I had been with the last time, who had shut her eyes in fear and lain still as a corpse under me, had changed a great deal. Now she was passionate and without inhibition, and we spent a rapturous night together.

However, when the sun rose in the morning, I saw I had not made love all night to Ambika but her maidservant, who was like her in form and even their faces were similar. But there the resemblance ended. I began to laugh, and blessed that warm girl, 'You shall have a son, whole in all his parts, handsome, and intelligent and serene beyond all common measure. He shall be as an embodiment of dharma in the world.'

When he was born, her son was called Vidura. Strangely, now, in my own mind I began to think of those three princes as my sons, for so indeed they were. Slowly, the grief in my heart for my Suka who had died left me. I became a regular visitor in Hastinapura, as my sons grew into fine princes. Sometimes I would spend some months in that city, before I went back to my asrama beside the Saraswati.

When I felt I was, again, growing too attached to Dhritarashtra, Pandu and Vidura, I would tell myself, 'Can I really think of these boys as my sons? Why, when I die they can hardly perform my sraddha, considering how they were conceived.'

The three of them grew apace, and Dhritarashtra, the eldest, was made king. But since he was blind, his brother Pandu ruled. Pandu was a great conqueror, and the Kuru kingdom grew immeasurably during his reign. Then, Bheeshma had Dhritarashtra married to the princess Gandhari, of the Gandhara kingdom; and Pandu to two princesses: Kunti of the Vrishnis, and Madri of Madra.

I thought, O Narada, that now fortune smiled on my sons and me. How wrong I was. Fate was waiting in the wings to remind me powerfully that all attachment is folly. Once, Pandu took his two wives to a forest at the foothills of the Himalaya. There, he shot a Rishi and his woman with his arrows, while they were making love as a stag and a hind. As they died, the Rishi cursed Pandu, 'If you ever make love to a woman again, you will perish!'

Grief-stricken, Pandu abandoned his life as a Kshatriya. He decided he would never return to Hastinapura, and remained in the jungle with Kunti and Madri. Slowly, he learned to control desire, on pain of death. But, then, he yearned to have sons. Now, when Kunti was a young girl the Rishi Durvasa, who saw far into the future, had taught her a secret mantra. It was a mantra for summoning the Devas of heaven, and for having children by them. Using it in the forest, when her husband begged her to, Kunti had three splendid sons, by the Devas Dharma, Vayu and Indra himself.

Those sons of the Gods were born for a great purpose of destiny. They were born to rule the world. They were called Yudhishtira, Bheema and Arjuna. Kunti said the mantra for Madri, also, and she gave birth to magnificent twins, whose fathers were the Aswin twins of heaven. Those princes were called Nakula and Sahadeva. All five princes grew in the forest, and they had their early tutelage from their father, and the Munis of the vana. But one day, when Yudhishtira was sixteen, Pandu saw Madri bathing naked in a silvery forest stream. He was seized by such desire, that he no longer cared if he lived. He forced himself upon her on the soft moss beside the stream, and he died.

Later, Madri committed sati on his pyre. The Munis of the vana took Kunti and the five Pandavas back to Hastinapura, the city of elephants. Then on, the sons of Pandu grew in the city of their father. Bheeshma, Vidura and blind Dhritarashtra, the king, made no difference between the Pandavas and Dhritarashtra's own sons, the hundred Kauravas. But from the first, the eldest Kaurava prince, Duryodhana, and his brothers loathed their cousins.

Those hundred sons of the blind king were evil princes, and they hated the thought that Pandu's eldest son, the noble Yudhishtira, would sit upon the ancient throne of the Kurus one day. Meanwhile, the Brahmana Drona arrived in Hastinapura, and he became guru to the young princes. He taught them the Vedas and the Puranas, and, most of all, he taught them archery and the use of the occult weapons, the astras that belong to the Gods.

And then, even before she was married, Kunti had once used the mantra Durvasa gave her, in her father's palace. The burning Sun appeared before her, and sired a child on the young princess. Her son was born magically, immediately, and he wore golden earrings and armour at his birth, which grew mysteriously with him. Surya Deva vanished before her eyes, and she was left with the unearthly infant. In terror, she stole down to the river flowing near her father's palace, and floated that child down its currents in a wooden box.

A suta charioteer found the shining infant and brought him home to his wife Radha. That couple was childless, and they raised Karna, as they called him, as their own son. Later, he was not to become a charioteer like his father, but the greatest archer on earth. For, though he never knew it until near the end of his unhappy life, he was the purest of Kshatriyas. He was also the Pandavas' eldest brother. But, neither they nor he knew this, and

Karna became Duryodhana the Kaurava's dearest friend. Indeed, he became a sworn enemy of his own brothers.

Even when they were children, Duryodhana hated his cousin Bheema obsessively. Many a time, O Narada, that evil prince tried to kill Vayu's son. But, fortuitously, Bheema escaped each time, for his, like his brothers', was a great destiny. Ah, such a great and terrible destiny. When the princes were a little older, Dhritarashtra made Pandu's son Yudhishtira Yuvaraja. The elders of the city and its people were delighted. They could not have hoped for a better or wiser crown prince. They could not hope to have a better king to rule them, once the blind Dhritarashtra decided to relinquish power.

But Duryodhana and his brothers simmered with envy. Duryodhana built a palace of lac in the city of Varanasi, and persuaded his father to send the Pandavas there for a long sojourn. There, his man Purochana was to set fire to the treacherous edifice. But their uncle Vidura learned of the plot. He sent a tunneller to the Pandavas, who made them a subterranean passage through which they escaped, after setting fire themselves to the house of the lac one night, with Purochana inside; and, also, a Nishada woman and her five sons, so the world believed the Pandavas were dead.

Duryodhana rejoiced, and his father Dhritarashtra, too. The Kurus mourned the Pandavas, for they knew what a monster Duryodhana was. Muni, you can imagine my grief when I heard the Pandavas had been killed. But then, my heart insisted they were not dead, and I sought them out with my dhyana shakti. I found them in the wilderness, disguised as five young Brahmanas and their mother.

Now, Drupada of the Panchala kingdom held a swayamvara for his daughter Draupadi, who was the most beautiful woman in the world. Drupada held a tournament in his city for his princess' suitors. He hung a spinning fish a hundred hands high in the air. Only the archer who could bring down that fish with five arrows, aiming in a trough of water at his feet, would have Draupadi for his wife. The greatest Kshatriya archers on earth failed to find the target. But Arjuna, disguised a Brahmana, brought it down.

But then, by a strange turn of fate, all five Pandavas married the exquisite Draupadi, who had once been born from a sacred fire. Word flashed across the land that the Pandavas had risen from the dead. It was in Drupada's city Kampilya that Krishna, the Avatara, first met his cousins. It was a fateful meeting, Narada, one that would change the fate of the world.

Dhritarashtra gave Yudhishtira and his brothers an arid wasteland as their inheritance: accursed Khandavaprastha. But when Krishna arrived there with his cousins, the ancient curse ended. He called upon Indra and Viswakarman. They transformed the desolation and, with divine power, raised the splendid city of Indraprastha in the wilderness.

Arjuna and Krishna helped Agni Deva burn the Khandava vana, and they saved the Asura Mayaa's life. In gratitude, that greatest of all builders, who was once lord of the fabulous Tripura, created a matchless sabha in Indraprastha for Yudhishtira and his brothers. Soon, persuaded by you, O Muni, that it was the only way to help their fathers' souls ascend to Indra's heaven from Yama's halls, the Pandavas performed the Rajasuya yagna. They conquered all the kingdoms of Bharatavarsha, north, south, east and west. Those kings came to Indraprastha with treasure and tribute, and Yudhishtira was crowned Emperor, a king of kings.

How his cousin Duryodhana burned with envy he could not bear. Conspiring with his father and his uncle, the perfidious Sakuni, Duryodhana invited his cousins to play dice in Hastinapura. With the invitation coming from his uncle, my son the blind king, Yudhishtira could not refuse. He came with his brothers and their queen to Hastina. At first, Yudhishtira refused to play, but then Sakuni taunted him in the public sabha, saying the emperor of all Bharatavarsha was afraid to play a game of dice. And Yudhishtira allowed himself to be provoked.

Sakuni was known to be the best dice-player on earth, and the noble Yudhishtira was perhaps the most naive. Moreover, the dice Sakuni used were loaded. Once Yudhishtira lost the first game of dice, he lost his head as well. He wagered everything he owned, and lost it to Sakuni, who was of course playing for his nephew Duryodhana. Why, when Yudhishtira had lost his army, his treasury and his kingdom, he wagered his brothers, then himself and, finally, even Draupadi.

Duryodhana won all this. He had his brother Dusasana drag Draupadi into the Kuru sabha, and try to strip her naked. But, from afar, Krishna's grace clothed her in an endless garment of many hues. Growing afraid, Dhritarashtra restored their freedom to the sons of Pandu and their queen, but the condition was that they spend twelve years in exile in the forest, and the thirteenth in disguise in a city of men. If any of them was recognised during the thirteenth year, they must spend another twelve years in exile. At the end of thirteen years, Duryodhana would return their half of the kingdom to his cousins.

O Narada, I have no peace worrying about the sons of Pandu. Yet, are they truly my grandsons? Though their father was born of my seed, all right. Ah, Muni, every few weeks I go off into the forest to see if the Pandavas and their Draupadi are well. Anguish clouds my very soul. I fear I am fervently attached, as no Rishi should be."

THIRTY-EIGHT

THE SUTA SAYS, "VYASA WENT ON, 'NARADA SAID TO ME, O KING, "MUNI, which embodied soul exists in this world without attachment? Why, Brahma, Vishnu and Siva are in the grip of samsara, why speak of the rest? Look at me, Vyasa, do you think I am a true gyani? Do you think I am never deluded by maya? Then, listen to a story I have to tell you about myself.

Once, my sister's son, the Rishi Parvata and I came down from Devaloka to Martiloka, the world of mortals, to wander the sacred land of Bharatavarsha. We went from tirtha to holy tirtha, on a great pilgrimage, stopping on our way in the sylvan asramas of the Munis of the earth. Before we set out, we had agreed we would not hide anything from each other, least of all what we felt, be it good or bad, be it anything at all. After we had ranged the fascinating world for some months, we arrived at the end of summer, when the monsoon was just beginning, in the city of king Sanjaya.

This king was a kindly and generous man, and for the four months of rain, he kept us willingly and with honour in his palace. Sanjaya had a daughter called Damayanti, and he asked her to look after us. She was a beautiful girl and began to serve us diligently, drawing water for our baths, bringing us fresh towels every morning, and our food thrice a day. We two Munis were well looked after indeed, and lived under Sanjaya's roof studying the Vedas.

As you know, Vyasa, I am fond of singing, and the Lord has blessed me with a voice. So, I would sing the Sama Gayatri songs in King Sanjaya's palace, accompanying myself on the vina. As you know, Muni, the Sama songs are enchanting. The princess Damayanti would come and sit raptly at my feet as I sang. From then on, she was specially affectionate towards me. Day by day, I could see how she always wanted to be close to me. Why, there was little doubt the young girl was falling in love with me! And, she was so exquisite and her nature was so sweet, that I too was powerfully drawn to her.

Damayanti began to make subtle distinctions between Rishi Parvata and me. She would bring me better food than him, and warm water for my bath while he got cold. I would get curd with my rice, while Parvata only got whey. I slept on a fine mattress of down, while my friend had to make do with just a sheet, which was not changed very often. And, always, she would turn her big eyes on me, full of love.

One day, Parvata took me aside and said, 'What is going on here, Narada? It seems the princess is in love with you. Why, with the distinction she makes between you and me, I would say she wants you for her husband. And, when I see you cast burning glances at her, Muni, I fear you would not be averse to it yourself. Come now, tell me all. We swore when we set out from Devaloka that we would hide nothing from each other.'

Ah, I felt shy, Vyasa, but I said to Parvata, 'It is true, the princess and I are drawn to each other. I want to marry her.'

Then, a strange thing happened. Suddenly, a great rage seemed to grip Parvata. For some reason, he felt humiliated, even betrayed. Perhaps, the truth was that he had eyes for the princess Damayanti himself, but the matter remains hidden from me. Anyway, his eyes turned crimson in a moment, and he cursed me. 'Base deceiver! It is because she finds you handsome that she favours you so. Wear a monkey's face from now! We shall see how long her love lasts.'

No sooner did the words leave his lips, than my face was a baboon's. And, though he was my nephew, I cursed him back, crying, 'Arrogant Muni, you have cursed me like this for hardly any fault. You shall not travel back to Devaloka, but remain here on earth for ever!'

Vyasa, even with my baboon's face, Damayanti's feelings for me did not cool. When Parvata stalked away from that kingdom in wrath, she began to serve me even more devotedly. And, she would come every day, and sit in my room, to hear me play on my vina and sing."

Narada paused, sighing to remember. Vyasa cried eagerly, 'What happened then, Muni?'

"I was dreadfully anxious, as you might imagine Vyasa. What would I do now, with my monkey's face? And I was still fervently in love with the princess. She had come of age, and the King Sanjaya called his ministers together, and told them to find a prince from a noble house to marry his daughter.

But when Damayanti heard of this, she sent a sakhi of hers to her father. That young woman came and said to Sanjaya, 'My lord, Damayanti has lost her heart to the Rishi Narada. She sits for hours listening to him play on his vina. She wants only him for her husband.'

Sanjaya's queen Kaikeyi sat beside him. The king turned to her and said, 'Did you hear this? My Damayanti has chosen a beggar for herself. And, no common beggar, but one with a monkey's face. I will never allow this! Talk to the child, Kaikeyi, make her see sense before it is too late.'

The queen called her daughter, and said gently, 'Ah, my child, what is this I hear? How can a beautiful young woman like you want the monkey-faced Rishi for a husband? We will find you a handsome prince. Give up this foolishness, Damayanti, you will never be able to spend the rest of your life with that crude hermit. Your father is anxious, set his mind at rest.'

But her daughter said, 'Mother, a man cannot be judged by his face and his body. These are superficial things. I have lost my heart to Narada because of his music, his soul. Why, the deer of the forest are enchanted by perfect naadam, mother. I have heard that they even give up their lives for the sake of sweet song. Love is not a thing of the eyes, but of the heart. Listening to Narada's vina, and his singing, I lose myself in joy. Where else will I find such rapture, Mother? Oh, I cannot live without it.

If a woman follows a man who knows music, he leads her to heaven. Has my father forgotten who Narada Muni is, that he balks at giving me to him? In the three worlds, in the three times, there is no singer like Narada, why, there is no bhakta like him. Mother, the Kinnaras of Devaloka have horse's heads. But don't they bewitch even the Devas and Gandharvas with their songs? You are a woman yourself, mother. You know how little a man's appearance counts in love. I beg you, convince the king that he must give me to Narada, and no one else.'

Queen Kaikeyi was moved by what her daughter said. She went back to Sanjaya, and said to him, 'Our child has already given her heart to Narada. She will not marry anyone else. And, if you force her to, I fear she will take her life. She is no foolish child, she is truly in love.'

The king took a day to think about this, then, he fixed an auspicious day for Damayanti to marry me. We were married with every ceremony, and began to live together as man and wife. My Damayanti shone with joy, whenever she saw me. She never tired of hearing me play my vina and sing, she was always eager to make love with me. But, Vyasa, my heart burned within me, when I thought of my long monkey's face. I had no peace even when I slept, for my ugly face haunted my dreams and gibbered mockery at me. And, when I was awake, I thought of hardly anything else.

A few years passed, and then Muni Parvata returned to my father-in-law's kingdom, after his long pilgrimage that had taken him to all the tirthas of Bharatavarsha. It seemed that his yatra had purified my nephew, and rid him of anger. He came to see me in my apartment. Without a word, he sat down before me, and I saw that tears rolled down his face.

After a moment, he took my hand, and said, 'Uncle, I cursed you in anger, and I regret what I did. Let my curse end, this moment, and your old face be restored to you.'

I felt my long snout and furry features vanish, and when I jumped up and looked into the silver mirror on the wall I saw I was myself again. With a shout of joy, I clasped Parvata to me, and cried, 'Your journey to Devaloka shall no longer be impeded either!'

And, Muni, when Damayanti saw me she was so happy. The king and queen were delighted, too, and declared a celebration in their city. Sanjaya gave away gold and jewels as alms, and all was well that ended so! But, the point I was making, O Vyasa, was that no creature great or small is free of desire, delusion, anger, envy, vanity, and the inevitable suffering they bring. All that exists is pervaded by the three gunas of nature: sattva, rajas and tamas. Everything that happens in the three worlds is by these three essences of nature.

All existence is maya, Muni. Why, once when I was walking through a forest with Bhagavan Vishnu, suddenly, the strangest transformation came over me! Would you hear what happened?" said Narada.

"I would indeed!" cried I, eagerly, for his stories were marvellous.

"The power of Maya is incomprehensible to the wisest of the wise. Once, I was seized with an irresistible urge to see my Lord Vishnu. I set out from Satyaloka, my vina in my hand, and went by Rishi-marga to Sweta dwipa, the blessed island where Narayana dwells. I went singing my favourite Sama hymns.

Soon, I walked into Vishnu's presence, and my heart was full. He was illustrious and four-armed, with the Sudarshana chakra in one hand, the

Saringa, the Kaumodaki and the Panchajanya in the others. His presence was of a great, fresh rain-cloud, and his skin was smoky blue, the hue for which he is known as Shyama. He wore fulvid silk, and the great ruby, the Kaustubha, shone like a red star on his deep chest, next to the Srivatsa curled there. He wore a sparkling crown on his head.

But, Muni, he was not alone. Lakshmi was with him. She covered herself quickly, when she saw me, and ran into the next room. But ah, Vyasa, I clearly glimpsed her breast before she could go. I offered Narayana the garland of wild flowers I had brought for him, and said, 'Lord, why did the Devi leave as soon as she saw me? I am a Rishi, and a master of my desires.'

Vishnu said to me, 'As Lakshmi was, a woman should never stay before another man, whoever he may be. Narada, the greatest Rishis are deluded by Maya. Why, you love music so much. Isn't music sensual, aren't the sweetest songs also Maya's enchantment? Maya is mysterious and subtle, Narada. No one has ever conquered her.'

I was amazed. I said, 'What is this Maya truly like, Lord? Show her to me.'

'Maya is everywhere, Narada. Her nature is the three gunas; she is the foundation of all existence. But, if you would see her, come with me.'

He summoned brilliant Garuda, with just a thought, and we climbed astride the great eagle. Vishnu spoke no word to Garuda, but he knew where to go. Swift as the wind, he flew us across continents, over mountains and jungles, rivers laid like threads upon the earth, villages and cities of men, fields like emerald carpets, tanks and lakes, herds of deer and elephant, prides of lions and lone panthers sawing up at us, to a place near Kanauj.

There was a crystalline lake there, overgrown with the most vivid lotuses. All sorts of water birds swarmed on its banks and swam on its clear surface. The sounds of goose and teal, cormorant and crane rose like a quaint symphony around us. It was a charmed place, where teeming flocks of pink flamingoes fished.

Garuda set us down softly, and Vishnu took my hand and said, 'Come, Narada, let us bathe in this lake before we enter Kanauj. You go first, and I will follow you.'

I gladly set aside my deerskin and my vina, and walked into the water. I tied my hair up in a kondai, pulled up some kusa grass that grew conveniently near, and performed achamana. The water was cool and invigorating, and scented sublimely with the lotuses that grew on it. I plunged in, Vyasa, and began to bathe. After my first immersion, I turned and I saw Vishnu gazing at me with a strange look in his eye. I felt the queerest tingling in my body, and when I looked down at myself, I cried out. Vyasa, I had turned into a woman! I stood thunderstruck and saw Vishnu pick up my vina and my deerskin. Smiling, he mounted Garuda and flew into the sky.

As he went, it seemed he took my memory with him, for I no longer remembered who I was. I forgot all about Narada and his vina, why, I even forgot his Lord Narayana. In a daze I came out of that lake, mother-naked, and ravishing, too, and sat on the velvet mosses on the lake's side, gazing out over the breeze-swept water, wondering who I was and how I had got here.

Then, I heard horses' hooves behind me, and turned to see a handsome king, staring at me. He called to me, 'Lovely one, who are you? Are you a Nagina or an Apsara, a Gandharvi or a Devi? Ah, whoever you are, do you belong to any man? If you don't, marry me, for I have lost my heart to you!'" said Narada,' Muni Vyasa told Janamejaya," says Suka to the hermits of the Naimisa vana.

THIRTY-NINE

"VYASA WENT ON, 'NARADA CONTINUED HIS AMAZING STORY, O JANAMEJAYA. "That king's name was Taladhvaja. And when he proposed to me so forthrightly, I thought earnestly for a moment, and said, 'I don't know whose daughter I am. I do not know who my father and mother are. All I know is that a dark man brought me here, to this lake. He, also, has gone away and I do not know where. My lord, I don't even know my own name. I am an orphan, and I am lost and helpless. Will you help me?'

Taladhvaja asked a golden palanquin to be fetched, some fine silk clothes for me, and he took me home with him to his palace. Muni, you will understand, I no longer knew who I was. Within the week, on an auspicious day, that king took me for his wife with all ceremony. Taladhvaja named me Saubhagya Sundari, and I was dearer to him than his life.

Day and night, Vyasa, he wanted just to be with me, and he was a handsome Kshatriya, and we spent most of our time at passionate lovemaking. We would both drink quantities of heady varuni, and we ranged the kingdom together, city and forest, lake's green bank and wooded hill, in the flush of our love. I knew only that king's ardour, and remembered nothing of the Brahmagyana, the Vedas or Shastras. Thus, my friend, twelve years flitted by as if they were just some weeks.

One day, I realised I was pregnant. Taladhvaja was beside himself with joy. He spent all his time cosseting me, bringing me anything I wanted, whether it was a piquant pickle made of mangoes brought from a distant kingdom, or exotic sweets made of milk and honey. He brought me lotuses for my hair, and silks obtained from ships that came from across the sea.

In time, I was delivered of a son. Taladhvaja's delight knew no bounds, and he named that child Viravarma. Two years passed, and then I became pregnant again. Again, a fine prince was born to us, and we called him Sudhanva. Why, in time, O Vyasa, I gave birth to twelve boys, and spent my days raising them. Our lives were perfectly happy, and soon our princes came of age, and we found suitable brides for them. Before we knew it, the king and I had become grandparents. Our palace was full of bright voices and laughter, and all the things that are most precious to human happiness.

Of course, I grew increasingly entangled in attachment. No trace of who I really was remained, either upon my person or in my mind. Only when any of my children were ill did I suffer. But soon, our sons and their wives fought among one another, and then I felt anguish, and was helpless against time's ravages that all the living must endure. I sank deeper and deeper into the bondage of samsara. Why, I grew proud thinking of what a good wife I was, and what an able mother, what a kindly mother-in-law, and loving grandmother. I also thought of myself as a sage queen, who had her husband's ear.

But, fate moves on ineluctably, and sweeps everything before her. My husband had an implacable enemy in the king of a neighboring kingdom. One day, this Kshatriya arrived with his legions to attack Taladhvaja. Kanauj was besieged, and my sons and grandsons rode out to defend their city. The battle was swift and savage; all my children were slain. My husband barely escaped with his life, and the enemy rode away having achieved the revenge he wanted for an old slight.

I went wailing to the battlefield; grief ripped through me, and I could hardly stand it. I flung myself across my sons' and grandsons' dismembered and, sometimes, decapitated bodies, and my screams rang across that bloody field. Just then, Vishnu arrived there in the guise of an ancient and splendid Brahmana. He said to me, conversationally, 'Why are you crying, gracious woman? You seem to belong to a good family, and to be a woman of wealth besides. Your tears are caused by moha. You are too attached, you are deluded. Go and bathe at some sacred tirtha, and offer til and tarpana for your dead. Stop tormenting yourself, beautiful queen. Come, come with me. I will take you to an auspicious tirtha not far from here. If you bathe there, you will find peace.'

I rose and followed that lustrous Brahmana blindly, and with me was my stricken husband Taladhvaja. I could not for the life of me tell why I went, except that I was desperate, and somehow felt sure the Brahmana would ease my anguish. We arrived at the lake called Pumitirtha.

The Brahmana said to me, 'Go and bathe now. Just think that you have lived a million lives before this one. In each one, you had sons and daughters and grandsons. Tell me, for which of them will you grieve? All this world is an illusion, dear lady, more than you know. Embodied souls inherit suffering, anguish, and little else. Enter the water, it will bless you with peace.'

He stood on the bank, with a faint smile on his lips. My eyes swimming with tears, I walked into that lake. As I immersed myself, strange calm washed over me, in tide, as if a sea of peace swept me away from my grief. I rose spluttering from the water, and lo, I was Narada again! The Lord Vishnu was also himself, dark blue, and clad in fulvid yellow. He stood smiling at me, and cried, 'Ah, Narada, you are taking your own time with your bath. Come on now, hurry a little. I have stood here for so long.'

The king Taladhvaja was astounded to see Narada Muni, with tangled jata piled high over his head, wade out from the lake into which his queen has gone for a bath. For a time, he had quieted his grief over our children's death. But now, he began to wail loudly, 'My love, where are you? Ah, first I have lost my sons, and now my queen is snatched from me. Have you drowned yourself in grief? Or does a shark or crocodile lurk under this lake? This is not the time to abandon me, my queen. How will I bear my sorrow without you at my side? Ah, my life is over. If only men were allowed to commit sati when their wives died!'

Now Vishnu spoke gently to the king, saying, 'Haven't you ever read the Shastras, O King? That you succumb to sorrow like this. Haven't you learnt that the union of wives and sons in this world is momentary, like people crossing a river in boats meeting? All that happens in this world is by fate. It is no use crying. This is where you found your queen, and now you have lost her here, as well. What time gave you, it has taken from you. You never really knew who she was. It is like the tale of the crow and the tal fruit: you gained her magically, and so, too, you have lost her.

Don't cry anymore, Taladhvaja. Go home, and know that time rules you. No man can conquer time. Not for all your tears will your queen return to you. Go back to your city, and rule wisely. Tread the path of yoga, and find peace for yourself. Everything in this life is transient, only the Truth never changes. It is rare to be blessed with a human birth, O Kshatriya. A man should do everything in his power to attain moksha.'

That king, who was in the grip of such shock, grew calm at what Vishnu said to him, though he still saw Narayana only as a bright Brahmana. Taladhvaja bathed in the lake and returned to his city. There, he slowly gave his power into the hands of his grandsons that still lived, and then took to sannyasa in the forest, where one day he did gain nirvana.

When Taladhvaja left Vishnu and me beside the magic lake, the Lord began to laugh heartily. I said to him, 'Hari, Maya is powerful indeed. But, Lord, how did I lose my memory so entirely, when my soul was my own all the time? For, how else could I remember every moment of Saubhagya Sundari's life as I do? Yes, every moment! And I blush to think of many of them.'

Vishnu said, 'There are more dreams and lives in your body than you realise, Narada. They all exist together, for the mind is a miraculous thing, and it is much more than any man realises. The mind itself is maya. Muni, when you sleep, do you remember what you dream? Yet, while you are asleep all that happens in your dreams is real enough, isn't it? All lives are dreams of one kind or another. They are all the work of Maya, and Maya is inscrutable, even to me."

With that, we mounted Garuda again and flew back to Sweta dwipa," said Narada Muni to me. Janamejaya, we always live in the midst of fathomless mystery and, try as we will, we can never comprehend it with our minds. We can only surrender ourselves in bhakti to God, and to the all-merciful Devi Bhagavati,' said Vyasa to the Kuru king at his sattra," says the blithe Suta in the Naimisa vana.

FORTY

"JANAMEJAYA ASKED THE GREAT VYASA, 'CAN YOU TELL ME THE ORIGINS of the race of the Sun on earth, Muni?'

Vyasa began, 'Narada told me how the Suryavamsa began in the world. He sat with me once in my asrama, and I asked him, "Muni, can you tell me how the House of the Sun, of the family of the seventh Manu began?"

Narada said to me, "As everyone knows, Vishnu Narayana lay on the coils of the serpent Ananta, upon the single and eternal sea Ekarnava. A golden lotus thrust itself out of Vishnu's navel, and Brahma was born within it. First, Brahma created seven sons from his mind. Marichi was the first, and then there was Kashyapa. Kashyapa Prajapati had thirteen wives, all daughters of Daksha. From Kashyapa came the Devas, Daityas, Yakshas, Punnagas, the beasts and birds of the earth. So, indeed, is creation called Kashyapi.

Among the Devas, Surya the Sun has the most fame. He is the most lustrous Deva, as well. He is also called Vivaswan, or Vivaswat. Surya Deva's son was called Vaivaswat Manu. This Manu had ten sons himself; Ikshvaku was the eldest of them. The others were Nabhaga, Dhrishta, Saryati, Narishyanta, Pransu, Nriga, Dishta, Karusha and Rishadra. Ikshvaku had a hundred sons, and Vikukshi was the eldest and wisest of them.

Of Manu's other sons Nabhaga had a son called Ambarisa, who was also a great king of the earth, sage and just, truthful, and a man of immense power. Dhrishta's son was Dharshtaka. Though he was born a Kshatriya, he was hardly a warrior by nature, and was always drawn, rather, towards learning and wisdom, that are the callings of a Brahmana. Indeed, he became a Brahmana during his life, and had moksha.

Saryati had two children whose names are legends in the world: Anarta, his son, and Sukanya, his lovely daughter. Saryati gave Sukanya to the blind Rishi Chyvana, to be his wife. Why, by Sukanya's purity the Aswin twins, who are Surya Deva's sons, gave Chyvana back his sight."

I asked Narada, O king, "How did Saryati give his daughter to a blind man? She was a beautiful princess, and whole in every part."

The Muni smiled and said, "King Saryati, who was like a God upon the earth, had four thousand wives. But, from them all, he had just one daughter, Sukanya. The father and all his wives doted on that princess, and she was like a piece of the moon fallen into the world. Not far from Saryati's capital was a lake as delectable as the Manasarovara. A ghat of steps led down to the pellucid water, on which swans, karandavas, chakravakas, datyuhas, sarasas, and all kinds of water birds swam, fished, and played. Five different kinds of reverberant lotuses grew in profusion on the lake, and their scent mantled its surface.

Tal, samala, tarala, punnaga, ashoka, pipal, nyagrodha, kadamba, panasa, and many other trees grew around that lake in an airy and fragrant forest. Yuthika and mallika vines entwined themselves like lovers around these trees and all that vana was swathed in a scent of heaven from the flowers blooming on those creepers. Peacocks lived in those woods, dancing to the rhythms of the seasons, their fans like scintillant miracles in the world. They sang dissonantly under the trees, while, from the branches above koyals lit up the air with snatches of song so enthralling that all the jungle creatures paused in rapture to hear them.

In the heart of that forest was a secret grove, a tapovana where blind Chyvana Maharishi lived in dhyana. The Muni had taken a vow of mowna, and as he sat with his breath perfectly controlled, he neither ate nor drank anymore. He meditated upon the ultimate truth, the Parabrahman. So immaculate was the Muni's tapasya, a great anthill grew up around him, and he sat unmoving within it. A mallika creeper wound itself around that anthill, but still Bhrigu's son sat on, unmoving, lost within himself, in his timeless Atman.

One day the king Saryati came to that lake with some of his wives, and with his daughter Sukanya and her sakhis. The king and his women waded into the water to bathe, and Sukanya and her friends began to explore the woods, plucking mallika flowers to make garlands for their hair. Sukanya's anklets chimed delicately in the spring air, as she ran here and there finding jasmine bushes, until suddenly she came to the anthill within which Chyvana sat absorbed.

The princess went nearer, and saw two holes in that anthill covered over with jasmine. They shone strangely, as if two fireflies were trapped inside. Intrigued, Sukanya picked up a sharp branch with thorns, and was about to poke those holes, when a voice spoke from them, "I am a Rishi at dhyana. You have such big eyes, how is it you can't see me? Go away, young woman, leave me in peace."

But all the playful princess saw was an anthill before her, with two shining holes and she poked them smartly with the thorn-branch. Without knowing what she did, Sukanya put out Maharishi Chyvana's eyes. His roars of agony rang through that forest, and Sukanya fled through the trees. Then the strangest thing happened: all the king's men and beasts, who were relieving themselves in the woods, found that suddenly their bowels and bladders were frozen within them! The king could not ease himself, neither his queens, nor anyone of his party.

Saryati was beside himself. He roared, 'Who has cast this spell? Let the man be found and punished.'

One of his trusted counselors said, 'Sire, the Maharishi Chyvana sits in dhyana in these woods. I fear someone from our party has provoked his wrath, and this is his curse.'

But the king's soldiers said, 'None of us has even been near the Muni.'

The king's women and friends said the same thing. Then, Sukanya said, 'Father, I saw a big anthill in the forest. There were two holes in it through which I could see two shining fireflies. I poked them with a sharp stick, and I heard a ghostly voice cry, "Ah, I am killed!" I saw the end of the stick was red and wet. I threw it down, and ran from there in terror.'

Saryati realised his daughter must have unwittingly disturbed the Rishi Chyvana. He had no idea what she had actually done. He hurried to the anthill, from which anguished groans and cries came. The king broke the hardened hill, and saw Chyvana inside, holding his eyes, that bled through his palms. Saryati quickly had the Muni's face bound with medicinal herbs to ease his pain. Then he stood before Chyvana with folded hands, and said, 'Holy one, my daughter did not realise what she did. I beg you, Lord, forgive her. Don't curse my child.'

Chyvana knew from his voice how genuinely distressed the king was. He said gently, 'Kshatriya, I am not angry with your child. Indeed, I have not cursed her at all. But tell me, Kshatriya, how will I live? I am old, and infirm by my long tapasya, and now your daughter has blinded me. I don't know how I shall survive, any more.'

Saryati said, 'I have a host of servants who will look after you, my lord.'

But the Muni replied, 'I doubt they will care for me for long. Servants are not relations, that they will love a helpless man. No, that is insufficient atonement for my injury. If you truly want to atone let your daughter, who did this dreadful thing, stay with me and look after my needs.' He smiled, 'If she does, I think the strange affliction that has seized yourself and your men will vanish gently. Otherwise...'

Saryati was shocked. He thought to himself, 'My child is young and beautiful, and this Muni is old and ugly, and now he is blind as well. How will Sukanya be happy with this man? How will he satisfy her? Why, young women can hardly remain faithful to their husbands, even when they are young, handsome and virile; so powerful are a woman's desires. Ahalya was beautiful, and she was married to the Rishi Gautama. But, when Indra importuned her, she couldn't resist him, and her sin with the Deva earned her husband's curse, so she became a heap of dust upon the ground, until Rama of Ayodhya set his blessed feet on her.

How can I condemn my child to a similar fate? Surely, if she is married to this blind old man, she will stray. And if she does, she will hardly escape the consequences of her sin.'

The king was distraught, and he asked Chyvana for some time to consider his proposition, for it had taken him by surprise. Saryati gathered his advisors around him, and asked them, in despair, 'What shall we do now? If I do not give my child to the Muni, we shall all die of our strange sickness.'

Those wise men said, 'But how can you even think of your delightful child with the ugly old man?'

But suddenly, a clear, bright voice spoke to the anguished king, 'Father, are you worried for my sake? That I will not be happy? Don't be anxious, my lord, nothing will make me happier than to be given the chance to serve the Rishi I have blinded so wantonly.'

Saryati clasped her to him and cried, 'But have you seen the Rishi, my child? He is old, ugly and feeble, and, as I have heard, he is very irritable as well. Then, he lives here in the midst of this jungle. You have grown up in a palace. How will you bear this life in the wilderness, with no servants to attend on you, but a servant yourself? Who are this old man's relatives and friends, what wealth does he have, that he can look after you, my child? Why, to my mind the choice is clear. It is better that my men and I die here, than for me to give you to the Rishi to be his bride.'

She began to speak, but he held up his hand, and cried, 'Say no more! I will not give you to the old one.'

But his daughter said, 'At least hear me out, father. I will not be unhappy in the forest. I adore the jungle, its sights and sounds, its scents, its untamed creatures, its lakes and streams, its trees and flowers, its birds. I have known all the worldly pleasures any soul needs for a lifetime, now the forest attracts me more than the palace.' She lowered her voice, 'And then, the Muni has such a sacred aura. I am drawn powerfully to him, father. I will be perfectly happy serving him, and learning wisdom at his feet. You need have no fear; I am not tormented by desire, as many young women are. I will be a chaste wife, and bring no sin upon myself or any shame to you.'

The king's ministers stood dumbfounded to listen to the princess. She spoke quietly, and with dignity, and it was obvious she meant what she said. Saryati hesitated only for another moment. Then he took his child's hand and led her to Chyvana.

Bowing to the Muni, the king placed his daughter's lissom hand in the sage's gnarled one. He said, 'Holy one, I give this child of mine to you for your seva.' The king's priests chanted the Vedas, and the marriage was sanctified. At once, the strange constriction that gripped the bowels of king Saryati and his army left them, and they evacuated in huge relief!

His heart heavy, Saryati turned to go. But Sukanya called him back. She took off her golden ornaments, gave them to him, and said, 'God has blessed me with skin smooth as honey. I have no need for these, nor for the costly silks I am wearing. I mean to wear tree-bark and animal-hide, like the wife of any Rishi, and to serve my husband so devotedly that your name, father, will be a legend in the three worlds. I mean to be like Vasishta's Arundhati, or Maharishi Atri's Anasuya.'

Deeply moved, her father had some deerskin and valkala fetched, and gave them to her. But when he saw her clad in those rough garments, tears sprang to his eyes. All his queens wept to see the princess transformed suddenly into a Rishi's bride. Saryati could not bear it at all, and he turned back quickly to his city," said Narada to me,' Vyasa told the king.

Janamejaya asked, 'And then, my lord?'

'Narada said, "Sukanya devoted herself to her husband, and she worshipped the sacred fire without fail. It was she, the princess, who now fetched his food for Chyvana: roots and fruit she foraged from the jungle. It was she who made a fire, drew water from the river, and heated it for the blind Muni's bath. Why, Sukanya bathed her old husband herself, lovingly, put his deerskin on for him, and sat him on his darbhasana. Then she would set kusa grass, til and his kamandalu before him, and say, 'Everything is ready for your nitya karma.'

When he had finished his daily worship, she would take his hand and lead him to another seat, where she fed him, often with her own hands, and always cheerfully, laughing and chatting with him, for her heart was full of joy.

When he finished, she would wash his hands, help him rinse his mouth, and then eat whatever was left over, and wash the earthen dishes. Only then did she bathe herself, and come and sit next to him. And she would say, 'Lord, tell me what I can do for you now.'

At nights, she would massage his body, and his legs, and, when he slept, she would curl up at his feet and fall asleep, exhausted by the day's chores, and as happy as she could be. That lovely princess, raised in a palace with a hundred maids attending on her every whim, served the old and blind Muni as few women had ever served their husbands.

One day, Surya Deva's sons, the Aswin twins, arrived in that forest. Sukanya was returning to the asrama through the jungle, with the water she had drawn from the river, where she had also bathed. The brilliant Aswins saw her, and stood transfixed by her beauty. They thought she must be a Devakanya, and accosted her. Their auras lit up the trees.

One of them said, 'Lovely one, who are you? Whose daughter? Who is your husband, do you have one? Why, you are as beautiful as Lakshmi herself!'

The other Aswin was not far behind; in an ecstasy he said, 'Ah, your feet as fragile as lotus petals. How is it you go barefoot in the forest? You are certainly a princess, where are your sakhis? Why are you carrying this water yourself?'

His twin took up again, 'The deer and birds of this vana are so fortunate, that they can see you whenever they like. The earth here is more blessed than Devaloka that your feet walk upon it! Tell us if you are a princess or an Apsara.'

Shyly, Sukanya said to the two Devas, 'I am king Saryati's daughter, and the wife of Maharishi Chyvana, who has his asrama in this forest. Won't you come to my husband's hermitage, and bless it?'

But the Aswins cried, 'A jewel like you, and that old man's wife! Passing strange. Why, you are like a streak of lightning frozen in time.'

'We have never seen anyone like you, even in Devaloka. You should wear the cloths of heaven around your delicate form, not this tree-bark and deer-hide. You should adorn your body with the ornaments of the Gods, so they shine more brightly with your beauty, and your beauty with them.'

'Ah, how exquisite you are,' said his twin, 'And, folly of follies, fate has given you a blind husband!'

'And an old one. God hasn't been kind you, why, he hasn't been just.'

'We say you should find yourself another husband, and quickly, before the brief season of your youth passes.'

'We offer ourselves, choose one of us.'

'Or choose both! Come away with us to Devaloka, and we will spend sweet hours together in the Nandana.'

'This is not the age for a woman like you to be a servant to an old man. This is the time for love! Come away with us, forget your Muni.'

Sukanya trembled when she heard their flagrant advances. But, she controlled herself, and said levelly, 'You are Surya Deva's sons, and they say that there is nothing you do not know in the three worlds. But then, you should know that I am a chaste woman. You are great Kashyapa Muni's grandsons, how can you speak to me like this? I am a wife, a Rishi's wife besides, and you are asking me to come away with you for pleasure's sake, like some whore?

I beg you, Devas, leave me in peace, and go away from here. Otherwise, I will curse you!'

Now her eyes glittered dangerously, and they knew that she was indeed chaste. Those splendid gods smiled at her, and said, 'Chastity like yours is hardly mortal. We are the physicians of heaven, there is nothing we cannot do with our powers.'

Knowing his twin's mind as if it were his own, his brother said, smiling brightly, 'We have a boon for you, Sukanya. We will make your old husband as radiant and handsome as ourselves. Why, we will restore his sight to him, and he will be as youthful as we are.'

She stood breathless. The other Aswin said, 'But, there is a condition. When we have transformed Chyvana he will look exactly like us, so you won't be able to tell him and us apart. Then, you must choose one of us three for your husband!'

She gasped at the thought, and ran back through the vana to her Muni, who sat lost in dhyana in their asrama. She burst in on his contemplation, and cried, 'My lord, my lord, the Aswin twins are here in our jungle! Surya's sons said to me they would make you as young and handsome as themselves, and they would restore your sight to you. But there is a condition. You would look exactly like them, so I would not be able to tell the difference between themselves and you. And then, I must choose one of you three to be my husband.'" said Narada, to me,' Vyasa told Janamejaya," says Romaharshana.

FORTY-ONE

THE MUNIS OF THE NAIMISA, OF WHOM SAUNAKA WAS FOREMOST, ASKED, "What became of Sukanya?"

The Suta said, "Vyasa told the king, 'Narada said to me, "Breathlessly, Sukanya told Chyvana of the Aswins' strange proposition, then, she said, 'My lord, I don't know what I should do.'

The Muni cried, 'What is there to think about? Bring the Aswins here at once, and agree to their condition!'

Like the wind Sukanya ran back through the forest to the splendid twins, and said, 'Devas! I will do as you ask. Come with me, and transform my husband.'

The Aswins came with her to the asrama. They said, 'Let us go to the lake, and bathe in it.'

Sukanya led her husband to the water by his hand. On its banks, the Gods from Devaloka said, 'Muni, enter the lake and immerse yourself.'

Sukanya helped the Rishi into the clear water. As he waded cautiously in, the Aswins also went with him. On either side of the Rishi, they took his hands, and led him into deep enough water so all three of them could immerse themselves entirely. So they did, as Sukanya watched them. They submerged for a long moment, and when they emerged again, the ancient Muni Chyvana had vanished, and instead three shining Aswins walked out of the lake. All three were young, wore the same ornaments, and each one was exactly like the others!

They said to her, all together, 'Now, choose one of us, whom you love best, to be your husband.' And their voices were exactly alike, as well.

For her life, which she felt was at stake if she chose a Deva who was not her husband, Sukanya could not tell one from the other. She thought that, perhaps, the third figure of light was yet another Deva. Trembling, she began to meditate on the highest Prakriti, the Devi Bhagavati.

'Mother of worlds,' Sukanya prayed desperately, 'I offer myself at your feet. Preserve my chastity! Show me which of these is my husband.'

Moved by the young woman's sincerity, the Devi blessed her with the subtle Sattva gyana. Again, Sukanya looked at the three Devas before her, and they were identical. But, now, her mind clearly knew which one her husband was. She went up and took his hand, saying, 'This is my lord Chyvana, and I choose him for my husband.'

The Aswins were enchanted. They cried, 'There is no one as chaste as you are, Sukanya! We bless you.'

But as they prepared to leave that forest, Maharishi Chyvana said, 'Devas, I thank you! A thousand times, I thank you! You have blessed me with youth and beauty and, most of all, with my sight again, that I can now see and please this wife of mine. I also have some punya shakti, Devas. Let me grant you a boon, anything your hearts desire.'

For just a moment, the Aswins were thoughtful, then they said, 'We have everything we want, with our father's blessing. Yet, at Brahma's great yagna on the golden mountain Kanakachala, Indra said that, because we are physicians, we should not drink the Soma rasa. It is the one thing we thirst for, O Muni, for we have heard there is no drink to match the ambrosial Soma. If you can, help us to drink the Soma rasa.'

Without a moment's hesitation, Chyvana said, 'Aswins, king Saryati will perform a yagna, and there you shall drink the Soma rasa in the very presence of Lord Indra!'" said Narada to me,' Vyasa said.

Janamejaya asked, 'But, how could Chyvana, who was only a Rishi, go against the word of mighty Indra, the king of the Devas?'

'Narada said to me, "One day, after some months of her being married to the Muni, Sukanya's father came across his wife, the queen, sobbing her heart out in her chamber. He took her hand and cried, 'My love, what ails you that you cry like this?'

She groaned, 'Every time I think of my child, I feel as if my heart will break. Ah, how can any mother endure this? My princess, who was raised in the midst of every luxury, now spends her days tending to that decrepit old man. She lives on roots and leaves like a slave in the forest. She must be wan and wasted with tapasya, and is this the age for her to be doing penance? Then, her husband is blind! Ah, I cannot bear to think of the torture she undergoes, day after day.

I beg you, my lord, go to my child and make sure she is well. Ask her if there is anything we can do to alleviate her misery.'

Saryati arrived in the forest asrama. As he walked towards the Muni's hut, he paused in the trees, for what he saw there shocked him. He saw Sukanya sharing an intimate moment with a splendid young man whose body shone like a God's. Indeed, he saw them kiss tenderly. Then, the young man went back into the asrama, and Sukanya began sweeping the yard. Her father hidden in the trees saw how radiant his child looked. But nowhere did he see the wretched Chyvana.

The king's chest heaved with outrage. He thought his princess had killed her old husband, and was now living in dreadful sin with the brilliant young man. But there was no crime as heinous as killing a great Rishi, and her own husband besides. Saryati had tears in his eyes. He thought this was the expiation for his own sins of the past: that he must live to see his daughter fallen so low. Ah, she was a stain upon the blemishless line of Manu Prajapati.

But then again, he wondered that she seemed so lambent, as if the spirit's purest light still burned brightly in her heart. No woman who had committed the sin he suspected her of could be as carefree and joyous, as he saw she was. For, once done, her sin would consume her, body and soul.

Suddenly, as the king stood thus distraught, his daughter saw him through the trees. With a cry she ran to him, and flung her arms around his neck. 'Father! How wonderful to see you here!'

Then she paused. She saw how pale and strained he was, she saw that he wept. She cried, 'What is the matter, father? Why are you crying?'

Saryati turned his face away from his daughter, and said grimly, 'Sinful child, who was that young man I saw you with? Aren't you at least ashamed of yourself, and the sin you live in?'

She began to laugh, as sweetly as ever. Then, in a moment, she was solemn, and her huge eyes were full of tears. Sukanya said, 'Father, how can you doubt me like this?'

But he raged, 'Don't lie to me! I saw you kissing the young man full on his lips, with my own eyes.'

Sukanya cried, 'The young man is my lord Chyvana! The Aswins gave him this lustrous body and his youth. They restored his sight to him. If you still doubt me, come and ask him yourself.'

Saryati came to the young man, and said, 'Son of Bhrigu, where has your age vanished?' But doubt seized him again, and he cried, 'How can you be Chyvana? Tell me, young man, who are you? And where is the Muni?'

Then Chyvana said in his own voice, 'Kshatriya, the Aswin twins blessed me, and in return I have sworn that I will help them drink Soma rasa at an Agnistoma yagna that you will perform.'

Saryati peered closely at the youth's eyes, and saw that he was indeed Chyvana Muni transformed. The king bowed to the sage and said, 'I swear I will perform the yagna.'

So, Saryati undertook the sacrifice. He spared no expense on the arrangements, and Chyvana himself invited Vasishta, Narada, and the holiest Rishis on heaven and earth. When the yagna was underway, Indra came there with his Devas to drink Soma rasa. Then, the Aswins arrived as well, in the yagnashala. Chyvana proffered the golden chalice that contained the Soma rasa to them, but Indra cried, 'Stop, Muni! These are vaidyas, they may not drink the Soma rasa.'

Chyvana said, 'Lord, these are Surya Deva's sons. They are born from his wife. What is their fault that they should not drink the Soma rasa? I have sworn they shall drink the Soma, indeed, this Agnistoma yagna is so that the Aswins may drink the rasa. Look what they have done for me, I cannot break my word to them.'

Indra replied, 'These twins have been made the physicians of the Devas. They serve the rest of us, and we look down on them. They shall not drink the Soma.'

Maharishi Chyvana's eyes blazed at the Deva king. He said softly, 'You committed adultery with Ahalya, why, you killed Vritrasura with treachery. Who are you, then, to sit in judgement over the Aswins? They shall drink the Soma at this sacrifice.'

A hush fell on the yagnashala, but it seemed everyone there, even the other Devas, saw the justice of what Chyvana said. They all knew that his ancient enmity with Surya Deva was the true reason for Indra barring the Aswins from drinking the Soma rasa. But now, the illustrious Bhargava brought the golden chalice of Soma to the Aswins.

Indra hissed, 'Stop, Chyvana! Or I will have your head.'

The Muni ignored him, and held the chalice of Soma out to the Aswins. Indra roared, 'Rishi, beware! Take that cup back, or I swear I will sever your head with my Vajra!'

But Chyvana paid him no mind; he gave the chalice into the Aswins' hands. In a flash, Indra cast his Vajra like jagged lightning at the Rishi. But Chyvana merely raised his palm, and that ultimate weapon was arrested in the air. It hung still, as if petrified. His eyes crimson with rage, Chyvana threw some potent oblation onto his yagna fire. A huge kritya sprang from it, her body and hair were scarlet flames, and her eyes were a nuclear fire.

She stood blazing there for a moment, then, her body seemed to cleave itself in two, and from her issued an immense Asura. He was awesome, he was dreadful, and he was called Mada, the mad one. His body was like a mountain, his arms long as rivers. His face was like a planet, with fangs ten yojanas long. He yawned his maw wide as the sky, and, in a wink, swallowed Indra's Vajra. Then, growling like the thunder of the apocalypse, he rushed at the Deva king. Indra flew from that yagna, swift as light, and the Demon after him.

Indra fled to Brihaspati, and fell sobbing at his feet, 'Ah, Guru, save me!'

With his antaradhrishti, his inner eye, Brihaspati saw what had happened. Then he saw the Demon Mada swarming up the sky to find Indra and devour him. The Deva king's lustre had faded in a moment, he stood shaking before his wise master, and whimpered, 'Guru, subdue the monster with a mantra!'

But Brihaspati replied, 'No mantra can subdue this Asura. He is born from the Parashakti, whom Chyvana worships. There is only one person who can save you from the Demon, Chyvana Muni himself.'

In a wink, Indra flew down to the yagna again, and prostrated himself before the Maharishi. 'Forgive me, my lord! Call off your Asura. Let the Aswins drink the Soma rasa from now. I swear they shall always drink the Soma! I beg you, Mahamuni, spare my life.'

By now, Mada arrived at the yagna. The kritya from whom he had sprung had vanished back into the flames of the yagna fire. Chyvana raised his hand over his head, and murmured an arcane mantra. Earth and sky shook at the incantation and Madasura found his huge body scattered like dust; and his ferocious spirit was divided in four, it is told, and given among women, wine, gambling, and the beasts of prey of the world. The Devas heaved a sigh of relief; their lord Indra stopped trembling.

Chyvana set the Devas in their places of honour again, and completed his sacrifice. With his own hands, he made both Indra and the Aswins drink the Soma nectar. Great auspiciousness spread across the earth after Chyvana's yagna, and his asrama became renowned through the three worlds as a most blessed place. Manu's son Saryati's fame also spread, and, after the Agnistoma yagna, he ruled his kingdom in peace and no blemish marred his long and just reign. The earth was, indeed, like a part of heaven when Saryati ruled from the throne of the Sun.

King Saryati had one son called Anarta, and Anarta had a son called Revata. Revata built the city called Kusasthala out in the midst of the ocean, and began living there. All the kingdom he ruled was named for his father Anarta. Revata had a hundred sons, of whom Kakudmi was the eldest. The noble Revata had a chaste and beautiful daughter, as well, whom he named Revati. When Revati came of age, her father ruled his people, the Anartas, from the Raivataka hill in the midst of the Anarta country.

Revata wondered to whom he could give his precious child in marriage. He decided there was one person who would advise him wisely. Taking the princess with him, he went to Brahmaloka," said Narada to me,' Vyasa Dwaipayana told king Janamejaya," says Suta Romaharshana to Saunaka and the rest.

FORTY-TWO

THE SUTA CONTINUES, "JANAMEJAYA OBJECTED, 'BUT REVATA WAS A Kshatriya! How could he go to Brahmaloka, where only Brahmanas who know the Brahman may come? Or men who have died and left their gross bodies behind them.'

Vyasa said, 'Above golden Mount Sumeru are Indra's heavens, and his city of Amravati, the abode of those who do not die. But in ancient times, men of the earth were so like the immortals they also journeyed freely to the subtler realms. Why, your great-grandfather, Kunti's son Arjuna, travelled to Devaloka in a vimana and stayed there with Indra for five years. The ancient king Kakutstha went as he pleased to Devaloka, in his human body.

Once, the king Mahabhishek was flying to Brahmaloka when he saw Ganga also travelling there, by the paths of the air. The wind parted the garment she wore, and Mahabhishek was smitten by lust to glimpse her exquisite nakedness. She noticed his arousal and smiled at him, for she also desired that mighty king. Then, Brahma cursed them to be born on the earth again, as a mortal king and his wife.

So, O Janamejaya, Revata was by no means the first or last Kshatriya who travelled to Brahmaloka along the pathways of the sky. When they arrived in Brahma's sabha, there was unearthly music playing there, and the king and his daughter sat entranced by it for a long time. When the music stopped, Revata bowed deeply to Brahma, and said, "Lord, this is my daughter Revathi. I have come to beg you to find the right groom for her. Let him be a Kshatriya, my Lord, good-natured and invincible."

For a moment, Brahma gazed at the beautiful Revathi, and at her father. Then, he laughed softly, and said, "Revata, a hundred and eight yugas have passed in the world, while you listened to my musicians playing. It is the twenty-seventh Dwapara yuga now on earth. I am afraid all the Kshatriyas of your clan are long dead. The Daityas attacked your city, and sacked it many times. But now the Yadava king Ugrasena rules from your city and it is called Dwaraka.

It is a long story, Revata, but an Avatara of Lord Vishnu has been born into the world to rid the earth of her burden of evil. He is called Krishna, and he has come to break the power of the race of Kshatriyas forever. You see, it is the end of the Dwapara yuga, and the Kali is rising over the earth. Vishnu's rest, Anantasesha, has been born as Krishna's mighty brother Balarama. This Balarama will make the perfect husband for your child. Take her to him, and let them be man and wife, you have my blessing."

The stunned Revata bowed again to his Pitamaha, and flew down to the earth. He could hardly recognise it, for its lustre had faded so abjectly in the evil time. Then, Balarama was magnificent, and he was delighted to make the lovely Revathi his wife. After the wedding, Revata made his way slowly to Badarikasrama where, at last, he found his peace,' Vyasa Muni said.

Janamejaya cried, 'But how astonishing, Muni, that a hundred and eight yugas passed, while Revata and Revathi listened to the music in Brahma's court! How did they live so long?'

Vyasa said, 'Brahmaloka is a sinless realm. There is no sickness or death there, not even weariness. When Saryati was in Brahmaloka, the Rakshasas killed many of his sons. Those that escaped fled Kusasthala in every direction, and hid themselves at the ends of the earth.

Meanwhile, Saryati's elder brother Ikshvaku was king in Ayodhya. Vikukshi was his eldest son. He sent fifty of his sons, Sakuni and the others, to the northern and eastern parts of Bharatavarsha, to rule in his name. He sent another eight sons to the south, and kept two princes beside him, to help him.

Once, the time of the astaka sraddha came round, and Ikshvaku sent his son Vikukshi into the forest to fetch fresh meat for the sacrifice in the name of the dead ancestors. Now, the meat used in any sacrifice must be perfectly clean. Vikukshi hunted a while in the vana, and he killed all sorts of animals, boar and deer, rabbits and fowl. But suddenly, he felt a powerful pang of hunger. He roasted and ate one rabbit from the many he had hunted.

Vikukshi came home with the rest of the meat, but when it was brought to Vasishta, the Kulaguru of Ikshvaku, that Muni knew at once that a portion of the game had already been eaten, making the rest leavings. The Shastras clearly say that leftovers are never to be used as sacrificial meat. Vasishta told the king that the meat his son had brought was tainted. Ikshvaku flew into a rage, and banished Vikukshi from his kingdom.

Then on, the prince was known as Sasada. And he was content, living in the forest among Rishis from whom he learned prayer, wisdom, and restraint. When Ikshvaku died, Vikukshi inherited his father's kingdom. Sasada himself had one son, called Kakutstha, or Indravaha, and also Puranjaya.'

Janamejaya said, 'Tell me how that Kshatriya had three names.'

'When Sasada left this world, Kakutstha became king of the House of the Sun. He was a powerful sovereign, a great bhakta, and a man of perfect dharma, besides. In those days, Indra and his Devas were routed in battle by some Asuras, and driven out from Amravati. They fled to Vishnu, and begged him to help them.

Vishnu said, "Ikshvaku's grandson Kakutstha is a Kshatriya upon the earth. Go and ask him to help you against the demons. He worships Parashakti, and has great prowess by her blessings."

Indra and his luminous people came to Ayodhya, and the king received them reverently. When they were seated in Kakutstha's majestic sabha, he said to the ones of light, "My lords, I am thrice blessed that you have come to my city. Tell me, how can I serve you?"

The Devas replied, "Great Kshatriya, the Asuras have driven us from Amravati. We have come to seek your help against them."

Kakutstha considered this for a moment, then, said with a smile, "It is a difficult task you assign to me. But I will come to fight the Danavas, if Indra will bear me into battle upon his back."

Indra was startled, he was outraged. But then, he had to agree, or the king of the earth would not come to fight for him. Indra became a great Bull and, mounted on his back, Kakutstha went into battle against the Asuras. By the Devi's grace, he was invincible, and the demons were slaughtered. Since Indra became a Bull, a Kakuda, and the Ikshvaku king rode on his back, he was known, then on, as Kakutstha. For Indra having been his mount, he was called Indravaha, and since he vanquished the Asuras, who are the first race of creation, he was called Puranjaya.

Kakutstha's son was the legendary Prithu, lord of the earth, who was an amsavatara of Mahavishnu. Prithu's son was Viswarandhi, and his son was called Chandra. One of Chandra's sons, who became king after him, was called Yuvanashva, and his son was Savanta the pious. Savanta built a city called Savanti, and it was like an Amravati on earth. Savanta's son, who ruled after him was Kuvalayasva, who killed the Danava Dhundu, who had overrun the world. That king became celebrated as Dhundumara.

Dhridasva was Dhundumara's son, and his son was Sriman Haryasva. Haryasva's son was Nikumbha, who was also a king. Varhanasva was Nikumbha's son, and Krisasva, his son. Krisasva's son was called Prasenajit, and he sired Yauvanasva, whose son was Sriman Mandhata, the great. Mandhata built a thousand and eight palaces in the name of the Devi Bhagavati in Varanasi, and the other most sacred tirthas. It is told Mandhata was not born of his mother's womb, but from his father's belly.'

'Passing strange!' cried Janamejaya. 'How can a man be born from his father's belly?'

'Mandhata's father Yauvanasva had a hundred queens, but he had no sons. He was obsessed by his lack. Yauvanasva performed a hundred yagnas in his palace, yet his wives did not give him an heir. Finally, in despair, the king went into the deep jungle where the holiest Rishis sat in tapasya. He flung himself down at their feet, and wept. The Brahmanas asked him gently, "What grieves you, Kshatriya, that you cry like this?"

Yauvanasva said, "Munis, there is nothing in the world that I do not have as king of the House of the Sun. I have vast lands, immense wealth, power, and a hundred chaste queens. I have no enemies in the world, for there is no one in it stronger than me. I am indeed a king of kings, but, holy ones, God has not blessed me with a son. My lords, my kingdom has no heir, I will do anything to have a son. Help me!"

The Rishis were moved, and they undertook a putrakama yagna for Yauvanasva in his city. They performed the sacrifice in the name of Indra, Lord of the Devas. They filled an earthen vessel with sacred water and blessed it with powerful Vedic mantras. The water vessel was left overnight in the yagnashala. But, that night, Yauvanasva awoke with a hot thirst searing him. He staggered about in the darkness, but found no water to drink anywhere. Then, he saw the water in the sacrificial vessel glimmering by a slender moon that had risen. Hardly knowing what he did, Yauvanasva picked up that vessel and drained the holy water in it. Then, he went back to sleep, and dreamt brilliant dreams.

The next morning, the Rishis saw the water vessel empty, and were aghast. They asked Yauvanasva, "Who drank the pavitra jala?"

Shamefaced, the king said, "I think I did, my lords. But I hardly knew what I was doing for thirst."

The Rishis conferred among themselves briefly, and decided this was a daiva, an act of fate. They completed the yagna, and returned to their asramas. In some weeks, Yauvanasva's belly began to swell, and he realised that he had become pregnant himself, with the water he drank. All his ministers and people, his queens and family, were astonished. But, when his time came, the king went into labour. His physicians incised his right bowel, and from it delivered a fine infant son. By God's grace, Yauvanasva himself did not die, but recovered fully from his extraordinary confinement.

But now, who would suckle the little prince? It is told that Indra himself reached his forefinger down into the bright child's mouth, and he sucked on it and was nourished. Thus, he had his name Mandhata, which means My Finger,' said Dwaipayana Muni to the Kuru king," says Suta.

FORTY-THREE

SUTA SAYS, "MUNI VYASA CONTINUED, 'WHEN MANDHATA BECAME KING after Yauvanasva's time, he conquered all the earth, and was called Sarvabhauma. He married Sasabindu's gorgeous daughter, Bindumati. He had two sons by her, who were to become legends in their time: Purukutstha, and Muchukunda. Purukutstha's son was Anarya, who was known as Brihadasva. Brihadasva was a devout king; his son was Haryasva, who became a realised soul, and Haryasva's son was Tridhanva, and Tridhanva's son was Aruna. Thus far, all the kings of the House of the Sun were God-fearing men of deep dharma.

But Aruna's son, Satyavrata, was a spoilt, self-indulgent prince and a philanderer. Once, he saw a young Brahmana woman and, smitten by her beauty, abducted her from her very wedding. All the Brahmanas of his city came together to the king to protest. They came into the court lamenting loudly, and cried repeatedly, "Alas! We are ruined! Alas! We are ruined! O king, your son has ruined us."

Aruna asked them, "What has my son done to you, holy ones?"

They said, "Our child had already been given to be a Brahmana's wife, but your prince took her from before the sacred fire."

The righteous king called his son and cried at him, "O, you disgrace to our ancient House! To what have you stooped? Leave my kingdom, let me never see you again."

The prince moaned, "Where shall I go, father?"

"You have behaved like a Chandala, go and live among the Chandalas!"

Satyavrata went sadly from his father's kingdom, and began living among the Chandalas of the forest, truly like one of them. His heart burned with resentment, most of all, against the king's Kulaguru, Vasishta, whom he held mainly responsible for his father's high-mindedness that had fetched him this wretched exile. Satyavrata was also convinced Vasishta could have prevailed upon Aruna not to punish him so harshly, but that Muni had said nothing.

Some years went by, and then Aruna himself, grief-stricken at what he had done to his son, left his kingdom and went to live in the jungle and perform tapasya, so the sin in the family may be forgiven. Indeed, Indra had not sent any rain to his kingdom for twelve years.

It was in those days that king Kaushika, who would one day become the Brahmarishi Viswamitra, abandoned his wife and children in the very forest Satyavrata lived in, and went away to the banks of the river Kaushiki upon the Himalaya, to sit in relentless dhyana, to have the power of a Brahmana. A famine came to that forest and, soon, Viswamitra's wife was in desperate straits. Her children, of whom there was a fair brood, had nothing to eat, and she had no notion how to feed them. Then, hardening her heart one day, she took her eldest boy, tied a rope around his neck, and went out.

It so happened that Satyavrata, who was out hunting in that forest himself, with his bow, saw the strange sight of a noble-looking woman walking through the forest with tears in her eyes, and a boy going before her, around whose neck she had tied a rope, the end of which she held in her hand. Stirred by the sight, Satyavrata accosted the woman and asked, "Who are you, beautiful one? Why do you lead this boy about on a rope? Why is he crying?"

She replied, "I am Viswamitra's wife. My husband has gone away to the mountains to perform tapasya. My children are starving, and this is my eldest boy. I have brought him to sell him, so the others can eat. The rope is so he won't run away, and he is crying because he knows what I mean to do."

Tears sprang in Satyavrata's eyes. He said to her, "Untie the rope, and go back to your asrama. Until your husband returns, I will bring you food from the forest every day. I will leave it hanging on a tree near your asrama."

She did as he asked and, then on, that child was known as Galaba, since she had tied a rope around his throat. In time, he became a great Rishi, for, that day's torment, when his mother led him around like a beast on sale left an indelible wound on the child's mind. Satyavrata kept his word to Viswamitra's wife faithfully, and, indeed, he felt he now had something to live for. Every day, he would hunt wild boar and deer, rabbits and pheasant, skin and pluck these and leave their meat on the tree as he had promised. Viswamitra's wife fed her children with what the prince brought her, and they grew into strong and happy children.

But, one day, Satyavrata found no animal to kill in the forest. In some despair, that he would have to break his word, he plunged through the forest in search of game. Now, Vasishta still kept an asrama in that forest, where his disciples lived in dhyana. The Rishi also kept some cows in his hermitage. Satyavrata on his hunt arrived at the edge of Vasishta's asrama, and saw a plump white cow cropping grass.

The prince had never forgiven Vasishta for not stopping his father from banishing him. Now, when he saw the cow and knew it was that Rishi's animal, he did not hesitate, but killed it with an arrow. He dragged it away into the forest, skinned it, ate part of it himself, and took some meat for Viswamitra's wife and children. They never knew it was the flesh of a sacred cow, and ate it quite happily.

But when Vasishta heard what Satyavrata had done, he came in a rage to where that prince lived, and cursed him, "You have killed my precious cow, like a pisacha you have killed her and eaten her flesh. You abducted a Brahmana's wife from her very wedding. For these three crimes, let there be three leprous marks on your face, like a demon's, and for the three shankus you shall be known as Trishanku. Let all the world know your true nature that you are a pisacha!"

At once, three leprous marks appeared on Satyavrata's face, and he became Trishanku. Pisachavata was upon him; he was like a demon, violent and terrible. But it seemed the curse made prince Satyavrata a more devout man than ever. He began to worship the Devi Bhagavati with the mantra of nine letters. One day Satyavrata decided that he wanted to perform the purascharana homa, in which a Deity is worshipped with oblations, mantras and burnt offerings.

He came to the Brahmanas of the forest and, bowing deeply to them, said, "I beg you, my lords, be my ritviks in the yagna I want to perform. I am a Kshatriya and a prince. My name is Satyavrata, and I am Aruna's son."

But the Brahmanas cried, "You are a pisacha, and your guru has cursed you. You have no right to the Vedas, or their rituals. You may not perform any sacrifice."

Satyavrata was stricken; this seemed the last straw in his tragic life. He decided to do away with himself. He piled a pyre from dry wood, then bathed in the river to purify himself. Finally, he lit the pyre and stood before it, chanting the Devi's mantra, before he immolated himself. Suddenly, the Devi Bhagavati appeared before him, mounted on her lucent beast, bright herself as a hundred suns!

"What are you doing, Satyavrata?" cried the Devi in a voice like a rain-cloud rumbling. "How can you abandon patience like this? Never think of killing yourself, Kshatriya, it is a sin worse than murdering a Brahmana. Why, tomorrow your father's ministers will come to this forest to fetch you home, and Aruna will bequeath his throne to you. Your father's time has come to embark on a life of tapasya, and yours to rule a great kingdom."

With that, the Devi vanished before his eyes like a dream, and the pyre Satyavrata lit had burned down to ashes. Trembling, and with tears in his eyes, the prince sat on the ground, in shock and elation. To his amazement, he found his pisachavata had left him. The Devi had undone Vasishta's curse, and blessed him with a radiant Kshatriya's body again.

Meanwhile, in Ayodhya, king Aruna had an illustrious visitor. Narada arrived in his court and told him all that had transpired with his son. Aruna began to cry. He said, "How my child has suffered! First, I turned him out in anger, then, he lived like a Chandala in the forest, and finally Vasishta cursed him to pisachavata. And now, O Muni, you tell me that he was about to kill himself when the Devi herself appeared before him. I have sinned more than my child has, let him be brought back at once, and I will make him king."

So, even as the Devi had predicted, Aruna's messengers arrived the next morning in Satyavrata's asrama, with the message that his father begged him to come home, and be crowned. Giving thanks to the Goddess who was the cause of this good fortune, Satyavrata went back to his father. Sobbing in delight to see his son, the father clasped him in his arms and would not release him, but kissed him over and over again. Finally, making the prince sit next to him, Aruna discoursed to him a little on the dharma of a king.

"Your highest dharma is to be devout, and a bhakta. Never lie or walk down the paths of evil. Never be influenced by men of dubious character, but keep truly wise men near you, Brahmanas and Rishis, and listen to their advice. Your senses, my son, must be your slaves. That is the first enemy a king must conquer: himself; the rest will be easy. Ministers must be consulted on every important decision, but none of them must be trusted completely.

Keep your enemies in your thoughts, constantly; never forget even those you consider the least of them. Every enemy, even the least, is dangerous to a king. Your spies must keep a close watch on your friends and your enemies alike. Never trust women, or men who are inordinately attached to women, nor gamblers and drunkards. Lead a sparse and an ascetic life, for only when the material life is simple, can the inner life be rich. And, only with a rich inner life can a man be a king.

I know you worship the Devi Bhagavati; Narada Muni told me how she saved your life. Always keep her next to your heart, pray to her every day, at all three sandhyas; invoke her blessing for everything you do. For, the Devi delivers her bhaktas from sorrow and evil, and he who drinks the Charanamrita, the water with which her feet are washed, will never enter a mother's womb again.

Never transgress dharma, my child, and remember that the Brahmanas who know the Vedas and Vedantas are like Gods on earth. Consult them always, revere them, support them with gifts of wealth and lands, cows and gold. But, if a Brahmana is not learned, do not give him more than what he needs to fill his belly. But worship the learned Brahmana. For he is like the fuel out of which the fire that is the Kshatriya's power comes. The Brahmana's power flows everywhere, my son. No king who opposed a wise Brahmana ever triumphed.

I mean to make you king now, for my time has come, and I must renounce the world."

With tears in his eyes, Trishanku prostrated himself at his father's feet, and all was forgiven between them. Aruna clasped his son to him, then called for the Brahmanas of his sabha to prepare for crowning Satyavrata king. He sent his soldiers out to the far corners of the land, to fetch water for his son's abhisekha from the ocean and the sacred rivers. When the holy water arrived, Aruna sent messengers to all the kingdoms of Bharatavarsha, to invite his friends, the other kings, to attend his son's coronation. In some surprise, for they knew that this prince had once been banished, those Kshatriyas arrived in Aruna's city.

With ceremony, Satyavrata Trishanku was crowned king of the House of the Sun. When this was done, Aruna and his son gave away lavish lands and wealth to the Brahmanas who had sat over the abhisekha. Then, with his wife, Aruna turned his back on his kingdom and retired into the forest, became a vanaprastha, and performed tapasya in an asrama on the banks of the Ganga. In time, he realised the immortal Brahman within himself, and, leaving his body, ascended into heaven, where he shone like another sun beside Indra.

Trishanku ruled the kingdom sagely, with dharma as his sceptre. He was just and generous, and there was no better king in all Bharatavarsha. In time, he was married and had a brilliant son whom he named Harishchandra, whose dharma would also be legend one day.

However, Trishanku always had an eccentric strain in his character. Once, he was seized by a strange and irresistible ambition: he wanted to rise into Devaloka, the realm of the Gods, in his human body! At first, he tried to dismiss the weird desire, telling himself that he was slipping back into the old spoilt ways of his youth. But it would not leave him in peace, and obsessed him day and night, his waking and sleep.

When he could not bear it anymore, he went to Vasishta in his forest asrama and confessed his extraordinary preoccupation. He said, "Try as I will, I cannot banish the obsession from my heart. Guru, you have the power to send me up into Devaloka in this human body. I have no peace, but dream of being with the Apsaras and listening to the Gandharvas' songs in the Nandana. I beg you, Muni, help me!"

But Vasishta said, "Who can live in Devaloka in a mortal body? Why, even the dead only live in heaven as long as their punya lasts, then they are born again into the world. Trishanku, how can a mortal man enjoy the Apsaras, or even listen to Gandharvas' songs that are like amrita? Be patient, and you shall indeed enjoy Devaloka, when you die."

Trishanku had always held a grudge against Vasishta, especially after he cursed him the last time. Now he turned on that Rishi and cried, "If you won't help me, haughty one, I will find another Brahmana who will!"

And he was about to stalk out of the Muni's presence, when Vasishta cursed him again, "Evil king! Your heart is still full of darkness and vanity. Be a Chandala from now, for you have the spirit of one. And I, your guru, curse you that you will never find Devaloka for yourself, not even when you die!"

At once, Trishanku found his body had turned into a black Chandala's. His features were coarse and his red eyes bulged from his crude face. His golden ornaments had turned into base iron ones, the sweet sandal-paste his women had anointed him with smelt like excrement, and his skin was thick and hirsute. With a howl, Trishanku fled from Vasishta's presence. He ran through the jungle, his eyes streaming, like a man who had demons after him.

He could not go back to his city now, for even his wife would not recognise him, or his son. The people would surely beat him, if he told them he was Trishanku. He thought it was better to die, than to live again in exile in a wretched Chandala's body. But then, he knew that a suicide would be born as a Chandala again. So there was no escape for him, even by killing himself.

Wisdom dawned on Trishanku; he told himself, "I must suffer for whatever I have done, for there is no escape, in a hundred lives, from the fruits of one's karma. I will live a forester's life, near some Rishis' asramas, and visit the sacred tirthas of the earth. I will worship the Devi more fervently than ever. And, perhaps, I will be forgiven my sins, and even realise my dream of rising into Devaloka in this gross body."

Trishanku began living beside the Ganga, in tapasya, as a penitent. But word got out about how he had been cursed, and his son Harishchandra heard of it. In grief, that prince sent his ministers to his father in the wilderness. They came and said, "Lord, we know who you are. Your son Harishchandra begs you to return home with us. We, and all your subjects will implore Vasishta to withdraw his curse or, at least, favour you with a blessing; and your anguish will melt away like snow on the Himalaya when summer comes."

But Trishanku, the Chandala, said to them, "Go back to the city and tell my son that I will not return. Make Harishchandra king in my place, and serve him well."

The ministers wept, and begged him again, but their king would not relent. He insisted he would remain beside the river, in atonement, and they must return to Ayodhya. And so they did and, on an auspicious day, crowned the noble Harishchandra king of the House of the Sun. And Harishchandra ruled with dharma, in his father's name, and the kingdom prospered,' said Dwaipayana Muni to king Janamejaya,' says Romaharshana Suta in the blessed forest.

FORTY-FOUR

SUTA GOES ON, "JANAMEJAYA ASKED, 'MUNI, HOW DID TRISHANKU RECOVER, or did he? Was he purified in the Ganga, or did Vasishta Muni withdraw the curse?'

Vyasa said, 'Peace stole over Trishanku beside the murmuring Ganga, for he worshipped the Devi Bhagavati unceasingly, her precious name was always on his lips. Meanwhile, Viswamitra returned to that forest, after he completed an austere tapasya on the Himalaya. Indeed, Brahma had appeared before that Kshatriya who had become a Rishi, and blessed him.

When Viswamitra saw how healthy and happy his wife and children were, he asked her, "How did you feed the children during the famine? I was anxious about you on the mountain, but I thought to myself even if I did return there was very little I could do, since I have given away all my wealth. I would only be another mouth to feed. But I did not escape the famine on my way home.

One night, I was so hungry that I crept into a Chandala's home, to steal some food for myself. As I was about to eat some cooked dog's flesh that I saw in the Chandala's kitchen, I became aware that someone had come into that dwelling, and was watching me. I almost dropped the dish in my hand in alarm, but the young man did not seem angry.

Quite gently, he asked me, 'What are doing here at this hour? You look like a noble soul. Who are you? What do you want in a Chandala's kitchen?'

My voice quivering with hunger, I said to him, 'I am a sannyasin, young man. I have been starving for many days, and I have come looking for something to eat in your home. I beg you, let me eat this curried flesh in your cooking-pot. I will die of hunger if I don't!'

But he said to me, with annoyance in his voice, 'This is a Chandala's house. You belong to one of the higher varnas. You must never touch my food, or you will be defiled.'

I was a little surprised at his concern. Moreover, he spoke in chaste language, such as I had heard spoken in royal sabhas. But he had not finished his advice, 'A human birth is exceedingly hard to have in the world, and then to be born a Brahmana is harder still. You must not dream of tainting yourself by eating dog's meat in a Chandala's house. We are the seventh caste, and Manu has declared us to be untouchables, for our sins of past lives.'

I replied, 'Intelligent Chandala, what you say is true, yet it isn't the whole truth. For, in times of danger and crisis, a man may have recourse to solutions that he is not allowed in ordinary times. The body must be maintained in health, always. If a man must sin to achieve this, if there is no other way for him, that sin shall not adhere to him, as long as he performs some prayaschitta for it. But, if a man dies of hunger, when he can eat even by stealing, that sin clings to him.

Chandala, if a man steals during a famine, his sin does not go to him but to the God of rain, Indra himself, until he sends a monsoon to the parched lands.'

I spoke with conviction and, at that very moment, as if Indra had heard me, thunder and lightning exploded in the sky, and it began to pour, even like water gushing from a million elephants' trunks! I felt a deep joy, and left the Chandala's hut without eating the dog meat for, suddenly, I was not hungry any more. But, tell me, how did you and the children survive the famine?"

She said, "When the famine began, I would go out into the forest to forage for wild rice, roots and fruit. But, as the days passed and there was no rain, I couldn't even find these any more. The children were crying piteously, and I thought they would all die. So, one day, when I could not bear to see them suffer, I decided I would sell our eldest boy to a rich man, to be his servant, and get some food in return.

I tied a rope around his neck so he would not run away, and led him out of the asrama. Our son realised what I meant to do, and began to cry loudly. The prince Satyavrata, who had been banished to the forest by his father king Aruna of Ayodhya, heard him. He accosted me and asked who I was, and where I was taking the boy with the rope around his neck, and why he was crying.

When I told him, the noble prince said, 'Take your son back to your asrama. I will bring you some meat to eat every day, until the famine breaks or your husband comes home.'

Crying myself, I thanked him and went back home. The prince kept his word; every day we would find some fresh meat tied to a tree outside the asrama, venison, boar and rabbit. The children and I had more than we needed to eat, and, indeed, the children grew healthy and strong.

But, one day, Satyavrata could not find any game to hunt in the forest, and he went to Vasishta's asrama and killed the kamadhenu, his sacred cow. Vasishta cursed him, first to be a pisacha, and to be called Trishanku. But Satyavrata worshipped the Devi and she restored his human form. Aruna called his son home and made him king, but then Vasishta cursed him again, to be a Chandala. Trishanku is living in exile again, in the forest, while his son Harishchandra rules Ayodhya. Satyavrata saved our lives, my lord, now you must help him."

Viswamitra wanted to know why Vasishta had cursed Trishanku a second time, and his wife told him about Satyavrata's obsession: to rise into Devaloka in his human body. Viswamitra realised the mission of helping Trishanku would not be an easy one; for that Kshatriya wanted heaven for himself, and his guru's curse was upon him.

Viswamitra, who also bore an old enmity for Vasishta, went through the forest looking for Satyavrata of the unusual destiny. He found him living in a Chandala village, himself an ugly Chandala now, why, he was the very man whose dog's flesh the Muni had almost eaten! When Trishanku saw Viswamitra, he fell at his feet and wept. Viswamitra raised him up, and blessed him. Then, with tears in his eyes, he embraced Trishanku and thanked him for what he had done for his wife and children.

They sat together beside the murmurant Ganga and, slowly, Viswamitra drew his sad story from the Chandala who had been a great king. He was deeply moved, for that Rishi had been a king himself, once, called Kaushika; but he had renounced his throne to seek Brahmagyana, the eternal Spirit. Now, in Satyavrata, he saw another Kshatriya whose path through life was at least as extraordinary as his own; he felt compassion for Trishanku, and swore he would help him. Since Satyavrata had saved his family's lives once, Viswamitra said he would use his punya to help Trishanku realise his exceptional ambition. He would send him to Devaloka in his human body!

Viswamitra arranged to perform a yagna, and he invited all the Rishis of the world to attend. He planned to have them bless the ritual, and use their powers to make Trishanku's wish come true. But Vasishta heard of the yagna, and forbade the other Munis to attend it. Seething in anger, Viswamitra roared, "I will send you to Devaloka by myself, Trishanku!"

He poured some holy water into his palm, and recited the Gayatri mantra resonantly. He laid that hand on Trishanku's head and cried, "I, Kaushika, give you all my punya. Rise, O Trishanku, rise into Devaloka in this Chandala's body!"

Like a bird, Trishanku rose into the air; crying out in exhilaration he arrived at Indra's Amravati. But when Indra saw the dark Chandala flying towards him, he cried in alarm, "Who is this, flying towards us like a black comet?"

Then he saw who it was, and said, "Trishanku! You are a Chandala, how dare you try to enter Devaloka? Begone, Untouchable, back to the earth where you belong!"

Indra raised his hand, and like a bird shot with an arrow, Trishanku fell down towards the earth, below. As he fell, he screamed, "Viswamitra, save me!"

Down in the world, the Muni heard him, and he raised his hand over his head and roared, "Trishanku, stay where you are!"

And, by Viswamitra's tapasya shakti, Trishanku was suspended between heaven and earth. His eyes blazing, the Maharishi poured some more sacred water into his hand, performed achamana, and began to create another Devaloka, a new heaven around Trishanku! Indra saw this and cried in panic, "O Muni, what are you doing? Why are you so angry, great Kaushika? There is no need for you to make another Devaloka, just tell me what you want, and you shall have it."

Viswamitra said in a voice like thunder, "Trishanku is a pure soul, and he must have his heart's desire fulfilled. I mean to create another Swarga for him, and he shall be its Indra."

Indra moaned, "Muni, don't waste your punya! I will take Trishanku into Devaloka. I beg you, Kaushika, desist."

Viswamitra said, "If you take Trishanku into Devaloka."

Indra flew down to the king with the Chandala's body, who hung between heaven and earth. With a touch of his palm, he gave Trishanku a Deva's lustrous body, and then he took him into Devaloka in a shimmering vimana, and made him a great lord of the realm of light. And Viswamitra was satisfied, but the stars and galaxies he had already created for Trishanku remained where they were in the firmament, and Indra agreed that Satyavrata would be master of them, even as he, Indra, was of Amravati.

But Viswamitra's vast store of punya was exhausted by what he had done to help Trishanku, and he went again to the mountains, to resume tapasya. In Ayodhya, Harishchandra heard about his father's salvation, and was glad. He began to rule the kingdom with a lighter heart, and his was a golden reign. Time wore on, but Harishchandra's lovely queen, Saivya, did not conceive and the throne of Ayodhya had no heir. The king performed countless sacrifices in his city, but to no avail.

At last, in despair, Harishchandra took himself to the forest, to his Kulaguru Vasishta's asrama. He prostrated himself before that Rishi and said, "Help me, Guru, for I have no son, and my line will end with me." ' said Vyasa Muni to the king," says Romaharshana the Suta.

FORTY-FIVE

IN THE NAIMISARANYA, SAUNAKA AND HIS MUNIS URGE THE SUTA TO continue. Romaharshana takes up his Purana once more, "Dwaipayana Muni said to Parikshita's son, 'Vasishta, who was a trikalagyani, said to Harishchandra, "Worship Varuna Deva, he will bless you with a son."

Harishchandra worshipped the Lord of the ocean with a solemn yagna. In streams of spectral light, Varuna appeared before Harishchandra, and said in his sea-voice, "You shall have a son. But do you swear you will give him to me when he is born?"

Desperate as he was, Harishchandra vowed he would. Within the year, by the ocean's blessing, the king's wife bore him a son. Harishchandra called the boy Rohita, and he was as dear to him as his life. But he had not enjoyed his Rohita for a day, when Varuna came to him, and said in his voice full of the soft thunder of waves, "I have come for your son, O King. Give him to me now, he was the offering of your yagna."

Harishchandra said quickly to the Deva of the deeps, "O Varuna, a newborn child is unclean. Come for him in ten days."

Ten days later Varuna came to the king again, and said in his voice of moon-tides, "I have come for your son."

Harishchandra said, "Lord of waves, a yagnapasu must have teeth. Let Rohita cut his teeth, before I offer him to you in dignity."

When Varuna came again, Harishchandra said milk teeth were not enough, let them fall; and next, that the child's new teeth should grow; and, later, that the sovereign of the oceans should wait until Rohita wore armour, because a Kshatriya is pure only when he dons mail. And so on, making great Varuna seem like a collector who came, repeatedly, for a bad debt.

Meanwhile, Rohita grew up. One day, in anguish, his father told him about his pledge to Varuna. He could not put the Deva off forever. Rohita was terrified. Taking just his bow and arrows, he ran away from his father's palace, and into the forest.

When Varuna heard this, he cursed Harishchandra. He visited him with mahodara, and the king wasted from that disease. Rohita learnt of this in the jungle, and started back to offer himself to the Sea God. But Indra accosted him on his way, appearing suddenly before the boy, refulgent. The Deva king said to Rohita, "Go on a yatra to all the tirthas in the land, and your father will recover."

Rohita went to the sacred rivers. He bathed in them, and worshipped their divine waters. Word came to him that Harishchandra was well again. Rohita returned to his hide in the forest. But, in a year, Varuna's affliction, caused by an imbalance in the bodily fluids, returned to Harishchandra. Again, Rohita set out on his pilgrimage to the tirthas. His father got better once more. But, after a year, the mahodara returned to Harishchandra, more virulently than before.

Five times this happened. Then, one day, when Rohita was on his tirtha-yatra, he met an impoverished Brahmana travelling with his wife and three grown sons, who were about the same age as the prince himself. A bizarre idea struck Harishchandra's son. He said to the brahmana, whose name was Ajigartha, "Brahmana, I will give you a thousand cows, if you let me have one of your sons."

Ajigartha wanted to know a little more. Rohita told him all about himself and his father, and the offering to Varuna. The Brahmana and his wife stood listening carefully on that path in the wilderness. Ajigartha said, "I cannot part with my eldest son, he is like my life to me."

At once, his wife cried, "I will not give you my youngest, he is my very breath. It is always thus, prince. The eldest is the father's favourite, and the youngest, the mother's."

Now, they both looked at their second son, whose name was Sunashepa. That boy stared back in disbelief, his eyes turning from his father's face to his mother's. Then, in a stricken voice, Sunashepa said, "Prince Rohita, take me with you. My mother and father have sold me for a thousand cows."

It was high noon, one day, when Sunashepa and Rohita arrived at Pushkara. Rohita fell asleep at the foot of a tree. Sunashepa sat numb with grief, that his own parents had sold him for some cows. He was thirsty and hungry, and he knew he was to be sacrificed to Varuna. Then, the Brahmana's son saw Viswamitra sitting under a tree, in unmoving dhyana. Sunashepa ran to the Rishi and flung himself sobbing at his feet.

Startled out of his samadhi, Viswamitra saw a fine young Brahmana boy lying before him in tears. At once, Viswamitra's soft heart was full of pity. Stroking the lad's head, he said, "Tell me, child, what grieves you? I will set it right."

Sunashepa sobbed out his tale. Then he said, "I don't want the yagna for which my father sold me to be spoilt. Nor do I want to die. I want to live long, so I can do enough tapasya to reach Swarga. Help me, Muni, I have no one else to turn to."

Viswamitra summoned his own sons. He said to them, "Which of you will go to his death in place of this unfortunate child? You are rich in punya, by your very birth. One of you can easily be the yagnapasu at Harishchandra's yagna."

But Madhuchandas, his eldest son, thought his father was joking and began to laugh. Viswamitra's other sons laughed with him. Madhuchandas said, "Father, how can you sacrifice one of your own sons because an orphan comes and cries at your feet? Next you will tell us to eat the flesh of a dog."

Rage, his old enemy, sprang up hotly in Viswamitra. His eyes blazed, and he cried, "A son who disobeys his father is not worthy of being called a son. Be you all Chandalas, like Vasishta's sons. And you shall indeed eat the flesh of dogs for a thousand years!"

His boys fled howling from there. Viswamitra was lost in thought for a while. Then he turned to Sunashepa and said, "Go with Rohita to the sacrificial stamba. They will tie you to the pole with ropes purified with mantras. They will smear your body with red sandal, and drape wild-flower garlands around your neck. I will teach you two mantras. You must sing them at the yagna, and no harm will come to you. And the yagna shall be complete, as well."

Sunashepa learned those secret hymns from Viswamitra. He went back to Rohita, who still lay asleep, and shook him awake. "Come, my prince, let us hurry to your father's sacrifice. I am prepared for what comes to me."

Rohita embraced him. The prince was glad the wonderful Brahmana boy had accepted his fate with such serenity. They came to Harishchandra's palace. The king lay in his sickbed in a dark room, because no light should touch him. Five men carried Harishchandra to the yagnashala.

They tied Sunashepa to the yupasthamba. They smeared him with the red paste of sandal, and adorned him with garlands of bright flowers, as an offering fit for a Deva. Suddenly, in his unbroken voice, the boy began to sing. He sang so sweetly: the magical hymns that Viswamitra had taught him. At first the singing was greeted with silence, it was so unexpected. But when those gathered there understood the meaning of the songs, they began to cheer the brave child.

Two unearthly flashes of light lit that yagnashala, and Indra and Varuna himself appeared before Sunashepa to bless him. Because of Viswamitra's brilliant songs, Harishchandra was forgiven by the Lord of oceans. But that king had learnt a lesson from his long illness: that excessive putrasneha is a curse to any father. Now he wanted to go himself to Viswamitra, and learn the profound Brahmavidya from that Rishi.

Meanwhile, Viswamitra's hundred natural sons agreed to accept Sunashepa as their eldest brother, and their father took back his curse. From that day, all the descendants of those hundred and one were known as Kaushika and that was their gotra.

In time Harishchandra performed the Rajasuya yagna, the greatest sacrifice any king can, one that is done perhaps once or twice in an yuga. Vasishta was his guru for the yagna, and he rewarded that Muni lavishly. One day, Vasishta and Viswamitra happened to come to Indra's Devaloka together.

In the shining Sudharma, Viswamitra said to his old rival, "Muni, you are more radiant than I have ever seen you. Might one ask the cause of your joy?"

Vasishta replied, "Harishchandra has performed the Rajasuya, and I am his guru. Ah, there is no king as pure and as truthful as Trishanku's son."

Viswamitra laughed, "Harishchandra! Truthful and pure, you say. I say to you, he is a liar and a cheat. Why, he promised to give his son Rohita to Varuna Deva, but when the time came, he promptly went back on his word. He is a liar and a cheat, and should proclaim it to the world!"

Vasishta said quietly, "Harishchandra has learnt his lesson; there is no king as righteous as him in the three worlds. I defy you to prove him a liar, and I will wager all my punya against yours."

Scornfully, Viswamitra said, "It will be the easiest wager anyone ever won. Why, I will make Harishchandra himself declare that he is a liar and a cheat!"

For a thousand years, Viswamitra sat in intense tapasya beside Brahma's sacred lake in Pushkara. One day, Harishchandra was out hunting in the forest, when he heard anguished sobbing from a dense copse. He saw a beautiful woman there. Her body was luminous, but her face was tear-stained, and great sobs wracked her slender form.

The king said, "Who are you, lovely one? How did you come to this forest, and why are you crying? I am Harishchandra, and I am the king of these lands. Tell me who has harmed you, and I swear he shall be punished."

She wiped her eyes, and said, "I am Siddharupini, O Kshatriya, and I am crying because the Rishi Viswamitra sits in tapasya to have me for himself."

Harishchandra said at once, "Be at peace, I will go to Viswamitra and tell him to stop his tapasya."

That king went straight into the deepest heart of that same forest, where Viswamitra sat in searing penance, like a flame. Harishchandra went before him, and said, "Muni, for what great cause do you pray so fervently in my kingdom? Surely, it must be for the welfare of all mankind, so austere is your dhyana."

He saw a flush of shame on the Rishi's face, and went on, "Muni, my people complain to me that they are terribly disturbed by your prayatna. It is my dharma as king to beg you to desist from this worship. Please leave my country and take your dhyana elsewhere."

In dharma, Viswamitra could not refuse to do as Harishchandra asked. But he was furious with that king. Without a word, he turned his back and stalked away; he left that jungle and went away to his old asrama in another kingdom. But then, he created a Rakshasa from his tapasya-shakti, to have revenge on Harishchandra. That demon had the shape of a wild boar, and was big as a small hillock. Viswamitra sent it to Harishchandra's kingdom, to the king's private forest where he went frequently to hunt.

That boar was a spirit of havoc and, crying shrill cries, it fell keenly to its task. With curved tusks, the boar began to destroy that forest. Parts of it were carefully tended garden, maintained by Ayodhya's army for the king's pleasure, when he came here with his queens. There were fine lotus-pools here, painstakingly laid rockeries, and groves of shade trees planted by the palace gardeners. The demon boar savaged all these, leaving a shambles wherever it went. The king's forest guards tried to chase it away, but, crimson eyes glittering, and with unnerving squeals of rage, the creature flew at them. The soldiers' arrows and swords glanced off the great pig's hide, and it managed to gore some of them, before they escaped with their lives.

Those forest guards flew back to Harishchandra, and told him what had happened. The king asked, "What Danava or Yaksha is this?"

His men replied, "It is a great boar, Lord, its back is as high as a man's head. It tusks are like swords, and its hide is so thick our arrows fell off it like wisps of straw."

When Harishchandra heard what the boar had done to his woods, he called for his horse, and a small army to follow him into the forest. With elephant and horsemen, foot soldiers and warriors in chariots, the king set out to kill the beast. Before they saw the animal, they heard the keening noises of delight it made, as it continued to devastate everything it saw.

Then, coming into an open glade the king saw the boar, and it was bigger than he had imagined. Erupting into shrill screams when it saw Harishchandra, the boar charged him in a thunder of hooves, earth flying around it. The king raised his bow and, quick as thinking, shot ten scorching shafts at the creature. But they fell off the demon boar's hide like stalks of grass. The boar still came on, and Harishchandra drew his sword and held it before him in both hands to impale the brute. But when the boar was a few feet away from the king, it leapt right over his head!

Whirling around, Harishchandra shot another brace of burning arrows at the animal, but it had gained the trees at the far end of the clearing and the king heard it crashing away through the undergrowth. Leaping onto his horse, Harishchandra pursued the demon boar through the forest, with his soldiers after him. But that creature set such a pace, that soon only the king himself remained on its trail, all his men fell far behind.

Plunging through the denser jungle, the boar led Harishchandra farther and farther away from his city and his army. But, furious as he was, the king pursued the animal, determined to have its hide today. He rode perhaps two hours, and, soon, ploughed through trackless forest, that grew more and more strange around him. The going now was slow, and suddenly he did not hear the beast ahead of him anymore, making its frenzied way through the trees. All was silence, and the king knew that he was very lost.

He dismounted from his horse, and made his way through the trees, in the direction he imagined he had come from. But the truth was that Harishchandra no longer knew where he was going. Very little sunshine pierced the thick canopy above him, and he could not even find his way by the sun, it being directly overhead. Panting, exhausted, and frustrated that the demon boar had eluded him, he broke into a small clearing through which a merry stream chatted through the looming jungle.

The king knelt eagerly to drink, and his heaving horse drank beside him. The boar had vanished as if into thin air, which was not far from the truth, for the Muni who had created it with his sorcery had undone its mortal elements, now its mission was fulfilled. As the king finished drinking, he became aware that he was not alone. An old Brahmana had materialised at his side, and stood looking gravely down at him. Despite his apparent frailty, this person seemed possessed of an exceptionally vigorous manner, and was a radiant presence in the forest dimness.

The Brahmana said, "O King, for that I can see you are, what are you doing in this grim vana, all by yourself? Where are your soldiers and trackers? Are you looking for treasure, perhaps, that you have come here all alone? Tell me, who are you?"

Harishchandra folded his hands, and bowed to the bright mendicant. He said, "Muni, I am Harishchandra of the House of the Sun, and I am the king of Ayodhya. This morning a demon pig rampaged in my private woods, and I gave the beast chase. It led me deep into the jungle, and my men could not keep up. I lost them along the way, and now I am lost myself. Brahmana, can you help me find my way back to Ayodhya? I give you my word that you shall find me grateful, O Sage," ' said Vyasa Muni," says Suta.

FORTY-SIX

"VYASA PAUSED, AND JANAMEJAYA URGED HIM, 'TELL ME MUNI, WHAT happened next?'

'The frail old Brahmana, who was Viswamitra himself, said to Harishchandra, "This is a very sacred tirtha, O Kshatriya. Anyone who bathes in it is cleansed of all his sins, and virtue springs up in him. I suggest you bathe here, and offer tarpana to your fathers on high. And give generous charity to the poor and deserving. For Svayambhu Manu has said, 'He who comes to a punya tirtha and does not perform ablutions and offer charity is a man who deceives himself, a slayer of his own soul.' So bathe, O Harishchandra of the House of the Sun, and then I will show you the way home to Ayodhya."

Poor, lost, Harishchandra did as he was told. He set aside his armour and his clothes, tied his horse to a tree, and entered the river to bathe. He offered tarpana to his fathers in heaven. When he came out, he said to the old mendicant, "My lord, now ask me for whatever charity you want, and it shall be yours. Land, horses and cows, gold and jewels, chariots and elephants, anything you want shall be yours."

The Brahmana said, "I have heard that there is no other man in all the world as generous as yourself, Harishchandra. My daughter has come of age, and I want to have her married. I beg you, give me enough wealth to perform the ceremonies."

"Decide on a date, Brahmana, and be sure that you shall have more than you ask for from me."

"The bride and her groom wait a short way from here, my lord, for I set out with them in search of a kindly patron."

When he dissolved the maya that created his demon boar, Viswamitra had made a handsome Brahmana youth and a comely young Brahmana girl, also with his tapasya-shakti. Now, he brought them to Harishchandra and said, "These are my daughter and the boy she will marry. Today is an auspicious day, my lord, and I mean to marry them straightaway. But do I have your word you will give the young man the wealth that I ask for as my daughter's dowry? Also, O King, you performed the Rajasuya yagna, and you must give me two and a half loads of gold as dakshina for myself."

"You have my sacred word on it, Brahmana, and may a curse fall on me if I don't give you whatever wealth you ask for, and the two loads and a half of gold, in addition. But first you must show me the way back to Ayodhya."

Viswamitra, the emaciated Brahmana, did so. Harishchandra went home in relief but, bright and early the next morning, even as he sat at his first sandhya puja of the day, the old Brahmana appeared in Harishchandra's agnishala, where the sacred fire burned. He came with his daughter and her young suitor, both the Muni's own creatures of illusion, though the king was not to know this. The king rose with a smile to welcome them. He embraced the Brahmana who had shown him his way home.

The Brahmana said, "My lord, I have married my child and the young man. I have come for the dowry you promised me."

"Tell me what you want, and you shall have more than what you ask."

Quietly, that Brahmana said, "Give my son-in-law your kingdom as his dowry, and your treasury, your granary, your army, your horses, indeed, everything you own. And, for dakshina, give me two and a half loads of gold."

Suddenly, the Brahmana stood transformed before him, and Harishchandra saw Viswamitra had tricked him. Numbly, he said, "All that was mine is yours, Muni."

He called his wife and his son Rohita, and told them what had happened. He said to Viswamitra, "Apart from our three lives everything in Ayodhya is now yours."

But Viswamitra said, "What about the gold you promised me as dakshina, O King?"

"I have given you everything I own, now where shall I go for gold?"

"You are a liar and a cheat, Harishchandra. You have broken your word to me," hissed the Muni.

Harishchandra said, "You shall have your gold, Dvija, be sure of it. I will not eat until I have given you the two and a half loads of gold. But you must wait a month, and I will pay you what I owe."

The Rishi laughed. "You have no kingdom, no treasury and no army left. How will you get the gold? I think it best you acknowledge that you cannot keep the oath you swore to me, and I will go away."

"Brahmana, be patient for a month, and you will have the gold you want. I still have my wife, my son, and myself. We three are healthy enough, and I will sell us to get you the gold I have promised you as dakshina. I beg you, inquire yourself if there is anyone who can buy us, and we shall be their slaves in return for the two loads and a half. I will return in a month, Muni."

Harishchandra took himself and his family to Varanasi, where the Lord Sankara dwells in spirit, with Uma. Just seeing Kasi filled that king with soft ecstasy. He went down to the Ganga, bathed in her and offered tarpana to the Devas and the Pitrs, and worshipped his own Ishta Devata. He then thought, no king rules Kasi, but only Siva; and Kasi was not part of the kingdom he had given away to Viswamitra. So Harishchandra, his wife Saivya and his son Rohita began living in Varanasi, in prayer to the Lord. But, when a month passed, Viswamitra appeared there, and said, "Where is the gold you promised me? A month has passed and you haven't given me my dakshina."

Harishchandra said, "Half a day remains of the month, wait just half a day and you shall have your gold."

"So be it. But if you don't keep your word when I return, I will curse you."

Harishchandra thought feverishly, "I am a Kshatriya, and I may not beg for money. Moreover, who will give me so much gold? But if I die without keeping my word, I will be born as a worm or a pisacha in my next life; for, I shall be damned with the sin of stealing a Brahmana's property."

He saw his wife Saivya weeping beside him. She sobbed, "My lord, you must keep your word to the Muni somehow. For, if a man breaks his oath, all his punya, all his tapasya comes to naught, and he is dragged down into hell. Why, Yayati performed the Rajasuya and the Aswamedha and found Swarga for himself. But he spoke just one lie and was cast down from heaven."

Harishchandra cried impatiently, "Say what you have to plainly, woman! Don't speak in riddles."

Saivya blurted, "I have given you a son, and my nature is fulfilled. So sell me, my lord, and give the gold you get for me as dakshina to the Muni."

But Harishchandra fainted just to hear this. When he awoke, he sobbed, "How can you say this to me? Have you forgotten all the sweet times we spent together? Ah, don't even think of it!"

And he swooned again. When Saivya saw him thus, she wailed, "Harishchandra, lord of the earth, look at you now! You were master of a great kingdom; you slept in a palace as big as a city, and gave away as charity what other kings hardly own. Oh, look at you now."

And she fell over him unconscious. Then, their small son Rohita began to cry, "Mother! Father! Feed me, I am hungry!"

Just then, Viswamitra appeared there again and sprinkled some water on the king's face. The Rishi cried, "Wake up, Harishchandra, and pay your debt to me. A man who owes money suffers great torments, that increase day by day."

The water was cold as snow, and Harishchandra awoke spluttering. But when he saw Viswamitra before him, he promptly fainted again. The Rishi dashed more cold water into the king's face and, at last, Harishchandra awakened with a groan. Viswamitra said, "It is the truth that makes the sun shine, and moves the earth in her place in the sky. Heaven is founded on the truth and the greatest dharma as well. If you weigh the punya of a thousand Aswamedha yagnas against a single truth spoken or done, the punya of the truth would outweigh the yagna by far. Do you know what I am saying, O King? If you don't give me my dakshina by sunset, I shall curse you. There is not much time left, Harishchandra, I will return at sunset."

With that, Viswamitra left again. Harishchandra was alarmed at the thought that the Rishi would curse him if he did not get his dakshina. But he was even more tormented to think that if he did not somehow give the Muni his gold by twilight, he would break his sacred word and violate the truth.

At this time, they saw a Brahmana passing by, who seemed like a man of some wealth. Saivya said to her husband, "My lord, a Brahmana is meant to be like a father to the other three varnas. A son can certainly ask his father for help in a time of need. Why not beg some gold from this Brahmana? There is no sin in it."

But Harishchandra said, "A Brahmana may beg, but it is forbidden to us Kshatriyas. I am a king, I cannot take alms from anyone, let alone from a Brahmana."

His wife said, "My lord, fate keeps some men in wealth, but others it throws on hard times. Fate alone makes kings and beggars, at different times, of the same man. It is fate that tests you, my husband, through the angry Muni who is meant to be a tapasvin and a master of his rage. You must bow to fate now. There is no sin in your begging for alms to pay the Rishi's dakshina."

But Harishchandra said, "I would rather cleave my tongue with a sword than beg for alms. I am a Kshatriya, I live by the strength of my arms."

His wife said quietly, "My lord, there is only one way by which you can pay the Muni's dakshina. You must sell me. It is in a noble cause, of keeping your sacred word, and no sin will come from it."

With a desperate sigh, his chest heaving, Harishchandra said, "Come, then, and let me do the thing that not the basest men stoop to."

He took her to the city's main thoroughfare, where all the shops were, and standing upon the pavement began to cry in a loud voice, "This woman is for sale! Does anyone need a maidservant? This lovely woman is for sale! She is my wife, and I mean to sell her for two loads and a half of gold!"

Some Brahmanas crowded around him, and asked, "Who are you, fellow?"

His eyes full of tears, Harishchandra replied, "I am a Rakshasa, friends, whom no one will call a man from today. But, speak to me only if you have the price to pay for my wife."

Viswamitra saw all this from a distance and, assuming the guise of an old Brahmana, came up to Harishchandra, and said, "I will pay half the price you want. Here it is, now give me the woman."

Harishchandra saw the man was a crude old fellow, but he was so relieved to have the gold he handed Saivya over at once. The old Brahmana seized her roughly by her hair and began to drag her away, when she cried, "Ah, let me look at my son's face a last time."

Sobbing, she said to her child, "Rohita, look, your mother is a slave now, and you mustn't touch her any more. I am going now, child, and I may never see you again. Look after your father for me."

Harishchandra was so stricken, he stood as if he had turned to stone. But Rohita cried out for his mother, and ran after her as the Brahmana hauled her away. Often, the child tripped and fell into the dust of the road, but he would pick himself up and run after Saivya again. Finally, he seized her garment in a small hand and would not leave it. He ran along with his mother. The old Brahmana grew annoyed, and began to slap the child.

Saivya screamed, "Have mercy, Brahmana! Buy my son as well, he cannot live without me. If I don't see my child's face, I won't be able to work for you."

The old man went to Harishchandra and said, "Here is some more gold, give me the child also."

Numbly, Harishchandra took the gold coins. But now Saivya fell at his feet and sobbed, "If I have been a chaste wife, may you be my husband again."

But Harishchandra could hardly speak for the thought of being separated from his son. He stood like a man who had been struck by lightning. He said to the Brahmana, "How will I live without my son? Why, I did not feel a thousandth part of the pain I am feeling now when I lost my kingdom." He turned to Saivya and wept, "Ah, my love, you were given to me by your father to be the queen of Ayodhya. And so you were. But now I have sold you into slavery. What fate could be crueller than this?"

But the old Brahmana growled, and began to drag the woman and the boy away, slapping them, now and again, or kicking them: they must learn how he treated his slaves. Harishchandra stood sobbing piteously, hardly able to believe the fate that had overtaken him, the king of the House of the Sun. When the old Brahmana had vanished with his wife and his child, and Harishchandra stood desolated, suddenly Viswamitra appeared before him, with his disciples in tow.

Harshly the Muni said, "The sun is sinking. Pay me the dakshina you owe or declare yourself a liar and a cheat."

Numbly Harishchandra handed him the gold he had, and said, "Here is your dakshina, Muni, as I promised."

Viswamitra said, "Where did you come by this gold?"

The king replied with a deep sigh, "Ah, don't ask me that."

"I will not take tainted gold. Tell me how you got these mohurs."

"I sold my wife and my son for this gold. Take it, Muni."

"This is only half what you owe me. Just a few hours remain of the day. Pay me what you promised, or declare yourself a liar and a cheat."

"My lord, I have sold my family to get you the gold. Wait till sunset, and you shall have the rest of it, as well."

The Rishi growled, "Very well, till sunset then. But, after that, be sure I will curse you if you haven't paid my dakshina in full."

He stalked away with his sishyas, and was lost in the crowd of the market place of Kasi,' Muni Vyasa told the king Janamejaya," says the Suta.

FORTY-SEVEN

WHEN HE WAS ALONE, HARISHCHANDRA BEGAN TO SIGH LIKE A SERPENT from a grief that would destroy him. In a while, he began to cry, "I am a preta now. If anyone wants to buy a preta for a slave, let him do it before nightfall."

It is told that Dharma Deva, the God of righteousness, decided to test Harishchandra's honesty. He came down to the street where that king stood, trying to sell himself. The Deva came in the guise of a coal-black Chandala, his skin rough, his features coarse, his hair crinkly, his belly enormous, his teeth like fangs, his face hidden in a thick beard, and stinking to high heaven. He held a bamboo staff in one hand, around his neck hung a necklace of bones, and his chest was hollow and scarred. Altogether hideous, the Deva came to Harishchandra and said in a grating voice, "I need a slave. Tell me, what price do you want for yourself?"

That Chandala looked so villainous the king asked him, "Who are you that wants to buy me?"

"I am Pravira the Chandala, and all the world knows me. When you are my slave, your task will be to steal the clothes from the corpses of the dead."

Harishchandra said, "I want to be bought by a Brahmana or a Kshatriya. I cannot observe my own dharma if I live in your house. You are low-born, and your dharma is low, as well."

The Chandala said, "Why did you say anyone can buy you, if you were so particular? You should have said that only a Brahmana or Kshatriya could buy you. Unless you are a liar, and go back on what you said first, then I have bought you in dharma. I will pay the price you ask, and you shall be my slave from now."

Harishchandra murmured, "He who lies goes straight to hell. To become a Chandala is far better than that."

As this was going on, Viswamitra arrived there, impatiently. He rolled his eyes and said, "The Chandala is willing to pay the money you owe me. Why are you hesitating?"

Harishchandra moaned, "Muni, you know who I am. This body of mine is born in the House of the Sun. How can I sell it in slavery to a Chandala?"

Viswamitra said between clenched teeth, "Be sure of my curse, if you don't. I don't care how you get the gold you owe me, but I must have it now. The sun is setting, Harishchandra, your time is almost up. If you don't pay me, I mean to burn you with fire from my eyes!"

Harishchandra fell at the Rishi's feet, and sobbed, "My lord, I beg you, don't be so harsh. Please don't make me this Chandala's slave, my very soul will be lost. Viswamitra, friend of the universe, take me for your own slave instead. I swear I will serve you humbly, till there is life in this body of mine."

Viswamitra did not hesitate, "Very well, be my slave from now."

Harishchandra wept for joy, as if his life had been saved. He cried, "Tell me what you want me to do, Muni, I am your slave from now."

Viswamitra turned to the Chandala, and said, "Give me the gold for this slave of mine. I will sell him to you."

The Chandala was delighted, and cried, "Dvija! I will cover you in gold and jewels." And so he did.

Viswamitra left with the treasure the Chandala gave him, and a voice spoke out of heaven to Harishchandra saying, "The dakshina is paid, you are free from your oath now."

But, now, the triumphant Chandala tied a rope around the king's throat, and dragged him away. He struck him, kicked him frequently, and abused him often. Overwhelmed with grief as he was, at losing his wife and son, Harishchandra fell unconscious on the road. When he awoke, he found himself in the Chandala's house, in chains.

That suffering king did not eat at all but wept without pause for his queen and his prince. He imagined his wife longing for him, living in the hope that he would come with gold and buy her back from the Brahmana. He saw his son's face before his eyes, calling to him, piteously. But what hope had Rohita of seeing his father again? His father was a vicious Chandala's slave.

Four days passed, and then the Chandala arrived in the room where Harishchandra languished. Greeting the king with a sundry slap or two, and a torrent of filthy abuse, he unfastened his chains, dragged him out into the open, and said, "Yonder is the smashana. Go and fetch me the clothes of the corpses that haven't been cremated but buried."

The Chandala handed the king a jarjara, a club, and sent him off to the cemetery, saying, "Tell anyone who asks that you are Viravahu's slave, and that he gave you this club."

The smashana lay to the south of the city of Kasi. It stank of rotting flesh and rotted garlands, and smoke issued over it from a hundred pyres. Jackal packs stalked that smashana, and their dismal howling echoed all around. There were kites and vultures, on the ground and in the air. Hyenas with yellow eyes slouched at the edges of that field of death. At times Harishchandra heard their maniacal laughter, and it seemed to him that some half-burnt corpse, its teeth exposed, was laughing at him.

Besides the dreadful noises the scavengers made, a sea of crying could be heard: a hundred relatives of the dead, wailing for lost husbands, wives, fathers, mothers, sons, brothers and sisters and friends. Flesh and fat, marrow and brain burned in the merry fires and their various smells rose into the air. Harishchandra heard some quaint popping sounds that punctuated the rest of the noises of death. He wondered at these, first, then realised it was the skulls of the dead exploding softly as the flames breached them.

There was enough grief and horror in that smashana to make a man believe that the universe was ending there. Harishchandra was overwhelmed and, squatting on the ground in misery, he began to sob again. "Ah, my ministers and generals, my servants and women, where are you all today when I need you most? Where is my kingdom and my army, my great treasury and my golden throne come down to me through the ages from Surya Deva himself?"

Gradually the storm of grief passed, and he remembered the ghastly task for which the Chandala, his master, had sent him here. In anguish, the king began to gather the clothes from the dead. The days passed. He grew lean and pale as a corpse himself, working at his demeaning task under the pitiless sun. He was covered in dust and ashes, like the most wretched Chandala himself, and soon he knew exactly how many gold coins each corpse's clothes would fetch. He wore a ragged cloth around his waist, with a score of patches, and his feet were smeared with burned flesh, blood, marrow and melted fat. He tied the garlands of the dead around his own head, and ate the food that was set out for them, as pinda for their last journey.

He hardly slept, and a year went by like a hundred.

Meanwhile, his son Rohita made some friends and, one day, when he went with them to play near the city of Kasi, he saw some kusa grass and began to pull them up. His companions asked him why he was doing this, and he replied, "My master is a Brahmana, and he can use these for his worship." And, then, the boy began to gather palasa branches as well. He made a bundle of these and, placing it on his head, set out for home.

That bundle was heavier than he could manage easily, and he felt thirsty. He saw a pool of water, and went to drink from it. He set the bundle of branches down on what looked like an old, hardened anthill. In fact, it was a snake pit, and Viswamitra had created it with his maya. When he had quenched his thirst at the pool, Rohitasva came to fetch his bundle of palasa and darbha, when out darted a king cobra from it and stung his hand. The boy fell down with a cry, turned blue in a moment, and died.

His friends, who saw all this, ran to the Brahmana's house, and called Saivya, who was now a maidservant there. They cried to her, "Come quickly, your son has died of snakebite."

She fell like a plantain tree cut down with a sword. The Brahmana arrived there, and threw some water on her face. When she sat up, she began to wail loudly. He gave her a slap and cried harshly, "Why are you crying, you wretch? Don't you know it brings misfortune to howl like this in the evening? The Devi Lakshmi will be angry, and she will curse me and my house."

But the queen only rolled in the dust again and wept. Soon, her face was covered with dirt, and her hair was loose and disheveled. But she wailed on. The Brahmana rounded on her again, and shouted, "Wretched woman! I paid so much gold for you, and now you will bring misfortune down on me. Why did you take my money, if you didn't want to work for me?"

And he gave her a kick or two. Then she managed to sob, "Brahmana, a snake has bitten my son, and he is dead! I beg you, let me go and see my child one last time, for I will never see him again."

"O Rakshasi! Don't you know that she who takes money for her keep and then does no work goes to the hell Raurava?" Being a Brahmana, he knew the details of the punishment for such a heinous crime. "After a short stay in that naraka, you will be born as a cockerel. Ah, but what use is it my telling a cheat and an ingrate all this, it is like sowing seeds in a desert. I say to you stop malingering, woman, if you have a care for your soul! Come in at once, and do your work."

But she cried, "I beg you master, let me go and see my son for just a moment. Let me touch his face one last time." She laid her head at his feet, and bathed them in tears.

But the Brahmana said, "Of what use will it be to me, if you go to see your son? You have forgotten my temper, woman. Do you want to feel my whip on your filthy hide again?"

He had whipped her once, and she had fainted from the pain. In terror, that queen went into the house and began to do her work, while she wept often. Night fell, she gave the Brahmana warm water for his bath, then his food, and then she pressed his feet until half the night was over. As he began to feel sleepy, the Brahmana said, "You can go now and cremate your son. Be sure to be back early in the morning."

With a cry of joy, she ran from the house, and all the way out of Kasi, in the direction the children had told her to go. The risen moon bathed the world in silvery ghostlight. She saw her child laid on the ground like a beggar's boy, lying on fallen leaves, and his bundle of palasa branches and kusa grass lying near him. The queen fell across her child's body and began to sob.

"Ah, why have you left me, my Rohita? How will I live now? As long as I heard your voice calling me, 'Amma! Amma!' I could stand every misfortune fate brought. But now how will I live? Ah, Harishchandra, where are you now? Don't you see your precious Rohita lying dead upon the earth? Come and look at him, my lord, ah, come and see our son."

And she fainted. When she opened her eyes again, she saw that her child still lay motionless. She said softly, "Rohita, my son, the hour is late. It is time for us to go home to sleep. Come, get up now, and let us go back to the Brahmana's house. It is almost time for the dew to fall, my child, and you will catch a cold. Ah, it is the hour of Yakshas and Bhutas, Rohita, can't your hear the jackals howling? I hear the dakinis and pisachas riding on the wind, in search of human blood to drink. Come, my child, get up, you can sleep at home now."

She spoke earnestly, and when he did not reply, she began to shake him and cry, "Why don't you answer me, you naughty child? We are slaves now, even your great father has sold himself to pay the Muni's dakshina. When the astrologers cast your horoscope at your birth, they told me of all the wonderful things that would happen to my prince. They were liars! Here you lie, clutched tight in death's embrace. They never told me this. They said you would be a mighty Kshatriya, a great king, a devout man, and they said you would have a long life. They showed me all the auspicious signs on your palm: the whorl and the fish, the lotus, the thunderbolt, the svastika, the flag, the jar and the umbrella. What have they all come to, today? That you lie in the dust like a beggar's boy who has died of starvation. Your face is caked in mud, and the fly-swarms are asleep on it, waiting for your sweet face to putrefy so they can begin their feast."

"Oh son, my Rohita!" she screamed over and over again. The wardens of the city of Kasi heard her in the night's last yaamas, and they came to where she lay wracked across her dead child.

The wardens asked her, "Who are you, woman? Whose child is this? Where is your husband? How are you here, at this hour? Aren't you afraid?"

But she only sobbed dementedly in reply. Then the guards grew afraid themselves, their hair stood on end.

They walked a short way from the queen, and one of them whispered, "She isn't speaking. She must be a Rakshasi to be out here at this hour."

"I've heard of her kind, they are vampires that drink children's blood."

"She brought the child here to devour him."

They laid hold of queen Saivya, and dragged her to the Chandala's house. They roused him from his sleep and said, "We have brought you a child-eating Rakshasi. Take her to the slaughter-house and have her killed."

The Chandala held up a torch, and peered closely at the queen. Rolling his eyes, he said, "I know this Rakshasi well. She has killed more than a hundred children, and we have been looking for her for years. You will all have great punya, when we cut her head off and burn her body. Go back to your homes now, I will deal with the demoness."

The Chandala seized the queen by her hair, and began to whip her with a length of rope. He woke his slave, Harishchandra, and ordered him, "Kill this woman, she is a murderess."

But, though Harishchandra did not recognise his wife, he shuddered at the thought of killing a woman. He said, "Master, let one of your other servants do this thing. I cannot kill a woman, however evil she may be."

But the Chandala growled, "You will find not sin but a great blessing for yourself, if you kill this monster. She eats the flesh of small children."

But the king said, "Women are meant to be cared for, never killed. Any man who kills a woman burns in maha raurava."

"Quiet, slave! When you kill a fiend like this, you have the blessings of the whole world. Here, take this axe and hew off her head. All Kasi will bless you."

"Master, I swore in my childhood never to kill a woman."

"Villain, no oath is greater than your master's command. If you don't do as I say, you will find yourself in Raurava anyway."

Harishchandra begged him, "Give me any other task you will, master. Have you an enemy you want murdered? I am the man for you. Just tell me his name and he will be dead by evening. Why, even if Indra and his Devas, the Danavas and Uragas, the Kinnaras, Siddhas and Gandharvas came to fight you, I would face them all for your sake, master. But, I beg you, don't ask me to kill a woman."

"How dare you?" cried his master. "You are the slave of a lowly Chandala, and you speak of Devas and Danavas, Gandharvas and Siddhas? If you were so proud, why did you sell yourself to be a slave in a Chandala's house? Not a word more, take this axe and off with her head."

Meanwhile, neither the king or the queen recognised one another, they had both been transformed so much in a year. Harishchandra looked every bit the Chandala slave who stole the clothes from corpses in the burning ghat, and Saivya like a Rakshasi, indeed, with her hair all wild and her face caked in ashes and dirt.' said Veda Vyasa to the Kuru king," says Romaharshana Suta.

FORTY-EIGHT

"SIPPING SOME WATER, VYASA CONTINUED, 'AXE IN HAND, HARISHCHANDRA led the queen outside, and said, "Young woman, I must be a great sinner indeed that I have to do this heinous thing. Come and sit before me. If my hands find the courage they will cut off your head, and may God forgive me."

She cried, "Chandala! I beg you, listen to me for a moment. My child is lying dead in a field outside the city. Let me fetch him here, and cremate him in your burning ghat. Then you can cut off my head, and I will die gladly."

Harishchandra said, "Very well. We will go and burn your child, and then I'll do what I have to."

So he went with her to where his son lay dead from the serpent's bite. Saivya had covered her child with a cloth and, when the king pulled the cloth away from the child's face, he saw how noble that young face was. Yet, so much had anguish transformed his very mind that, for a moment, he did not recognise his son.

Strangely moved, he muttered, "Every auspicious sign is upon this child. Why, he may be a prince, he is so beautiful. His face is noble, his limbs are long and fine, and his hands are strong and elegant. Surely, he was born in some royal House of the world."

Squatting impulsively on the ground, the king took the child's head on to his lap, while queen Saivya stood by, sobbing uncontrollably again. The moment Harishchandra's fingers touched his dead child's face, remembrance flooded over him. He gave a dreadful cry, and began to wail, "Oh! This is my own son, my Rohita! My child, what sin did you ever commit that you have died of a serpent's sting?"

At which, Saivya peered at him closely, and recognised her husband. She fell into his arms sobbing, "My Lord! It is you. Ah, look at you, great king, what fate has reduced you to. She has made a Chandala of you."

And she swooned. And, when he knew her, he fainted, to think he had been about to cut off her head. When he came to his senses again, he flung himself across Rohita's body and wept.

Saivya took him in her arms tenderly, and said, "My lord, tell me how you came to this pass, to be a Chandala's slave."

Sobbing, he told her what had become of him after he had sold her to the Brahmana. She wept more than ever to hear him. Queen Saivya moaned, "I have worshipped the Devi Gauri, and every other God, that you will be my husband again in our next birth."

He wailed still louder at this. "Ah! My soul is on fire, but I can't even kill myself, for I shall be born as a Chandala's slave again, in my next birth. Besides, he who kills himself goes to a worse hell than the one he is in on earth. But what hell could be worse than this world, when my precious child is dead? Nowhere in all the worlds is there any agony like losing a son. Yes, I shall put an end to myself, I will throw myself into the same fire that consumes my child."

He turned to his wife again, "Go back to the Brahmana's house. All is lost in this life. But, if I have been a man of dharma at all, we three shall be united again in the next life. I beg you, my love, if I have ever offended you in any way, forgive me now, at this hour of parting. Pray, pray, Saivya, that we meet again. Forget that you were ever a queen. Look on your master as a Deva, serve him faithfully; that is your way to salvation."

Saivya cried, "Ah, my lord, I too will burn myself on your pyre, and go with you to the next world, whether it be to heaven or hell."

Grimly, Harishchandra piled some firewood into a funeral pyre, and lifted his dead child onto it. Then, the king and queen sat beside it in padmasana, and worshipped the Devi Bhagavati, Queen of the Universe, who reigns within the five sheaths, who is an ocean of mercy. As they chanted her thousand sacred names, Indra and his Devas appeared in that cremation ground. With them came the Maharishis, the Sadhyas, the Maruts, the Lokapalas, the Charanas, the Nagas, Gandharvas, Siddhas, Rudras, the Asvins, and Brahmarishi Viswamitra himself.

Dharma Deva, the God of justice, arrived there and said, "Harishchandra, your truth is immaculate. There is no cause to kill yourself."

Indra said, "You have conquered all the worlds, that you have conquered yourself. You shall sit beside me on the throne of Devaloka, Rajarishi. There is no man like you in all this world. You, your wife and child shall come into my heaven."

The Lord of the Devas sprinkled some amrita over Rohitasva's corpse, and, at once, that prince rose from the dead. With a cry, Harishchandra and Saivya clasped their child to them, and their tears fell on his radiant face. The child looked as if he had had a deep and refreshing sleep. Wonderfully, Harishchandra and his Saivya were also restored to their regal forms. Their appearance were of a great king and queen of the earth; they wore silken garments and golden ornaments and jewels upon their bodies.

Indra said to them, "Come into Devaloka with me."

But Harishchandra said, "My master, the Chandala, must be waiting for me. He must give me freedom before I can go with you."

Dharma Deva laughed, and, then, he was the coarse Chandala before the astounded king. He said, "I release you from your bondage, it was only a test of your heart."

Saivya said, "My master, the Brahmana, waits for me. I was sold fairly to him. I cannot abandon him now."

Then, Viswamitra showed himself as the Brahmana, and as the serpent that stung Rohita. The Rishi said, "I was wrong about you, Harishchandra, you have passed every test I put you to. There is no man on earth or any Muni in heaven or earth, I dare say, who can match your perfect dharma. Vasishta was right about you, you are truly a just man."

Indra said again, "Come, Harishchandra, my vimana waits to take you into the realm of the Gods."

The king folded his hands, and said, "My Lords, hear me a moment. My people of Kosala wait anxiously for me to return to them. How can I leave them, and go away even to Devaloka? They depend on me, they have need of me, and I cannot abandon them. There is no worse sin than if I did. I cannot hope to be happy even in your blessed realm, if I forsake my people, who love me. My fate is bound with theirs; they are like my own children. Where they are, so must I be, whether it is on earth, in heaven or hell. Only if they can all come into Devaloka with me, I shall go with you, my Lord Indra."

"But, there are both sinners and virtuous men among your people. How can all of them come into Swarga with you?"

"A king's strength is his people, without them he is nothing. So, my Lord, if not all my people are virtuous enough to go into Swarga, let the punya I have be divided equally among them. So, if I was to live a hundred years in Devaloka by my punya, let that time be reduced to even a day, so my people are forgiven their sins and find heaven."

A shower of petals fell out of the sky, celestial music sounded in the azure vaults, and the very earth cried out great Harishchandra's name, the trees and mute rocks.

Indra said, "Peerless Kshatriya, let all your people of your generation, and the old, find Devaloka for this great sacrifice of yours. And, in no way, shall your punya be diminished, not by a single deed or moment."

The Gods and Viswamitra with them, that Muni most pleased of all, arrived in Ayodhya instantaneously by the Devas' power. That ancient city was lit up as if the sun had risen in its streets. The people gathered round their king and queen and the shining Gods, in awe. Indra, Lord of Devaloka, said to them, "You shall all come into Swarga with us today, for the dharma of your king."

Grace flowed from the Devas and every sinner in that city was healed of his sins. They all shone like Gods themselves. Rohita was installed as the new king of Ayodhya and, so, too, the men of that city gave away everything they owned to their sons and daughters. Then the sky seemed to part, and from it flew down a great and shimmering vimana, large as a city itself. The people of Kosala, their king and queen, rose into that craft and flashed away up into the realm of Gods.

When Sukra Bhargava saw half a city fly up into Devaloka in the luminescent vimana he said to the Daityas who are his pupils, "Look at this miracle. Nothing like it has ever happened before on earth, that a whole nation has been saved by one man's suffering. Time tried Harishchandra to the ends of human endurance, through Viswamitra and Dharma Deva, but he never lost his faith. And now he is like a God himself, he shall sit beside Indra on his ruby throne."

O King, the name of great Harishchandra is an immortal one. Why, he who merely hears this story has his sins taken from him, and peace comes to his spirit. It is a magical tale, and those who study it have all their hearts' desires fulfilled, in time, whatever they may be. The childless shall be blessed with sons and daughters, the unhappy shall find inexplicable joy, and the indigent shall find wealth. Kings who have lost their kingdoms shall regain them, why, beggars become like kings if they hear the story of Harishchandra and understand its deep meaning, and those who want even heaven for themselves, will surely find Swarga.' said Vyasa Muni by the river," says Suta.

FORTY-NINE

SUTA CONTINUES, "AT HIS YAGNA, JANAMEJAYA ASKED THE MUNI VYASA, 'Guru, I have heard the Devi Parvati is called Sataksi, thousand-eyed. How did she get this name?'

Dwaipayana, my master, said, 'In time out of mind, when all beings were immensely greater than they are in these diminished times, there was a Danava called Durgama. He was Ruru's son, born in direct descent in the line of the awesome Hiranyaksha, who plunged the earth into the primal waters, and then Mahavishnu came as the Varaha to lift her out of the black Ekarnava, into light and grace again.

Durgama once thought to himself that the Munis who sustain dharma in the three worlds have their strength from the Vedas. For, it is with mantras and yagnas prescribed in the sacred books that they worship the Devas, who, in turn, are sustained by their worship. If the Vedas could be destroyed, that Demon calculated, so could the Munis' power, and, thus, the Devas themselves could be destroyed.

Durgama took himself to the loftiest Himalaya and sat in a freezing drift of snow, and began an intense, unequalled tapasya. He worshipped Brahma, the Pitamaha of creation, the Creator of all the races, in the space within his heart. Unflinching, never opening his eyes, breathing just once or twice every hour, and then, only as many times every day, that great Demon sat yoked into his single, obsessive purpose.

A thousand years passed, and the Asura's dhyana grew so powerful that the tejas, the lustre from his head spiralled through the three worlds as subtle fire. All the finer realms were pervaded by this heat, and the Devas grew terrified. No God can ignore such a tapasya as Durgama sat in, and, at the end of the thousand years, Brahma appeared before that Danava in a coruscating form that lit up the very mountain on which he sat. The Pitama arrived mounted on his white swan.

Durgama was dazzled by the splendour of the four-faced apparition, and, opening his eyes, prostrated his emaciated form before the Creator.

Brahma said, "Ask what boon you want of me, Asura, and it shall be yours."

"Lord of worlds," replied the Demon, "let the Vedas belong just to me. Let the power of every mantra in all four Vedas suffuse me, so that I can conquer the Devas, and be sovereign of the worlds. From this moment, let no one else have the Vedas but me."

After his searing penance, Brahma could not refuse what he asked. Brahma, the author of the Vedas, flinched to hear what that Demon wanted, but he said, "Let it be so," and vanished.

At once, the Brahmanas forgot the Vedas. No longer did they perform the sacred rituals that keep harmony in all things, and peace and light in the world. No more did they offer worship to the Devas. The rites of sandhya, homa, sraddha, yagna, japa, and all the rest became extinct, as if they had never been. No longer did the Gods receive the havis that makes them strong, and with which they, in turn, nurture the worlds.

A dreadful cry arose from Swarga, Bhumi, and Patala, as if the very soul of creation had perished. The Brahmanas trembled for strange oppression, and wailed, "How has this happened?"

Soon, everything was to be explained. The Asura Durgama, radiant with the immense power of the Vedas, shining like ten suns, arrived at the gates of Amravati and blew an echoing challenge on his war-conch, like the thunder of the apocalypse. The Devas were so weak, they fled from the Demon, knowing they could not fight him in their condition. Indra and his people hid in the secret caverns of Mount Sumeru, and began to worship the Parashakti, the Devi Bhagavati.

Meanwhile, with the Brahmanas having lost the Vedas, all homa ceased on earth. Great epidemics stalked the world, terrible plagues visited the sons of men, and even the natural beasts suffered since not a drop of rain fell. Rivers and pools, tanks and lakes all ran dry; a savage drought swept the earth. Indeed, for ten years this drought lasted and millions perished, man and beast, bird and insect, and even the plants of the world, all except the eldest trees that plunge their roots into Patala itself and sustain themselves on the darkling waters of the nether-realm.

Corpses and bones were strewn across the lands, and, in the case of men, no one could be found to perform the last rites, or even set the dead alight, so their souls may be gathered to their fathers on high. The Brahmanas of the earth met together and climbed the blessed Himalaya, and, there, sat in tapasya to the Devi Bhagavati. Ceaselessly they chanted her sacred names, and begged her to save the world.

At last, pleased by their devotion, the Devi appeared before those Brahmanas one day. She was effulgent; she was black as kohl. She was four-armed, with a bow and a quiver, a lotus and the bright seeds of life in four hands. She was entirely beautiful and, when the Brahmanas prostrated themselves at her feet and begged her to help them, it is told the Devi suddenly had a thousand eyes all over her dark body. These eyes were wide open and full of grief to see her bhaktas' misery. She began to weep from those thousand eyes, and her tears flowed as precious streams and rivers, down into the world.

Then, she raised her fourth hand, and scattered the divine seeds she had in them everywhere. From them sprang up fruit trees and every kind of plant and vegetable, grass and grain, all over the famined world. The Devi's tears rose into heaven as vapour and thunderstorms lashed the parched earth, which drank down the life-giving waters in gratitude.

When all this happened in less time that it takes to tell, the Devas also emerged from the caves on Sumeru where they huddled in fright like hunted animals. They drank the tears of the Devi's mercy, and were renewed by them. And, with the Brahmanas, they, too, began to hymn the Mother of the universe. She fed them unearthly roots and fruit with her own hands, and they had their strength back.

For her thousand eyes that wept in mercy, the Devi was called Sataksi, and for the precious green food she gave the starving Brahmanas and Devas, and, indeed, the Earth, she was called Sakambhari. Now, the Devas and Brahmanas implored her, "Mother, restore the Vedas to us, or how will we sustain even ourselves, let alone the three worlds?"

Meanwhile, the sinister Durgama, who ruled in Amravati now, heard the thunderstorm of the Devi's tears, he saw lightning gash the sky, and knew that danger threatened. That Demon set out for the Himalaya with an army of a thousand aksauhinis. Seeing him come, the Devas and Brahmanas cried to the Devi in terror, "Save us, Bhagavati, or we die!"

Smiling, she drew a luminous circle of protection around them with her hand. She stayed outside the circle herself. Durgama and his army arrived, and a frenzied battle broke out. The face of the sun was covered with blizzards of arrows, so darkness fell over the world, and the archers of both sides could not see clearly any more. But when the astras of the two armies fused in the sky, it seemed a thousand suns had risen in place of the one obscured, and brilliant light flooded the earth. The mountain shook with the virile twanging of bowstrings.

Pierced with a thousand Asura shafts, the Devi gave a scream to freeze the rivers of the mountain. She grew vaster still, brighter still, and now, from her body there issued the Mahashaktis, the ferocious Goddesses: Kalika, Tarini, Sodasi, Tripura, Bhairavi, Kamali, Bagala, Matangi, Kamakshi, Tulaja Devi, Jambhini, Mohini, Chinnamasta and ten thousand Guhya Kalis. They sprang howling from the black body of the Devi Bhagavati in a moment.

And, in a moment too, the rampaging Shaktis consumed a hundred Demon aksauhinis, of some million Danavas and Daityas, with fire, calid banks of arrows, immense swords that hewed the heads off ten thousand demons at once, and some of the more savage Goddesses swept up a thousand Asuras and stuffed them into mouths wide as valleys, and chewed on them, their screams echoing from sheer mountainsides, and their blood flowing down the Shaktis' jowls like betel-juice.

Durgama's roars shook heaven and earth, and woke the Nagas in Patala from their slumbers of a thousand years. In a froth he charged the Shaktis with his other nine hundred legions. Ten days and nights that battle lasted, and not only the Ganga, the Brahmaputra, and their tributaries flowed down the white Himalaya now, but new rivers, shining scarlet under sun and moon. On the tenth night, Durgama performed a long and potent ritual of darkness, invoking the Atharva Veda, and, on the eleventh morning, he came to battle smeared in red sandalwoodpaste, wearing vermilion garlands, like a crimson mountain himself. He came in his black crystal chariot like a second ominous sun risen at dawn.

With the arcane strength from the Vedas coursing through his body, the great Asura faced the Mahashaktis. They fought for barely an hour and then those elemental women fled from him, for he was irresistible. Durgama came face to face, at last, with the Devi Bhagavati. They were like two figures out of a cosmic dream of darkness and light: the Devi entirely beautiful, serene and effulgent, and the Demon dread incarnate, evil embodied. For twelve hours they fought and, while they did, the earth no longer rotated on her axis, so terrific was their contention. The sun stood still at his zenith gazing down in awe at that battle. The Devas and Brahmanas, the spirits of the Himalayas, the Gandharvas and Kinnaras, the Charanas and Yakshas, and the Asuras whom the Shaktis had not slain, all cowered in terror at its ferocity.

Then, with a roar that sent avalanches hurtling down the mountain slopes, the Devi loosed fifteen sizzling arrows at Durgama, in the blink of an eye. The first four killed the Asura's horses, the fifth beheaded his sarathy, the sixth and seventh put out Durgama's eyes, the eighth cut down his flagstaff, the ninth and tenth severed his arms, and the last five smashed into his heart, so it blew apart in an explosion of blood. The Demon fell at the Devi's feet, and, as the Devas and Brahmanas watched wonderstruck a lucific light, of his spirit, emerged from his body, and merged with the Bhagavati.

The Devas and Rishis fell on their faces before the Devi and sang her praises. They saw that, in her delicate hands, which had strewn the seeds of plants across the earth there shone something else now, blinding. With an ineffable smile, she returned the Vedas to the Brahmanas, and vanished. And because she slew the Demon Durgama, she was known as Durga from then on,' said Vyasa Muni," says the Suta.

FIFTY

"VYASA SAID, 'THE DEVI BHAGAVATI IS THE KERNEL WITHIN THE HUSK that is all the other Gods. She is the Parashakti who sets men free from the bondage of birth and death. She is the highest Deity, and the final aradhana any man can aspire to; the ultimate worship and bliss is when his heart is melted into the Parashakti, which is the Devi.'

Janamejaya asked, 'The Bhagavati came as Uma, Lakshmi and Saraswati for Siva, Vishnu and Brahma. How is it, my lord, that Uma and Lakshmi were also daughters of a mountain and the sea?'

'Once, there were some Danavas called the Halahalas. They were terrible past imagining, and as powerful. They had a boon from Brahma with which they conquered the three worlds, drove the Devas from Amravati and then laid siege to Kailasa and Vaikuntha.

Siva and Vishnu came forth to fight the Asuras, and a stupendous battle ensued, that lasted sixty thousand years. At last, the two great Gods slew the demons, and returned to their homes. And they boasted about their exploit to their wives, Gauri and Lakshmi. In truth, finally, the Goddesses themselves had subtly infused their lords with their own irresistible Shaktis, and it was thus that the Halahalas were slain. So, when Vishnu and Rudra bragged about their victory, their women laughed softly at them, with a trace of gentle scorn.

Growing incensed, and deluded by Parashakti, the Gods spoke in anger to their women, they even abused them. Whereupon Gauri and Lakshmi left their husbands and vanished. At once, with their Shaktis gone, the two Gods grew wan and dull. Their power, all their majesty, faded in a moment, and they became like two beggars, or madmen even. They gnashed their teeth and cried out all sorts of wild nonsense, and there was chaos in heaven and earth, and in the nether realms as well.

The Devas, and indeed all the living, were gripped by strange panic. Day and night no longer followed each other with order, but the sun was a wayward spirit in the sky, and so too the moon and the stars. Thunderstorms lashed the earth, and the oceans of the world breached their shores in fury and swept over the continents. Icy mountains spewed lava from their crowns, and the homes of men and beasts were threatened.

Brahma saw all this and grew anxious. He was obliged to assume Vishnu and Siva's tasks as well. He feared the pralaya had come betimes, and that all of careful creation and long, delicate time, would be laid waste. He called his son Manu and the Rishis, Daksha, Sanaka and the others, and said to them, "Bring peace again to Vishnu and Siva. I am bound with too many tasks, and cannot do this myself. Worship the Parashakti, for, it is by her wrath the two Gods are desolated."

The Rishis took themselves to a Himalayan forest and, there, began to chant the bija mantra of the Devi Bhagavati, without pause. A hundred thousand human years passed. At last, the Devi appeared before them. She was three-eyed and of the triune form of Satchitananda, absolutely merciful.

Overwhelmed, the Munis prostrated themselves at her feet, and cried, "O Mother of the universe, bless us!"

She said, "Ask me for anything, Munis, I am pleased with your tapasya."

They said, "Bhagavati, be united again with Hari and Hara."

Daksha said, "Be born as my daughter and marry Rudra."

Another Muni said, "Be born as the daughter of the ocean, and be Vishnu's Shakti again."

The Goddess murmured, "Hari and Hara are paying for their own pride. They must repent. I will give them the Maya mantra, soon, and they shall have their Shaktis again."

And she vanished before their eyes. Daksha and the Munis came to Brahma, and told him what the Devi had said. When Vishnu and Siva were told, they were contrite, and their arrogance left them like a spirit in the night. The Devi blessed them, and they had back their former splendour; and harmony and peace were restored to creation, for, the Trimurti ruled again.

Then, in time, the Devi herself was born to Daksha Prajapati and his wife Asikni, as a brilliant child. The quarters were tranquil when she was born, the three worlds were suffused with grace, the sky echoed with the sound of the Devas' dundubhis, and the air was laden with the subtle music of Gandharvas. The rays of the sun were like shafts of bright crystal, somehow purer that the Devi had been born as a child of flesh and blood. The winds were auspicious and fragrant that day, as were Devaloka, Bhumi and Patala. A sacred current coursed through creation and bliss pervaded all things and creatures. Why, the mute rocks seemed to sing for ecstasy that she, the immaculate one, had been born to be Siva's bride.

Siva lived as Rudra on white, mystic Kailasa, which communes with the stars. Daksha and Asikni named their daughter Sati, for she was an embodiment of the truth, and, when she came of age, they gave her to Siva to be his bride. But, ill omens attended the wedding of Siva and Sati, for the planets were not worshipped, as they should be before the marriage rites. Siva himself was too eager, after being separated from his Shakti for an age, to return to his home in Kailasa with her, and, indeed, to make love with her. This haste was inauspicious, and Daksha, who was loth to be parted from his child whom he doted fiercely on, was unhappy.

Now Daksha Prajapati, sire of the races of the earth, was not above being arrogant himself. After he gave his exquisite Sati away to Siva, he began to compare himself to his son-in-law and, indeed, to envy him. Once, at a certain yagna the Devas held, Siva and Sati did not rise to greet Daksha when he entered the yagnashala. It would have been sacrilege to do so, since they attended the yagna as Mahadeva and his immortal Shakti, and not as Daksha's daughter and son-in-law. They were his superiors, and he would have been cursed if they paid any homage to him, by rising or bowing.

But that Muni was incensed. He screamed at Siva, "All the yagna rises to greet him when Daksha Prajapati enters, but not his own half-naked son-in-law, who lives in a burning ghat, his body smeared with ashes, his hair matted in filthy jata, snakes coiled round his body, and bhutas and pretas his only friends. Arrogant fool, I rue the day I gave my daughter to you. I sinned when I did, and this is my payment for that sin!"

Siva's bull, Nandiswara, roared at Daksha, "Vainglorious Prajapati, it is the Parabrahmam whom you dare curse. May you and your race of Brahmanas lose the Vedas one day. In the Kali yuga, witless wretch, your kind shall still chant the Holy Scriptures, but you will have forgotten their inner meaning! And, in this life, you shall have a goat's head for what you dared say to my Lord."

"I expel your naked master from the yagna!" hissed Daksha, and stalked out from the sacrifice.

"Siva is the yagna, fool!" Nandiswara roared after him.

Daksha was so angry that, soon, he held another yagna of his own, on the banks of the golden Ganga. It was an unparalleled sattra, and he called all the Devas and Rishis to it. He called all the Brahmanas and Gandharvas, the Siddhas and Charanas. Everyone who was anyone was present at Daksha's yagna, but he did not call Siva, or Sati.

One morning, a few days before the yagna began, Sati saw her sister Rohini passing the Himalaya with her Lord Soma, the Moon. She sent a sakhi to ask Rohini where she was going clad in her finery.

Soma said to the sakhi, "Why, we are going to Daksha's sattra. Aren't Siva and Sati going?"

The sakhi brought this news back to Sati, who ran to Siva with it. She was in tears when she came into the crystal cave where her lord sat among his ganas. Siva made her sit beside him, and wiped her tears. He asked in concern, "What has happened, my love? Why are you crying?"

She sobbed, "My father is holding a great yagna beside the Ganga. All the Devas and Rishis have been called, Brahma and Hari have been invited. But not us, Siva."

Siva said gently, "Your father thinks of me as his enemy."

"Oh no, I am his daughter, you are his son-in-law; how can he think of us as enemies? It is just that one does not formally invite one's nearest and dearest ones, but takes it for granted they will come. Come, my lord, let us not waste any time. The sattra is to begin tomorrow, we must set out at once."

But Siva said, "I will not go to Daksha's sattra. I tell you, he thinks of me as his enemy, and he has not called us purposely, to insult you and me."

But Sati sobbed, "My lord, he is my father, how can I not go to his yagna?"

"You can go, if you like. Take Nandin and some ganas with you, take my vimana and attend your father's sacrifice. But I will not come."

So, with some of her sakhis and some of Siva's ganas, Sati set out in Siva's vimana for her father's yagna. Nandiswara went before her through the air as a great and resplendent bull. As she left, Siva clasped her in his arms, and a pang of anxiety wrung his heart. But he said nothing of it at the hour of her leaving. Indeed, this was the first time they had been parted since the day they were married, and Sati went weeping from Kailasa.

She arrived at Daksha's glorious yagnashala, where the Gods and sages had gathered to bless the Prajapati's yagna. Daksha and Asikni were radiant today, and everything was quite splendid. Her mother Asikni, and her sisters, the nakshatras, ran forward to embrace Sati. But Daksha ignored her, and glowered at his wife and other daughters, so they quickly left Sati alone.

She cried in dismay, "Father, why are you ignoring me? Aren't I your daughter, too? Why did you not invite Siva and me to your sattra?"

He replied, "Invite that half-naked upstart yogin! I am not mad to call every beggar on earth to my yagna. This is a solemn and auspicious occasion, I shan't have a naked fellow covered with ashes and serpents, who has no mother or father, at my yagna." Then, he softened, "But you are our daughter, and you may have your share of the havis, but not as that smashanavasi's wife."

Sati said in deadly calm, "He who speaks like this of Siva, the dust from whose feet the Devas wear on their heads, must surely go to hell. And those who listen unprotesting to him. My Lord was right when he said you were his enemy, I should not have come here. I am defiled by your arrogance, father. I should have stayed with my husband, for now I cannot return to him. I am still your daughter, your flesh and blood, though I would not be. O evil father, how I hate myself that I am your child!"

Her eyes blazed, and she said, "Look, I cast off this body born from your loins as if it were a corpse. I shall be my Lord's wife again when I am born to a father I can love."

Sati grew awesomely still. She sipped holy water, covered herself, head and face, with her garment and, thinking of Siva, she entered into a yogic trance. She balanced the winds, pana and apana; she lifted the third wind, udana, from her umbilical chakra up through her heart, through her throat, and fixed it between her eyebrows. In a flash, a fire from within consumed her body and it fell apart in pale ashes.

When Siva heard what had happened, his roar shook heaven and earth. From his body, he extruded the dreadful gana Virabhadra, and also a Shakti black as the void, terrible Bhadrakali, with wild elephants for her earrings. With a thousand other ganas, those two came howling down upon Daksha's yagna, and devastated it. With their Lord's power, they killed most of the Devas and Munis. Virabhadra struck Vishnu down, and Brahma fled. Finally, Virabhadra and Bhadrakali caught Daksha, as he tried to flee, and plucked his head off with their nails. Then, for a time they kicked his head back and forth between themselves in a ghoulish game.

At last, Siva himself materialised there, and the Devas and Rishis that remained alive fell at his feet and begged his forgiveness that they had come to Daksha's yagna, when the haughty Prajapati had not invited him; more than anything, that they had stood apart when Sati consumed herself with fire. Siva forgave them; he restored all those whom Virabhadra, Bhadrakali and their ganas had slaughtered.

Then, he asked, "Where is Daksha?"

Virabhadra brought that Prajapati's head and flung it down before Siva, with a grin. The other Rishis begged the Lord to forgive Daksha, and restore his life. And Siva, who is always Sankara the Merciful, did so. He had the sacrificial goat beheaded, and gave his father-in-law that goat's head, and his life back.

Then Siva took up Sati's ashes; he wore her delicate bones around his neck as a garland, and ranged the earth like a mad man, howling in grief. It is told he fell into the Yamuna, and that river was burned its midnight-blue colour from his sorrow. And as Siva roamed the earth, east and west, north and south, dementedly, Sati's ashes fell from his hands across the Holy Land, and wherever they fell the very earth became sacred in the Devi's name, and those tirthas are called Siddhapithas.'

'Which are they, O Muni?' asked Janamejaya.

Vyasa said, 'Those Pithas of Sati's ashes destroy the sins of men who worship at them, by the Devi Bhagavati's grace. Men who sit in dhyana at Pithas gain great siddhis, and peace comes to their spirits. The ashes of Sati's face fell in Kasi, and she is known as Visalakshi in that holiest tirtha. Her ashes that fell in the Naimisa vana are called Linga Dharini, in Prayaga as the gentle Lalitha Devi; in Gandhamadana she is known as Kamuki; in the southern Manasa as Kumudaa, in the northern Manasa as Viswakamaa; in Gomata as Gomati, and as Kamacharini upon the Mandara mountain. In Chaitraratha, the Devi is called Madotkataa, in Hastinapura as Jayanti, in the Kanyakubja as Gauri, upon the Malaya range as Rambha; in the Ekamprita as Kirtimati, and in Viswe as Visweswari.

She fell upon sacred Pushkara too, and there she is known as Puruhutaa; she is called Sanmarga Dayini in the Kedara Pitha, and Mandaa upon the highest crown of the Himalaya, as Bhadrakarnikaa in Gokarna. She is Bhavani in Sthaneswara, Vivapatrikaa in Vilvake; in Srisaila as Madhavi, as Bhadraa in Bhadreswari. In Kamalalaya, she is Kamala, Jaraa in the Varaha Saila, as Rudranila in the Rudrakoti, and as Kali in Kalanjara. She is Mahadevi in

Salagrama, Jalapriyaa in Sivalingam, Kapilaa in Mahalingam, Mukteswari in Makota, Kumari in Mayapuri, Lalitambika in Sanatana, Mangalaa in Gaya, and Vimala in Purushottama.

In Sahasraksha, she is Utpalakshi, in Hiranyaksha she is Mahotpalaa; she is Amoghakshi along the river Vipasa, Patalaa in Pundra Vardhana, Narayani in Suparshva, Rudra Sundari in Trikta, Vipula Devi in Vipula, Kalyani in Malayachala. In Sahyadri, she is called Ekaviraa, in Harishchandra she is Chandrika; she is Ramanaa in Ramatirtha, Mrigavati upon the Yamuna. At Kotatirtha, she is Kotivi, Sugandhaa in Madhavavana; on the Godavari, she is Trisandhyaa, Ratipriyaa in Gangadvara.

In Siva Kundam, she is Subhanandaa, Nandini in Devikatataa; she is Rukmini in Dvaravati, Radha in Vrindavana. In Mathura, she is Devaki, Parameswari in Patala; in Chitrakuta, she is Sita, Vindhyadivasini upon the Vindhya Mountain. In holy Karavira, she is worshipped as Mahalakshmi, as Uma Devi in Vinayaka; she is Arogyaa in Vaidyanatha, Maheswari in Mahakala.

In all the Ushnatirthas, she is Abhayaa, Nitambaa, also, in the Vindhya ranges; in Mandavya, she is Mandavi, Svaha in Maheswaripura. In Chagalanda, she is dreadful Prachandaa, Chandika in Amarakantaka; in Someswara, she is Vararohaa, Pushkaravati in Prabhasa. In Saraswati, she is Devamata, in Samudratata she is Paravaraa. In Mahalaya, she is Mahabhagaa, Pingaleswari in Payosni.

In Kritasaucha, she is Simhika, Atisankari in Kartika; in Utpalavartaka, she is Lola, Subhadra in Sona Sangama. In Siddhavana, she is Mahalakshmi, Anangaa in Bharatasrama; in Jalandhara, she is Viswamukhi, Tara in Kishkindha. She is Pusti in the Devadaru vana, Medha in Kasmiramandalam; she is Bhimaa in Himadri, Tusti in Visweswara Kshetra.

In Kapilamochanaa, she is Shuddhi, in Kayavarhana Mataa, in Sankhodhara Dharaa, in Pindaraka Dhriti, on the Chandrabhaga river Kalaa, in Achchoda Sivadharini, in Vena Amritaa, in Vadari Urvashi. She is Aushadhi in Uttara Kuru, Kusodhakaa in Kusadvipa, Manmathaa in Hemadri, Satyavadini in Kumuda, Vandaniyaa in Aswattha, Nidhi in Vaisravana, Gayatri at the mouth of the Vedas; she is Parvati beside Siva.

In Devaka, she is Indrani, Saraswati in the face of Brahma; she is Prabhaa in the Sun's relucent disk, Vaishnavi with the Mattrikas. Among the Sati Savitris, the chaste women, she is Arundhati; she is Tilottama among the Ramas. And, of course, she is Brahmakalaa in the hearts of all beings.

These are the hundred and eight Pithas and Devis, O King. He who hears these sacred names of the Devi in these holy tirthas is set free from all evil, and attains the realm of the Devi in time. His heart is purified, and he comes finally even to moksha, and is liberated from the sea of samsara. Why, even a home where the names of the Devi are kept, say in a book, is freed of all evil. If a man worship the Goddess with these hundred and eight names, the Devas themselves will worship that man, in time. The Rishis of Devaloka will bow down before him, and he attains the very nature of the Devi herself. The Pitrs in heaven are pleased with him, and they too are blessed by the names of the Devi.

So, O King, turn your heart to the Devi's blessed names. Each one is a holy mantra, and there is nothing you cannot have by just saying them,' said Muni Vyasa to Janamejaya," says the Suta.

FIFTY-ONE

"JANAMEJAYA SAID, 'MUNI, TELL ME HOW THE DEVI RETURNED TO THE world, for we know she did.'

Vyasa said, 'Siva ranged the earth, dementedly, with Sati's ashes and her bones. Wherever he rested, he began to meditate, slowly mastering his grief by dhyana. But all the worlds were distraught, as if they had lost their inmost grace. All creatures, God, demon, man, beast and bird, were as if their hearts had run dry, for joy had left them. Strange anxiety and indifference had its way with them, macabre diseases of body and spirit stalked heaven and earth, and creation was full of unease. Misfortune seemed to be the pivot around which life revolved, and the planets of fortune were retrogressive in their orbits.

It was at this time that a great Asura, a Demon of awesome powers, obtained a boon of invincibility from Brahma, and began to rule the worlds. His name was Taraka, and the boon he had was that no one except a son of Siva himself could kill him. Of course, he was also immeasurably strong. Taraka collected a fell army of Asuras and Rakshasas; he vanquished Indra's Devas, and assumed sovereignty over the three worlds.

After Sati's death, there was small chance of Siva taking a wife, or having a son, and the Asura was secure in his vast power, for no army of heaven or earth could vanquish him. Taraka cast the Devas out of Amravati, and sat upon Indra's throne. His chosen Danavas ruled earth, fire, sea and the air, they had power over the sun and moon, and the planets. Creation was mantled in darkness, and evil held sway over the hearts and lives of all the living.

The Devas lost their power, their lustre, and hid from the hunting Asuras in deep jungles, in the hearts of deserts, and in lonely mountain caves.

Finally, when it dawned on them that they had, indeed, become like beggars in creation, Indra's people went in distress to Vaikuntha, to see Blue Vishnu, who is always their saviour.

In tears, his vanity quite crushed, Indra prostrated himself abjectly before Narayana, and cried, "Lord, save us from Tarakasura, only you can!"

Vishnu said, "It is the Devi Bhagavati who can help you. When a mother scolds her children, it never means she has stopped loving them. She only does it for their own good, so their carelessness may not lead them into deeper trouble. Go, pray to the Devi, she will deliver you from Taraka."

So the Devas went to the Himalaya and performed a fervid tapasya, fuelled by their plight. They performed the purascharana karma, repeating the Goddess' sacred names, and making burnt offerings to her. The Devas lost themselves in that worship. Years passed, thus, and the Gods of light grew wan and wasted from their austerities, for they purified themselves with harsh rigors.

Then, one day, the ninth tithi of the month of Chaitra, a Friday, the Devi appeared before the prayerful Devas on that mountain. Her lustre was that of a lakh of suns, and it seemed the mountain had been subsumed into a higher realm, into the heart of all the light in the universe. The Vedas were there, hymning her, and the mass of flames she appeared in the midst of was ubiquitous; there was nothing in the three worlds, in all the galaxies, it did not engulf.

She was a blinding light, and the Devas shut their eyes for they could not bear her effulgence. But when they looked again they saw she, the Parashakti, had turned herself into an incomparable young woman, so exquisite that beauty began with her. Her youth was just blooming, her breasts were like lotus buds, she had golden ornaments on her hands and arms, and a splendid necklace set with unworldly gems around her darkling throat, casting its lambency across the pale mountain like an enchanted sun. Her hair was luminous and hung down to her ankles. She wore a delicate, tinkling waistlet and anklets above her fine, dark feet. Her mouth was perfect, tinted scarlet with the betel she chewed. She bore the Moon in a crescent on her forehead, her eyebrows were long and arched, and her eyes were reddish like the crimson lotus. Her teeth were like flowering buds of kunda. She wore a string of pearls as well, round her fluted throat, and they glowed like small moons; on her head, she wore a coronet worked, again, with matchless jewels.

She wore mallika and malati flowers in her hair and kashmira kumkuma teardrops. She carried a shining goad in one hand, and a brilliant noose in the other: the symbols of her sovereignty over time. Her other two hands were formed in the mudras of granting boons and deliverance from fear. Her eyes were like soft stars upon her face; the third one slumbered on her brow. She wore a crimson silk garment, and she was as bright as the flowers of the darima tree.

Stormed by her grace, the Devas were speechless before her. Then, slowly, as she stood smiling mysteriously at them, they began to chant the mantras that worship her, to sing her many names in ecstasy.

She said to them, so gently, "Tell me, Suras, what ails you that you worship me so fervently? Ask me for any boon, for I am a tree from which my bhaktas can have any fruit they like."

Swept by a gale of joy, the Devas said, "Mother of worlds, save us from the terror of Taraka. The Asura has a boon that only a son born to Siva can kill him. But, O Devi, how will Siva have a son when he has no wife? We fear he will never take a wife unto himself after Sati ashed herself. All the worlds are ruled by fear and despair, for Siva is grief-stricken. Mahamaye, Parashakti, we beg you, incarnate yourself again and be Siva's wife. Or Tarakasura will destroy the worlds. And, Mother, lastly, grant that we Devas always be devoted to your lotus feet."

And the Devi said, "My Shakti shall incarnate as the mountain's daughter, and she shall be Siva's wife. And they will have a son who will rid you of the Asura. And, I bless you, Suras, you will always have bhakti in your hearts, and my grace be upon you and yours." Smiling now, she added, "Not only your tapasya brings you this boon. Himalaya has also worshipped me, and I shall come as his daughter."

At which the Lord of mountains, the mighty spirit of the Himalaya stood embodied upon his loftiest peaks, a great white figure, and, tears flowing down his craggy face, said, "Mother, no boon in all the worlds can be higher than this one you have blessed me with. I shall be renowned across the universe now on, that the Creatrix of all things incarnated herself as Himavan's daughter! Who can be as fortunate as he whose child is the One in whose belly all the millions of brahmandas exist? Ah, peerless fortune, my sires shall find the highest Swargas for themselves, after this fortune of fortunes. But

I beg you, Mahadevi, Parameswari, enlighten me now, that vanity and darkness leave my heart and I become worthy of this boon of boons you have granted me!" said the august Lord of mountains,' said Vyasa Muni to Janamejaya," says the most erudite Suta.

FIFTY-TWO

SUTA SAYS, "VYASA MUNI SAID, 'THE DEVI SAID TO THE DEVAS AND THE Mountain, "Before creation, only I existed. That Form of mine, that formlessness, is called Chit, Sambit, Parabrahmam, and by other names, too. But that Self of mine is beyond the mind's comprehension, it is past even the Gods' thought. It transcends all its names and symbols. It is One, unequalled, beyond birth, death, and change, Un-born.

As heat arises from fire, as rays emanate from the sun, so, too, Maya does from the imperishable Atman. All these worlds and time are that Maya. Maya, also, has no beginning, but it surely ends with moksha. I, the pristine Soul, who am attributeless, Nirguna, become Saguna, diversely embodied when I am united with Maya. Then, I am Shakti, the cause of this and every world.

Maya is also twain: avidya maya, which binds in darkness and ignorance, and vidya maya that liberates. This Maya, too, is known by many names: Pradhanaa, Shakti, Prakriti, and Ajaa. She is known as Avidya, Samsara, Vimarsha and Jada.

In creation, Samsara, there are jivas and there is Iswara. Both have three bodies and three names. When the jiva dwells in his causal body he is Prajna, in his subtle body he is Taijasa, and in his gross body, he is Viswa. So, too, with Iswara. He is Isa in his causal body, Sutra in his subtle one, and Virata in his material form. It is Iswara who creates the universe, impelled by my Brahma Shakti. I am the Parabrahman, the cause of causes, and the Iswara is conceived in me as a serpent is imagined in a rope.

Many are the jivas, the mandalas and the Iswaras, as well. But I am one, the Parabrahman, the Adi Parashakti. The Brahman is the ground upon which all the worlds are created, the fabric from which time is woven. I enter the worlds as subtle breath and sustain them, and, when I leave, I destroy them, transmute them. And just as the rays of the sun are not defiled when they fall upon the gross earth, I am untainted by the worlds I enliven.

I am actless. The worlds and time flow from me, but not because I exert myself to create them. All the mandalas are based upon me, but not because I make any effort to sustain them. They are not real, as the Brahman is: they wither and die, they are made of illusions, of maya. Even the Iswaras are, finally, illusory; they are born, they live and die. Though the worlds and their creatures, their very Gods appear to be myriad, in truth, they are all founded in just One, and that One is all there ever was, is, and shall be. Only ignorance sees the many in the one. O Devas, O Himalaya, all creation is made of me; I am the Srutatman, Hiranyagarbha that dwells in every spirit.

I am Brahma, Vishnu and Maheswara. I am the Brahmi, Vaishnavi and Raudri Shaktis. I am the Sun, I am the Moon and all the stars; I am birds, beasts, Chandalas and the thief, as well. I am the savage hunter; I am the virtuous Mahatma. I am all men, women and every eunuch too. Be sure that if you see anything at all, I dwell in it and that is why it exists. No more can anything on any world exist without me, than a son be born to a barren woman.

I am the ground upon which all being and time are founded, and all that are found in these," said the Devi.

Himavan, Lord of mountains said, "Bhagavati, if you are pleased with me, show me your cosmic Self, show me your Virata Rupam."

The Devas echoed his wish, and the Goddess stood revealed before them, and she was everything that existed, or ever did, or shall. Upon the crown of her head the highest worlds of Satyaloka, the realms of truth and bliss rested. The Sun and Moon were her eyes, the quarters her ears, the Vedas issued from her as sacral speech, the universe was her pulsing heart, the earth was her loins, Bhuvarloka was her navel, the Nakshatras were her thighs, the Maharloka her neck, the Janarloka her face, the Taparloka her brow, just below Satyaloka, Indra and Devas and their Swargaloka were her arms, the Aswins were upon her nose, Agni was her face, day and night were her wings.

Four-faced Brahma sat upon her forehead, between her eyebrows, the ocean of purity flowed from her mouth, as her saliva, Yama was her teeth, Maya was her smile, all gross creation was her sidelocks, modesty her upper lip, covetousness her lower lip, adharma behind her. Prajapati was her vagina, the gross seas her bowels, the mountains were her bones, the rivers her veins, and the trees and plants her body hairs and down. Youth, virginity and old age are masks she wears, the two sandhyas are her raiment; the Moon is her mind; Vishnu is her vijnana Shakti, and Rudra her apocalyptic power. The beasts of nature are her loins; the nether worlds, Atala, Patala and the others are her legs and feet.

The Devas and the Mountain gazed upon her, they were within her as well, and were rooted with wonder. She contained everything within herself, all the worlds and all creatures, and she was irradiant as a million suns. As they watched they saw her smile, they saw her begin to lick up the universe with her crimson tongue. She chewed all creation with fangs as long as time, and the sounds she made doing this were awful. Her soft eyes grew fierce and spewed flames longer than imagination.

Before the Devas' terrified eyes, before Himavan's shocked, staring gaze, she became an apparition of absolute dread. She had a million arms and hands, all bearing horrible weapons; she had a million heads and faces, each one wild and dark. Her demented, scarlet eyes were everywhere, numberless suns and awesome gashes of lightning shone and played across her faces. Galaxies erupted and died upon her velvet skin, her brilliant pores. The Devas began to scream in terror. The Mountain roared in fear, and, in a moment, Himavan and all the Gods swooned at the Devi Bhagavati's feet.

In a while, the embodied Vedas roused them with soft mantras, and the Immortals and the Mountain prostrated themselves at the Goddess' feet, and hymned her in awe, in fervor.

"Obeisance to thee, Mother of worlds, of the nature of Pranava. Ameyaa, who can measure your greatness, when you are all there is, all place, all time, and the great peace beyond these? You are the One of whom the Vedanta speaks, you alone. Obeisance, O Hriim, without whom nothing would be. You are the Self of all the living, from you the fire and the sun, the moon and the earth have flowed. From you the healing herbs have come, why, from you all the Gods were born.

You are the source of all the worlds and all their creatures, from the smallest to Brahma, Vishnu and Siva. We tremble to see your cosmic form, Mother. We beg you, be as you were before, so we can bear to look at you. Be soft and lovely again, ah, dreadful, unbearable One!"

And she stood before them, exquisite and kindly again. She was four-armed, and held the noose and the goad in two hands, and the others were formed in mudras that dispel fear, and grant boons. She was gentle and smiling, and her presence was of such grace their minds were washed by a wave of joy and relief to see her like that.

Kindly she said, "Suras, O Himavan, only the Brahmam is real. Everything else, all the worlds, is illusion, it is maya. In samsara the soul incarnates in myriad wombs, good and evil, and is never free. Karma turns the wheel of life and death round, interminably. Ignorance is the root of karma and of these lives, their pleasures and agonies, of death and rebirth. Only when ignorance is dispelled with wisdom do these lives and deaths end, and the soul realises its eternal nature. Only then, is it set free from the cycle of births and deaths.

Gyana is wisdom, and true wisdom is only the knowledge of the Atman, the imperishable Soul: the Brahmam that was never created, but always was, and shall be, which is the foundation and the source of lives and worlds, the condition beyond change, the undying peace and ecstasy.

Desire prompts karma, action, and desire causes attachment. A man expects to enjoy the fruits of his karma, what he does. Lost in a jungle of deeds and desires, darkness engulfs him, and he seeks his peace outside himself, where it is never to be found. Enduring happiness, the joy of the soul, exists only within you: the bliss of the soul, immaculate, untouched by sorrow, attachment or desire, welling as naturally in the depths of your own hearts as breath does in your bodies. That is gyana, which ends the darkness of the mind, and liberates the embodied soul from incarnation, reunites him with the eternal Truth.

Yet, the Srutis do not advocate sloth. An embodied being must spend his years engaged in karma; for, deeds performed without desire for their fruits, but done with perfect relinquishment, as worship: these, too, are liberators. Whatever you do, offer it as devotion to the Brahmam, why, to me; and you shall come to salvation, to moksha from which there is no return to the realms of sorrow.

Seek perfection in your every deed, and you shall come to peace one day. Seek wisdom, too, for deeds without wisdom are hollow. The embodied being has as much need of karma as of gyana; just as he has need of day and night. Some of the wise say that, at last, just as day and night cannot exist at the same time, so, too, karma and gyana cannot. Karma loosens the bonds of desire and attachment that bind all creatures in darkness, while gyana severs those knots. But, then, both time and the path to enlightenment are not short, but span many lives. And each soul must pass through all the stages and shades of evolution and experience before coming to nirvana, which is the final aim of the incarnate lives the spirit assumes.

Slowly, taking many steps forward and many back, also, the soul treads the long way to mukti. Learning many lessons, unlearning them, and learning them again; purified by thousands of births and deaths, the spirit rises towards the light of the Brahmam, from where it will never return."

Himalaya asked, "Devi, Mahamaye, tell me about the last Yoga, and its eight angas, the limbs of that ultimate samadhi."

"The union between the Jivatma and the Paramatma is samadhi. Six enemies intervene between the soul and its primal source: lust, greed, anger, ignorance, vanity and envy. The eight angas of Yoga wear away these sins, and set the spirit free, so it flies towards its eternal sanctuary. Yama, niyama, asana, pranayama, pratyahara, dharana and samadhi, these are the eight yogangas.

Yama is ahimsa, non-violence and truthfulness; it is asteyam, honesty, where a being renounces the thievishness in his nature; it is brahmacharya, continence; it is daya, compassion; it is forgiveness and steadfastness, and frugality in food and speech, and purity of the body and the spirit.

Niyama is tapasya, ascetic penance; it is contentment; it is astikya, faith in God, in dharma, the Vedas and Devas, and the recognition of adharma; it is charity; it is hri, modesty; it is srarddha, the performance of rituals; it is japam, chanting the Gayatri, the Puranas, and other sacred mantras; it is homam, offering oblations to holy Agni.

These are all purifiers of the wise. Then, there are the asanas, the postures of dhyana. Five of them are main: padmasana, svastikasana, bhadrasana, vajrasana and virasana. When the aspiring yogi sits comfortably in any of these asanas, he then performs pranayama, the way of breathing. He draws in breath, slowly, deeply, through his left nostril, ida, counting sixteen AUMs. He retains the precious prana, the life-breath, for as long as he counts sixty-four AUMs, so it permeates his body, his very self. Then, he releases it gradually through the pingala, the right nostril, counting thirty-four AUMs.

The inhalation is called puraka, the retention kumbhaka, and the exhalation rechaka. All three together, that are hard indeed to do at first, are called one pranayama. To begin with, the acolyte will count less AUMs than sixteen, sixty-four and thirty-two. But, in time, he will master his breath. Some tapasvins will chant other mantras, or the name of their favoured deity, an ishta mantra, during pranayama; and this pranayama is called sagarbha pranayama. Vigarbha pranayama is when only AUM is chanted in the mind, and no other mantra.

The first sign of the successful pranayama is when the body begins to sweat. Later, the yogin will experience trembling. Finally, when pranayama is truly mastered, the yogin will rise from the ground and levitate.

After pranayama comes pratyahara. If the senses are unchecked they flow spontaneously towards the objects of the senses, and are frustrated, for there is no lasting fulfillment in the union of the senses with their objects. Drawing the senses back from their illusory objects to their very sources within the body and the mind is pratyahara. When the consciousness is fixed upon its fonts in the body—the toes, the heels, the knees, thighs, the scrotum, the genitals, the navel, the heart, the throat, the palate, the nose, the space between the brows, the top of the head—this indrawing is dharana. And, when external consciousness is subsumed slowly into the great Self within, the Ishta Devata, the personal God, that is dhyana. After long dhyana, comes samadhi, which is the ultimate union in which the sense of the individual self is lost entirely in the consciousness of God.

Samadhi also is of two kinds, savikalpaka and nirvikalpaka. When there is consciousness of the Brahman, but awareness of the jivatman also remains, that samadhi is called savikalpaka; and where there is consciousness only of the Brahman, single and undifferentiated, when the individual self is entirely subsumed and ceases to be, that is the final samadhi, the nirvikalpaka.

In the human body, there are three hundred and fifty thousand nadis; of these, ten are main and, of the ten, just three are principal. The sushumna nadi is within the spinal column, and is red and of the nature of fire. It extends from the base of the spine to the Brahmarandhra at the top of the head, where it resembles an unfurled dhustura flower.

To the left of this nadi is the ida nadi, white, and of the Moon's essence; this is the ambrosial nadi, gentle, feminine and blissful. To the right of the sushumna is the pingala nadi, of the Sun's nature, masculine.

At the base of the sushumna nadi, in the anal region, is the chitrini bhulinga nadi, formed like a gossamer cobweb. In the midst of this, ichcha Shakti, jnana Shakti and kriya Shakti dwell, resplendent in the spirit realm as a million suns. Above the bhulingam Hrim dwells, the Maya bija, and Chandrabindu that embodies the sacred nadam. Above the Hrim is the flame, the red kula kundalini: the serpent fire, intoxicated.

Around the coiled serpent is the yellow adhara padmam, fulvous, four-petalled lotus, with va, sa, s's and sha inscribed on each petal, and a hexagon at its corolla. Yogins meditate on this lotus, first. It is called the muladhara, the base of the six chakras that are above it.

Immediately above the muladhara, along the spinal stem, is the svadhishtana chakra, fiery, lustrous and coloured like a diamond, and six-petalled, with ba, bha, ma, ya, ra and la inscribed on each petal of light. This is the masculine chakra, for sva means parama lingam. Brahma, the Creator, resides in it.

Above svadhishtana is the manipura chakra. This has the colour of lightning in clouds, fiery. It has ten petals, with the letters da, dha, na, ta, tha, dda, ddha, nna, pa and pha inscribed on each letter. This lotus is like a great pearl, hence the name manipadmam. Vishnu dwells in it. Meditating on this chakra leads to a vision of Him.

Above the manipadmam is the anahata padmam, with twelve petals that have the letters ka, kha, ga, gha, ng, cha chcha, ja, jha, ya, tta and ttha upon them. In their midst is the luculent banalingam, bright as a sun seen from near. This padmam emits the sabda brahmam spontaneously, without being struck: hence, its name, anahata. Rudra lives in this lotus, and joy with him.

Above this padmam, along the spine, is the vishuddhi chakra, sixteen-petalled, with a, aa, i, ii, u, uu, ri, rri, li, lri, e, ai, o, ar, am and ah upon its smoky crystal petals, brighter than suns. This padmam is at the throat. The yogin who meditates on this lotus has a vision of the Paramatman here, and it purifies him, hence its name vishudhdhi. This chakra is also called the akasa chakra.

Above the akasa chakra, is the incomparable ajna chakra, between the eyebrows, with just two petals, with the letters ha and ksha inscribed on them. The Atman, the highest Self, dwells in this lotus, and the yogin who finds the ajna knows all things, past, present and future, and from here the highest Deity tells him what he must do, hence its name, ajna chakra.

Above the ajna is the kailasa padmam, and above that the rodhini, both ineffable, mysterious. And those who have gone beyond the rodhini say there is a final chakra above it: the thousand-petalled lotus, the Bindusthana, the final mystery, the Singularity, within which the Parabrahmam resides, and nirvana."

Himavan asked, "How, Bhagavati, does a bhakta begin his sadhana of discovery?"

She said, and her words have come down the ages, "First, assume a yogasana. Then, with puraka pranayama, fix your mind upon the muladhara padmam at the base of the spine. Take the vital prana down between the anus and the genitals, and rouse the serpent that slumbers there, the kundalini.

Once roused, the kundalini rises up along the spinal stem and pierces the higher chakras, awakening the radiant lingas along its subtle journey, until the prana arrives at the highest chakra, the lotus of a thousand petals, where the Svayambhu Adi Lingam dwells. Give your prana, your very heart, over to the precious sahasra padmam. Give yourself in deep dhyana to the Siva united in the final Lotus in the brain with his Shakti.

An ambrosia of bliss flows in the bindu padmam, from the eternal coition of Siva and Shakti, it resembles a crimson lac. The wise, who have achieved yoga, union, sip that amrita, then, worshipping all the Devas in all the chakras, the yogin brings the Shakti down into the muladhara again. This he does every day, and by this sadhana, frees himself from samsara, from every attachment, severs any bond that ever bound him through all his many lives, and becomes an enlightened one.

This, O Mountain, O Devas, is the pavana dharana yoga. There is another path to salvation, the dharana. Those who live in the Kali yuga, or those whose hearts are not pure, can fix their minds and hearts on Me, on my form of light. I pervade all Creation, and the dharana yoga leads as surely to moksha as the pavana dharana yoga.

But, if a yogin finds even this dhyana more than he can do, for the darkness and fear that beset him from within or without, there is the avayava yoga, where he does not conceive me entirely, but only my hands or feet, or any other limb or organ of mine. By this, he shall find enough purity of heart to then perform the dharana yoga.

Japam, homam, and mantram are what dissolve a bhakta's heart, his very life, into the Godhead that I am. Mantra and yoga are the two paths to moksha; each one is of little use without the other. O Himalaya, Devas, you have heard this secret of secrets from me today, and someday it shall set you free. For, I have become your guru. A man must learn the yoga from a realised guru; else, all the millions of Shastras can never make him truly understand the truth. He will only be lost in a bewildering jungle of fantasies. The guru is the key to wisdom, without a guru no sadhana can be fruitful." said the Devi Bhagavati, the greatest, primal guru upon the Himalaya,' said Vyasa Muni to the Kuru king, once," says Suta to the Rishis of the Naimisa vana.

FIFTY-THREE

"VYASA CONTINUED, 'O KING, THE DEVI BHAGAVATI SAID TO THE DEVAS and the Mountain, "The Brahmam is everything, nearer than you imagine, moving in the hearts of all creatures, of all the worlds. He is the final goal of all things great and little. Every existence is founded in him. He is the ultimate, holy ground, higher than being and nothingness, higher, even, than wisdom. He is the light of lights, infinite and infinitesimal. He is immortal, the target to strike!

Vishnu is prana, and Prananatha, too; he is the Word, Vak. He is Jagadguru, the preceptor of the universe. He controls every jiva.

Let Pranava be your mystic bow. Fix the arrow of your heart to it, sharpen it with dhyana, and take careful aim at the Brahmam. The man with the single-pointed mind finds his eternal mark, even if it takes him a hundred lives to do so.

In him all the mandalas and brahmandas dwell, into him the nadis, the lattices of life, are threaded. He is the Atman that pervades the heart, and manifests himself as all the living. He is that Pranava, the AUM from which every life springs, the Turiya, the fourth dimension. His ways are always mysterious as he leads all jivas on their long and brief journey, along pathways through stars and time.

Five bonds bind the embodied in darkness: avidya, lingadeha, pramachadaka prakriti, kama, and karma too. A vision of the Brahmam severs these fetters, and liberates the Atman into the Santamka loka, a higher realm. At the threshold of this world, the gyani salutes the Sisumara, the hub of the universe.

The Sisumara is the 'infant-slayer', the constellation of the dolphin in the north. He is a mystical one, the doorkeeper to the universe! He is Hari, say some; some say he is the Brahmam himself, manifest in the highest sheath of the Golden Egg, the light of lights, the fire of every sun. In the jiva he is the auric egg, in the cosmos the great Golden One.

He is worshipped, in the first, as Gayatri and, then, as Sisumara. The golden sheath is the solar sphere, and Narayana, Sisumara, dwells in it, pure and single, without parts or limbs. Because of him the sun burns, why, every sun of every nebula. But they do not illumine him; rather, he illumines each light in the universe.

The Brahmam is eternal freedom, boundless; he pervades all the directions, and transcends them too. And he dwells in the heart; verily, he is the heart entirely. The man who realises this final Self, becomes the Brahmam himself, and he is set free. He is perfectly fulfilled in the ocean of spirit, he has no needs or wants, he knows no fear or danger. He knows the unity of all things, and that he too is that One.

Know, O Mountain, O Gods, I am that One. I am She, the Parabrahmam. And I dwell not in any tirthasthana, not in Kailasa Vaikuntha or Manidvipa, but in the hearts of my bhaktas, the souls of wisdom, the gyanis, the illumined ones. The yogin who attains moksha, whose heart is dissolved in the Brahma gyana, be certain he purifies the whole world, why, the very brahmanda, the universe.

This, O Parvata, O Devas, is the essential Brahma gyana, that must be taught to the eldest son who is devout or, indeed, to anyone who has an upright character; and never to the man whose nature is mocking, or sinful.

The guru who imparts the Brahma vidya: he is like God himself to his sishya; the gift of the Brahma vidya is one that can never be repaid. Why, a man's natural father is hardly as important as his master, the spiritual father who gives him birth into the eternal Brahmam. For the incarnate life ends in death, but the life of the spirit into which the guru gives a man birth, is immortal. Indeed, this is why the guru is to be worshiped like God.

Even if Siva in angry with a man, it is said his guru can save him. But if a guru becomes angry, even Sankara cannot save the sishya from his master's wrath. A man who is ungrateful to his master who teaches him the way of the spirit, why, he can never have salvation, not in a hundred births.

But Brahma gyana is hardly easy to acquire. Listen to a tale from me. Once, in certain kalpa, a Muni from the Arthavana family, whose name was Dadhyama, went to Indra and asked him for the Brahma gyana.

Indra said, 'You can have the final vidya from me. But if you ever tell it to anyone else, I will have your head.'

Dadhyama swore he would not breathe the last secret to anyone, and Indra taught him the Brahma gyana. A few days later, the Aswin twins arrived in the Muni's asrama, and worshipped him to have the Brahma vidya from him.

Dadhyama said, 'If I teach you the Brahma vidya, Indra will cut off my head.'

But the Aswins hardly needed to think before they surmounted this obstacle. 'We will sever your head, and keep it elsewhere, and give you a horse's head. Teach us the vidya.'

The Muni could not resist such pupils. He taught them the Brahma vidya, and Indra cast his Vajra down at him and struck his horse's head off. But then, the Aswins arrived with their guru's real head, and restored it to him. Of course, Dadhyama, the realised one, only laughed as if the two beheadings tickled him.

So, blessed are they who gain the Brahma vidya, and a yogin will do anything to have it; for, it sets him free for ever," said Devi Bhagavati.

Prostrating a hundred luminous peaks at the Goddess' holy feet, Himalaya Parvata asked, "Mother, tell us about the bhakti marga now, by which ordinary souls, who have not the dispassion to gain the Brahma gyana by tapasya, come to grace."

"By three paths, embodied souls arrive at moksha: karma yoga, the way of deeds, dhyana yoga, the way of meditation, and bhakti yoga, the way of worship. Of the three, bhakti is always the easiest, and bestows the same nirvana as the other two.

Bhakti requires no great rigors of body or spirit, and just as the essences of nature are triune—of sattva, rajas and tamas—so, too, is the yoga of bhakti. He who worships me to inflict harm on an enemy, his bhakti is tamasic, since he is full of vanity, malice, envy and rage. When a devotee worships me for his own ends, and not to cause injury to anyone, his bhakti is rajasic. Such a worshipper has some great desire he wants to fulfil: of wealth, pleasure, or achievement. But the bhakta who worships me to purify himself, and offers me all his karma, whatever he does, in a spirit of perfect relinquishment, he is a sattvik bhakta. But even he thinks of himself as being apart from that which he worships, and his devotion is less than the parabhakti, the supreme bhakti, the fourth, transcendent kind.

In that final devotion, the bhakta is absorbed in love for me. He has no trace of desire for the fruits of his karma, neither does he want any of the mokshas for himself: not samipya, sarishta, sayuja, salokya, or the others. He is perfectly absorbed by his bhakti; he does not even want nirvana! He is the immaculate sevaka, serving only me. Why, he hardly thinks of himself as being apart from me anymore, but says, 'I am she, the Devi myself.'

He sees me in all things and everywhere, in the low and the high, all the jivas, he hears the hymns of the stones that are meant to be mute. And when he but says my name, or my mantra, or sees a temple of mine, or my bhaktas, his heart wells in a font of ecstasy: his hairs stand on end, and tears of love course down his face. He sings my names then, in abandon, for the paraprema is a torrent of love hurtling into the ocean that I am.

He is hardly conscious of being apart from me, the Mother of the universe, the cause of causes. He sings, he dances, intoxicated with me. This bhakta's heart and his life are sage, serene. He knows that the prarabdha karma of past lives must bear fruit in this one, and he is imperturbable. He does not identify with his body or even his mind, and is far from concerned with their preservation. He sees his way ahead clearly, and that it will lead him to me.

This fourth bhakti is parabhakti, and there is none higher than it. It is unalloyed with philosophy. It is simple, pure, and consumes the bhakta, so he becomes one with me forever. Ahamkara dies in his heart, and he realises the Parabrahmam. When he dies, he does not return to birth.

O Devas, O Himavan, the Paramatman is seen in the Pitrilokas like an image in a mirror. But a man who attains the realms of the manes, or even the realm of Brahma, returns to birth, perhaps to one final one. But he who sees the light of the Brahmam, is not born again. This final salvation comes after many, many births. A human birth is rare, indeed, and he who does not strive for moksha even after being born human, let him know that his life has been wasted. Yet, the very desire for liberation arises only out of past karma; which is why some have it and others do not.

Self-restraint, yoga, knowing the Vedas, acquiring a real guru: these are the true treasures of life. Fortunate are they who gain these out of their punya, by leading as devoted and chaste a life as they can. And he who has these, naturally, in some measure, yet does not aspire to the final Gyana, truly his life is a desolate one, an incalculable waste.

The wise have said that as ghee dwells potentially in milk, so, too, does knowledge dwell in the human heart, why, even the Vijnana Brahma. Let a man's final purpose be clear to him, and then let him tread the long and winding way, let him truly make an effort, and he shall indeed come to grace," said the Devi to the Devas and the Mountain,' said Vyasa Muni to the king.

FIFTY-FOUR

"VYASA CONTINUED," SAYS SUTA ROMAHARSHANA, 'HIMALAYA SAID, "TELL us which places on earth are sacred to you, Mother, and the rituals by which men can purify themselves, and the auspicious times for observing them. Let what you say to us today be preserved in the memory of the races of the earth."

The Devi smiled, "O Himavan, the very Earth is sacred to me, and part of me. And every moment, each life is auspicious, precious. Yet, it is true there are some tirthas that are specially blessed, where my power and grace are most focused, and I will tell you of these now.

In the south, in the tirtha called Kohlapura, I dwell as Lakshmi. In Matripura, in the Sahyadri Mountains, you will find me as Renuka; in Tulajapura, in Saptasringa, in Hingula and Jvalamukhi you will find me always, as Sakambhari, Brahmari, Sriraktadantika, and as Durga. Among the finest tirthas are those of Vindhyachala Vasini, Annapurneswari, and Kanchipura Kamakshi.

I am Bhimaa Devi, Vimala Devi, Sri Chandra Devi of Karnat, and Kaushiki, too. Upon the Nilaparvata, I am Nilamba, and I am Jambunadeswari and Srinagareswari as well. In the land of Nepal, you will find me as Sri Guhya Kali, and in Chidamvaram as Meenakshi. In Vedaranya I am Sundari Devi, and in Ekamvaram. In Bhuvaneswara near Purushottama, worship me as Parashakti Bhuvaneswari.

In renowned Mahalasa, I am Mallari, in Varata, Yogeswari; in Vaidyanatha, I am Bangalaa, Nila Saraswati in China, and Srimati Bhuvaneswari in Manidwipa, the holiest of all my tirthas. In that whorl of time, Yonimandala Kamyaka, I am Tripura Bhairavi, the Goddess Maha Maya herself. This last is the most auspicious tirtha on earth, none more sacred than it is. It is here that I come each month, during my time of womanly blood, and here that you Devas dwell as holy mountains upon the earth, and where Rishis and Munis, Gandharvas, Kinnaras, Charanas and Siddhas, Nagas and Apsaras, and all sorts of exceptional beings live.

In Pushkara, I am Gayatri, Chandika in Amaresa, and Puskareksini in Prabhasa. In Naimisaranya, I am Lingadharini Devi, Puruhuta in Puskarksha, and Rati in Asadhi. In Chandamundi, I am Dandini Parameswari, Bhuti in Bharabhuti; in Nakula, I am Nakuleswari, Chandrika in Harishchandra.

In Srigiri, I am Sankari, Trisula in Japeswara; in Amarakeswara, I am Sukshma, Sankari in Ujjaina. In Madhyama, I am Sarvani, Marga Dayini in kshetra Kedara; in Bhairava, I am Bhairavi, and Mangalaa in Gaya kshetra. In Kurukshetra, I am Sthanupriya, in Nakula Svayambhu Devi too; in Kanakahala, I am Ugraa, and Viswesaa in Vimaleswara.

In Attahasa, I am Mahanandaa, Mahantakaa in Mahendra; in Bhima, I am Bhimeswari, and Bhavani Sankari in Vastrapadma. In Ardha koti, I am Rudrani, Visalakshi in Avimukta; in Mahalaya, I am Mahabhagaa, and Bhadarakarini in Gokarna. In Bhadrakarnaka, I am Bhadraa, Utpalakshi in Suvranaksha; in Sthanu, I am Sthanavisa, and Kamala in Kamalalaya.

In Chagalandaka, I am Chandaa, Trisandhya in Kurundala; in Makota, I am Mukteswari, Sandaki in Mandaleswara. In Kalanjara, I am Kali, Dhvani in Sankhukarna; in Sthulakeswara I am Sthulaa and Parameswari Hrillekha who dwells in the lotus in the heart of Gyanis, the Munis of detachment!

And in Kasi, O Himavan, all these tirthas exist together, and any bhakta who chants the Devi's name and worships at her temples shall have his sins burned up, and come to grace and to moksha. If a bhakta recites the Devi's sacred names during a sraddha for his dead ancestors, surely the Pitrs are purified of their sins in the mahakasa by the mahaprana of that chanting, and are set free."

Himavan asked now, "Mahamaye, tell us about the holy vows."

She said, "The vratas are for both men and women. Listen. On the tritiya, the third, tithi, observe the Anantatrithiyakhya vrata, the Rasakalyani vrata and the Ardanandakara. Then, the Sukra vrata, the Krishna chaturdasi vrata, the Mangala vrata, and the Suryastma sandhya vrata. This last because Mahadeva set me on a splendid asana at twilight, once, and he and you Devas danced before me. The bhakta must fast all day during this vrata, and in the evening worship me with song, offerings and dance. Hardly anything pleases me more.

For the Soma vrata, you must fast at night, and the two nine-night Navaratas of autumn and spring are most auspicious. Then there is the dol festival in the month of Chaitra, which I love well, and its meaning, as with all my other festivals, is deeper and more beautiful than most bhaktas imagine.

In Asadha on the day of paurnamasi, my bhaktas perform the sayanotsava, rolling upon the earth in worship; the jagaranotsava, of the awakening, they do on the paurnamasi of the month of Kartika. The third day of the white fortnight of Asadha is for the ratha yatra, the chariot procession, the damanotsava in Chaitra, and there are others, all holy and precious to me, in the months of Sravana, and every other month, for time itself is a perpetual festival of joy to those that can see.

The poor must be fed during these festivals, and the kumari virgins and young virgin boys worshipped like my very self. These, briefly, are my vows, O Mountain, but the festival dearest to me, that outstrips every other is the utsava of compassion and charity, the ritual of the heart.

And my worship is of two kinds—outer and inner. Outer worship is, again, of two kinds: Vaidik and Tantrik. Once more, Vaidik worship is of two kinds depending on which form of mine is being worshipped. Listen first to what Vaidik worship is.

You saw my Viswarupa, with endless heads and arms, countless hands, feet and eyes, the Illuminer of the buddhi of every jiva in the universe, omniscient, omnipotent, and awesome. The first Vaidik worship, O Himavan, is to bow to that eternal Rupa of mine. To install its image in the temple of your heart, and seek moksha for yourself.

Mountain Lord, dhyana mixed judiciously with karma, and gyana with bhakti, will deliver you. Bhakti arises from dharma, a righteous life, and from bhakti alone, the highest knowledge wells. If you doubt what is dharma, if your heart is not clear on it, consult the Sruti and the Smriti Shastras, or the other sacred books. For the Vedas flowed from my infinite nature, and they are blessed. And the Smritis came from the Vedas and the Puranas from the illumined maharishis who are my bhaktas, through whom I speak in diverse ways to commune with men of diverse times and natures. Let scripture be your guide for what dharma is, for the Vaidik scripture has come from me.

As for the Tantras, Mahadeva himself created the Kapalaka, Kaulaka, Bhairava, and other Tantra Shastras. For, once, some Brahmanas were banished from the Vaidik path by the curses of Daksha, Sukra and Dadichi. For their salvation, Siva made the five agamas: the Saiva, Vaishnava, Saura, Sakta and Ganapatya Shastras.

Many portions of these Shastras conform to the Vedas, and others appear to contradict them, even to be heretical. The Vaidik Brahmanas are not the adhikaris, the authorities, of these latter passages of the Tantras. But now, hear the method of the Tantrik puja from me.

The Tantrik meditates on an idol, or a yantra drawn upon a smooth patch of earth, on the sun or the moon, on water, on a vana linga, a yantra inscribed on a cloth, or on the lotus in the heart. He worships the Devi, cause of creation, sustenance and destruction, the blissful Mother of the universe, whose youth blooms eternal, who brims with mercy like a river from a spring, whose complexion is of the rising sun, from whom beauty begins, who is love incarnate, who feels the anguish of her bhaktas more sharply than they do themselves, on whose brow the crescent moon is always rising, whose hands hold the noose and goad, and the third and fourth hands formed in the mudras of fearlessness and boon-giving. Until the bhakta finds the inner bhakti, he must pursue the outer one; never must he abandon the image of the Devi.

Of course, his goal is transcendent: the Samvita, my very Consciousness, in which he seeks to dissolve himself for ever," said the Devi upon the holy mountain,' says Vyasa Muni."

FIFTY-FIVE

"VYASA SAID, 'THE DEVI SAID, ONCE, "RISING FROM BED BEFORE DAWN, THE bhakta meditates on the thousand-petalled lotus of the Soul, of the hue of camphor, within the highest bodily chakra in the brain. Within this, he pictures his Guru, immaculate and lustrous, his Shakti beside him. He bows to that Guru, and worships the Kundalini Devi thus:

I worship the highest Shakti, Kundalini, who is chaitanya along the journey up to the Brahmarandhra, and upon the nectarine Goddess along the return down the sushumna nadi. Then, the bhakta turns his thought to my form of bliss within the kundalini flame coiled in the muladhara, the anal chakra.

After this, he rises and answers nature's bodily calls, and performs the udaya sandhya vandanas, the rituals that begin the day. He then performs the agnihotra homa, worships the sacred fire sitting in an auspicious yogasana. Next he performs bhuta shuddhi, purifies the elements of the body with pranayama, and then, inscribing the alphabets of the mulamantra of Mahamaya, draws the hrillekha matrika nyasa. He emblazons the 'ha' upon the muladhara, the 'ra' upon his heart, the 'i' between his eyebrows, and the 'hrim' upon the crown of his head, on the subtle aperture there.

Having completed the other nyasas, he conceives dharma, gyana, vairagya and labha within his body as the four legs of the asana, and adharma, agyana, avairagya and durlabha as the seat of the asana in the four quarters, north, east, south and west. He then meditates on me, the Devi, seated within the mystic lotus in his heart, blown by the breezes of pranayama. The Devi sits astride the five Pretas. O Himalaya, Brahma, Vishnu, Rudra, Sadasiva and Iswara are the five Pretas at my feet.

The Pretas are of the nature of earth, water, fire, air and cosmic ether. They also have the natures of jagrati, waking, svapna, dreaming, shushupti, deep sleep, turiya, the fourth state, and atita rupa, the fifth. And I, who am of the nature of the Brahmam, am above these five, and thus my asana is above the five Pretas.

Now, his mind made steady, the bhakta begins slowly to intone my names, which are sacred mantras. After this japam, he offers me the fruits of his worship, setting the arghya before the agni, sprinkling them with the pavitra jala, the holy water, while chanting the astra mantra, 'Phat'.

He seals the ten quarters by the chotika mudra, and bows down to his guru. Asking his master's leave, he meditates upon the external asana, which is sthula, gross, and with prana pratishta exteriorizes the resplendent Devi within his heart, and enthrones her upon the outer asana. He performs avadana, and offers her arghya (green kusa grasses, rice grains, etc.), padya (water to wash her feet), achamana (water for her bath), some clothes, ornaments, flowers, perfumes. All these he offers the Deity of the yantra.

If he cannot worship thus every day, he must do so at least on each Friday.

He worships the Devi whose nature is of light, Prabha, whose splendour pervades the universe. He worships Bhuvaneswari Devi again, Mistress of the earth-jungle, with naivedya and other sweets and foods. He recites the sahasranama, her thousand blessed names, and the Devi sukta stotra—Aham Rudrebhih, and so on, and Deva Devi mupatasthuh. He chants the Devi atharva siro mantra, the Upanishada mantra of Bhuvaneswari, until bhakti wells in his heart, in his body, in tide.

His hair stands on end with the current of ecstasy, tears flow down his face, and now, rising, he sings and dances for me. When he has finished this worship, and made the offering of homa, he feeds Brahmanas, the virgins, and any others that come to him, thinking of them all as manifestations of me. After this, he prostrates himself before me, who dwells in the heart, and ends his devotion with the samhara mudra.

The Hrillekha mantra, O Mountain, is equal to all the other mantras put together. It is a mirror in which I appear quickly. And the bhakta who worships the Devi Bhuvaneswari, has all the desires of his heart fulfilled, and finds Manidwipa for himself when he leaves his body. Why, he has my very form by his worship, and the Gods bow down to him.

Let this, the way to approach me, be handed down from you to the generations of men of the earth. Yet, let no one who is an enemy of dharma, or base or cunning or Godless ever learn this Shastra Devigita. For, it is like a mother's breast being uncovered before lewd strangers. Let is thus be precious, and a secret shared between the devout, for it is the final secret, the path to nirvana.

O Devas, O Himavan, I know the reason for which you have worshipped me today. I say to you, the boon you want shall be yours."

And she vanished before them like mist before the sun,' said Vyasa Muni to the king.

In time, the Devi was born as Himavan and his wife Mena's daughter Parvati. Siva married her, and they had a son, born not from Parvati's body but from Siva's seed, his golden Hiranyaretas ejaculated onto a rocky cave-floor, when an impatient Vishnu and the Devas called him out of love. That magnificent son of Siva's was called Karttikeya, or Kumara, Guha, Sanmukha— for he had six faces, Subrahmanya, Muruga, Agneya, and he slew the Asura Taraka in a great battle fought between the forces of darkness and light beside a stormy sea, on a fateful silver shore," says the Suta to the enchanted Rishis of the Naimisa vana, in a certain kalpa.

FIFTY-SIX

SUTA SAYS, "MUNIS, THEN JANAMEJAYA ASKED THE BLESSED DWAIPAYANA, 'Tell me, Master, about the true tattva of the Viratarupa. Tell me how the Devi Bhagavati of that cosmic form was worshipped in each manvantara, by its sovereign ruler and the earthly kings of its centuries. With what mantras was she worshipped? Describe all the forms of Adi Shakti to me, so I can seek the final freedom.'

Vyasa Muni said, 'Then listen, O King. In time out of mind, the Devarishi Narada wandered the earth, as was his wont, and came upon the asrama of the Rishi Narayana, who was an Avatara of the Lord. He prostrated himself at that greatest of Munis' feet, and sat with him, sharing in a deep and serene silence.

In a while, Narada asked Narayana, "O Holder of the universe, in whom all worlds, all things, begin and end, tell me where does the universe have its beginning, in what is it founded, whence does it rest? Into what does the cosmos dissolve at the end of time, when the pralaya drowns creation? Where does the karma of all beings go? Answer me these questions, holy one, so I may scatter your knowledge like seeds upon the wind, and men of the generations of the earth bask in the shade of the trees of wisdom that sprout from them, and have some respite and comfort even amidst the sea of grief, this samsara."

Ancient Narayana replied, "Listen, then, O Narada, to what the tattvas of this world are, and, listening, never be entangled in the world's illusions again.

All the Shastras say that the Devi Bhagavati creates, preserves and destroys the akhanda, that she is the Mother of this universe and its death, as well; and all that ever is resides only in her, finally. The Devas, Gandharvas, Siddhas, Rishis, Charanas and, indeed, all the immortals worship her, and she grants them their hearts' desires—in artha, dharma, kama, and moksha also.

In the first kalpa, the powerful Svayambhuva Manu, who is Satarupa's lord and the sovereign of every manvantara, worshipped the immaculate and sinless Prajapati Brahma with an immaculate tapasya. When the Creator was satisfied with Manu's devotion, he spoke to his resplendent son.

'Worship the Devi Bhagavati, my child, seek her blessing and then embark upon your enterprise of creation!'

And so the Vibhu Svayambhuva Manu did. He worshipped Mahamaya with an unprecedented tapasya. He sang her holy names, he danced for her, he prayed to her with a mind like a frozen bolt of lightning.

The Devi appeared before him bright as a million suns. She said, 'Son of Brahma, I am pleased with you. Ask me for any boon, and it shall be yours.'

Svayambhuva Manu asked, 'Devi, grant that my creation meet with no obstruction, and that it is even as I intend it to be. Let my creatures multiply and be fruitful; let them prosper and finally have moksha from you.'

She raised her sacred hand over him, and granted his wish. Then she vanished like dew before the sun, softly, while her grace lingered over him, filling him with light. Manu remembered his sire Brahma again and, when his father appeared before him, the son asked his Pitamaha, 'My lord, let me have a solitude in which to sit fervently, and begin the task of creation.'

Brahma mused, 'But the worlds with all their jivas are plunged in Ekarnava, the single sea. Yet, perhaps, if Vishnu were to help us...'

Even as he spoke, thus, to Svayambhuva Manu and the other Munis, who are born from his thought and are sinless, there emerged from Brahma's nose a young boar, small as a thumb! It was an exceptional beast, shining; and in a moment, before their wondering gazes, that boar grew big as an elephant, and began to roar as loudly as the clouds of the pralaya.

Brahma, Svayambhuva Manu, Sanaka and the other Kumaras, Marichi and the Saptarishi cried, 'This is the Lord Himself!' and they began to praise him. They sang the Vedas to that Adi Purusha, the Bhagavan.

With a smile, surely, the great Boar plunged into the primal sea of dissolution that lay all around. The ocean, Sagara, trembled with the Boar's fierce dive, and his fiercer bristles, and cried, 'Lord of Gods, Hari, have mercy on me!'

The Boar dived down, right down into that plumbless sea, and by now, he was bigger than a planet. Brushing aside schools of whales and sharks, and timmingalas, he sought the Earth everywhere, the precious Earth, repository of the jivas. At last, he caught scent of her in those black waters. She lay glimmering upon the pale sea-bed of that sea, blue-green, glowing with all the rich spirit-life she contained, pregnant with the times that were yet to be, the lives, the forests, rivers and mountains, and the days, years and centuries, and the ages, the yugas, and all, all the races and destinies, great and small, to be born upon her yet.

With a roar of joy that sent bubbles big as galaxies streaming to the surface, Vishnu the Varaha tore the Asuras that guarded the earth in the deep to shreds, dug his snout into white sands, and with tusks like cosmic lightning bore the round world up out of the dark and singular sea, and broke out into the sunlight above, roaring in exultation! Ah, he was like one of the Diggajas that support the quarters who had just torn up a mythic, thousand-petalled lotus by its very roots. He was splendourous, sunlike, his grace blinding, though he was such a strange beast, the lucific Lord Vishnu.

Brahma said, in a rapture, 'Lord, by your grace do I create the worlds from kalpa to kalpa! O Devadeva, by your grace Indra's Devas churned the Kshirasagara and drank the amrita. By your grace, Indra has sovereignty over the Triloka.

By your power, Agni burns and dwells in the bellies of the Devas of light, the Asuras of dark, mortal men and every beast that lives in the world, and stokes their hearts. By your power, Yama, lord of dharma, rules the southern quarter, of the manes, and is the judge of karma, meting out reward and punishment.

By your grace, Nairrita, lord of the Rakshasas, who is the universal witness, destroys obstacles from the paths of all the living. Yes, though he is a Yaksha.

At your command, does Varuna, lord of waters, rule the earth. At your instance, Vayu, lord of airs, has become a Lokapala and the guru of the universe. After your word, did Kubera become lord of the Yakshas and the Kinnaras, and of the nine treasures.

Isana, who destroys all the living, has his lordship over a quarter and his power by your grace. All the Rudras, Devas, Gandharvas, Yakshas, Kinnaras, all men, why all living creatures, exist because of you, and they do so by your law.'

The Lord, that Boar, gave Brahma and the Devas a sidelong glance of infinite mercy, even as he lifted the Earth out of the primal and terrible sea. Just then, Hiranyaksha, the golden Asura, appeared in the Lord's path, and sought to obstruct his passage with the Earth in his tusks. But the Varaha shattered the Demon's body with a stroke of his club, the Kaumodaki, and was splattered with his dark blood. And, covered in gore, the Lord emerged from the depths of Rasatala, and floated the earth upon the surface of the sea again.

Narada, child, he who hears this tale of the Lord Vishnu shall have mukti from his sins, and come to live in the Lord Vishnu's realm," said the Muni Narayana in time out of mind.

Then, after pausing a moment, he continued, "After rescuing the Earth from hell's watery deeps, Vishnu went back to Vaikuntha. Then Brahma said to his son, Svayambhuva Manu, 'Now begin your creation.' And, blessing him, went back to his own loka.

Manu began. At first, he created two magnificent sons, Priyavrata and Uttanapada, and three exquisite, brilliant daughters called Akuti, Devahuti and Prasuti. Akuti married the Maharishi Ruchi, Devahuti the Prajapati Karddama, and Prasuti the Prajapati Daksha. And know, O Muni, that all the beings of this earth had their origin from this third daughter of Svayambhuva Manu, from Prasuti.

Mahamuni Ruchi sired one son, whom he named Yagna, upon his wife Akusi. Yagna is an amsa of the Bhagavan Adi Purusha Vishnu. Devahuti became a mother, too, by her lord Karddama Maharishi. From her womb, she bore Bhagavan Kapila Deva, who created the Samkhya Shastra. And Prasuti was mother only to some daughters, by her lord Daksha, who created all the Devas, Gandharvas, men, birds, beasts and insects, besides.

The children of the children of Svayambhuva Manu were the first creators of the races of men. In the Svayambhuva manvantara, the Manu himself was set upon by some sinister Rakshasas. His grandson Yagna saved him, with the help of Yama Deva. And the lord of yogins, the brilliant Kapila, revealed his Samkhya Shastra to his mother Devahuti, while he stayed briefly in her asrama. He also taught the dhyana marga, with all its refinements. Finally, he went away to Brahmarishi Pulaha's asrama, to seek samadhi, and Samkhyacharya lives there even today. Ah, I bow to the Deva Kapila, who makes fruitful every desire of the heart, whose very name reveals the Samkhya gyana to the yogin!"

Narada asked, "Tell me more about the sons of Svayambhuva Manu, Lord."

Narayana Rishi said, "Svayambhuva's eldest son Priyavrata served his father faithfully, and was an embodiment of truth. He married Prajapati Viswa Karma's daughter, the lovely Brahishmati, who resembled him not only in appearance but in her devotion to dharma as well. They had ten splendid sons, and a daughter called Urjasvati. She was the youngest; her elder brothers were Agnidhra, Idhmajiva, Jajnabahu, Mahavira, Rukmasukra, who was also called Hiranyareta, Ghritaprishta, Savana, Medhatithi, Vitihottra and Kavi. The name Agni suffixed each of the above.

Of these ten, Kavi, Savana and Mahavira were absorbed in themselves, indifferent to the world. In time they attained atma-vidya, the knowledge of the soul, and became paramahamsas.

Priyavrata had three sons by another wife: Uttama, Tamasa and Raivata. In time, each became lord of a manvantara. Priyavrata lived for eleven arvada years, and he did not age a bit, nor did his body show the least sign of decay. Once, Priyamvrata saw that, even while he was sovereign of the earth, the sun did not light the entire globe, but there was night in parts of it. In annoyance, he created a refulgent chariot for himself, great and bright as the sun, and flew up to dispel the darkness, wherever it was.

Seven times round the earth he flew and, wherever his chariot-wheels touched the ground, an ocean appeared. Thus, there were seven seas upon the world. And between them was land, the seven great islands, the dvipas.

This first is Jambu, then Plaksha, Salmali, Kusa, Krauncha, Saka and Pushkara. Plaksha, the second dvipa, is twice as large as Jambu, and so on. Of the oceans, the first is Ksharoda, the salt water sea, then Iksurasa, the sugarcane sea, Sura, the sea of wine, Ghritoda, the sea of ghee, Kshiroda, the sea of milk, Dadhi Manda, of curd, and the last, Svadu sagara, of crystal water.

The Kshira samudra surrounds the Jambu dvipa. Priyavrata made his son Agnidhra lord of this continent. He gave Plaksha dvipa amid the Iksu samudra to Idhmajiva, the Salmali dvipa in the Sura sagara to Yagnabahu, the Kusa dvipa to Hiranyareta, the Krauncha to Ghritaprishta, to Medhatithi the Saka dvipa, and to Vitihottra the Pushkara dvipa.

Priyavrata gave his daughter Urjasvati to be the lord Usana's wife. And upon her did Sukracharya beget his daughter, whose name is a legend—Devayani. When Priyavrata had thus made his sons masters of the islands and the oceans, he embraced the way of yoga and sought his own final deliverance.

Now listen, O Narada, to the division of the earth into the dvipas and the varshas by the Devas. Jambu is a hundred thousand yojanas wide, and is round like a lotus. It has nine varshas, continents, and, but for Bhadrasva and Ketumala, each one is nine thousand yojanas wide and long. There are eight immense mountain ranges in these varshas, bounding them. The two varshas in the north and the south are bow-like, curved and segmented. Four others are long and straight. At the heart of these is a rectangular mountain, a lofty tableland called Ilavarsha. Out of its nave, golden Sumeru, the corolla of the lotus, thrusts its pinnacle at the sky, a hundred thousand yojanas into the air.

The top of Sumeru is thirty yojanas wide and only part of it is above ground while its great roots thrust themselves down, deep into the earth. To the north of Ilavarsha are the mountains Nilagiri, Svetagiri and Sringavada, which bound the three varshas Ramyaka, Hiranmaya and Kuru. These slope down gently into the sea of salt, Lavana samudra.

Numerous rivers have their sources in these mountains, and to the south of Ilavarsha are three delectable ranges called Nisada, Hemakunta and Himalaya. Each one is an ajuta of yojanas long. These form the frontiers of Kimpurusha and Bharata varsha. To the west of Ilavrata the mountain Malyavan looms, and to its east Gandhamadana, Neela and Nishada, powerful naves of grace upon the earth, each one two thousand yojanas long. Mandara, Suparshvaka and Kumuda stand in the Ketumala and Bhadrasva varshas, but these are counted as pada parvatas, foothills of golden Meru. They form, as it were, the pillars around awesome Sumeru, on four sides.

Upon these four mountains four crystalline lakes shimmer, one of milk, another of honey, a third of canesugar juice, and a fourth of sweet water. Near these lakes are the enchanted gardens of the Gods—Nandana, Chaitra, Vaibhrajaka and Sarvatobhadra. In these gardens, the Devas dwell, the Gandharvas, Apsaras, Kinnaras, Bagas, and other marvellous beings that are divine, with their women of untold charms. They live in love and some abandon, for the lives of the immortals are always freer than those of mortal men.

On the peak of Mount Mandara, grow the celestial mango-fruit trees, each one eleven hundred yojanas tall. They are the sires of the mango trees of the later ages, and from their fruit that fall to the ground, each one big as a mountain-crag, flow crimson, delicious juices. Why, they flow down into the world as a river, scarlet as the rising sun, the Arunodaya. At the feet of those magical trees, the Devas worship the Devi Bhagavati as Aruna, who destroys all sins, grants every desire.

In another age, lost in time's labyrinths, the lord of the Daityas worshipped Devi Aruna upon Mount Mandara, and had vast power and great blessings from her. He who worships her is cured of all his ailments, has back his health and grows miraculously wealthy and happy, too. Thus, she, the Devi, is called Adya, Maya, Atulaa, Aanantaa, Pushti, and Iswaramalini. By her grace, the river Jambunada flows, bearing divine gold on her currents," said Narayana to the wanderer, Narada Muni, in a certain kalpa,' says Vyasa to the Kuru king," says Romaharshana Suta to the Rishis of the sacred vana.

FIFTY-SEVEN

"VYASA MUNI SAID, 'NARAYANA SAID TO NARADA, "THE ARUNODAYA SPRINGS upon Mandara and flows east of Ilavarsha. Vayu Deva wafts the fragrances of the bodies of the Yakshis and Gandharvis and the sakhis of the Devi Bhavani, and pervades the air for ten yojanas around with them.

The rose apples that grow upon Mandara, each one big as an elephant, also fall on to the ground and their juices flow down the mountain as a river. And this is the Jambu, which flows south of Ilavarsha. Here the Devi who loves the jambu fruit is called Jambadini. All the Devas, Rishis and Nagas worship her, and pray for every living jiva in creation. She dwells on both banks of the river Jambu, and mortal men who chant these her sacred names, each one a mantra—Kokilakshi, Karunaa, Kamapujitaa, Kathoravigrahaa, Devapujyaa, Dhanyaa and Gavastini— have her blessings both in this world and the next.

Unearthly gold is created from the juice of the jambu fruit, the essence of the wind and the rays of the sun. The Vidyadharis and other immortal women wear ornaments fashioned from this magical svarna, and it is called jambunada svarna. Lovelorn Devas, too, make crowns, armlets and waistbands for their flames from this gold, and they never tarnish, not in a kalpa.

On Mount Suparshva, there is a giant kadamba tree. The five rivulets of honey called the madhudhara flow from cavities in the vast trunk of this tree, big as caves, and flow west over the land. The Devas drink from these streams and their mouths are always sweet. Pavana Deva carries the scent of this honey for even a hundred yojanas.

Dhareswari Mahadevi dwells on the banks of the streams of honey, her nature of kaala, the fulfiller of desires, having a thousand faces, turned everywhere to hear every bhakta's prayers. She is the Goddess of forests and woods. She is worshipped as Karala Devi, Kaalamgi, and Kamakotiparvatini.

On top of the Kumuda Mountain, there grows the enormous banyan tree Satabala. From this pristine tree, as well, many great rivers flow. Their waters bestow their hearts' desires on bhaktas, and so they are known as kamadugha. They flow slowly down the north of Ilavarsha. The Bhagavati Meenakshi dwells in these rivers, and is worshipped by the Suras and the Asuras alike.

The Devi there is fierce to behold, her raiment blue, and her hair, and those that worship her call her by her names Atimanyaa, Atipujyaa, Mattamatanga Gamini, Madanonmadani, Manapriyaa, Manapriyataraa, Mayuravarshobhadayaa, Marabegadharaa, Marapujitaa, Maramadini, Sikhivahanagarbhabhu. And the Goddess Meenalochana Ekangarupini and the Lord Parameshwara bless them.

If they drink the lucid waters of those rivers, they are set free from old age, anxiety, from every disease and from an early death. They are blissfully happy as long as they live, and no danger comes anywhere near them.

Now listen, O Muni, to the names of the other nineteen mountains that ring golden Sumeru round, as if they were the petals of a flower, and Meru its corolla. They are Kuranga, Kuraga, Kusumbha, Vikankata, Trikuta, Sisira, Patanga, Ruchaka, Nishada, Sitivasa, Kapila, Samkha, Vaidurya, Charudhi, Hamsa, Rishabha, Naga, Kalanjara, and Narada named after you!

Sumeru is also flanked by eight other massive mountains—Jathara and Devakuta in the north, Pavamana and Pariyatra in the west, Kailasa and Karavira in the south, and Sringagiri and Makaragiri in the east. And, amidst these, Meru is splendid as the Sun surrounded by the planets.

In the heart of Sumeru, there is a secret city, ten thousand yojanas long and wide. It is Brahma's city, Brahmapuri, at the heart of the earth, and everything in it is made from the Devas' gold. And around Brahmapuri are eight other mysterious golden cities, one for each Lokapala. These are two thousand yojanas long and wide.

Their names are Manovati, Amravati, Tejovati, Samyamani, Krishnangana, Sraddhavati, Gandhavati, Mahodaya, and the ninth is Yasovati. Brahma and the Dikpalas rule over them.

When Mahavishnu came as the Vamana, the Trivikrama, some thousand yugas ago to curb the power of the Asura Mahabali, the nails of his foot cracked the Brahmanda kataha of this auspicious mountain. Through that cleft the Bhagavati Ganga flows, she who washes the sins of those who bathe in her. And she is known as Vishnupadi.

The Ganga first fell from the heavens upon Vishnudhama. Here, the pure Dhruva saw the Lord's lotus-like feet, shimmering, and he has remained there ever since, in samadhi. There, too, the Saptarishi dwell, in spirit, praying for all the lokas. In Vishnudhama, where the Ganga springs, moksha is to be had most easily in this world, and here through the ages do Rishis dwell in dhyana and bhakti, their hair matted in jata, bathing frequently in the holy Ganga, seeking the final freedom.

The Ganga flows from the Dhruva mandala where Vishnu dwells, in a million luminous channels, down into the Chandra mandala, the realm of the Moon, and then on into Brahmaloka. Here she divides herself in four channels, Sita, Alakananda, Bhadra and Chaturbhadra and, flowing across the earth, enters the sea.

The all-purifying Sita flows across the mountain filaments of Sumeru, and onto Gandhamadana; and flows on across Bhadravavarsha, worshipped by the Devas, and into the salt sea in the east. The second dhara, the Chakshu, emerges from the Malyavan range of mountains in a cataract, hurtles past Ketumala and on into the western ocean.

The third dhara, the shining Alakananda, flows down from Brahmaloka over the Girikuta Mountain, through some impenetrable jungles, and falls onto Hemakuta. She flows across Bharatavarsha and into the southern sea. Words cannot describe the power of the Alakananda. Let it be said, though, that those who go to bathe in her have a lifetime of their sins burnt away for each step they take along their pilgrimage. Some say each step is equal to an Aswamedha or Rajasuya yagna.

The fourth stream of the Trilokyapavani Ganga Devi is called Bhadra, and she falls down from the mountain Srigavana in a swift and wide dhara, flows by the northern Kuru kingdom, and into the sea. Numerous rivers flow out of the great and blessed mountains Meru, Mandara and the rest and flow through various varshas, the continents, and into the plumbless ocean. But the wise who know say that, of all the varshas, Bharata varsha is the karma kshetra, the field of fate.

The other eight varshas, though they are on earth, bestow the pleasures of heaven. For, it is souls that exhaust their punya in heaven who are born into them. The people of the eight continents live for ten thousand years. Their bodies are magnificent and hard as diamonds, and they have the prowess of a thousand elephants, more. They live lives of immense pleasure, and neither the men nor the women ever tire of their ecstatic dalliances. Their appetite for love is prodigious, and their virility and femininity, as well. These eight are continents of miracles, and it is told the people born into them grow in miraculously short time. So, the women conceive even a year after they are born! Life in those continents is hard to describe; everything in them is so unearthly.

In those eight varshas, Vishnu and the other Devas worship the Devi Bhagavati. Why, worshiping the Devi in those enchanted realms, Vishnu remains there in deep samadhi, and his grace is upon all the wonderful men and women of those continents. In Ilavarsha, however, there is only one man—Rudra— who lives surrounded by countless lovely women. They were not all women always, for once Bhavani laid a curse on Ilavarsha that any man who enters that continent would be transformed into a woman, instantly.

Rudra, Bhavani's Shakta, remains there worshipping the Un-born, unmanifest Lord Samkarsana. To bless humankind he worships his own turiya form, the transcendent state, of the nature of tamas.

In Harivarsha, Vishnu dwells as the splendid Narasimha, the Manticore, and the lord of the Daityas, his most devoted bhakta Prahlada worships him. In Ketumalavarsha, Bhagavan rules as Kama Deva, the God of love. The ocean's daughter, Indira Devi, worships him there, and she is mistress of the varsha.

In Ramyakavarsha, Vishnu is worshipped as the Matsya, the Fish. Both the Suras and the Asuras worship him, and Manu, ceaselessly. In Hiranmaya varsha, Hari dwells as the Kurma, the primeval Tortoise, the Lord of yoga, which is union. He is worshipped there by Aryaman, the sovereign of the ancestors.

In the Uttara Kuru mandala, the Bhagavan is manifest as the Adi Varaha, the primordial Boar. Bhumi Devi, the Earth herself, worships him there. In the Kimpurusha varsha, the Bhagavan Vishnu manifests himself as Rama, and great Hanuman worships him there, and is lord of that varsha.

And in this Bharatavarsha, O Narada, I am here before you, as a Rishi, and a man, and you are the one who worships me here!" And Narada sang his praises.

The Bhagavan Narayana was pleased and said, "Hear from me about the rivers and mountains of Bharatavarsha. The main mountains are Malaya, Mangalaprastha, Mainaka, Chitrakuta, Rishabha, Kutaka, Kolla, Sahya,

Devagiri, Rishyamooka, Srisaila, Vyankata, Mahendra, Varidhara, Vindhya, Suktiman, Riksha, Pariyatra, Drona, Chitrakuta, Govardhana, Raivataka, Kakubha, Nila, Gaurmukha, Indrakila, Kamagiri; and a hundred other lesser mountains. Thousands of rivers issue from these, and bathing in them or even drinking their auspicious waters destroys the sins of men.

The main rivers and the most blessed are Tamaraparani, Chandravasa, Kritamala, Vatodaka, Vaihayasi, Kaveri, Vena, Payasvini, Tungabhadra, Krishnavena, Sarkara, Vertaka, Godavari, Bhimarathi, Nirvindhya, Payosnika, Tapi, Reva, Surasa, Narmada, Saraswati, Charmanvati, Sindhu, Andha, Sona, Rishikulya, Trisama, Vedasmriti, Mahanadi, Kausiki, Yamuna, Mandakini, Drishadvati, Gomati, Sarayu, Oghavati, Saptavati, Susama, Satadru, Chandrabhaga, Maharudbhrida, Vitasta, Asikni, Viswa, and a thousand streams besides.

All jivas that incarnate in Bharatavarsha enjoy the three kinds of pleasures, divine, worldly and bestial, too, in accordance with their store of karma. And the wisest Munis have always said that Bharata is the foremost varsha, for it is Holy Land and the grace of God is most easily obtained here. They say that not even in Devaloka can the Bhagavan Hari be worshipped as he can in the land of Bharatavarsha. It is better, they aver, to be born a short-lived mortal in the land of Bharata than be born in any other varsha, even as a being who lives for a kalpa.

And men who do not try for moksha even after being born in the Holy Land of Bharata are certainly lower than beasts, and so will they devolve. It is true, indeed, that the Lord gives his bhaktas in Bharatavarsha most of what they ask him for, but it is rarely that he will give them moksha, or a vision of the Paramatman, that will set them free. This he does only to the rest of his worshippers who have been born repeatedly, and been his bhaktas for many lives.

There are eight upadvipas of the great Jambudvipa. When king Sagara's sons were searching for the white horse of their father's Aswamedha yagna, they found these. Their names are Svarnaprastha, Chandrasukra, Avartana, Ramanaka, Mandaropakhya, Harina, Panchajanya and Lanka.

Jambudvipa is surrounded by the Kshara, the salt sea. Even as golden Meru is surrounded by Jambudvipa, the salt sea is bounded by Plakshadvipa, the continent of the fig tree. The plaksha is of a golden hue, and fire burns at its roots. Idhmajihva, the son of Priyavrata is lord of Plaksha. In Plaksha, too, there are four castes, called Hamsa, Patanga, Urdhayana and Satyanga.

The people of the plaksha live for a thousand years. They are of motley and marvellous appearance, and worship the Lord Surya, the blazing Sun, and are bright and powerful folk.

The Ikshurasa, sugarcane sea, bounds Plakshadvipa, and the Salmala, silk-cotton tree, dvipa bounds this sea. Salmala is twice as great as Plaksha; and on the tree with the name Salmali, Garuda roosts. Priyavrata's son Yagnabahu is king in Salmala dvipa. Here, too, there are four castes and they are Srutadhara, Viryadhara, Vasundhara and Isundhara. The people of Salmala worship Lord Soma Deva, the nectarine Moon.

Salmala dvipa is bounded by the Surasagara, the sea of wine, and the Kusa dvipa, of grasses, bounds that crimson sea. It is twice as great as Salmala, and luminous kusa grasses grow everywhere. Priyavrata's son Hiranyareta rules Kusadvipa. The four castes of this realm are Kusala, Kovida, Abhiyukta and Kulaka. The people of this continent are as powerful as Indra and the Devas. They are all said to be omniscient. They worship Agni, the Fire God, and live for many thousands of years.

The awesome Ghrita sagara of ghee bounds Kusadvipa, and is in turn bounded by the Krauncha dvipa, of the curlew. The Krauncha Mountain stands vast and dominating upon this dvipa. Once, in dim time, the brilliant Lord Karttikeya burst this mountain asunder. Priyavrata's son Ghritaprishta rules this continent, and its people are divided into the castes Purusha, Rishabha, Dravina and Vedaka. Varuna Deva, Lord of the seas, is worshipped by them.

Krauncha dvipa is bounded by the Dadhisagara, and the sea of curd is encompassed by the Saka dvipa, of the teak tree. And, indeed, there stands an ancestral, numinous teak in the midst of this dvipa. Priyavrata's son Medhatithi rules Sakadvipa, and its castes are Satyavrata, Kratuvrata, Danavrata and Anuvrata. They worship Lord Hari himself, as pranavayu, life-breath, and are all masters of pranayama, by which they control their senses, and their very hearts and destinies.

Kshira sagara, of milk, bounds Saka dvipa, and is bounded by Pushkara dvipa, of the blue lotus. The leaves of the gigantic Pushkara tree are golden and innumerable, like flames. Brahma Paramesthin, creator of all the continents and seas, dwells in the great blue lotus at the heart of this dvipa and is worshipped by the people of Priyavrata's son Vitihotra.

Pushkara dvipa is bounded by the Svadu sagara, of pure, crystalline water. And then there is the mountain called Lokaloka, which stands like a sentinel upon the plain between this world and the next, loka and aloka. This mountain stands upon a plain of pure and unearthly gold, smooth as a mirror. No living beings dwell here. The rays of the sun, the moon and the planets pass through this mountain and then only shed their lustre upon the Triloka, the three worlds," said the Muni Narayana, who is God himself,' said Vyasa Muni."

FIFTY-EIGHT

THE SUTA TELLS HIS MUNIS, "VYASA DEVA SAID, 'NARAYANA SAID, "THIS subtle mountain Lokaloka is so lofty, that none of the planets on their deepest orbits pass out of it. Brahma Paramesthin has set the four great Diggajas on four sides of this mountain. Their names are Rishabha, Pushpachuda, Vamana and Aparajita. These four leviathans hold all the worlds in their places. The Bhagavan Hari pours his infinite strength into these elephants, and so do Indra and the Devas who are his Vibhutis.

Beyond the mountain Lokaloka, a resplendent path leads directly to Yogeswara, within the great egg formed by heaven and earth. When the egg, which is twenty-one koti yojanas from tip to base, grows inert the Sun flames into it as Vairaja. Hence, he is called Martanda. He is Hiranyagarbha, when he is born from the Golden Egg, and he ordains the quarters and where Swarga, Bhumi and Patala shall be. The Sun is the atman, the soul, of Swarga and Moksha, of the Patalas, of the Devas, men, birds and beasts, insects, of trees, reptiles and of all the living. He presides over their vision.

Even as the halves of a gram are of equal size, so, too, heaven and earth are equal to one another. The space between them is called Antariksha. The Sun, blazing at the heart of this space, illumines the worlds, and heats them. When he travels north during Uttarayana, he moves slowly, in mandagati. And when he goes south, he does so more swiftly, in shighragati. By his sojourns, the lengths of day and night are determined.

Every planet has three positions, Jaradgava, at the equator, Airavata in the north, and Vaiswanara in the south. So, too, the Sun. When Dhruva the pole star hauls in his rope of air in the north, it is Uttarayana.

East of Meru, there is a city of the Gods called Devadhanika, Indra's city, glorious past imagination. South of the golden mountain lies Yama's city, Samyamani. West of Sumeru is Varuna's magnificent pura, Nimnochani, and to the north is Soma, the Moon's, glimmering city Vibhavari.

The Brahmavadis say the Sun rises first in Indra's city, at noon he is over Samyamani, at dusk over Nimnochani, where he sets, and at midnight, he shines upon nocturnal Vibhavari. Those who dwell on Meru always see the Sun in the middle of the sky. For himself, of course, Surya Deva never rises or sets, only burns on and on, but he is the manifestor of time, and the zodiac is his atman! The Sun's chariot runs up the sky at the speed of a hundred and forty-two thousand yojanas per muhurta, and he traverses the entire zodiac in the time of a year. Why, the learned call the very chariot of the sun the year; its spokes are the months, the three fourth-months are the nave and the six seasons the circumference of the wheel.

The axle points of the wheel are Meru on one side and Manasottara on the other; the wheel marks are kaala, kaastha, muhurta, yaama, parahara, day and night, and the fortnight. The wheel is fixed upon the nave, and the sun goes round it, like an oilman oiling his machine, round and round the Manasottara Mountain! The eastern extremity of the wheel is fixed upon the pole star.

The seat of the Sun on his chariot measures thirty-six lakh yojanas. The chariot is yoked to seven horses. Garuda's brother, the legless Aruna, is his sarathy, and the horses always whinny for joy. Though Aruna sits before the Sun, he keeps his face turned west. Sixty thousand Balakhilya Munis, each the size of a thumb, chant the ambrosial Vedic hymns before him. The Rishis, Apsaras, Urgas, Gramanis, Rakshasas and all the Devas worship the relucent Sun. The Sun flies over the great earth in just a moment, and he never rests, not for a moment.

Now listen to the movements of the planets in the sky; for the fates of men, and of humankind, good and evil, are determined by these. First, the Moon. The Moon, the Lord of night, is situated a lakh of yojanas above the Sun. Soma takes a month to traverse the zodiac, across which the Sun moves in a year. He brings joy to men of the earth during his bright fortnight, and to the Pitrs when he wanes above the world.

The Moon travels one nakshatra in thirty muhurtas, and twenty-eight nakshatras spread across the twelve signs of the zodiac in a month, at the rate of a two and a quarter nakshatras per sign. The Lord himself made the nakshatra Abhijita, the twenty-eighth asterism, to align with golden Meru upon the earth. These nakshatras are, of course, bright stars in each sign. He is called Manomaya, for he stokes love and fulfills the desires of the heart. He is Annamaya, as well, being Lord of herbs and plants, and all green, living things.

Soma is nectarine in his nature, and bestows liberation and ecstasy. He is usually a beneficent luminary.

The planet Sukra, Venus, orbits two lakh yojanas above the Moon. He travels with the Sun at times, but then again behind or before him, too, taking a year more or less to traverse the zodiac. He is a benign influence, mainly, the Lord of love, the Bhagavan Sukra Bhargava, the son of Bhrigu, Acharya to the Asuras.

Budha, Soma's illegitimate son Mercury, moves beside Venus. He also moves with, behind and ahead of the Sun. He seldom takes a year to travel the zodiac. When he is far from the great star, hurricanes and tempests blow across land and sea, and there is fear of drought, and danger in general. He is usually a benefic, too, and is the Lord of intelligence.

The Earth's son Kuja, Mars, is a red and warlike planet. He takes forty-five days to cross each rasi, each sign of the zodiac, a distance the Sun covers in a month. This reckoning for Mars' movement is when he is not retrograde. Mars is generally a malignant and mischievous planet. The Lord of courage and war, he does bring misery.

Two lakh yojanas above Mars is Brihaspati, the Acharya of the Devas, the sage Jupiter. He takes twelve years to traverse the zodiac, spending a year in each sign. When he is not retrograde, he is always the most benign planet, doing greater good than any other does. He is the Lord of wisdom, prosperity, and all things auspicious.

Two lakh yojanas above Brihaspati, there revolves the son of Surya, Sani, the much feared Saturn. He takes thirty months to pass over each rasi of the zodiac, and is known as a mandagraha, a slow and malefic planet. He is the great balancer, but works with sorrow and unrest.

Next to Sani is the Saptarishi mandala, the great Bear, the seven stars that revolve around Dhruva, the pole star. These seven sages always grant very special boons to all that come under their influence. They are called Vishnupada.

Thirteen lakh yojanas above them is Dhruva, Uttanapada's son, and the greatest of bhaktas. He dwells there, constant and unmoving, and with him are Indra, Agni, Kashyapa, Dharma Deva and the Nakshatras. All men and all the Devas, too, pay homage to the blessed Dhruva, and he is the patron of the immortals that live until the end of the kalpa. He serves the Lord's starry, lotus feet. He is the pillar around whom all the other planets revolve on their ropes of air, like beasts of draught, some near and some further away, each by his own karma and blown by mystic Vayu of the airs, and kept aloft by the mystery of Purusha and Prakriti.

Some say this jyotishachakra is Sisumara, the Dolphin, the Lord himself. On his right are the Uttarayana nakshatras, fourteen of them from Abhijita to Punarvasu, and on his left the fourteen Dakshinayana nakshatras, from Pusyami to Uttarashada. Thus, the asterisms of the zodiac form the coiled body of the Sisumara. His back is upon the Ganga of heaven, called Ajavithi. Punarvasu and Pusyami are the right and left side of his loins, Ardra and Aslesha are his right and left feet, Abhijita and Uttarashada are his left and right nostrils, Sravana and Purvashada are his eyes, Dhanishtha and Mula are his ears, Magha and the eight Dakshinyana nakshatras are the bones of his left side. Margasirsha and the Uttarayana nakshatras are the bones of his right side. Satabhisha and Jyestha are his shoulders. Agasti from the upper jaw and Yama the lower. Kuja is his face, Sani his sexual member; Brihaspati is the hump on his back. Surya is his breast, while Narayana remains in his heart and the Moon is his mind.

Sisumara is also sometimes the one the wise call Dhruva and the whole concept of the Sisumara remains shrouded in mystery. Yet, they also say the Aswin twins form the nipples on his chest, Usana is his navel, Budha is his prana and apana, his breath, Rahu is his neck and Ketu all over his body, and every star in heaven in the most distant mandalas rules over one hair on his form! The Devas are this cosmic form of the Bhagavan, the Sisumara. The knowing meditate upon this Form of the Lord at the sandhyas, in perfect silence and with all their hearts.

They say, 'We worship the Lord, in whose body all the stars and planets dwell. Who destroys the sins of those that compose the mantras, and of any that worship thee in the morning, noon or at twilight.'

O Narada, the realm of Rahu is situated an ajuta of yojanas below the Sun. Rahu, who is the Rakshasi Simhika's son, moves like any nakshatra. He once drank the amrita and Vishnu struck off his neck with the Sudarshana chakra before the nectar of immortality went down his throat. So, his head is immortal and stationed in the sky whence the chakra bore it like lightning.

It was Surya and Soma Deva who warned Mohini, the enchantress that Vishnu had become, that a Demon was drinking the amrita she meant to give only to the Devas. So, Rahu, in unending hatred, swallows the Sun and the Moon every now and again, in baleful eclipse. Then, again, Vishnu casts his flaming Sudarshana into the sky and Rahu, who cannot bear its fires, retreats, and the luminaries shine forth again. Else, we should all be left darkling forever, from Rahu's ancient ire.

Below Rahu's realm are other lokas, all pure and sacred, where Siddhas, Charanas and Vidhyadharas dwell. Below these live the Yakshas, Rakshasas, Bhutas, Pretas and Pisachas in their enchanted worlds and palaces. The wise call these zones the Antariksha. It extends up to where the wind blows violently, and where the clouds appear. Below the Antariksha is Bhumi, the earth of a hundred yojanas. On the underside of this Bhumi are seven cavernous regions, secret, dark and wonderful.

The first of these is Atala, the next Vitala, then Sutala, Talatala, Mahatala, Rasatala and the seventh, Patala. They are, respectively, white, black, red, yellow, tan, gray and gold. These are called the Vila-swargas and are places of greater, more intense happiness than the heavens above! There are awesome, splendid palaces in them, where thousands of Danavas, Daityas and Yakshas dwell, all beings of great power. They are all mayavis, mages, and their resolves are never thwarted.

The Patalas are illumined by the huge gemstones set in the emerald heads of the thousands and thousands of Nagas that live here in these glimmering worlds, serpents of every kind, the magnificent Vasuki their Lord. Ah, which liberated Muni, even, is not aroused to see the exquisite daughters of the Daityas and Danavas and the Naga princesses that dwell in the Patalas?

Mayaa, the demon emperor of limitless power, and master builder of the Asuras, has created many marvellous cities here, with immense places and numberless mansions of untold brilliance amidst charmed gardens, with streams and luminous pools full of lotuses not found either on heaven or earth, and lakes swarming with birds of stunning plumage, and sweetest-throated warblers that sing in tongues that the inhabitants of these realms know well.

The Asuras and Nagas anoint themselves with magical medicaments and oils when they bathe, and cook their food using magic herbs, as well. So, they know no illness. The wine they drink is such that even the Devas of Amravati hardly taste anything like it. The only thing the Asuras of the nether worlds fear is the tejas of the Lord Vishnu, who is always on the side of the Devas and thus the Danavas' enemy, and his Sudarshana Chakra.

In the highest of the lower realms, Atala, the haughty son of the Asura Mayaa, architect of the legendary Tripura, rules. He is Bala, the mighty. He is the creator of the ninety-six sorceries, the mayas. The other mayavis of the Patalas and the Earth, the best of them, hardly know two of these; yet, even they are so powerful. When awesome Bala yawned, legend has it, the three kinds of seductresses of his realm were made, who fascinated mankind everywhere, in all the lokas. These were the Pumschalis, the Svairinis and the Kaminis.

They will seduce any man who happens to wander into secret Atala, and so sweet and deep are their embraces and caresses, Narada, that their lovers begin to believe themselves to be Gods after they lie with these enchantresses, who, in truth, drain them of their strength, their very life-force. And these unfortunates are then sent back to the higher worlds, wasted in a night, never able to forget their delirious seduction, and they die thus, soon, pining for a woman they never knew was a vampire.

The realm below Atala is Vitala, and here the Bhagavan Bhava himself rules as Hatakeswara. He dwells there with Bhavani, forever, and with his wild and devoted ganas around him. The river Hataki flows from here and it springs from the juices of the ceaseless lovemaking of Bhava and his Bhavani. Agni, the Fire God, urged by the Wind, Vayu Deva, begins to drink from this river of infinite excitement. It burns him, the hiranyaretas, the fiery golden semen of Siva, and he spits it out with a phutkara sound. Thus, the gold of the Asuras, hataka, is made, and the demons are passionately fond of it. The Daitya women use no other metal for their ornaments.

Below Vitala is Sutala, said to be especially important. Virochana's son, the great, great Mahabali, lives here. At Indra's behest, the Bhagavan Vamana, Vishnu who came as a Dwarf, thrust Bali down into Sutala. He gave the noble Asura all the Lakshmi of the worlds and made him Lord of the Daityas. Why, it is told the Devi Lakshmi herself followed Mahabali down into the Patalas, when the Lord thrust that Asura of immaculate dharma down there. The fearless Bali dwells there still, worshipping Vasudeva.

It is told the Bhagavan hardly shows his favour to us when he gives us the greatest wealth and apparent prosperity. For, riches are the offspring of maya, and with them come anxieties, worries, and the lack of mental peace. He gave Bali, the just Asura, peace, when he took earthly kingdom from him by stamping on his head. Earthly treasure is a most ephemeral thing, and of hardly any account. Thus did my grandfather Prahlada ask the Lord for but one boon—to serve Him, always. The truth is none of us know the nature of the Bhagavan Vasudeva, and what methods he employs to favour us when he is pleased. Truly, at times what he does seems at first anything but his good favour. But, in time, a man realises how the Lord was always with him, and how he blessed him precisely with what once seemed like hardship, even torment.

Thus the Bhagavan once bound Bali with the Varuna paasa, thrust him down into a mountain cave in Sutala, and is now his dwarapalaka, his gatekeeper. Once, mighty Ravana who had limitless strength stormed down into Sutala to conquer that hidden realm. It is told the Bhagavan, who is Bali's gatekeeper, flicked his toe at the Rakshasa and flung him an ajuta of yojanas away," says Devarishi Narayana to Narada,' Vyasa Muni told the king."

FIFTY-NINE

"KRISHNA DWAIPĀYANA, THE BLESSED ONE, TOLD JANAMEJAYA OF THE Kurus, 'Narayana said upon Badarikasrama to the Devarishi, "Below Sutala is Talatala. The Lord of Tripura, the peerless Mayaa Danava, is sovereign of this realm. Siva burnt up his triune cities with a shaft of fire, but then rescued his bhakta Mayaa, and gave him sovereignty over wonderful Talatala.

Mayaa is the Acharya of all the mayavis of the nether realms, for there is no sorcerer as powerful or as wise as he is. He once had the Surya Siddhanta, the secrets of the stars, from the Sun himself. And he was to Asura creators and artisans, what Viswakarman is for the Devas—an artist of fathomless genius.

Below Talatala is Mahatala. The ferocious Nagas, the sons of Kadru rule here. Their hoods are as wide as rivers, and they are legend for their swift and vicious rage. The foremost of them are Kuhaka, Takshaka, Sushena and Kaliya. The only one they truly fear is Vishnu's golden eagle Garuda. They live in Mahatala in peace and pleasure, with all their marvellous kin.

Below Mahatala is Rasatala, where the Daityas, Danavas and Pani Asuras live. There also dwell in Rasatala the Nivatakavachas, whose armour is impenetrable, and the awesome Kalakeyas of the golden city of the air, Hiranyapuri, who are the witch Puloma's sons and sworn enemies of the Lord Indra and his Devas. There are other mighty Asuras who dwell in Rasatala even like snakes in their holes—the Demons who have fled down here and cower in terror of Indra's sorceress Sarama, and her feral mantras.

Below Rasatala is Patala, where the great Naga, Vasuki of a thousand coils rules, with his kinsmen Sankha, Kulika, Shweta, Dhanajaya, Mahasankha, Dhritarashtra, Sankhachuda, Kamvala, Asvatara Devpadattaka, all virulent.

Some of them have five and ten hoods, others twenty, fifty and a hundred, while a few have a thousand hoods, and others have jewels in their heads like small suns! They are all irascible in the extreme.

Thirty yojanas below Patala is the void, the eternal darkness that is also the Bhagavan. His bhaktas call him Sankarshana in this Form. He is thousand-headed here; he is Sesa, who holds the entire universe like a mustard seed upon his head. When he wants to end the worlds, Rudra springs forth from him with eleven savage vyuhas. Rudra is three-eyed, his trisula in his hand, ablaze with the three apocalyptic flames.

At nights, all the great Nagas come to Ananta Deva, and bow to him, the jewels in their hoods shimmering. The Naga women come to him as well, sinuous and exquisite, their velvet bodies anointed with sandal, aguru and kasmiri. Their bodies exude the musk of their lust as well, and it is told the Lord Ananta's thousand eyes roll in desire.

In his human form, the omnipotent Lord Ananta is kindly and merciful. He is sattvika, intoxicated always, and speaks only the sweetest, most loving words. The vaijayanti hangs from his neck; his complexion is fair as lotuses. He wears just one earring and deep blue silk, and his immense ploughshare weapon, the Halayaudha, is never far from him."

Narada asked, "Lord, why has Bhagavan created such diversity, when the laws of karma are the same for all the living?"

Narayana Muni said, "It is the mixtures of the gunas, of sattva, rajas and tamas, that cause the infinite variety in nature. Below the earth and above Atala, the manes called the Anisvattas dwell in deep samadhi, blessing their own gotras, their own kith and kin. Here Yama, the Lord of the ancestors, punishes those that die and are brought to him for judgement. Yama is master of the Narakas, the hells, which are not to be confused with the Patalas.

The wise Munis who have composed the Shastras say that there are twenty-eight Narakas: Tasmisra, Raurava, Maharaurava, Kumbhipaka, Kalasutra, Asipatrakanana, Sukaramukha, Andhakupa, Krimibhojana, Taptamurti, Samdamsa, Vajrakantaka, Vaitaranai, Puyoda, Pranarodha, Visasana, Lalabhaksha, Sarameyadana, Avichi, Apahapana, Ksharakardama, Rakshogana, Sambhoja, Sulaprota, Dandasuka, Avatarodha, Paryavartanaka and Suchimukha.

Jivas are taken to these hells to pay for their sins. The torments of these Narakas vary according to one's crimes, from being brutally whipped, to being devoured by animals he has harmed during his life, to being cooked in oil, burned by fire, driven mad, cut in slivers by plants sharp as razors, ground to paste, transformed into a hideously ugly being, reduced to an insect and eaten by other insects, skinned alive, made to embrace the red-hot iron form of a woman, this the adulterers, impaled, thrown into rivers filled with urine, faeces, pus, blood, vomit, fat, marrow, flesh, phlegm, and made to eat and drink these, torn to bits by packs of dogs, flung down from steep cliffs onto rocks below, cut up in small pieces, made to drink molten iron, to eat human flesh, to kill and eat friends and lovers, starved to death, hunted by great birds with beaks like swords, eaten by five-faced worms big as pythons, shut up in black, stinking holes, have their eyes gouged out by vultures, pierced all over with long needles.

These are just some of the torments that the Narakas have to offer sinners, and the erring soul's sojourn in a hell can last for ten thousand years, more, before his sins are washed from him, and he has paid for them in full.

There are those who believe that in some ages the earth and the hells overlap each other, when the punishments of the Narakas may be found in this world itself. But those who worship the Devi Bhagavati, even if they are the worst sinners, she saves them from these Narakas and their kundas, their dreadful pits. Where the Devi is worshipped all sins are burnt to ashes, and the bhakta becomes a free man, and a liberated soul. A man who has the Devi's grace does not suffer even in his dreams. All manner of prosperity becomes his," said the Mahamuni Narayana to Narada, listening avidly to him.' Vyasa said to the rajan," says the Suta.

SIXTY

"VYASA MUNI CONTINUED, 'NARAYANA SAID, "THE HIGHEST PRAKRITI appears as the five-fold Goddess. She manifests in creation as Ganesha's mother Durga, as Radha, as Lakshmi, as Saraswati and as Savitri."

Narada would know, "Why is she called Prakriti? Why does she manifest herself as five?"

"She is more mysterious than we can ever fathom. Yet, I know something of her from my father Dharma Deva; so, listen. Pra means exalted, surpassingly excellent, kriti means creations. Thus, she the Devi is the transcendent, most marvellous Creatrix. Also, Pra is sattva, kri the rajoguna and ti is tamas. When the Brahmam, the pristine holy Ground upon which everything is founded, is tainted with the three gunas, then the Brahmam is known as Prakriti.

Yet, the mystery is that Prakriti exists before creation; she precedes the gunas. With yoga, the Paramatman, the first God, divided himself in two. His right side was male and his left, female. Thus Prakriti is eternal; she always was and shall be. There is no distinction between the Atman and his Shakti, between Purusha and Prakriti.

And before the Paramatman, even, there was the Devi. From her came the five Devis who bestow all their hearts' desire on her bhaktas. This primordial Devi is Maha Maya, of the nature of the universe. She is the Shakti of Krishna, who begins the kalpa. She is Durga, Siva's queen. She is intelligence, sleep, thirst, hunger, shadow, tiredness and mercy, memory, consciousness, nurture, prosperity and fortitude. Indeed, her qualities, like her nature, are infinite.

The Paramatman's second Shakti is the Devi Lakshmi. Her nature is shuddha sattva, which transcends the sattva guna. She is the presiding Deity of wealth and fortune. She is beautiful, benign, and perfectly auspicious. She is free from any vanity, lust, anger, greed or egoism. She is devoted to her Lord and her bhaktas. Indeed, she is the very life and soul of the Lord Vishnu. She is the source of life in all beings, and dwells in every green and living thing.

She dwells in Vaikuntha as Mahalakshmi. She dwells in Devaloka as Swarga Lakshmi, in palaces as Raja Lakshmi, and in every home as Griha Lakshmi. All the beauty that exists in this world, whether in places or people, in beasts or inanimate things, is hers alone. She is the fame of men of great deeds; she is the power of kings, the skill in trade of merchants, the compassion of Munis.

The third great Shakti in creation is the Devi Saraswati. She is the Goddess of speech, learning and intelligence, the Devi of the fine arts. She is all the learning in the universe and dwells in the hearts of men as medha, intelligence. She is the genius of poets; she is memory, wit and understanding. She is the inspiration of musicians and singers, artists and sculptors, too. She is a Goddess of peace, and, four-armed, holds a vina, a string of beads and the Vedas in her hands. She is of shuddha sattva guna, entirely pure. She is fair as the ice on the Himalaya, white sandalwood, the kunda flower, the moon, or the white lotus.

She chants the name of the kalpa's Paramatman, Sri Krishna, while she tells the string of beads in her hand. Her nature is ascetic and she bestows the fruits of tapasya on tapasvins. She is siddhi and vidya, and blesses her bhaktas with success in their endeavours. She is Vakdevi, the Mother of the holy word; why, without the Devi Saraswati all of creation would be dumb.

The fourth Shakti is the Devi Savitri. She is the mother of the four varnas, the source of the six Vedangas, the seed of every sandhya mantra in the three worlds, and of the mystic tantras. She is a Muni herself, and the tapasya of the Brahmana; she is the tejas of the sacred fire and the japam as well. She is purity itself, and is called Gayatri too. She dwells in Brahmaloka, and in every holy tirtha in the three worlds. Every yatri is thirsty for her blessed touch, which sets men free.

She is perfectly white, like soft crystal. Her nature is shuddha sattva, also, of the highest, transcendent bliss. She is the Parabrahmam, and gives moksha. She is the Shakti of fire, and mistress of the Brahma tejas. She is the Devi of the Brahmanas. She is the fourth Shakti, by the touch of whose feet the earth is purified.

The fifth Shakti is the Devi Radhika. She is the sovereign of the panchaprana, the five scared breaths: the elements. She is the life of all lives, dearer to Sri Krishna, the Paramatman, than his own prana. She is the most beautiful, highest Devi. She is fortune, saubhagya, and she is the left side of Krishna himself, and in no way less than he is.

The Devi Radha is the essence of all things, the infinite One, the First, eternal One, her nature of bliss, and she is worshipped by every being. She is the spirit of the mystic rasalila, the round dance of Krishna, and the rasa mandala was created for her, and she is its grace and its jewel.

She dwells in rasa, in Goloka, the realm of the sacred cow, and she is always joyful; and from her the exquisite gopikas have come, they are her amsas. She is beyond the three gunas, and is nirkara, formless. She takes form, now and again, only to bless her bhaktas. She is ubiquitous and immanent, but unattached and free. She is the soul of nature, of all beings and all things.

The wise recount her deeds and her mahima, they hymn her greatness and fame. She has no ahamkara, no ego, and makes no effort to do all that she does, so gloriously! To behold the Devi Radha is like looking upon the light of a million full moons.

In the Varaha kalpa, she is born into the world as a gopika, as Vrishabhanu's daughter, and she dances the Raasa lila in enchanted Vrindavana with her Lord Krishna. The very earth is blessed by the touch of her lotus-feet. At Krishna's breast, she is like streak lightning among deep blue thunderclouds. In time out of mind, Brahma undertook a fervid tapasya for a vision of her feet, but could not see her even in his dreams. He saw her then, incarnate in Vrindavana, and experienced her grace.

Every woman in the universe, it is told, O Narada, is born from some part of the Devi Radha's body. These five, O Muni, are the highest manifestations of the Parashakti. Listen now to the amsavataras of these five Devis.

The Devi Ganga, who washes the sins of men and the Devas alike, springs from Vishnu's holy feet. She is fluid, lustrous and eternal. She delivers those that bathe in her to Goloka. She is the best of the sacred rivers that flow in the world; she is the string of pearly water-beads that adorn the Lord Siva's jata! She is the incarnate tapasya of the Rishis of Bharatavarsha.

She, too, is an amsa of the Mulaprakriti, the Devi Bhagavati Mahamaya. Embodied, she is like the full moon, white as the pale lotus, as milk. She is also of the essence of shuddha sattva, lucid as heaven's crystal, quite free of ahamkara, chaste, and loved by Narayana.

Tulasi Devi, who lives in the world as a sacred plant, is also the Lord Mahavishnu's consort, and dwells at the Lord's feet. The wise say that, at her very touch, and by her scent, bhaktas achieve samadhi! She, too, burns the sins of the Kali yuga with fragrant fire. She is herself of the nature of agni. Ah, she is like a kalpa-vriksha, and mistress of all plants, great and small, in the land of Bharatavarsha.

Manasa Devi is the Muni Kashyapa's daughter, and Ananta Deva's in the world. She is the mother and queen of all Nagas, and they adore her. She sleeps on a bed of serpents. She is a Siddha yogini, a Vishnubhakta, and the kindly bestower of the fruits of tapasya. For, she herself once spent three hundred thousand years at tapasya, by the count of the Devas, and became the greatest tapasvin on earth.

Her fine body always radiates the Brahmatejas. She has Brahma's very nature and is always meditating upon the Parabrahmam. In a human life, once, she was the chaste wife of Jaratkaru Muni, and bore Astika as her son.

Then, there is Sasthi Devi, Devasena's mother. She is the best of the Matrikas; she is the foster-mother of the world, the bestower of sons and grandsons. It is told she lives beside every child as an aged yogini. She is the sixth amsa of the Mulaprakriti, and hence her name Sasthi, the sixth one. She is worshipped in Visakha, this subtle guardian of children everywhere.

The Devi Mangala Chandika goes from house to house, bestowing blessings and boons. She journeys by land, air, or through water. She was born from the face of the Devi Mulaprakriti. She is Mangala Chandi, because she is joyful and auspicious always, and does only great good wherever she goes. Yet, during the dissolution, there is none fiercer than she is. She is worshipped on the day of Mars, on every Tuesday. She, too, is a great granter of boons, of sons, wealth, fame, and indeed the gifts of all things a bhakta may want.

Then, there is she who is half of the Devi Durga, who sprang from the brow of the Mulaprakriti to kill the Asuras Sumbha and Nisumbha. She is Maheswari Devi Kali, who can destroy the universe in a wink, if she is roused. She is fiery, full of energy. Her splendour is that of a million suns, incredible! Her body is black from the fierce tapasya she does to Sri Krishna, the Kaalapurusha.

The Devi Vasundhara, the Earth, is also part of the Mulaprakriti. Brahma and the Devas, all the Munimandalas, the fourteen Manus and all men worship her, the blessed Mother. She is the source of sustenance and nurture, of precious jewels and metals that form in her great womb. She is the refuge, whom kings adore, for she bestows prosperity and is the life of the jivas that dwell upon her.

Of course, there are also the Devis who are the consorts of the Gods. The Devi Svaha is the consort of the Lord Agni, and without her, he is powerless to receive any oblation. Dakshina and Diksha are both queens of the Lord Yagna; diksha is given at the beginning of any auspicious ritual or sacrifice, and dakshina at the end.

The Devi Svadha is the wife of the manes, the Pitrs. She must be worshipped when the ancestors are, or the worship is futile. Vayu, the Wind's, lady is Svasti; Pusti is Ganapati's queen, and bestows health and strength, for she is nurture, too. Tusti, who is contentment, is the Devi of the splendid Lord Anantasesa, and Sampatti is the Lord Isana's mistress. Without her, the earth would be plunged in poverty.

The Bhagavan Kapila Deva's wife is the Devi Dhriti, and she is the wellspring of patience. The Devi Sati is the Goddess of truth, the Lord Mahadeva's consort, and he is known as Satya Deva as well. She is the mother of friendship. The Deva Punya, the Lord of merit's, lady is the Devi Pratishta, who is the Goddess of celebrity. She is the enlivener. Daya, she who is mercy, is the queen of Moha Deva. She is the source of hope in the world.

The Lord of good works, Sukarma Deva's, Devi is Kirti. She is fame. Kriya, who is deeds, is the consort of the Deva Udyoga, who is effort, industriousness.

Adharma, too, has a Devi, Adharmaa, who is the mother of lies, and the Goddess of cheats everywhere in the world! She was never seen on earth during the immaculate Krita yuga, but her influence has grown enormously, since the Treta yuga, when Rishis of tapasya could see half of her sukshma rupa, her subtle form. Then on, she has become more and more evident, and there is none to match her in brazen assurance or shamelessness. She has a nameless brother, Deceit, who is always at her side as she ranges the earth.

But there are the Devis Shanti, Paativratya and Lajja, peace, chastity and shame, who curb the wild influence of Adharmaa and her brother. It is only thus that the world has not yet gone entirely mad and vicious, even in the engulfing darkness of Kali yuga. Buddhi, and her sisters Atibuddhi, who personifies genius, and Kshema, who is fortitude, are the Lord Gyana's

Devis, and they help hold the world somewhat steady against the onslaught of reckless evil.

Dharma Deva's Devi is Murti. She is lovely, and the refuge of the Lord. She has the Devi Lakshmi's own nature, and beauty and her fortune as well. The Siddha yogini Nidra is the consort of Rudra Deva, when he is Kaalagni, the fire of time. All jivas spend their nights with her. The three sandhyas, day and night are also Kaala's queens. Who could keep count of time, if they did not exist?

Hunger and thirst, Bhuka and Daha, are the consorts of Lobha Deva, the Lord of greed. They, also, have their parts to play in keeping the world upon an even keel. Tejas too has his queens, splendid and iridescent. Mrityu and Prayaa, death and old age, are the consorts of Jvara, who is the Lord of illness and disease.

Sraddha and Bhakti are the queens of Vairagya Deva, who is the Lord of detachment. Then, there is Aditi, the mother of the Devas, Surabhi, the mother of sacred cows, Diti, the mother of the Daityas, Kadru, the mother of serpents, Garuda's mother Vinata, and the Danavas' mother Danu. All these Devis are amsas of the Mulaprakriti.

The Moon's wife Rohini, Surya Deva's queen Samjna, Manu's Satarupa, Indra's Sachi, Brihaspati's Tara, Vasishta's Arundhati, Atri's Anasuya, Kardama's Devahuti, Daksha's Prasuti, Himavan's Mena, Lopamudra, Kunti, Vindhyavali, the wives of Varuna, Kubera, Mahabali, the Devis Damayanti, Yasodha, Devaki, Gandhari, Draupadi, Saivya, Satyavati, Vrishabhanu's wife who is Radha's mother, Mandodari, Kausalya, Kauravi, Subhadra, Revati, Satyabhama, Kalindi, Lakshmanaa, Nagnajitaa, Mitravindaa, Lakshana, Rukmini, Sita, Kali, Usha, Chitralekha, Prabhavati, Bhanumati, Mayavati, Renuka, Balarama's mother Rohini, the Devi Sati—all these are, truly, amsas of the Devi Bhagavati, the Mulaprakriti.

Why, all women everywhere, every female of every species is an aspect of the great Prakriti. And women, too, differ from one another depending on which guna dominates in them. The sattvikas are always chaste and good-natured, and like Lakshmi herself in their homes. Women born of the rajoguna are middling in their appearance and their qualities, too. They are excessively fond of their pleasures and of wealth; and women in whom the tamoguna dominates are loose, and cheats and liars. They, it is told, are born in unknown families and often become whores in this life, and Apsaras in the next!

The hijaras, the hermaphrodites, are also amsas of Mulaprakriti, and they are of tamoguna as well.

All men and women born in the punyabhumi, Bharatavarsha, worship the Devi Bhagavati. The great king Suratha worshipped her in the most ancient days, and then Sri Rama did as well, when he wanted to kill Ravana. She was born herself in the world, once, as the Devi Sati, Daksha's daughter, and later as the Devi Parvati, Himavan's blessed child, whom Rudra married.

The Devi Lakshmi was born in unremembered times, when the Kshirasagara was churned for the amrita of immortality. Mangala Raja, the Lord Mars, first worshipped the Devi Lakshmi, and since, all the worlds have, as well, mortals and immortals too.

When the Devi Saraswati was born, the Lord Brahma worshipped her first. And after him, the Devas and the Munis did. On the night of the full moon, in the month of Kartika, Sri Krishna himself adored the Devi Radha in Vrindavana, within the Raasa mandala," said Narayana to an avid Narada,' said Krishna Dwaipayana," says Suta.

SIXTY-ONE

"VYASA WENT ON, 'NARADA THEN ASKED, "BHAGAVAN, THE DEVI ALWAYS was, I have heard, long before this world of the five elements. Why did she incarnate herself as five separate Devis?"

Narayana said, "Indeed, even as the Atman, the nabho mandala of cosmic space, Kaala who is time, the ten quarters, the Golden Egg of the universe, Goloka and Vaikuntha dhama below are eternal, so, too, is the Mulaprakriti, the Maya of the eternal Brahman. Atman and Prakriti are fused, inseparably, just as the sun and its light, or fire and its heat, the lotus and her beauty. Even as the goldsmith can make no ornaments without gold, so, also, the Purusha can create no worlds or lives without his all-powerful Prakriti.

'Sha' means grace and 'kti' is power. The Devi bestows both these. Once, in the beginning, the Lord who was neither male nor female, and both potentially, divided himself into two: a Purusha and a Shakti. His left half was a woman, and his right a man. The woman, the Goddess, was absolutely beautiful. The male looked upon this female and was stricken with pristine love, and he wanted to fill her with it, with himself.

She was as luminous as the lotus of a thousand petals, the bloom of the soul. She glanced at him, sidelong, and he was lost. And she, too, was lost in love with that dark Krishna, who was the other half of the Paramatman. Her great eyes greedily drank the light of his perfect face. The Purusha, Krishna, lord of the kalpa, took her hand and drew her into the Raasamandala. There, they made love for the first time ever, awesome love.

It is told she sweated at his embrace, and the sweat pouring from her body inundated the universe. It became the salty oceans! At his thrusts like starflares, she gasped, cried out, panted. Her breath became the life-breath, the prana of all the jivas. From that prana, too, a Devi was born, from his left side; and they saw each other, were seized with desire, and began to mate.

From that tumultuary coition, which lasted aeons, five sons were born to that primeval Vayu and his Shakti: Prana, Apana, Samana, Udana, and Vyana, who are the five vital vayus of all living beings. Also, from their loving came Naga, and the four lower Vayus.

The sweat that poured from the rapturous exertions of the Shakti of the Kalpa-Krishna, became Varuna, the Lord of the sea. From Varuna's left side also, there was born a Devi, and she was his consort, and was called Varunani.

But the pregnancy of the first Shakti was interminable; it lasted for a hundred manvantaras. Her form was refulgent with the Brahmatejas, and she rested upon Krishna's darkling breast. When a hundred manvantaras had passed, the first Devi gave birth to a lustrous golden egg! Within it, was the whole universe. But when the Devi saw the golden egg, she was sad and angry, and flung it from her down onto the seas of her salt sweat.

When the Kalpa-Krishna saw this his eyes blazed, and he cursed her, 'Cruel One! You have forsaken our first-born son. Never have any more sons from now, and let the daughters who are born from you be issueless, as well, and let them never know motherhood but remain youthful forever!'

Even as he cursed her, O Muni, there sprang from her tongue a girl-child, fair as a white lotus, exquisite. She wore shimmering white raiment, and carried a vina and a sacred book, and she was adorned with brilliant ornaments. She was the Goddess of the Shastras, the Devi Saraswati.

Then, later, Krishna's love became twain herself. From her left side there issued Lakshmi, and from her right Radhika. Krishna, Kalpa-Purusha, also, became twain. From his right side, there sprang a two-armed God, and from his left a four-armed one. The two-armed Kalpa-Purusha said to Saraswati Devi, 'My four-armed amsa shall be your lord from now. Go with him.'

Turning to Radhika he said, 'You come with me, my haughty love!'

He turned again to Lakshmi, who stood quivering, 'You go with four-armed Narayana, let him be your lord as well.'

Thus, Narayana took the Devis Lakshmi and Saraswati to Vaikuntha. And both of them, having been born from Radha, were barren. From Narayana's very body there issued a host of divine servitors, all four-armed like himself, all splendid, all wise and dark as him.

From the Devi Kamala Lakshmi's body there arose millions of bright women, to be her sakhis. They were lovely as the Goddess they had been born, immaculately, from.

Then, from the Lord of Goloka, Krishna's, pores there arose a great, shining host of gopas. They were all like him in appearance, in prowess and wisdom. Each one was as dear to him as his very life. And to be their consorts, Radha exuded from her pores the gopikas, every one as sweet and delectable as herself. And they, too, were barren women like her, for Kalpa-Purusha Krishna's curse, and they would remain forever young.

Then, all on a sudden, Vishnu's Maya, Sri Durga, arose here, Svayambhuva, of herself, from herself, and she adored the Kalpa-Purusha as well. She was the avatara of the Mulaprakriti, not of Radha, the Kalpa-Prakriti.

Durga is Narayani, she is Isani, she is the Parashakti, and the very mind and heart of Krishna. She is tejas. Her complexion is like molten gold. She is as lucific as ten million suns, and she has a thousand arms and hands, each one bearing an awesome weapon. She is three-eyed and all the women of time, that are jewels of their kind, have come from her alone.

O Narada, this Durga Mulaprakriti is the seed of the Tree of this world. She stood, thousand hands folded before Krishna Kalpa-Purusha, and he offered her a throne to sit upon. At that instant, from his navel there sprang four-faced Brahma, with his Savitri, holding a kamandalu in one hand, and hymning Krishna from four mouths.

Krishna gave Brahma and his Savitri, dazzling like a thousand full moons, a lofty, jewelled throne to sit upon. And then, Krishna divided himself again. His right side became Mahadeva, and his left side the dark and indigo lord of the gopikas. Mahadeva's colour was white as snow and moonbeams, and he shone like the finest crystal. In his hands, he held the trisula, and the sharp pattisa. He wore a tiger-skin, and his hair was matted in tawny jata that was the colour of the sun in the late afternoon. He was also digambara, the quarters of the endless firmament being his raiment. Upon his camphor-white body, he wore ashes, his throat was blue where he had once drunk poison, his ornament was a great serpent, and in his right hand, he held a string of rudraksha. He was Mrityunjaya, death's conqueror, and he took his place upon the throne that Krishna offered him."

Narayana paused, and Narada asked him, "And the Golden Egg, Master?"

"The Golden Egg floated upon the Ekarnava, the single and primordial sea for an incalculable length of time, they say for as long as Brahma's life. Then it was cloven into two equal halves. Within that egg lay a lambent child, splendid as a thousand million suns. But his mother, Radha, had forsaken him, and he could not feed at her breast, or drink mother's milk. And he began to cry.

That child, who would be the Lord of numberless brahmandas, countless universes, was an orphan, and he looked up into the sky with tears flowing down his face. Later, he was called Viraj, and he had a sixteenth part of the power that Krishna wields. Truly, he was the Lord of all the galaxies, and there were spiral nebulae in his every pore, so many that even Krishna could not count them.

There were countless numbers of Brahmas, Vishnus and Sivas, ruling these brahmandas. Each brahmanda had its own separate lokas, stretching from Patala to Brahmaloka. Above the brahmandas is Vaikuntha, and beyond that is Goloka. Goloka dhama is as eternal as Krishna himself is.

Just as there are seven oceans and continents in the world, and seven Patalas below Bhumi, so too are there seven Swargas above it. In order of ascent from the earth, they are Bhurloka, Bhuvarloka, Svarloka, Janarloka, Taparloka, Satyaloka, and finally Brahmaloka. The luminescence of Brahmaloka has been likened to that of gold. But, even these heavens are transient. Like the Earth and the Patalas, when each brahmanda dissolves they are also put out even like bubbles that have formed and floated briefly in the eternal current of time!

It is told, O Muni, that in each brahmanda there are thirty million Gods that live and die between its inception and its end! Some of these are Dikpatis, regents of the quarters, others are Dikpalas, guardians of the quarters, some are Grahas, planets, and others Nakshatras, stars. In Bhurloka, there are the four varnas of Gods, and in the Patalas the Nagas rule.

When the Viraja Purusha, the splendourous child within the Golden Egg that had cracked open, looked up into the sky he saw nothing but the sunya, the void. A dreadful pang of hunger convulsed him and wailing loudly, he fell into a swoon. When he awoke again, that awesome infant began to think of his father, Krishna. At once he saw the immortal light of the Brahman, and within that light he saw Krishna, blue as thunderclouds, wearing a fulvous pitambara robe, a radiant smile on his face, a flute in his hands, and grace flowing from him in tide!

Seeing his father, the child grew glad and smiled sweetly. Krishna blessed him, saying, 'May you have all the knowledge that I do. May your hunger and thirst vanish. May the numberless brahmandas be contained by you until the pralaya. Be without ego, or fear, and be the bestower of boons to all the created. Let not age, sorrow, disease or death afflict you ever.'

And bending down, he whispered the six-syllabled Krishna mantra in that child's ear, **AUM Krishnaya Namah!** And he decreed that a sixteenth part of any offering made upon any world in all the brahmandas, the countless universes, shall go to Narayana, and the rest to the boy Viraj. Sri Krishna kept nothing for himself, for he is always content within himself.

Granting the magnificent child these boons, his father Krishna asked, 'Now tell me, what other boon do you want from me?'

And in his immense voice his son replied, 'Only grant me, father, that for as long as I live I have perfect bhakti for you.'

And Krishna said, 'Be always as I am. Not even if a thousand Brahmas are born and die, shall you know age or tiredness. But cleave yourself into as many Virajas as there are brahmandas and, thus, rule each cosmos separately. In every universe, from your navel shall spring the lotus in which Brahma is born.

And from Brahma's brow shall spring the eleven Rudras who will destroy his creation. They shall issue from Brahma's face, but they shall be amsas of Siva. Of these eleven, the Rudra called Kaalagni shall be the destroyer of the universe.

Also, from your amsas, the numberless Virajas shall be born, countless Vishnus who shall preserve creation, in all the brahmandas. And, indeed, you shall have infinite bhakti for me, so that you need but think of me and you will see me before you. And you shall see your mother, this Radha who dwells in my body, in my heart. I must leave you now, for you have your great task of creation to embark upon. Dwell here at your ease, and bless you, my son, bless you, bless you.'

Krishna vanished back into Goloka, the loftiest realm, which is immortal. In own abode, he spoke to the primal Brahma and Sankara. To Brahma he said, 'Go and be born in amsa from the lotuses that sprout from the navels of all the countless Virajas that arise from my child's pores. You shall be the Creator of all the universes.'

To Siva he said, 'And you be born from the brow of all the Brahmas that Brahma becomes. For, you shall be the one who destroys creation.'

And those two Gods went forth to their missions. The Viraj, who now lay asleep upon the Ekarnava, the single cosmic sea, began to divide himself in a trillion trillion parts, as, from every pore of his skin an Amsaviraj was born.

From the navel of each Viraj, a lotus thrust itself, and within its petals, a Brahma was born. For a hundred thousand yugas, Brahma wandered along the stalk of the infinite lotus, yet could not discover from whence it sprang. Then, Narada, your lotus-born father returned to the pavilion of his birth, and began to meditate upon the immaculate feet of Sri Krishna.

And now, in his dhyana, behind the petals of his eyelids, each Brahma saw the amsa Viraj of his brahmanda lying asleep upon the eternal sea. And, beyond that vision, the Brahmas all saw the great, original Viraj upon his sea of seas, in whose pores all the universes existed. And, beyond that vision, he saw Sri Krishna in Goloka, the imperishable realm. Brahma hymned that Krishna, and embarked upon creation.

From Brahma's ancestral mind, first, were born Sanaka and the other Munis who are the children of Brahma's pristine thought. Then, the eleven Rudras issued from his brow. Then, from the left side of the Amsa Viraj, came Vishnu the blue saviour. Vishnu journeyed to Swetadvipa, where he remained.

All the Brahmas created all their brahmandas, like great symphonies in time and matter, in life, death and rebirth, and they all had three realms, Swarga, Bhumi and Patala," said Narayana Muni to the absorbed Narada,' said Vyasa."

SIXTY-TWO

"VYASA SAID, 'NARADA THEN ASKED, "GURU, YOUR PURANA IS LIKE AMRITA to me. Tell me how the five great Devis, and all the others who are amsas of Mulaprakriti, are worshipped in the world. Tell me more about their lives."

Narayana said, "The Vedas, the Puranas, the Tantras, and the other Shastras describe how Durga, Radha, Lakshmi, Saraswati and Savitri are to be worshipped. So, their worship I need not dwell upon. The other Devis who are amsas of Prakriti are Kali, Vasundhara, Ganga, Sasthi, Mangala, Chandika, Tulasi, Manasa, Nidra, Svadha, Svaha, and Dakshina. By and by, I will tell you more about their lives and qualities.

But it was Krishna himself who first introduced the world to the worship of the Devi Saraswati, who holds the vina in her gentle hands, who is the mother of speech, and who illumines the hearts of even the most bestial man with knowledge if he but worships her. She sprang from the lips of the Devi Radha. She saw Krishna and trembled with love, with great desire. She wanted him, desperately.

Knowing her love clearly, Krishna said, "Devi, Radha is already with me, it is futile for you to desire me. Blue and four-armed Vishnu is born from me; verily, he is me. He is a great lover, O Saraswati, why, ten million Kamas dwell in his body! So, take yourself to Vaikuntha, and you shall find joy there with Narayana. Lakshmi dwells there, but she is beyond jealousy. Hari will treat you both equally.

And, I say to you, on the fifth day, the sukla panchami of the bright fortnight of Magha, the day when every child first sets out on his journey of learning, you shall be worshipped. A great festival shall be held in your name, and all men, Manus, Devas, Munis, Vasus, Yogins, Nagas, Siddhas, Gandharvas and Rakshasas shall worship you in every kalpa until the pralaya arrives.

Your mystic kavacha, the sacred syllable Humn shall be inscribed on the bark of the bhurja tree, and then set within a golden ring, a maduli, and tied as an amulet on the right arm, or worn as a talisman around the neck of your bhaktas.'

Thus spoke Sri Krishna, and he himself worshipped the Devi Saraswati, of moonbeam whiteness, of the soft, heartpiercing lustre of a million full moons, who holds the vina and the sacred books in her hands, whom Brahma, Vishnu, Maheswara and all the Devas worship. He worshipped her with the Saraswati mula mantras, **Aim Klim Saraswatyai namaha!** and **Srim Hrim Saraswatyai namaha!**, both of which are kalpa-vrikshas that yield every desire.

In time out of mind, this second was the mantra that Narayana himself gave Valmiki in the sacred continent of Bharatavarsha, on the banks of the golden Ganga. Then, Maharishi Bhrigu taught this mantra during a solar eclipse to Sukracharya at the Pushkara tirtha. Brahma himself taught Bhrigu the mulamantra in the Badarika asrama. Maricha Muni imparted the Saraswati mantra to Brihaspati during a lunar eclipse, Jaratkaru to Astika Muni on the shores of the Kshiroda sagara, Vibhandaka to Rishyasringa on Sumeru. Siva taught it to Kanada and Gautama, Surya Deva taught it to Yagnavalkya and Kartyayana, Ananta Deva did to Panini Maharishi, to Rishi Bharadvaja the intelligent, and to Sakatayana in Bali's sabha in Patala.

If any man chants the Saraswati mantra four hundred thousand times, he will become a Siddha, as powerful as Brihaspati.

In ancient times, Brahma gave Saraswati's subtle kavacha called Viswajaya to Bhrigu upon Mount Gandhamadana. Once, Bhrigu asked the Lord Brahma, 'Tell me about the Devi Saraswati's kavacha, the Viswajaya, Pitamaha. I have heard it embodies the essences of all the holiest mantras.'

Brahma replied, 'Once, just when time was beginning, Krishna told me about Saraswati Devi's kavacha in Vrindavana, in the Raasa mandala. It was a great secret, it was full of every sacred mantra in creation, indeed, it was wrought from them. By touching that kavacha, truly, did Brihaspati become the Devaguru, and wiser than anyone else. By the power of the Devi Saraswati's kavacha, Bhagavan Sukra became the Acharya of the Daityas and Danavas. By its power did Valmiki become Kavindra, and Svayambhuva Manu renowned through every yuga. By that kavacha have Kanada, Gautama, Kanva, Panini, Sakatayana, Daksha and Katyayana become great poets. And so many others, besides, owe their greatness to the Saraswati kavacha.

Dvija, the Prajapati himself, is the Muni of the Saraswati kavacha, and these are its mantras for each part of the body.

For the head, **Srim Hrim Saraswatyai Svaha**; for the forehead, **Srim Vagadevatayah Svaha; AUM Srim Hrim Bhagavatyai Saraswatyai Svaha,** for the eyes; **Aim Hrim Vagavadinyai Svaha** for the nose; **AUM Hrim Vidyadhisthatri Devyai Svaha** for the lips; **AUM Hrim Brahmyai Svaha** for the teeth; **Aim**, the singular, for the neck; **AUM Srim Hrim** for the throat; **Srim**, the shoulders; for the chest, the same as for the lips; **AUM Hrim Klim Vanyai Svaha** for the hands; **AUM Svarna Varnatmai Kayai Svaha**, the feet; and **AUM Vagadhishtatridevyai Svaha** guards all the body!

Let **AUM Sarvakanthavasinyai Svaha** watch over the east of he who has the kavacha; **AUM Sarvajivagravasinyai Svaha** safeguard the south-east; **AUM Hrim Srim Klim Sarasvatyai Budhajananyai Svaha**, the south; **Aim Hrim Srim**, the south-west; **AUM Aim Jivagrahavasinyai Svaha,** the west; **AUM Sarvam Bikayai Svaha,** the north-west; **AUM Aim Srim Klim Gadyavarinyai Svaha** the north; **Aim Sarvastra Vasinyai Svaha,** the north-east; **AUM Hrim Sarvapujitayai Svaha,** the sky; **Hrim Pustakavasinyai Svaha** the ground below, and let **AUM Granthavijavarupayai Svaha** protect all the quarters and directions.

This is the Visawajaya Kavacha of the Devi Saraswati, O Bhrigu, and it has my own nature,' said Brahma once to that Muni. And I heard this tale from Dharma Deva upon Mount Gandhamadana, the dwarapalaka to the heavens. Never tell this secret of secrets, O Narada, to anyone who does not revere his Guru absolutely. For, any man who repeats the Saraswati kavacha five hundred thousand times surely becomes a Siddha, with immense powers," said the immortal Narayana upon the sacred mountain to the wandering seer, Brahma's austere son, who is the dark blue Lord Vishnu's greatest bhakta among Munis," said Krishna Dwaipayana, Satyavati's brilliant son to the anxious Kuru king Janamejaya at his great sattra upon the bank of the sacred river, once," says the Suta Romaharshana to the enraptured Rishis of the Naimisa vana, that was sanctified long ago for Puranic revelation.

SIXTY-THREE

"VYASA MUNI HAS SAID, 'ONCE, WHEN HIS GURU CURSED HIM, YAGNAVALKYA forgot the Vedas. In sorrow, in anguish, he performed an incomparable tapasya to Surya Deva. The blinding Sun God appeared before the Muni, who broke down and wept at his candescent feet. When Yagnavalkya controlled himself, he managed to tell the Deva about his loss.

Bhagavan Surya Deva then taught Yagnavalkya the Vedas again, and the Vedangas. The God said to the seer, "Worship the Devi Saraswati, and she will restore your memory to you." With that, the brilliant Sun vanished before the Rishi's eyes.

Yagnavalkya worshipped the Devi Saraswati, he sang her praises night and day. And she materialised before him, luminous as a thousand moons. He lay at her feet in obeisance, and she blessed him, saying, "Be a Kavindra from now, be a river of wisdom to your sishyas!"

So he became, that foremost of Munis of yore.

The Devi Saraswati dwells in Vaikuntha, near Narayana. But, once, there was an altercation between her and the Devi Ganga. Ganga cursed her to flow in the world as a river. On her sacred banks, the greatest sages dwelt, until she vanished from the earth after the Mahabharata yuddha was fought. Yet, she flows as a spiritual river, and those that bathe in her subtle waters find salvation. And he who lives on the banks of the Saraswati and chants the Devi's mantra surely becomes a Mahakavi, a great seer and poet.

Narada now asked, "Lord, tell me about the altercation the Devi Saraswati had with the Devi Ganga."

"Once, when Narayana sat in Vaikuntha, in his antapura, with the three Devis who are his consorts, Lakshmi, Saraswati and Ganga, the Devi Ganga was seized by an overpowering amorousness. She flushed, she quivered, broke out in a fine sweat, and, right before the other two Goddesses, she began to cast sidelong, seductive glances at the Blue Lord, and to smile at him in the most suggestive, enticing way. And Vishnu smiled back at her in a rather direct manner. Ganga went nearer and let her satin side stroke his arm, at which he sighed, quite wantonly, Narada.

The Devi Lakshmi only smiled at this; she felt no envy or possessiveness. But the Devi Saraswati was perturbed, and then furious. She turned crimson with rage. Her lips trembled, her limbs shook. Lakshmi tried to placate her, but to no avail.

Beside herself, Saraswati turned on her Lord, on Vishnu, and said in a low voice, but hotly, 'The good husband looks upon all his wives with equal favour. But, Gadadhara, you are partial to Lakshmi and Ganga, while you always ignore me. What use is my life, when I must constantly endure seeing you fawn over the others, whilst I am left yearning, a woman whom her Lord does not love?'

She worked herself into a fair frenzy, Narada. 'Ah, you have little dharma, Hari! Knowing you better than anyone, I know what fools the Brahmanas are who worship you, and call you the greatest God!'

Vishnu listened to her tirade in silence, thoughtfully; then, he turned and, without a word, walked out of his antapura, his harem, smiling slightly to himself. When he had gone, Saraswati turned her wrath on Ganga directly. She abused her, O Muni!

'Shameless wretch!' she screamed, and worse, if truth were told, 'I will teach you a lesson today!' And she seized the Devi Ganga by her hair and began to drag her about. Lakshmi sprang forward in alarm and caught hold of her hands to stop her, at which Saraswati turned on her, as well, eyes flaming.

'You are no better! You saw what she did, and you only smiled. Are you a stone or a plant or a river, that you stand mutely watching this hussy do as she likes, wherever she likes? I curse you, Padme, be a river and a plant one day! Yes, I curse you, I curse you for being insensible!' she screeched at the Devi Lakshmi, who never lost her temper, though tears filled her lotus-like eyes.

Suddenly, Ganga raged, 'Let this wretch be by herself from now, Lakshmi! She wants to show her strength. So let her be alone! Let us have nothing to do with her.'

All three were trembling by now, and the air around them crackled with the anger of two of them, and with Lakshmi's sorrow. By now, Ganga had lost her temper completely. She cursed Saraswati, 'You have cursed Padma to be a river, and I curse you, irascible wretch, to be a river yourself. I curse you that the worst sinners on earth shall bathe in you, and you shall bear all their sins, and atone for them in anguish!'

And Saraswati screamed, 'So shall you flow in the world of men as a river, and let the most heinous sins be washed in you!'

At which juncture, Muni, the four-armed and immaculate Lord Vishnu returned to their midst, and gently gathered Saraswati to his breast. Kissing her fondly, stroking her face, her hair, so she melted at his touch, he began to tell them why rage had gripped all three of them, and so suddenly. As he spoke, Ganga and Saraswati felt their anger leave them, so they wondered that they had been beside themselves, and Lakshmi no longer felt impelled to cry.

Vishnu said, 'Lakshmi, my love, be born in amsa, in the king of the earth Dharmadhvaja's palace, and you shall be his daughter Tulasi. And there, the Asura Sankhachuda, who is also my own amsa, shall come to marry you. When you have lived that life, return here to my side in Vaikuntha. By Saraswati's curse, you shall be a plant, as well, the most sacred plant in the world: the fragrant tulasi, purifier of the three lokas.

She cursed you to be a river, too. So be a river now upon the earth, and be called the Padma, river of lotuses! And as a river, also, be only auspicious in the world.'

He turned to Ganga, 'You, too, my love, must be born in the world as a river, and absolve the people of Bharata of their sins wherever they bathe in you. The king Bhagiratha of Sagara's line, shall call you down into the world as a river, and you will be called Bhagirathi. Generations later, a king called Santanu will be born in the noble House of Kuru, and he will be my amsa. He will marry you in the world and be your husband for a time, and a great war will be fought on Bhumi, just before the Kali yuga enters the earth. And Siva shall wear you in his jata, as well.'

Then, with the strangest light in his eyes, he said softly to Saraswati, who lay against him in a swoon, 'And now, I must curse you as well, I fear, for the anger you showed me. Saraswati, go now to Brahmaloka, and be the Lord Brahma's Devi. And, you, Lakshmi stay here with me.'

He spoke with finality and what he ordained came to pass; and the three Devis knew that his decree was their destiny. And all women born into the world from the serene Devi Lakshmi are themselves of perfectly tranquil natures, devoted to their husbands, and beyond jealousy and anger.

Because of what happened in Vaikuntha of old, it is written in the Veda that there is no folly to compare with the one of keeping three wives, or having three servants, or even three friends of diverse natures meeting together. It is also told, that it is better to flee to the jungle, and live on fruit and roots amidst dangerous wild beasts, rather than remain in a home where one's wife is ill-tempered, foul-mouthed, and wounds a man's heart with the barbs from her tongue, from which he will hardly recover.

Men whom their wives rule shall never know peace of mind until they are laid upon their funeral pyres. They will hardly reap the fruits of their daily labours even, will have no honour or fame anywhere, in this world or the next. And he who has more wives than one, it is not hard to imagine his torment if he suffers so much already when he has just one! The man whose wife is not docile, but haughty and wanting her own way, he is dead even while he is among the living, a breathing, walking corpse."

Narada wanted to know, "What did the Devis do, when Narayana pronounced their respective fates?"

Narayana Muni said, "All three Devis began to sob piteously. They clasped one another and wept and wept. Then, Saraswati Devi said abjectly to Hari, 'Lord, how long will any woman live without her husband? Oh, I will die when I am parted from you!'

Ganga cried, 'Why do you abandon me like this, Lord? I too will die, if you do this, and you shall have the sin of killing a woman on your soul.'

Lakshmi said, and she still spoke gently, 'Lord, I marvel that you have been moved to such rage. But I beg you, Hari, forgive Saraswati and Ganga now. For, mercy is the highest quality of a good husband. As for me, I will go down to the earth as a plant and a river, by Saraswati's curse. But tell me, Hari, how long must I be gone, how long must I be apart from you? How long shall I be a river? How long will I be Dharmadhvaja's daughter and a plant?

And, if Ganga has to flow on earth as a river by Saraswati's curse, for how long will that be? And if Saraswati has to flow on earth as a river by Ganga's curse, for how long will that curse last? When shall we all be re-united? Ah, Lord, take back the curse by which my sisters must go away and be with Brahma and Siva! For, more than anything else, that will break their hearts.'

The gracious Devi Lakshmi bent down at her Lord's feet, and clasped them in her petal-soft hands. She wiped her own tears that fell onto those sacred feet, with her hair. With deep tenderness Vishnu raised Lakshmi up, and took her in his arms.

'Sureswari!' said he. 'I cannot break my word, yet I will also do as you ask. So, let what happens be a mixture of my curse and your plea. Let Saraswati be born in only one amsa as a river on earth. But then, she must take half her Shakti and be with the Lotus-born One as well. Yet, her ardhamsa, half of her, shall remain here with us.

Let Ganga, in two amsas be a river of the earth, as well as dwell in the Lord Sankara's jata. But, she too shall remain here with me in Vaikuntha, at the same time.

As for you, Sri, you must also be born in the world as the river Padmavati, and the auspicious tulasi. But, when five thousand years of the Kali yuga pass, the earth shall no longer be sacred enough to contain you, and you will return entirely to me. For, your part in today's anger was only of innocence and conciliation.

Danger and calamity are the roots of the happiness of all beings, even the Devas and Devis! For, without knowing the anguish of separation, how will the living know the joy of union and, indeed, the true nature of happiness itself? And then, my precious ones, how shall they who are mortal and sin in the Holy Land of Bharata be saved, when the age darkens and they can hardly hope to perform expiation by themselves, with tapasya. In those evil times, bathing in your grace-filled waters shall free them of the burden their crimes, and enable their spirits to soar in freedom and light again.

Why, even they who commit the mahapatakas, the direst sins, like brahmahatya, surapanam, steyam, gurubhanganaganah, mahanti patakanyahuh, tatsamsavrasesha panchamam, even these are liberated from the darkness that consumes them, from the very shadows of the dreadful crimes, if they bathe often in your waters with a repentant heart.' Now, he smiled, 'But, just a touch of my bhaktas' hands can save a sinner from his sins, sooner than any tapasya, or even bathing in your most sacred tirthas!'

Sri Lakshmi said, in some wonder, 'Who are these bhaktas of such marvellous power, my Lord?'

The Lord Hari said, 'The traits of my bhaktas are never generally described, for they are auspicious and secret, and no one who is not deserving should hear of them. No mocker, certainly. But you are chaste, my love, and pure, so let me tell you about my bhaktas, the purest of the pure.

In his ear, have no doubt, his guru has once murmured the Vishnu mantra, making him an initiate from that moment. A hundred generations of forebears of such a man are liberated instantly, be they not in Swarga or Naraka, or embodied on earth as a jiva! They find Vishnupadam, my feet, and dwell there in immortal bliss. My bhaktas are men, or even beasts, whose minds and hearts are full of me, who never tire of saying my name, or speaking of my deeds, my incarnations, of spreading them through the world. Tears flow from their eyes, my love, when they but hear my name. And those that are the greatest, the most evolved among them, why, they swoon in rapture upon hearing my name!

My bhaktas do not yearn for moksha, even, or the salokya, sayuja, samipya, or sarasti, not brahmatva, or devatva. They are perfectly delighted to just serve me, always, however hard the service, however evil the time in which they are called upon to spread light in darkness.

Yet, the birth of such men in the land of Bharata is passing rare,' said the Lord," said Narayana Muni to Narada,' Muni Vyasa has said."

SIXTY-FOUR

"DWAIPAYANA CONTINUED, 'NARAYANA SAID, "THUS, AN AMSA OF THE Devi Saraswati flowed as a river in Bharatavarsha, while she remained in Vaikuntha. She also came to Brahmaloka and became Brahmi, Brahma's consort. Since she flows, always, as speech and as river, she is called Saraswati, since 'saras' is a stream.

So, also, did Ganga and Sri flow upon the earth as rivers. But they shall flow only for five thousand years of the Kali yuga, and then return to Vaikuntha to Vishnu's side. And all the sacred tirthas shall return with them, save only Kasi and Vrindavana, which will remain in the world even in the deepest night of the Kali.

When ten thousand years of the evil yuga have passed, and darkness rules the earth completely, even the precious saligrama sila, the stone that is Vishnu himself, and Siva, Uma, and Jagannatha will all leave the soil of Bharata and return to their abodes on high. Their mahatmyas shall no more bless the land.

No more, then, will there be any true Rishis in the world, not of any sect, Siva Sakta, Ganapatya or Vaishnava. The eighteen Puranas, the auspicious sankhas, sraddhas, tarpanas and every Vaidik ritual and sacrifice will vanish from the face of the Holy Land, even as if they never existed. The Vedas and Vedangas themselves will not be heard of anymore! Why, men will no longer worship the Gods, or hymn them.

The sadhu satyasamghas, the sanatana dharma, the four Vedas, the village Devas and Devis, the vratas, the practice of austerity, fasting, all these will not be heard of any more. All men and women, too, shall be addicted to the left-handed Tantrik way, the rites of Vamachara, although they will hardly realise this is what they live by.

The truth will be mocked, and hypocrisy and lies, greed and thieving will be the acknowledged and revered ways of the world. If, still, any rare man does worship, his bhakti shall be performed without the sacred tulasi, which will long since have disappeared from desecrated soil. The most common relations between men and men shall be of suspicion and enmity, and so too with the women of the world.

Women will be universally harsh and greedy. They will cease to revere their husbands, indeed husbands shall be like their women's slaves! The old will be treated with contempt, harshly, even one's own parents. Wives' brothers will become the virtual masters of their sisters' homes, while the husband is reduced to powerlessness.

The four varnas will live like mlecchas. Brahmanas will no longer observe the sandhya vandanam, or even wear the sacred thread around themselves. Alien ways of the mlecchas will rule their lives, not their own Shastras. The three higher varnas will be the servants and bondsmen of the Sudras, their cooks and messengers. No man shall have the truth either in his heart or on his lips.

And the earth herself will respond to the evil by drying up, as if in agony. No more will the rains come in time, and the grains of the field and the fruit of the tree shall all shrivel, and turn sparse and bitter. Soon, the majority of human women will also be barren. Cows will hardly yield milk. The love between husbands and wives will be a dim memory and marriage shall be a transaction of convenience, if that. Not truth but greed and deceit will rule every hearth and home.

Rivers and streams will run dry, and even the mountain springs that are perennial. The very seas will recede for dreadful drought. One man in a hundred thousand may be virtuous, and the race of men will lose its beauty and lustre. Mostly, the people will be ugly and graceless, even deformed. And their speech will turn as coarse and vile as their hearts are, and be full of mere cleverness and obscenity.

By and by, men will quit their habitations and flee into the wilderness for succor and for sanctuary from the rapacity of their kings and the men of power that surround them, who will all be thieves and murderers. The beasts of the wild will roam the streets of men, baying into the evil age in dismal voices. And the men that dwell in cities shall be no better than beasts, for love and mercy shall not dwell in their hearts.

Yes, men and women everywhere in the Kali yuga will be dwarfish in spirit and body. They will be short-lived, prone to all manners of terrible diseases that stalk the earth in fury, at the sins of humankind. The young will be old when they are but twenty, and girls of eight will menstruate and become pregnant. Like rutting animals in season they will copulate and deliver every year. And when they are sixteen they shall be wasted, and old.

The four varnas will sell their daughters for dowry, like cattle. And not their husbands but their lovers, and their sisters' and mothers' lovers, who shall be their own as well, will support them. Men will fornicate with their brothers' wives, their sons' wives, their mothers-in-law, why, with their own sisters and daughters too. Ah, who is whose wife in the Kali yuga? It will be hard indeed to tell.

The current of sin will flow in a torrent through the earth and through the homes of rich and poor. Brahmanas will earn their livelihood by driving buffaloes and burning the corpses of Sudras. They will eat the food of Sudras and lie with whores. No longer will they observe the vows of old, that sustain the earth, and they will have no faith in yagnas.

There will be no distinction in society between the varnas, or asramas, why, no difference between the old and the young, the clean and the unclean, the wise and the ignorant. All men in the Holy Land of Bharata shall be as one, and they shall be mlecchas. Why, it is said that when the Kali yuga runs its course, the trees of the earth will stand just a hand high, and the lustrous, noble race of men be no higher than a thumb! Evil will sweep the earth in a tide, evil will rule everything.

Money alone will confer nobility, power will be the only sign of virtue. Pleasure will be the sole spur to marriage, lust the only endowment of womanhood. Honour will be measured by wealth alone, arrogance and violence will be thought praiseworthy. A bath in water will be considered the only purification, and charity the only virtue. To wear fine clothes will be considered equal to dharma, and pretending to be great will be equal to greatness itself. And powerful men with grave faults in their characters will rule the earth, in greed and rapacity. Thus, in time, humankind will be utterly ruined.

And, at last, when the sinister age has run its course, the Lord Vishnu Narayana will be born into the world in his tenth avatara, in the house of the Brahmana Vishnujasa. And, mounted on a pale horse, a blinding sword in his hand, he will rid the earth of the mlecchas in three days and nights! And with that, he will disappear from the face of the world.

Then, the pralaya. The stormclouds pushkara, avartana, samvartaka and drona will fill the sky and be rent with immense gashes of lightning, and cosmic batteries of thunder. Then the heavens open, and walls of rain fall from the stormclouds of the dissolution, solid cataracts from above. All the earth will be as an ocean at the end of that rain, no vestige will remain of the ages that have been, not of men or beasts, or even birds of the air. Of the cities of men, their villages and homes, not a stone shall be seen after the Deluge.

Then, the Lord Vishnu enters seven rays of the sun as Rudra, and he absorbs the waters of the pralaya into himself. With that invigoration, he begins to burn like seven suns himself, and the sky is alight with his awesome fires. He dries up the seas that cover the world, why, he dries up the darkling waters of Patala.

Fiercer and fiercer burn the seven suns in the sky, until they ignite all the worlds above and the surface of Patala. The earth is soon as bare as a turtle's back, all its forests and rivers gone, all its mountains consumed into mounds of ashes that ferocious winds have swept away.

Tempests of wild flames sweep Bhuvarloka and Svarloka. The three worlds burn like oil in a frying pan that has caught fire. Their tasks in the lower heavens fulfilled, the Devas fly up into Maharloka above, the dreadful firestorms searing them as they flee. The apocalypse rises inexorably into Maharloka, and the ones of light flee higher again to Janarloka.

The Lord Janardhana, straddling creation now as Rudra the Destroyer, breathes out clouds of fire. He roars, he laughs in great rage and glee, and the clouds that erupt from him are like herds of elephants in the sky. Some of these are dark as blue lotuses, others white as the water lily, some are mysterious and smoky, and other xanthic yellow. Some shall have the hue of a brown donkey, some shall be like crimson lacquer, gleaming. Some shall be the colour of the chrysoberyl, and some of the blue sapphire, crystalline and pellucid, glinting coldly, great jewels in the sky.

Yet other clouds he spews are like peacocks, and others like hosts of glimmering fireflies. There will be those that seem like scarlet or golden arsenic, and those like brilliant blue jay's wings. Some clouds in the extravaganza in the sky will be like great cities, some like mighty mountain ranges, snow-capped, some shall be like lone stupendous palaces, each one bigger than a city, and yet others like anthills and dust-heaps.

These billowing conglomerates of clouds fill the firmament, end to end, and then it begins to rain again, a deluge greater than the first one, before the fires swept the three realms. This pralaya douses the flames everywhere, hissing like unimaginable nests of serpents. Again, the worlds are flooded, first Patala, then Bhumi, and then the tidal waters of the deluge rise foaming into Bhuvarloka. For a hundred years, it rains without a moment's pause, for the clouds in the sky are replenished even as Jagannatha, Rudra the Destroyer, breathes from his fanged mouths.

At last, when the single sea has risen up to the zone of the Saptarishi, the rains stop. Now, fresh, wonderful winds issue from the Lord's mouth, for another hundred years, and blow the stormclouds of the apocalypse away. Then, the Lord Narayana consumes the great winds as well, draws them back into himself, and stillness rules over the Ekarnava, the single ocean in which everything lies dissolved.

When all is still, again, the Lord Janardhana is seen upon the ocean that covers everything. He lies asleep upon his immense serpent bed, emerald gleaming Anantasesha with his thousand hoods unfurled above Narayana. Vishnu fixes his dhyana on that form of himself known as Vasudeva, and he has the form of Brahma the four-faced Creator then. For a cosmic night, which lasts as long as all the ages of the three worlds have lasted, Brahma sleeps.

Then, day dawns again in the universe. Narayana who is Brahma awakens, and pours forth another creation. And this one, too, shall last for a day of the Creator, and end in another dissolution, another pralaya. And, then, Brahma will sleep again. A hundred and eight years of such cosmic days and nights, it is told Muni, is the span of each Brahma's life. And Narayana's life is said to contain a thousand Brahmas, and Sadasiva's life a thousand Vishnus, and the day of the Devi Bhagavati contains a thousand Sadasivas, and so on.

When Brahma awakens and a new day dawns over the earth, it is Satya yuga again, the pristine and perfect age when dharma prevails, immaculately, the blessed, tranquil, golden Krita, when men are like Gods in the world. It is told that when Hiranyagarbha, the golden-wombed Brahma, dies at the end of his life of a hundred and eight years, there is a Prakriti pralaya, more absolute than the thirty-six thousand pralayas that have gone before.

Now Brahma becomes the Lord Maheswara entirely, and thrusts his Atman into the Paramatman. He then burns up the Golden Egg, shell and everything within, the very meat of time. He consumes the Devas, the Asuras and all the living, every last jivatma. The red and blue God Maheswara appears in the most hideous form, and enters the orb of the sun.

When the three worlds are alight and blazing, he summons the Brahmasiras, the final astra that bears the four heads of Brahma upon its shaft. He looses that weapon into the luculent bodies of the Devas, and consumes them and their very lustre in white flames. Thus, the universe, that is made of the bodies of the Devas, the elemental and celestial ones, is consumed and returned to the divine dreams of which it was first conceived.

When all the other Gods and Goddesses have been consumed, the mountain's daughter Parvati, who is the Devi herself, stands alone, and she is Sambhu's sole witness, the only one who sees the tandava he now dances, in perfect ecstasy, in complete abandon and control. Uma stands more resplendent than all the galaxies that her Lord extinguishes with his dance. Siva wears a bright necklace made with the skulls of the Devas. He has a thousand arms and a thousand legs, his tawny eyes blaze a thousand fires, his thousand fangs are longer than the vaults of space. His body is white as moonbeams, he wears a tiger's skin around his body, wields his trisula spewing the mystic fires in which time dies. And as he drinks the ultimate, blissful amrita, as he dances, his great eyes are turned in absolute love on Parvati, the mountain-daughter's, dark face.

And she, the Goddess, enters into his white, immortal body and she drinks the amrita of his dance. Siva of light burns up the Golden Egg of creation, with all its Devas and Asuras, all its beings, until only he himself, Brahma, and Vishnu remain. The Earth he has already dissolved into the Ekarnava, the sea of time and timelessness.

Maheswara, the Trisulin's, fires consume the sea, and a great wind stills the fire. That wind is absorbed in space, in akasa, the cosmic ether. Akasa is dissolved in bhutadi, the Spirit of all things, and the faculties of the senses of every being are dissolved in lustre, in taijasa, the Deva hosts are subsumed into vaikarika. And then, the triune ahamkara, vaikarika, taijasa and bhutadi, is absorbed into Mahat, the Great. At last, the single, unmanifest, unchanging, undying Womb of all things and worlds, the Parabrahmam, takes back the Mahat with its triune modes into Itself.

When he has consumed all the jivas and all the elements thus, Siva divides the Un-born Pradhana, the womb of the worlds, and the supreme masculine Purusha from one another. This division and the dissolution that follows it, occur from Siva's deep, deep, desire. The Purusha, the lucific Self stands apart from the feminine Maya, the Prakriti, as the final, twenty-fifth principle. It is Alone, the singular, immaculate One, the Pitamaha, the Grandsire.

This is the great Prakriti pralaya, which occurs when Brahma's hundred and eight years are over. After this pralaya, Narayana lies again upon his serpent bed on the endless and single sea, and from his navel the interminable lotus stalk thrusts its way up into infinite space again, and another four-faced Brahma is born within the soft pavilion of that original bloom," said the divine Muni Narayana, who was Mahavishnu's very amsa in the world, once, to Narada the great wanderer.

Narada asked, "Tell me more about time, and its divisions, holy one."

Narayana said, "One day of the Devas is a year of mortal men. Three hundred and sixty-five human yugas make one Deva yuga. Seventy-one Deva yugas are a manvantara. Sachi's lord Indra, the sovereign of the Devas of light, lives for one manvantara. Twenty-eight Indras are born and perish during a single day in the life of Hiranyagarbha Brahma Paramesthin. And, he, the four-faced Creator lives for a hundred and eight years.

When Brahma himself dies during the Prakriti pralaya, the Devi Bhagavati also becomes one, as do all the other Gods and jivas, with the Parabrahmam, whose nature is Satchitananda, undiluted truth, consciousness and bliss. The Prakriti pralaya lasts for exactly a moment, a nimesha, of the Parabrahma Mulaprakriti. All the brahmandas are destroyed in that instant, and, when it is over, creation begins again. Countless times this has happened, and shall again, infinitely. All jivas and worlds, all the Gods and Demons, even Brahma, Vishnu and Maheswara live and die. Only the Parabrahmam is truly eternal, Un-born, Undying.

And from the Parabrahmam, Krishna, Lord of kalpas, is born, and Radha who dwells in his very body, his mystic left side, and in his heart," said Narayana Muni to Brahma's own son, the itinerant seer,' Krishna Dwaipayana, the dark and sage Vyasa, told the Rajarishi Janamejaya, once, upon a certain time, beside a holy river of the earth," says the gifted Suta to Saunaka's Munis in the Naimisa vana.

SIXTY-FIVE

"VYASA MUNI CONTINUED, 'NARADA ASKED NARAYANA, "LORD, THE Prakriti pralaya takes no more than the twinkling of an eye of the Devi Bhagavati. The Prapancha, the five elements, are dissolved, and the Devi Vasundhara, the blessed Earth herself. Tell me, master, where does the Earth dwell after the pralaya, and how does she manifest herself again, when a new creation begins?"

Narayana said, "Vasundhara is an amsa of Mulaprakriti, and at times she is absorbed into the Mahamaya, and at others, she emerges, and is manifest. And she, Bhumi Devi, is the love of the blue Lord Mahavishnu, when he comes as the Varaha, the great Boar, to lift her out of the sea of dread in which the Asura Hiranyaksha plunges her. She is called Varahi."

"How did she become his love, O Guru?"

"When the golden Demon Hiranyaksha thrust the earth down into Rasatala, the underworld, Vishnu plunged down through the ground, burrowing his way with tusks like streaks of solid lightning, long as the space between constellations in the sky. He slew Hiranyaksha and the Asuras in Patala with hooves like the thunder-flashes of the apocalypse, and set the round earth upon his tusks and brought her up to the surface of the ocean Ekarnava again, where she floated, bobbing gently.

Hari the Boar was lustrous as ten million suns, and his roaring shook the heavens. When he had rescued the Earth, suddenly he saw her spirit manifest in the sky above him, entirely beautiful and enchanting. She appeared in the firmament, flushed with the excitement of his having borne her up, blushing that he had touched her so intimately.

And he, the great, dark-hued Lord was smitten to see her sidelong glances. For, ah, she was bewitching. In a wink, Vishnu assumed a God's four-armed, dusky, brilliant form, and he flew up to her, and took her in his magnificent arms. And she melted against him in tidal desire, and they began to make love in the sky, and in the water, and his glad shouts and her soft screams rang everywhere!

For a year of the Devas their loving lasted, and not he, nor she, was conscious of what they did, but they were lost in a deep swoon of each other. At last, in sweet exhaustion, he drew himself away from her perfect body. Then, he was a great Boar again, and he worshipped her as the primordial Devi, with incense, dark blue lotuses, lamps, offerings of food and sindura, sandal-paste he anointed her limbs with, and silken garments.

'Auspicious One! Lovely One!' he cried fervently. 'Be the womb of all things, and the Munis, Manus, Devas, Siddhas, Gandharvas, Asuras, Bhutas, Rakshasas, why, all the created shall worship you!'

And, glowing with his love, she said, 'At your word, I shall be the white Varahi, your beloved for ever, Lord, and hold the earth of all beings and things upon my back. Yet, I cannot bear some things. The pearls, the little shells, the black saligrama of the river Gandaki, the Sivalinga, the murtis of the Devi Bhagavati, the ocean-sankhas, the sacred lamps of worship, the mystic yantras, diamonds, the sacred threads of the upanayana, flowers, gold, camphor, gorochana that is made from a cow's urine, sandal, and the water with which the saligramas are washed: these I shall not bear, my Lord!'

And he replied, 'Let any fool that sets any of these upon your back find himself in Kalasutra Naraka for a hundred years of the Devas!'

And he was quiet. But, now, the Devi Vasundhara was with child, a powerful male child: Kuja, whom the Lord set up in the heavens as a red and martial planet. And Varaha Deva worshipped the Earth again, and then Brahma worshipped her. After which, all the Rishis, Devas, Manus and men revered her with offerings and the mula mantra, **AUM Hrim Srim Klim Vasundharayai Svaha.** And with the Kanva sakha."

Narada said, "Now, tell me about the Devi Ganga. Tell me how she came to flow in the land of Bharata, and in which yuga this happened. Tell me how she appeared as Vishnupadi, who springs from Vishnu's feet. Lord, they say that hearing the legend of Ganga can make ashes of the sins of a thousand lives."

Narayana Muni said, "It was by the curse of Saraswati and the prayatna of king Bhagiratha of the House of Surya, that the Devi Ganga flowed upon the earth. Bhagiratha's ancestors, the wild Sagaraputras, had been turned into ashes by Kapila Vasudeva in a cave in Patala; for those violent and untamed Kshatriyas had rushed at him in anger, crying that he had stolen their father Sagara's horse. In fact, Indra had secreted that white beast of that king's Aswamedha yagna in Kapila's cave, where the Muni sat in samadhi, unaware of the world around him.

On their rampaging quest for their father's horse, during which they had despoiled the earth, uprooting whole forests, draining off rivers, and savaging the peace of the spirits of the earth, Sagara's thousand elemental sons arrived in wrath in the Muni's cave. When they rushed at Kapila, yelling that he was a thief, he blinked open his eyes, and with a soft, terrible 'Hummm!' made ashes of them.

The Sagaraputras' spirits languished in a dark limbo, a naraka, from which they could not rise into the realms of the Gods, the regions of light. Sagara's grandson Anshuman came reverently and peacefully to Kapila's cave, and the Muni gave him his father's horse, and told him how he had been forced to burn up that noble prince's uncles, when they attacked him.

Anshuman roamed the Patalas in some anguish, in search of expiation for his uncles' souls, in search of water pure enough, so he could wash their sins and set their spirits free. But their crimes were so brutal, when they ranged the earth in search of the white horse, that he found no water that was holy enough; why, he found no water at all. Then, his mother's brother, the Lord of birds, Garuda, flew down to him in compassion, and told him that there was only one way to redeem his uncles' spirits; he must wash the ashes that Kapila Muni had made of them in the waters of the Ganga. Otherwise, their souls would languish forever, and the royal line of Sagara would be cursed for all time.

Anshuman was aghast. How could he wash his uncles' ashes in the waters of the Ganga, when, in those most ancient days, she, Himavan's eldest daughter, flowed only through Devaloka?

Anshuman sat in tapasya for a thousand years, for of course, the kings of the Treta yuga lived long lives. But he also had to rule his kingdom, and he could not bring the Ganga down to wash his uncles' ashes. The curse grew in the House of the Sun. Anshuman's son Dilipa felt its shadow fall across his life. He also performed great tapasya, but to no direct avail; though

Dilipa's son Bhagiratha certainly inherited the punya of his father and grandfather's worship.

When Bhagiratha ascended the Ikshvaku throne, he found the clamour of his ancestors, who languished in a nightmare, had become unendurable in his very blood. The curse had grown so powerful in the royal House of Ikshvaku, that Bhagiratha could not father children. He knew he could not rule the kingdom of his fathers, as long as his grand uncles' souls remained in Patala, in agony.

Bhagiratha left his kingdom in the hands of some trusted ministers, and went to the Himalaya, and sat in a single-minded dhyana to achieve his impossible task—to bring the Ganga who flowed in heaven down into the world, and down into Patala to cleanse his ancestors' ashes and, thereby, end the curse that lay over the House of Ikshvaku.

When he had sat in relentless tapasya for a hundred thousand years, Krishna, Lord of the kalpa, appeared before Bhagiratha. The Lord came in his Gopala form, with a flute in his hands, and refulgent as a million suns. Bhagiratha felt a sea of bliss swell in his body, and prostrated himself before Krishna.

The Lord asked, 'What boon do you want from me, O King?'

The tapasvin king told him the boon he wanted. And Krishna called Ganga there, and said to her, his love, 'Saraswati has cursed you to flow for five thousand years in the land of Bharata. Let the curse be fulfilled now, help this great king in his need. Flow upon the earth, my love, and purify the ashes of the Sagaraputras. Their sins shall be taken from them by the tapasya of this son of Ikshvaku. They shall rise into Goloka in forms of light when your waters flow over their ashes, and they will be my gopas from then on, and they shall be free.

Why, any man who bathes in your sacred waters, Devi Ganga, shall be freed of a thousand births of sin, even the most heinous sinners among them!'

Her head bowed in bhakti, Ganga said, 'Lord, if every sinner who bathes in me upon the earth has his sins washed from him, tell me, how will I bear that terrible burden of sins? Shan't I be destroyed by it? And how long will I flow in the world, my Lord? When can I return to you on high?'

Krishna said, 'All that troubles your heart is known, Sureswari. The salt sea shall be your lord in the world, for he is my amsa, too. You will flow into him, and he will absolve you of every sin you bear into his plumbless depths. And I will absolve him of their pain, for he is part of me. Devi, you will have more honour than any other river that flows in the world, for you shall be the purest, the most blessed of them all. And, by Saraswati's curse you will flow for five thousand years on earth, and for your endless pleasure, you will flow into your lord, the Ocean, and he will embrace you without pause!

All the people of Bharata will worship you, Ganga, whilst you flow across their holy continent. And he who but says your name will be freed of his sins, be he not a thousand yojanas from your currents, and he will come to Vishnuloka. And he who dies beside you, why, he will surely find Vaikuntha and dwell there for as long as the sun shines upon the earth. For, only the man who has a great store of punya earned through many lives, can die in your waters.

That man will be blessed with many bodies so he can enjoy all his punya, and then he will have my own form, my svarupa, and dwell at my side for as long as Brahma's life. And he who remembers your name with bhakti, Ganga, will have a luminous vimana, and live through countless Prakriti pralayas in Goloka.'

Krishna turned again to Bhagiratha, and said, 'Now worship this Devi Ganga, my son, and she will grant you the boon you seek.'

And, tingling in awe with what he was privileged to see and hear, Bhagiratha purified himself once more by bathing in an icy stream of the mountain. Then, he worshipped Ganapathy, Surya, Agni, Vishnu, Siva and Sivaa, in that order, and now he was ready to implore the Devi Ganga for what he wanted from her, that she flow upon the earth. He worshipped Vighnesha so every obstacle may be removed from his path, he worshipped the flaming Sun for health, Fire so he may be pure, Vishnu so he may have wealth and power, Siva so he would have knowledge, and Sivaa so he would have mukti, one day.

And then, Bhagiratha worshipped the Devi Ganga with the Kanva sakha that burns up every sin, thus:

'Bless me, O Devi, who are white as the pale lotus, who destroy the sins of men, who have sprung from Sri Krishna's blue body, who are as powerful as he is, who are perfectly chaste, brilliant as a thousand autumn moons, always with a smile on your lips, always youthful, who wear malati in your hair and spots of sandalwood on your dazzling face, and the sindura in your hair, on your brow, and delicate musk upon your body, whose crimson raiment is immortal, made pure in the fire, whose lips are cinnabar like the bimba fruit, who teeth are pearls, whose eyes are ineffable, whose breasts are like two bhel fruit thrusting against each other, whose loins are, oh, indescribable, slender as the plantain tree's stem, whose pink feet are more beautiful than the sthalapadma, the lotus of the ground!

The Devas, Siddhas and Munis always offer you arghya, O Devi, and worship your feet tinged with the scarlet honey of the parijata Indra wears upon his head. And you give mukti to those that pray for mukti, and bhukti to those wanting boons of pleasure.

O Mother, who bestow the Vishnupada, who have sprung yourself from His holy feet, bless me now, O precious, precious Ganga. Be Tripathaga from now; you who flow in Swarga, flow on Bhumi and in Patala, too!

I bow to you, Devi, who sprang from Sri Krishna's body, who are enchanted by the Lord Siva's music, who bathed in the effusions of the Devi Radha's pristine form, her ambrosial sweat! I bow to you who first appeared in the Raasamandalam in Goloka, in the ecstatic dance of Radha, on the night of the full moon in the month of Kartika.

I bow to you who are a koti yojanas wide and a hundred thousand times as long in Goloka! And as splendourous in Vaikuntha, in Brahmaloka, in Sivaloka, in Dhruvaloka, in Chandraloka, in Satyaloka, in Tapoloka, in Janarloka, in Maharloka, on mystic Kailasa, who are the lustrous Mandakini in Indraloka, and the Bhogavati in glimmering Patala, and the Alakananda on earth.

I bow to you, who were the colour of milk in the Krita yuga, of the moon in the Treta, of cool, golden sandal-paste in the Dwapara, and are as water in the Kali. I bow to you, Devi, of whose water the touch of an atom is enough to make ashes of the most heinous sins, even the murder of a Brahmana!

I beg you, Mother Ganga, now flow down in the world in this chaturyuga for the sake of all men, flow down again into Patala, and liberate my ancestors from their sins.'

And then, she did fall down from heaven, as a mighty torrent, and flow upon the earth for the perfect tapasya of the noble Bhagiratha. So awesome was her fall that the earth would have shattered if the Lord Rudra had not risen upon the Himalaya and borne her mad descent upon his head. It is told the Devi Ganga was arrogant, for she had been worshipped in Indraloka so long by the Devas. She came laughing wildly down the mandalas, and the Lord Siva loomed up and contained her easily in his jata, indeed at the base of just one hair of his blessed head!

She raged there for a hundred years, in spinning cataracts and whirlpools, but she could not free herself at all. She grew quiescent, knowing she was helpless against Siva's immense power. Bhagiratha worshipped the Lord Siva with another fierce tapasya, and only then did He who is easily pleased let a chastened Ganga down into the world, drop by drop, so she formed a crystalline lake of holy water-drops upon the great mountain, the lake called the Bindusaras. And it is from that lake she flowed down into the land of Bharata.

The Devi Ganga followed Bhagiratha's chariot down through plains of Bharatavarsha, often meandering sinuously, like a woman, and at last she fell down through the crevice in the earth, and down into Patala below, and fell over the ashes of the sons of Sagara that lay in a grey heap in a rocky cave. And, palms folded and crying out their gratitude, a thousand great and grave spirit-forms rose into Vaikuntha, and the long curse that lay over the House of Ikshvaku ended.

When the Ganga flowed across the land of Bharata, she was called Bhagirathi for the pious king, whose tapasya had fetched her down from the sky. And, then on, the Gods said that any great feat performed in the world, against impossible odds, would be known as a Bhagiratha prayatna, for what that king of old achieved was truly, well nigh, the impossible."

Now Narada asked, "Muni, how did the Ganga first flow through the three realms, how was she worshipped in them all?"

Narayana said, "Sri Krishna worshipped his Radha on the night of purnima in the month of Kartika, in the Raasa mandala. Then, Brahma and the other Devas, Saunaka and his Munis, worshipped the Devi Radha. Then, inspired by bhakti, the Devi Saraswati sang to Krishna, and played on her vina. In delight, for her music was transcendent, Brahma gave her a precious necklace, Siva gave her rare jewels, Krishna the crimson kaustubha, Lakshmi Devi gave her golden earrings, and Radhika and Narayana gave her wondrous ornaments as well.

The Devi Bhagavati blessed Saraswati, then, with love and bhakti for the Lord Brahma, whose consort she must be from now. Dharma Deva gave her the highest fame, and devotion to the quality of dharma, which is righteousness. Agni Deva gave her shimmering raiment burnt pure in his flames, splendid clothes to wear that were indestructible. Vayu Deva gave the Devi Saraswati fine nupura, toe-rings, studded with jewels clearer and more resonant than any others.

Now, all the Gods and Goddesses were swept up in a storm of bliss, and Brahma asked Siva to sing there at Krishna's Raasa lila. And, when Maheswara sang the Devas stood transfixed, unaware of themselves, so marvellous, so profound was his singing. When they grew conscious again, they saw that Krishna and Radha had vanished from the Raasa mandala. They saw there was a tide of water flowing in that place, the sweetest, clearest current, a river in which everything was subsumed!

Brahma and the others began to pray, crying, 'Krishna, Lord, where are you? We are lost without you and the Devi Radha!'

And a disembodied voice spoke to them out of the sky, a reverberant asariri, 'I am with you always, and Radha is, too! We have assumed this fluid form only to wash your sins, and to bless you all. And, if you truly want to see my other form again, as I was before, O Brahma ask the Lord Siva to compose the Tantra Shastra for you. And let it be full of magical mantras and stotras, and subtle kavachas, and let my own mantra, stotra and kavacha, and Radha's as well, be embedded in it secretly, so no sinner in the ages of evil sees them, and uses their power against me.

It may be that one in a thousand worships my mantra, truly. And, those that do shall surely be freed of their sins and come to dwell with me in Goloka. Let Mahadeva swear that he will create this Shastra, and you shall see me again!'

The asariri, Krishna's voice, was full of playfulness, the bliss of the Raasa lila, and Radha's joyful laughter could be heard after it. The mood of exaltation and play was upon all the Gods, and Mahadeva Siva, Bhutanatha, the Lord of the elements, scooped up some water from the freshly sprung Ganga in the palms of his hands, and said, 'I shall, indeed, compose the Tantra Shastra, that will sing the Lord Krishna's and the Devi Radha's names, and their mantras, stotras and kavachas, all secretly, so only the pure-hearted may see them!'

At this, Krishna and Radha appeared again before the Trimurti and the Devas and Rishis. The eulogies of the Devas rang out in that blessed realm, and the flowing river sparkled. For, O Muni, that river, the golden Ganga, was, verily, Krishna and Radha, she was their own bodies become a river that would flow through all the realms of creation to bless every jiva in time," said the Muni Narayana, once, to Narada,' said Vyasa," says Romaharshana, the peerless Suta.

SIXTY-SIX

SUTA ROMAHARSHANA TELLS THE RISHIS OF THE NAIMISA VANA, "MY GURU Vyasa said to the king, 'Narada now asked Narayana, "Muni, where did the Devi Ganga go after she spent the five thousand years of her curse in the world?"

Narayana replied, 'To Vaikuntha, and the Devis Saraswati and Lakshmi also went back to their Lord Vishnu, when they had served the time of their curses in the world, flowing as rivers. And they are his eternal loves, and the Devi Tulasi as well.'

Now Narada asked, 'How did the Ganga spring from Vishnu's holy feet? Why did the Lord Brahma fill his kamandalu with her? I have heard, O Muni, that Ganga is Siva's wife; how then did she become Vishnu's love?'

The sage said, 'In time out of mind, in Goloka, Ganga first assumed her form of water, and she flowed from the bodies of Radha and Krishna. So, she has both their natures; she is the Goddess of all fluid beings. And her beauty is incomparable! Her face, when she was first born, was like the autumn lotus at noon, and her smile was entrancing. Her skin was like liquid gold, Muni, and she was like the full moon.

And, ah, what can one say about her form? Of her flaring hips, her slender waist, her high, full breasts? No poet can describe them adequately! She wore raiment purified in the fire. Her eyes were exquisite, and the sidelong glances she cast out of them enough to make anyone's heart beat fast. She wore her hair braided with malati flowers, sweet jasmine, and the pottu of sandalwood and vermilion on her forehead.

Musk leaves were drawn across her face, and her lips were as crimson as the bandhuka flower. Her teeth were like rows of ripe pomegranate and she sat beside Krishna, once, after she was born, quivering with shyness and desire in equal parts! She had covered her face with the end of her garment, and gazed at him through a gap between the cloth and her fingers. She gazed on, drinking the nectar of his dark face, and trembling with anticipation of his first embrace.

Radhika arrived on this scene in a vimana, with her gopis. Radha was as brilliant as a thousand moons, and a small army of gopis came with her. The vimana landed soft as a Devi's breath, and Radha alighted from it by a flight of crystal stairs. She stopped still, when she saw Ganga sitting beside Krishna, devouring him with her gaze. Radha's eyes turned red as plums. She stamped her foot like a maddened she-elephant, and the ground shook.

The scarlet sindur in her hair, where it was parted, shone like a flame. Radhika trembled with rage, and her plait, which fell to her ankles, was like an agitated serpent. Her lips had turned white, in a moment, and she stalked haughtily up to Krishna and Ganga, and sat on a jewel-encrusted throne beside them. The gopis stood at a safe distance in fear, their heads bent down, not daring to look at their mistress or their Lord.

Smiling serenely, dark Krishna rose and began to hymn Radha softly with the most wonderful stotras! He spoke to her, as well, whispering the sweetest things. He asked tenderly how she was. But her mouth was parched as if she had a desert in it. Now Ganga grew terrified to see Radha's wrath, and, rising hastily, she also began to flatter her with honeyed stotras.

Her sakhis brought the Devi Radha some betel, and she began to chew, she who is the most beautiful one of all. Before her even Krishna's lustre seemed faint. Ganga stood quaking, her gopis were full of fear. And then, at last, when her fragrant mouth was scarlet with betel-juice, Radha said sweetly to Krishna, "My Lord, who is the lovely woman? She trembles with wanting you, and you, also, I see are moved by her charms."

Krishna made no reply at first, and Radha went on, her rage a slow, quiet, terrifying thing, "Krishna, do you remember how you made love to the gopi Viraja? And I saw you with her, thrusting at her in the chandana vana. My sakhis begged me to forgive you, and so I did. And in shame, Viraja became a river, and she flows still in Goloka, murmuring your name.

When she had gone, you looked everywhere for her, calling to her desperately, 'Oh, Viraja! Viraja my love, where are you?'

And she rose out of her waters, as a Siddhi yogini. She was radiant in her spirit form, and what did you do then, my Lord? You drew her to you, and cast your seed into her, even as she was! And so the seven seas of the earth were born.

But that was not all, Krishna. One day I heard delirious screaming in the forest, and when I ran to it, I saw you making love with my gopi Shobha! You heard me coming, even as you were upon her, and you fled. In shame Shobha left her body and flew to the Chandra mandala, and the moon has his cool lustre from her. And you gave some of her soft light to gold, some to pearls, some to the faces of women, to the bodies of kings, to leaves and all green plants, to flowers and ripe fruit, to ears of corn, to palaces and temples, and to all creatures that are young. So, you could gaze on her always, anywhere you looked!"

Krishna stood at her side, the faintest of smiles playing on his lips. She, of course, grew angrier to see him so cool, and her voice tighter, went on, "Then, I caught you with Prabha, wrapped around you like your very skin! Again, you vanished from there, and she left her body and flew up to the sun. You moaned for her, Krishna, you cried out her name again and again. And, in your pang, you put some of her lustre in fire, some into Yakshas, some into lions, some into brilliant men, some into the Devas, some into serpents, some into Vaishnavas, some into Munis, some into Brahmanas, and some of her light you gave to beautiful and learned women! So, on her also you always gazed!

Then, I saw you with the gopi Shanti, don't think I did not. I saw you with her on a spring morning in a bejewelled, lamplit, pavilion in the heart of the forest, lying on a bed of flowers, your body anointed with sandal-paste. I heard her cries as you put yourself in her, again and again. So absorbed were you that you did not notice me for a time. You shared a betel leaf with her, both your mouths were stained scarlet by chewing the same leaf, your tongues entwined like serpents.

You grew aware that I watched you, and you vanished again! Shanti was so ashamed that she too abandoned her body, and she was absorbed into you, my Lord. Which is why she is a noble quality, and why you are so calm even at this moment!

Yet, you missed seeing her so much that you imbued part of her to the forests, part to Brahma, some to me, some to Lakshmi, some to those who worship you with your mantra, some to those that worship me with mine, some to the Munis, some to dharma, and some to all those who are devout.

Then, my Krishna, do you remember how once you lay in the arms of Kshama, in a green glade, upon a mattress of swan's-down, when I chanced upon you both? I had heard the very forest ring with her sweet cries and yours, and tracked you down. But when I arrived in your grove of love, I found you asleep in her golden arms, exhausted with your labours. I stole near, and removed your pitambara robe, your precious flute, your vanamala and kaustubha. And then you were as one demented! Only because my sakhis begged me to show mercy, did I return all these to you.

Your body turned black for that sin! And Kshama was so guilty, she fled down to the earth, and you gave her, who is forgiveness, many homes: in Vishnu, in his bhaktas, in dharma, in all the devoted, in the weak and the learned, in poets and scholars.

So that is how you have always been, Krishna, and now here you are with another woman! And, I wonder what is she going to do?"

With a moan to see Radha's wrath, Ganga flowed as a river, at once, with her siddhi yoga. Radha was ready to quaff all her currents in a gulp, but Ganga hid herself in Krishna's blue feet. Radha could not find her anywhere. She set out in a fury to look for her. She searched in Goloka, then in Vaikuntha and Brahmaloka. She searched every realm, high and low, but she did not find Ganga anywhere.

And when Ganga vanished all Goloka became dry, for she was the Devi of water. All the fish and every creature that lives in water perished. A terrible thirst parched the worlds. Brahma, Vishnu, Siva, Ananta, Dharma, Indra, Soma, Surya, all the Devas and Munis, all the Siddhas and Gandharvas were seized by the dreadful thirst. They flew to Goloka, and came to Krishna who is the Supreme God above whom there is no other, the Creator of creators.

The other Gods and Munis saw him, and were swept by a wave of ecstasy, such love! With Vishnu on his right and Vama Deva on his left, Brahma approached dark Krishna. All around him, he saw only the blue Lord. He saw him as the formless Light of lights, he saw him as the dark flute-player, and he saw him as lover and cowherd. He saw Krishna everywhere, and Brahma could not tell which Dark One he should speak to!

Brahma began to hymn Krishna silently, with perfect bhakti, in the lotus of his heart. Then, a smiling Lord stood before him, and said gently, "Tell me Brahma, O Vishnu and Sankara, O Devas and Munis, Siddhas and Gandharvas, why have you come all together to see me?"

Brahma murmured, "Lord, the Devi Ganga has vanished from creation and all the created are parched with thirst. Our bodies burn, our souls are seared. What shall we do?"

Krishna said, "Ganga has vanished in fear, for Radha wanted to drink all her water in a sip! If you want her to flow again through the lokas, worship Radha. Only she can remove Ganga's terror."

Brahma folded his hands, and said to the Devi Radha, "Devi, Mahamaye, when Krishna and you heard Siva's song, you were transformed into that music and became a river in the Raasa mandala. You became Ganga. She is your own child, your very self. Let her flow through the worlds again, a part of her on the earth; and let Varuna be her lord there, let her flow into him always. In Vaikuntha, let her be the Lord Vishnu's love. And in Goloka let her be your daughter and have your nurture. I will teach her the Radha mantra, and she shall worship you with it."

Radha smiled, and said, "So be it."

At which Ganga appeared again from Krishna's feet, from the tips of his toes. She flowed once more in Goloka, and she arose, embodied from her shining waters, and the Devas all received her with worship and praise. Brahma filled his kamandalu with a part of her, so he would never go thirsty again, and Siva kept a part of her in his jata.

And now, the four-faced Creator taught Ganga the Radha stotra, and covered her in the Radha kavacha, the subtle armour of protection spun from the Radha mantra. Brahma taught Ganga Radha dhyana, and the Radha purascharana too. With all these, Ganga worshipped the Devi Radha, and she went away to Vaikuntha.

Thus Muni, Lakshmi, Saraswati, Ganga and Tulasi became the four wives of Mahavishnu. When Ganga flowed through Goloka again, Krishna smiled mysteriously and said to Brahma and the other Devas, "My Lords, I fear that, while you have all been here with me, time has dissolved in every other realm. So go forth now, and create the universe again!"

And he took Radha by her hand, and walked blithely into his palace. Brahma and the others set about their task of creation again, and, when they had created a new brahmanda, yet another universe, the Devi Ganga flowed through it, through Goloka, Brahmaloka, Vaikuntha, Sivaloka, and every other realm, blessing them all, the queen of holy waters. Because she flowed once from Krishna's blue feet, she is called Vishnupadi, O Muni," said Narayana Rishi,' my guru Vyasa told me."

SIXTY-SEVEN

"MY MASTER SAID TO THE KING, 'NARADA MUNI ASKED THE RISHI NARAYANA, "We have heard how Ganga was married to the Lord Vishnu, but not how he married the Devi Tulasi. Who was Tulasi, whose daughter? What tapasya did she perform, that she became the Lord's wife? And, then, how did she become a plant?"

Narayana Muni said, "The Manu Daksha Savarni was an amsa of Vishnu himself, it is told, and he was an illustrious Prajapati. His son Brahma Savarni was as devout as his father was. His son was Dharma Savarni, and his son Rudra Savarni, and his son was Deva Savarni, and his son was Indra Savarni, and all of these were great Vishnubhaktas. Indra Savarni's son was called Vrishadhvaja, and he was an ardent Sivabhakta!

In Vrishadhvaja's home, Siva himself dwelt for three Devayugas, which are more than a thousand yugas of men. Indeed, Bhagavan Bhutanatha loved Vrishadhvaja more than he did his own son. And Vrishadhvaja worshipped no other God save Sankara. He did not worship Vishnu, Lakshmi or Saraswati. Why, he stopped performing the Lakshmi puja in the month of Bhadra, the Sri Panchami puja in Magha, and the Saraswati puja, as well.

At this the Sun grew angry, and cursed Vrishadhvaja. 'O King, since you worship none but Siva, let your wealth and prosperity desert you!'

When Siva heard this he was furious, and went after the Sun with his trisula. Surya Deva grew afraid and hid with his father Kashyapa in Brahma's realm. But Siva arrived blazing in Brahmaloka, and Brahma himself grew afraid, and fled with Kashyapa and Surya to Vaikuntha. They stood trembling before the Blue God, and, when they told him what terrified them so, he raised a dark hand over them and said, 'Abhaya! Do not fear the Auspicious One.'

Just then, Siva arrived in Vaikuntha, mounted on his Bull Nandiswara. Smiling, the Lord Siva came and bowed graciously to Blue Vishnu. Vishnu also bowed to Siva, and then so did Brahma, Kashyapa, and Surya Deva. Meanwhile, Vidyadharis sang and danced all around them in Narayana's fine sabha. Siva sat beside Mahavishnu, as Kashyapa and Surya Deva began to hymn him with resonant stotras.

Then Vishnu said, 'My Lord Sankara, tell me what brings you here. Has anything annoyed you?'

Siva said, bristling, 'My Lord, Surya here cursed my bhakta Vrishadhvaja, who is as dear to me as a son. I have come to take revenge, even as a father would for his son. I would burn the Sun to ashes with fire like he has never known, except that you protect him. But, tell me, what will become of my bhakta, the king of the earth?'

Vishnu smiled, he seemed to consider what Siva had said for a moment. Then, he murmured, 'My Lord, twenty-one yugas have passed on earth, since you set out in pursuit of Surya Deva. I fear Vrishadhvaja is dead, and his son Rathadhvaja too. Rathadhvaja has two sons, Dharmadhvaja and Kusadhvaja, but, though they are great Vaishnavas, fortune has deserted them because of Surya Deva's curse. They have no kingdoms, gold or children even.

Even as we speak, they are worshiping Mahalakshmi, and she means to be born in a twin Avatara, as their children. And then, they will surely find fortune again! They shall be kings of the earth, once more.'

Dharmadhvaja and Kusadhvaja worshipped Sri Lakshmi with a fervid tapasya, and they had the boons they wanted from her. Kusadhvaja's wife was called Malavati, and she bore him a daughter, who was indeed an amsa of the Devi Lakshmi. Immediately as she was born, that exceptional child began to sing Vaidik mantras, at her mother's side, in the very chamber of birth! The Brahmanas named her Vedavati.

As soon as she had bathed, after she was born, she said she wanted to go into the forest to sit in tapasya. Her parents did their best to dissuade her, as did everyone else. But she, of course, was adamant. She walked out of her father's home, and went to Pushkara, where she sat in dhyana for a manvantara. She ate not a morsel, yet she did not so much as grow lean. Instead, she grew into a most beautiful young woman.

One day, Vedavati heard an asariri speak to her from the sky,

'In your next life, young woman, Narayana himself will be born as a man, and he shall be your husband.'

Vedavati was beside herself with joy. She ran all the way to Gandhamadana, the fragrant mountain, and sat in even more fervent tapasya in one of its caves. When years had gone by—and she did not age at all by her dhyana – the awesome Ravana arrived on that mountain and in her very cave. When Vedavati saw him, she rose and made him welcome as she would any guest to her home. She gave him water to wash his feet, soft fruit to eat, and sparkling spring water to drink.

The Rakshasa accepted all this rather grandly, and he was a handsome devil, indeed, a Demon king with a reverberant presence. Then, he asked her, 'Who are you, lovely one?'

And he was so smitten that he reached for her hand, pulled her to him, quicker than thinking, and ravished her upon that very cave-floor! When she disentangled herself from him, and he lay in a swoon, she cast a spell on him with her tapasya-shakti so he could not move, but lay as if turned to stone. Only his lewd and burning eyes still watched her. But Ravana was a great tapasvin himself, though of the left-hand way, and he began to hymn her and the Parashakti of whom she was an amsa. He did this silently, since he could not even move his lips to speak.

At which, the Goddess in Vedavati grew pleased! The Devi blessed Ravana that in the next world he would have great punya. But Vedavati, the woman, cursed him. Her eyes blazing, she cried, 'Vile Rakshasa, you have desecrated the sanctity of my body, and you and all your family shall perish for this crime! And, look, I abandon this soiled body now, for I cannot bear to live in it for another moment.'

And in a flash of spirit-fire, she did as she said. Ravana lay sobbing desperately on the cold cave floor. At last, he roused himself, took up the exquisite body Vedavati had left forever, and floated it down the Ganga. Then he returned to Lanka, his home.

In her next life, Vedavati was born as Sita, and Rama of Ayodhya, who was an Avatara of the Lord Vishnu himself, became her husband. And, of course, Sita was to become the cause for the invincible Ravana's death. Yet, there is a strange tale that some of the knowing tell about Sita. They say that, shortly before Ravana abducted Sita and flew with her to Lanka, Agni Deva appeared in a dream to Rama in the forest to which he had been banished for fourteen years. The Fire God told Rama that, inevitably, precious Sita would be abducted now, and he would have to kill the Demon of Lanka, the master of evil on earth, and rescue her.

Agni suggested in the dream that he take Sita away with him for a year. Meanwhile, he would create a Chchaya Sita, a shadow Sita, who would be like Rama's wife in every way, and Ravana would abduct her and not the true Sita. Sita herself would, thus, never be in any danger of either dying or being molested by the Rakshasa, who was a mayavi, a master sorcerer, as well; and Agni promised to deliver her to Rama, after Ravana had been slain.

In his dream, Rama agreed, and Agni created the Chchaya Sita, and left her in the asrama in Panchavati where Rama, Lakshmana and Sita were living, and took the real Sita away with him. But, of course, Rama was born to suffer as a man, for the sins of all men, and because great evil can be overcome only after the warriors of dharma are purified with a great ordeal; and so, Rama remembered nothing of his dream when he awoke, and took the Chchaya Sita to be his own wife. And, of course, the Chchaya Sita also believed herself to be the real Sita, she owned her very memories!

The next day, Maricha the Rakshasa, Ravana's minion, came as a golden deer to enchant Sita. She begged Rama to capture the gleaming creature for her. And he set off after it into the deeper forest, leaving Lakshmana to watch over Sita, in their little asrama. Deep in the jungle, Rama realised the golden deer was a demon, and brought it down with an arrow. As he died, Maricha assumed his own fanged and clawed Rakshasa's body again. But, just before life left him, he screamed in Rama's very voice, 'Hah! Lakshmana, save me!'

When Sita heard this cry, she sent Lakshmana into the jungle after it, for she thought Rama was in mortal danger. Reluctantly, Lakshmana set out, and Ravana, who had sent Maricha as the golden stag, and who waited hidden near the little asrama, seized Sita, and flew with her to his island, Lanka. For an anguished year, Rama and Sita were parted from each other. But finally, with an army of vanaras, and with the Sea-God's help, Rama and Lakshmana arrived on Lanka, and slew most of its Rakshasas. In the end, Rama killed the sovereign of evil upon the earth, and rescued Sita.

But then, Sita had lived in an asokavana in Ravana's palace for a whole year, and the people would surely assume that the Demon had enjoyed her. Rama himself insisted that Sita underwent an agnipariksha, a trial by fire, to prove that she was still pure. On Lanka, Lakshmana kindled a fire, and the Chchaya Sita walked into it. In a wink, Agni himself emerged from the flames, bearing the real Sita in his arms!

But, now, the Chchaya Sita came before Rama and Agni, and said, 'Lord, what will happen to me now?'

They said to her, 'Go to Pushkara, and sit in tapasya there. And, in time, you shall be Swarga Lakshmi in heaven!'

It is told Chchaya Lakshmi sat in dhyana for three hundred thousand years, and, at last, she did indeed become Mahalakshmi. It is also known that, once, upon a certain time, Chchaya Sita appeared from king Drupada's yagna kunda, from the sacred fire in that pit of sacrifice. She appeared as a dark and ravishing princess, and she became the wife of the Pandavas. She was, in that incarnation, called Draupadi, or Panchali. This was when the Dwapara yuga was nearing its end. So, she lived in Krita, Treta and Dwapara yuga, as well. And, for this, she is sometimes known as Trihayani."

Now, Narada asked, "Lord, why did Draupadi have five husbands? I have heard there is a tale behind this."

Narayana Muni said, "When Chchaya Sita first worshipped Siva in the Pushkara kshetra, it was soon after the real Sita had been restored to Rama. Now, the Chchaya Sita was a virgin still, because she had not been with Rama, since Ravana had taken her his captive the day after she was first created, and the true Sita was restored to Rama that day after Ravana was slain.

Chchaya Sita yearned for a husband, Muni! So, when she asked Sankara for a boon, she cried, 'Lord, give me a husband!' five times. And Siva, with a smile at her eagerness, gave her five husbands in the Dwapara yuga!" said Narayana.

"And what happened to the real Sita, master?" Narada wanted to know.

"With his Sita beside him, Rama ruled Ayodhya for eleven thousand mortal years, and the grace of his reign blesses the land of Bharatavarsha even in the vilest night of the Kali yuga. But, when her time came, Sita was absorbed into the body of the Devi Lakshmi, whose amsa she was. And Rama, when his mission on earth had been fulfilled, walked into the sea once, and vanished from the world in mystic jalasamadhi. The ocean received his mortal elements and immortal Vishnu received his Avatara back unto himself," said Narayana,' Vyasa Muni told Janamejaya," says the Suta, once, in a certain kalpa.

SIXTY-EIGHT

THE SUTA SAYS, "MY GURU TOLD THE KING, 'SRI NARAYANA SAID TO THE Muni Narada, "Kusadhvaja's brother Dharmadhvaja's wife was called Madhavi. Once, they went to make love upon the fragrant mountain Gandhamadana. Those, O Muni, were times when love was still a long and most sacred thing, and a hundred years passed in dalliance for Dharmadhvaja and his Madhavi. Yet, she was not satisfied, that lustful woman, and Dharmadhvaja swooned away!

Then, the Devas took a hand in their fate, and Madhavi became pregnant. She conceived the amsa of the Devi Mahalakshmi in her womb. That queen shone like a bit of the sun on the holy mountain, the mountain was lit up with the lustre of the child growing inside her. And on a perfectly auspicious night, when the moon was full, and all the planets were in rare and harmonious aspects, and shone in the signs of their exaltation, Madhavi was delivered of a girl child, whose face was as bright as the autumn moon.

She was entirely aware, as soon as she was born, that holy child, and looked around her with knowing eyes, luminous as lotus petals. The palms of her hands and the soles of her feet were reddish, the colour of the Devi! Rishis and Siddhas from the world over, from severe mountains and mysterious jungles' hearts, arrived on Gandhamadana to bless that child, to adore her. And they named her Tulasi.

She was a miraculous infant, and she had grown into a perfect-bodied young woman within an hour of her birth! And she was incomparable. Though her parents tried to prevent her, she went away to the Badarivana, to sit in dhyana. Tulasi sat in tapasya for a hundred thousand years, for she wanted Narayana himself, Blue Vishnu for her husband.

In summer, she sat in panchatapa, the penance of five fires, four that she lit around her on scorching stone, and the fifth the sun above. In winter she sat in ice-laden mountain streams, and in every season, rain or shine, she sat bared to the elements; at times she was drenched to the bone, at others, great gashes of blue lightning struck the earth a few feet from where she sat. She lived on just fruit and leaves and water, for twenty thousand years.

Then, she neither ate nor drank any more, but survived on just the air she breathed, on precious prana. Next, she stood on one leg, her arms raised above her head, motionless. And, when Brahma saw her standing thus, for ten thousand years, he appeared before her, riding his white swan.

Tulasi saw the Pitamaha, and prostrated herself before him. Brahma said to Tulasi, 'Ask me for any boon, and it shall be yours.'

She said, 'Lord, you know who I am, and why I am here today. I was once a gopi in Goloka, and, when Radha Devi saw dark Krishna making love to me in the Raasa mandala, she cursed me to be born as a mortal woman on earth. But, oh, Pitamaha, I was not sated with his loving, I had not had enough! Krishna said to me then, "Perform a tapasya in the world, so the world is blessed for ever, and, when the Lord Brahma appears before you, ask him for the Lord Vishnu to be your husband. Hari is my own amsa, and being with him you shall be with me again." Lord, that is the boon I want, to be with the Blue One again! Nothing else, nothing else.'

Brahma said, with a slight smile, 'Do you remember the gopa Sudaman from Goloka, Tulasi my child? Do you remember how he wanted you, and how he almost thrust himself upon you in the forest, save that Devi Radha arrived there? She cursed him, as well, and he has been born as a great Danava now, on earth. He is also an amsa of Krishna, Tulasi, and he is soon to be Lord of the world. And he loved you so truly, then, and he wants you so much even now, that you must be his wife first, for some time, before you can be free of that karma, and have Vishnu for yourself.

But, now, let me teach you the Radha mantra, so you will never have to fear Radha again.'

And, when Tulasi knew the Radha mantra, she chanted it ceaselessly until she was overwhelmed by a huge surge of peace. All the rigor of tapasya vanished from her mind, she swooned for joy. Her soft body anointed with sandal-paste, she fell asleep on a bed of mallika flowers.

Tulasi slept deeply, for the first time in so many years! And, as she slept, her lovely lips a sigh apart, her full breasts heaving gently, Kama Deva the

God of love stole into the cave where she lay. He came with his sugarcane bow in his hand, and his five flowery arrows of enchantment. He pierced her velvet skin at will with his subtle shafts, one by one.

She felt no pain, of course, for Kama's arrows are like fine thoughts. But, even as she slept, the most delicious desire, which she had never known before, awakened in her body soft as the petals of the wild rose. The fine down on her skin unfurled and stood on end. She moaned in her sleep, she turned, she awoke. She found she was quivering all over, in a delirium she had never dreamt could even exist.

Soon, Tulasi felt uneasy with the strange and powerful sensations that swept through her. She fell back into sleep, then she got up again and was restless. She felt faint, her mouth was parched. She felt great joy, and then, again, pangs of inexplicable grief. She felt hot flushes flash through her body. As the day wore on, the extraordinary sensations did not leave her, rather they intensified.

She had the most eerie hallucinations. Her cave seemed like a hole in the ground to her, the flowers on her bed appeared to be full of thorns. Clear water in a tumbler seemed like dark and deadly nightshade, so she let the glass fall from her hand, and stood trembling, her eyes red as bimba fruit. And, most of all, she began to have visions, by night and day, asleep and awake, of a strikingly handsome young man, with a faintly mocking, haughty smile on his strong face.

He came to her in the warm nights, as she lay on her bed of the softest petals. He came to her as if he rode the moonbeams that flowed in through the cavemouth on Badari and caressed her fair, naked body in yearning. She did not know if she was dreaming or awake, but he came naked himself in the night, and he made such sweet, rampant love to her, that she screamed in transport. Then, she would wake up, suddenly, covered in sweat, shivering, aching for him; but he had vanished. For, of course, he had been a dream. She lay sobbing bitterly.

Meanwhile, some years before Tulasi herself, the gopa Sudaman had been born into the world as the Danava Sankhachuda. Sankhachuda had the Krishna mantra from Maharishi Jaigasavya, and great siddhis too, at Pushkara kshetra where the Asura sat in a long dhyana, worshipping Brahma. At last, Brahma himself appeared before the Daitya, and gave him Krishna's subtle armour, the kavacha called Sarvamangalamaya. And, Brahma told him to go to the Badarikasrama, where he would find the woman who would be his wife.

Sankhachuda was as handsome as if Kama Deva himself had been born in amsa as that Asura. He was fair as champaka pushpas, and the finest jewels glittered from the ornaments with which he adorned himself. The splendid young Demon arrived in Tulasi's cave, and she saw at once that it was him, the man of her recent dreams. But she was determined to test his mettle before she gave himself to her, if indeed that was what he had come for.

He saw her, and stood as if he had been struck by lightning. His eyes turned slightly red, with the shock of love he felt, he sweated. She covered her face with her cloth, and the smile that broke out on her lips, helplessly.

After standing speechless before her for an interminable moment, at last the Danava said hoarsely, 'Who are you, lovely one? Whose daughter are you? Why are you here in this mountain cave by yourself?'

She read everything else that he wanted to say in his voice, his eyes, and the flush that crept into his face. But she must try him, if she was to become his wife. In a cold voice, Tulasi said, 'I am king Dharmadhvaja's daughter Tulasi. I have come to this Badari to do tapasya, for I seek moksha for myself. And who are you, stranger? Don't you know it is forbidden for a man to speak to a chaste woman alone, especially a sannyasini like me?'

He did not reply, but just stood drinking in the sight of her, while ancient memories of another life stirred dimly within him; but, of course, he could not know what they were.

Seeing him standing there dumb, she said more combatively than before. 'Don't you know it is a sin to speak in private to a yogini? Besides, don't you know, O ignorant young man, that a woman is only beautiful to behold? She is the most dangerous creature in the world, her heart full of venom, greed and deceit. Don't you know a woman only wants to satisfy herself with every handsome stranger she meets? Ah, they only pretend to be shy and bashful, but with their lovers, young man, they are shameless, insatiable!

Why, the Rishis say of women that they will prefer their lovers, any time, to their own children! For, once aroused, truly there is no limit to a woman's lust. She devours her men even as a snake eats rats. And a woman's heart is as inscrutable as her passion is tameless. Women are born to be fetters to men in this world. A man may escape if he is bound in chains of iron and cast into the sea, but he shall never escape the bonds that a woman binds him with!'

She looked up into his eyes directly, for the first time now, and with such a sweet smile, that belied every word she had spoken so far, said, 'You still stand there gazing at me, young stranger. Run away quickly! I am dangerous.'

But he laughed, looked straight into her eyes, and said, 'What you say is true, indeed, of some women. But not all of them. There are women in the world, born of sattva guna, and they are as chaste as Goddesses. It seems to me, O Tulasi, that you are one of them. I am Sankhachuda the Danava, and Brahma himself sent me here. I have come to make you my wife.'

He spoke firmly, with no doubt about what he said, and she quivered to feel how strong he was. Turning her eyes down shyly, a delicate flush spreading up her throat, she said in a softer voice now, 'Truly, it is men like you whose fame spreads through the world. For, the man who lets himself be dominated by a woman has no escape from his shame except in death. Why, even the manes will not take the pinda and tarpana offered by such a man. Even the Devas will not receive flowers or holy water from him. For, he is hardly a man. But you are truly a man, my lord. You are not conquered by women's weapons, and I feel certain no man shall conquer you, either.'

Suddenly, in a swathe of light, four-faced Brahma appeared before Tulasi and Sankhachuda. The Pitamaha of the worlds said, 'Why do you waste precious time? Tulasi, do you seek to subdue this Danava of whom even the Devas go in fear? No, child, he will be the master of the three worlds, as soon as his shakti is with him. And you, precious child, shall be that shakti. As Lakshmi is to Vishnu, Radhika to Krishna, Savitri to me, Uma to Siva, Dakshina to Yagna, Sachi to Indra, Bhumidevi to Varaha, Anasuya to Atri, Ahalya to Gautama, Rohini to Soma, Tara to Brihaspati, Satarupa to Manu, Rati to Kama, Aditi to Kashyapa, Arundhati to Vasishta, Devahuti to Kardama, Svaha to Agni, Pushti to Ganapathy, Devasena to Skanda, Murtidevi to Dharma, so too shall Tulasi be to Sankhachuda.

Now take her to be yours in Gandharva vivaha, for, you were born to be man and wife! And, I bless you that, as long as this Tulasi is loyal to you, you shall be invincible.'

And, so he did, that Asura, and Brahma blessed them and vanished from there. When Sankhachuda married Tulasi in the free ritual of Gandharva vivaha, drumrolls sounded in the sky, and fresh, unearthly petal rain rained down upon the young couple. Straightaway, the Asura and his delectable bride fell to love in that same cave, where she had lain on her bed of flowers and dreamt of being ravished by him. And the reality of his lovemaking exceeded her wildest dreams. In the sixty-four different ways of the

Kamashastra, Sankhachuda made love to his Tulasi, and she to him, and there was no abandon they did not indulge in, nor any rapture they did not experience, for she was femininity itself, and he was as virile as only a great Asura could be, who would soon become emperor of all the world! His joyous roars and her sweet cries rang across Badari, and the Devas and Daityas smiled down on their delicious exertions.

And when they were sated for the time being they rose, and Tulasi playfully smeared her husband's nose with red sandal, mixed with kumkumam. She anointed all his body, and most delightedly its most delicate parts, with golden sandal, laughing throatily when she saw him aroused again. She made him wear a garment she had from Agni Deva, with her tapasya shakti, an indestructible robe that had passed through fire. She draped a garland of parijatas around his neck, to protect him from age and disease, and fed him scented betel from her own fragrant mouth.

And, he too had the most wonderful gifts for her, for, of course, he was a most blessed Danava. Sankhachuda kissed his Tulasi fervently on her cheeks, her lips, her fluted throat, her luscious breasts, and he gave her a rich, silken robe that he had from the Lord Varuna, and a necklace of priceless jewels, glimmering. He gave her Agni Deva's wife Svaha's anklets, Surya Deva's wife Chchaya's keyura, her armlets. He gave her Soma Deva's wife Rohini's earrings, the finger-rings of Rati, who is Kama's love, and a delectable sea-conch, encrusted with the rarest gemstones by Viswakarman himself, and more, much more that Asura gave his bride, for he was sovereign of the worlds.

Then, they left the asrama in Badari and ranged the earth together, the Danava and his beloved Tulasi. To the most sacred mountains they went, and to wondrous forests' hearts. They lay abandoned to wild love in mountain caves into which the moon stole in silvery tides, he in fever to see that beautiful couple. They lay entwined on deserted beaches, on glowing mosses beside exotic lotus pools in the most secret jungles, hidden away where no man, and perhaps no Deva or Gandharva, even, had ever come before.

They made enraptured love on the banks of the Pushpabhadra, and in the waters of that river, too, and in the Vispadana vana, with birds trilling above them to see delight such as theirs. From Vispadana they travelled to the Surasana vana, and then to Nandanam; thence, to the champaka vana and the chandana, the kunda, malati, kumuda and padmavanas, where they saw the parijatas and the kalpavrikshas that grew in dense groves, their leaves white, gold and silver, bright in the magical dimness.

Their wandering took them to Kanchana, and the Kanchivana, to Kinjalakavana, and to the gold mines at Kanchanakara. And everywhere they went, they lay on dewy moss, on velvet grasses, or on natural beds of flowers, and enjoyed each other interminably, and neither of them was ever satisfied, but wanted to make love more and more, again and again, even as they did so. Like a fire fed with ghee!

Finally, Sankhachuda, lord of the Danavas, brought his Tulasi home to his kingdom, to his majestic capital, and the splendid palace in it, and here also, in an opulent bedchamber, upon exquisitely carved beds, hung with strings of pearl and opal, and out in sequestered gardens, where koyals warbled in bright trees, the Asura drank deeply of Tulasi's love, and she from his potent manhood.

Meanwhile, by the power of her shakti, Sankhachuda extended his kingdom across the three worlds, Swarga, Bhumi and Patala. Every day, his power and wealth grew. The Devatas, Asuras, Danavas, Gandharvas, Kinnaras and Rakshasas were all his subjects, and he ousted Indra's Devas from their loka, from their crystal city Amravati, and they went like beggars in the world, and hid in obscure jungles and in unknown caves in distant mountains, where Sankhachuda's Daityas could not find them. And, the sovereignty of the great Asura was unchallenged," said Narayana,' my guru Vyasa said," says the Suta in the holy jungle.

SIXTY-NINE

"VYASA CONTINUED, 'NARAYANA SAID, "INDRA ARRIVED WITH HIS DEVAS in his father Brahma's sabha. They prostrated themselves abjectly before the Grandsire of the worlds and Indra moaned, 'Pitama, the Asura Sankhachuda tyrannises us, and he is protected by your boon. Help us, O Brahma, or we perish!'

Brahma took the Devas to Siva, and they came together to Vaikuntha. They passed numberless dwarapalakas, and sixteen occult thresholds, before arriving in Vishnu's presence, in his fragrant, peerless sabha, lit with clustres of moon-pearls, with opal and turquoise, parijata garlands hung everywhere, and all sorts of wondrous folk, Gandharvas, Apsaras and Vidyadharis dancing there. Lakshmi Devi, more beautiful than beauty, sat beside Narayana, and he held her hand in his.

The Devas wept even to see Hari, his very sight coursed such bliss through them. Vishnu rose to welcome Brahma and Siva. When they all sat together, and were at their ease, Brahma said, 'Lord, the Danava Sankhachuda has become master of the three worlds, and he terrorises your bhaktas, the Devas. He has driven them out of Devaloka, and set his Asuras to perform their tasks. Hari, the worlds have turned dark with the Daityas' crimes.'

Vishnu said softly, 'I know about Sankhachuda, he was my own gopa Sudama in Goloka, and he was my first parishada. Radha cursed him to be born a Danava.' The Blue One smiled, 'Do you know how it happened, O Brahma, Sankara, O Devas? I was with Viraja, the gopi, in the Raasa mandala, once, and we were making love, when my Radha arrived in the vana, in a rage, and all her sakhis with her. But she did not find me or even Viraja, who in a wink flowed as a river through that forest!

I went home to our palace, and Sudama was with me; he kept a watch for us in the vana, and warned us of Radha's approach. Back in the palace, precious Radha stormed into the chamber where I sat with Sudama, and she began to upbraid me. Sudama could not bear this. He turned on her, and cried, "Dare you rebuke my Lord? I won't stand for it!"

In the state she was in, this was an unwise thing to do. Her eyes turning crimson, she screamed for her sakhis to fling him out of our home. But he began to roar in anger, and advanced menacingly on her. At which, in a moment, thousands of Radha's Shaktis appeared and surrounded Sudama. But, undaunted, and quite beside himself, he continued to advance on her.

Then, in a ringing voice, she cursed him, "Vile gopa, dare you threaten me? Be born in a Danavi's womb!"

Sudama forgot his rage in a moment. Tears filled his eyes, and he bowed low to me, and then to Radha as well, and, without a word, he began to walk out of that chamber. And Devi Radha, who is mercy herself, cried to him with tears in her own eyes, "Wait, Sudama! Ah, what have I done? Where are you going? Don't leave us ever again!"

But go he had to, for the curse could not be in vain. But, then, he would go for no more than a moment, since Radha had also called him back, and said he should not leave us again. Yet, my Lords, a moment of Goloka is a lifetime in the world below. And, it seems, the moment is not yet over. Your Sankhachuda is my Sudama, and there is only one way in which he can be killed, and only one of us who can kill him.'

And Vishnu gave Siva the Trisula, saying, 'My Lord, impale the Danava upon this trident, and let him be my Sudama again, and return to Goloka.'

But the knowing Siva asked, 'Shall it be so simple, my Lord? Or is there something else that needs to be done?'

And, smiling, Vishnu said, 'Sankhachuda wears Krishna's kavacha around his neck, and there is a still more subtle and powerful armour which makes him invincible. His queen Tulasi's chastity. As long as Tulasi is faithful to her husband, no weapon, and not even you, O Sambhu, can harm him.'

Siva asked, innocently, 'And who shall cleave the kavacha of Tulasi's chastity, O Hari?'

Vishnu replied, 'She shall be mine again soon, Siva, so let it be me.'

Siva came to the ancient and immense vata vriksha that grew on the banks of the Chandrabhaga, and sat down under it. This was Siddhasrama, where once Kapila Muni sat in dhyana. He sent Pushpadanta, prince of the

Gandharvas, to Sankhachuda in his capital. It is told that, by now, the Danava's city was more beautiful than Indra's Amravati, and his palace more opulent than Kubera's.

Five yojanas long and wide was Sankhachuda's pura, and every Asura's mansion within it was encrusted with vaidurya and padmaraga. Magnificent highways connected its various suburbs, and it was encircled by seven deep trenches, some filled with water, others with sharp stakes in them, so it was impregnable. Bustling marketplaces had grown up within its precincts, a hundred of them, where merchandise from distant corners of the world was traded: the finest artifacts, the rarest silks and ornaments, the most delectable wines and exotic foodstuffs, everything under the sun.

There were vedis of worship all around, shrines at every street-corner, all worked with priceless jewels. And the stately mansions and homes that the Gandharva saw all around him, thousand upon thousand of them, took even his breath away. At the very heart of that amazing city, Pushpadanta saw Sankhachuda's own palace, a small city by itself, a circular edifice, and more splendid than every other. Four moats full of fire surrounded the palace of the sovereign of the worlds.

That palace had turrets that seemed to be made only of jewels, glittering diamonds, sapphires and glowing, thoughtful rubies. Twelve gates, one behind the other, through which a friend may enter, led into Sankhachuda's palace; and these were guarded by the most ferocious Asuras, whose very sight was enough to freeze the blood of any enemy.

Pushpadanta came to the first gate and he saw a single Daitya guard who sat in the middle of the road which led to this entrance to Sankhachuda's palace of a hundred thousand chambers! This guard was perhaps twenty feet tall, his skin was the colour of unburnished copper, and so was his hair. His eyes were two points of tawny fire, and he sat upon a great stool, with a shining trisula in his hand, smiling. His long red hair was tied neatly behind his thick neck, and his beard was clipped short. He barred Pushpadanta's way, and the Gandharva said sweetly, 'I am the Lord Siva's messenger come to see the emperor of the Danavas.'

The giant Asura scrutinised him for a long moment, then nodded his head slowly, that he may pass. Pushpadanta arrived at the next gate, and there, too, he was allowed to pass by a guard even more formidable than the first. Thus, he passed through twelve gates, and arrived at last in a sabha more magnificent than Indra's Sudharma, and there, upon a golden throne worked with jewels big as a child's fist, he saw Sankhachuda, master of the worlds.

In all his countless years, the Gandharva had never seen such presence and power in any king, not in Devaloka, Bhumi or Patala. Other Asuras held a jewelled parasol over Sankhachuda's august head, and fanned him with white chamaras. The Danava emperor smiled down at Pushpadanta, who stood before him, quite awestruck. He had, indeed, expected to find grandeur in Sankhachuda's city, and upon his person. But the reality exceeded his every expectation, and the majesty of the Asura left him speechless.

Sankhachuda said kindly, 'Friend Gandharva, what brings you to my sabha?' and his great, dark eyes appraised the Elf, so Pushpadanta felt his very soul was bared before the Demon on his throne.

Composing himself, finding his melodious voice again, the Gandharva said, 'Great Sovereign, I am Siva's messenger, and the Lord sends this message through me. May I repeat it, O Sankhachuda?'

The Demon smiled again, 'What else have you come for, blithe one? Have no fear in my sabha, speak freely.'

Pushpadanta drew himself up to his full, elegant height, and said, 'My Lord Sankara sits in dhyana beneath a vata vriksha, beside the Chandrabhaga. He says to you, "Danava, return what belongs to the Devas to them, or else come and fight me!"'

Sankhachuda seemed surprised for a moment that anyone dared send him such a message. Then he threw back his head, and huge laughter swelled from him, peal upon peal. At last, wiping the tears of mirth that flowed down his face, he waved his hand at the messenger and said, 'Gandharva, go back to your master, and tell him that Sankhachuda is not afraid of a half-naked yogin, whoever he may claim to be. I will leave at dawn tomorrow to fight him, for he leaves me no choice. Tell him I come with my legions, tell him to be ready to die!'

Pushpadanta bowed low and went back to Siva; for once, he was uncertain in his heart whether even the three-eyed Lord could vanquish the tremendous Asura to whom he had brought his message. Meanwhile, a brilliant host had gathered around Siva at his dhyana, under his tree.

The gana Lords Karttikeya, Virabhadra, Nandiswara, Mahakala, Subhadraka, Visalaksha, Bana, Pingalaksha, Vikampana, Vikata, Tamralochana, Kalakantha, Balibhadra, Kalajiba, Kutichara, and the eleven Rudras, eight Vasus, Indra, the twelve Adityas, Agni, Soma, Viswakarman, the Asvins, Kubera, Yama, Jayanta, Nala Kubara, Vayu, Varuna, Budha, Mangala, Dharma, Sani, Isana, Kamadeva, and the ganas Ugradamishtra, Ugrachanda, Kotara, Kaitabha.

And, besides, the eight-armed, dreadful Devi Bhadrakali had arrived on the banks of the river that was an amsa of the moon. She was black as night, and had smeared sandal-paste all over herself. She wore crimson clothes that seemed drenched in gore already, and bore a terrible weapon in each of her eight lovely hands. She swilled raw liquor from a skull she carried; she sang, she danced and her tongue, when she stuck it out, lolled for a yojana! And the rutilant shakti in one of her hands was as long.

Then, she would appear briefly as thousand-armed Mahakali, and there was no astra she did not bear—she had the mudgara, the musala, the vajra, kheta, the shield phalaka, the vaishnava, vaaruna, agneya, the nagapasa, the narayana, the gaandharva, the brahma, the garuda, parjannya, pasupata, jrimbhana, parvata, maheswara, vayavya, the sammohana, and a hundred recondite, hallucinatory and incendiary weapons besides.

Three crores of Yoginis made up the terrifying legions she brought with her, and another three and half koti Dakhinis, and numberless Bhutas, Pretas, Pisachas, Kusmandas, Brahmarakshasas, Rakshasas, Vetalas, Yakshas and Kinnaras, too.

Karttikeya came and bowed to his father, to serene Siva; and Siva set his mighty son on his left, to lead his army.

Meanwhile, after Pushpadanta left his city, Sankhachuda went into his harem at dusk and told Tulasi of the message the Gandharva had brought from Siva. He told her he meant to march the next morning to fight the great Yogin. Tulasi's hand flew to her mouth, she turned pale as a lodhra flower. Tears filled her eyes, and the world spun round her.

Trembling in every limb, she whispered, 'Oh my Lord, hold me close. I am terribly afraid.'

And when he did, she said, 'I beg you, don't go to battle against Siva. He is not just a Yogin, he is God Himself.'

But he laughed gently, that Danava, for his time had come, and replied, 'As long as I have Krishna's kavacha around my body, and the kavacha of your chastity, not even Siva can harm me.'

Tulasi remembered Brahma's boon, and was somewhat mollified, though her heart still misgave her. But now his great hands were undoing the bonds of the garment she wore, and she felt him aroused against her, and Tulasi forgot her fears. Their loving that night was more feverish, more ecstatic, than ever; even as if their bodies knew that this was the last night they would touch, caress, be rapturously joined. Until dawn, that matchless Danava and his queen were lost in each other. And his thrusts like fire, and her cries like those of a great and lovely bird, clove the night.

Then the sky outside lightened, and it was the Brahmamuhurta. Sankhachuda rose from beside Tulasi, he bathed and put on a fresh set of clothes laid out for him. He worshipped the rising sun, marked his brow with the crimson tilaka, and worshipped Brahma, his Ishta Devata. He gave away alms, of food and gold and jewels, to deserving Brahmanas in his court, munificently.

He called for his son, and left charge of his endless kingdom, and the care of his wife and his ministers and subjects, in his hands. He donned his precious kavacha, and his chariot was stocked with all his weapons. Outside, his stupendous legions, which had conquered the three worlds under his lead, began to congregate.

Three crores of horse, a crore of elephants, an ajuta of chariots, three crores of bowmen, three kotis of mail-clad footsoldiers and another thirty million trident-bearing Asuras. There were three hundred thousand legions in Sankhachuda's army, and each aksauhini had its own great Danava general.

Having worshipped Narayana and Brahma, Sankhachuda came to bid farewell to Tulasi. She clung to him softly, and tears flowed down her face. Despite his having Krishna's kavacha and the other armour of her own chastity, Tulasi felt strangely certain this was the last time she would see her husband.

She whispered, 'Ah, don't go to battle against Siva, my love. He is the Parabrahmam himself.'

But he laughed, 'Old wives' tales! How can any yogin, even if he is the Brahmam, face me on a battlefield? I have always returned to you from every battle I went to fight. It will be no different this time.'

And, with a last kiss, he left her. With ten thousand conches booming together and a sea of drummers beating up a storm, Sankhachuda set out from his city, his army flowing behind him like another Ganga. He came to Siddhasrama on the banks of the Chandrabhaga, bounded on the south by the Sri Saila Mountain and the north by Gandhamadana, and saw Siva beneath the vata vriksha.

The Lord sat in a yogasana, perfectly tranquil, a smile lit his face. He was white, and shone like lucent crystal for the light of the Brahmam, the Brahmatejas, issued from every pore of his body. He wore the skin of a tiger, and held the trisula Vishnu gave him in his hand, and Bhadrakali stood on his right and Karttikeya on his left. And, ah, he was a fathomless ocean of peace!

Sankhachuda was deeply moved, when he saw the Lord like that, waves of love streaming from him. The Danava alighted from his golden chariot, and prostrated himself before Siva. Siva, Kali, and Kumara raised their hands in blessing over the great Asura.

Soon, Sankhachuda sat on the ground before the Lord, and Siva said to him, 'Sankhachuda, we all know that Brahma Pitamaha is the Father of the worlds, and the Father of dharma. The Lord Hari's bhakta Marichi is Brahma's son, and so is Kashyapa Prajapati. Brahma's other son Daksha gave Kashyapa his thirteen daughters to be his wives, and the chaste Danu is one of them.

Danu had forty splendid sons, and they and their sons were known as Danavas. Viprachitti was the purest among them, and his son was Dambha, who was a great Vishnubhakta. Why, Dambha chanted the Vishnu mantra for a hundred thousand years at Pushkara kshetra, and you, Sankhachuda, are that Asura's son. And you, O King, were once the gopa Sudama in Goloka, all the wise know that. You were closer to Krishna than anyone else.

But Radhika cursed you, and here you are born as a Danava in the land of Bharata. You are not truly an Asura, Sankhachuda, you are Krishna's greatest bhakta. And no Krishna bhakta cares for any power or possession. Why do you covet what belongs to the Devas? Why have you taken their kingdom and wealth from them? Why do you hunt them across the worlds, like animals?

You have your own kingdom, you have unrivalled power and wealth. The Devas are your kinsmen, Danava; like you they are Brahma's children. Restore the Devas' dominions and their treasures to them, Sankhachuda, and live a long and peaceful life. Remember, the fortunes of all the living ebb and flow. Why, even those of Brahma, Vishnu and myself. The Sun is hot in summer and cool in winter, and the Moon waxes and wanes. You will find you feel lighter, less burdened, without the weight of someone else's kingdom upon your back.'

Thus, Siva said to the Asura Sankhachuda," said Narayana Muni to Narada,' Vyasa said to the king," says Suta Romaharshana.

SEVENTY

"VYASA CONTINUED, 'NARAYANA WENT ON, "WHEN HE HAD LISTENED TO Siva, and the Lord fell silent, still smiling quizzically, Sankhachuda said, 'O Sankara, you say that, as by nothing else, dharma is violated by hostilities between kinsmen. How, then, did Vishnu take everything he had from Mahabali, and thrust him down into Patala?

If the Devas and the Danavas and Daityas are cousins, how did Indra's people plot to kill Hiranyaksha and Hiranyakashyapu? Then, when both Deva and Asura toiled to fetch the amrita up out of the deeps, how was it that only the Devas drank the nectar of immortality, and my race was cheated out of it by Vishnu, who appeared as Mohini?

But, what point is there in talking about this now? All this universe is just the sport of the Paramatman, and the strife between Asura and Deva is only part of his lila. There will always be enmity and war between Deva and Asura, my Lord, and as we know, at times the Devas shall have victory, and at others we of the first race of the stars.'

Now, he paused and gazed directly into Siva's calm, sky-deep eyes. Sankhachuda said sadly, 'But you, my Lord, should be above our petty animosities. You are the Brahmam, and for you to take sides in a war between Deva and Danava is a shame. For, we of the race of Asura worship you, you are our God even as Vishnu is the Devas'.'

But Siva laughed gently, and said, 'O, you are the most invincible warrior in the three worlds. You are a Brahmana, Sankhachuda, you are Krishna's greatest gopa, and I find no shame in facing you in battle. Why, you are more powerful than Madhu and Kaitabha, than Hiranyaksha and

Hiranyakashyapu; for all the power in the three worlds belongs just to you. Oh no, Danava, I will find no disgrace by fighting a king like you!'

Sankhachuda gazed for another moment into Siva's lustrous, merciful eyes. Then he prostrated himself before the Lord for his blessing, and, without another word, rose, and turned back to his chariot and his teeming army. Siva made a subtle sign to Karttikeya, that the forces of light should also be ready for battle.

Conches deep as the gathering thunder of the pralaya sounded across that fateful field. Drumrolls like electric batteries of the air reverberated there. Then, with a roar to drown every other noise, Sankhachuda gave the command for his legions to attack. Siva also nodded his head, and the Devas' army and the Danavas' fell host rushed at each other, roaring like wild beasts of a hundred jungles.

Mahendra fought Vrishaparva, Bhaskara fought Viprachitti, Nisakara battled Dambha, and Kala faced Kaleswara. Agni and Gokarna fought, Kubera and Kalakeya, Viswakarman and Mayaa, Mrityu and Bhayankara, Yama and Samhara, Varuna and Vikamka, Budha and Dhridhaprishta, Sani and crimson-eyed Raktaksha, Jayanta and Ratnasara.

The Vasus and the sinister Varchasas did battle, the two Asvins and Diptiman, Nalakumara and Dhumra, Dharma and Dhurandara, Mangala and dawn-eyed Ushaksha, Bhanu and Sobhakara, Kandharpa and Pithara. The eleven Adityas fought Godhamukha, Churna fought Khadgadhvaja, Kanchimukha fought Pinda, Nandi fought Dhumra, and Viswa battled Palasa. The eleven Rudras and the eleven Bhayamkaras battled, Ugrachanda and the legion of Mahamaris, and Nandiswara and the rest of the Danavas.

Such a tremendous battle, and the Asuras prevailed! Bleeding, screaming, the Devas fled. But Karttikeya stood firm, mounted on his glittering peacock, an army by himself. In moments, with calific weapons he razed a hundred demon aksauhinis. Beside him, another great soldier of Siva's legions had not fled. Black, lotus-eyed, drunken, beautiful, wild and terrible Kali fought on. She wore a tiger and an elephant as earrings and, as she killed the Asuras before her as easily as she may a phalanx of children, she drank their blood as greedily as she swilled from her skein of wine.

And when she had warmed to her task and was truly blood-drunk, she felt a raging hunger. Now she began to devour all the Asuras she could lay hands on, either swallowing a thousand of them whole, or chewing delightedly on some hundreds, her eyes rolling and a smile curving her face to show she savoured what she ate. Not only the demons but also their beasts, horse and elephant, she devoured without favour. Blood leaked down her jowls in streams, and she was bathed in scarlet gore.

When she felt a little full, she only bit off her enemies' heads, and ate them, relishing the soft brain, and crunching on the skulls as easily as if they were eggshells. Thousands of headless demons' corpses littered the field. They loosed cloudbanks of arrows at her, fusillades that covered the face of the sun in darkness. But either these fell out of her tamely or she plucked them out like flower-stems that pierced her skin, and tickled her delightfully. And she sang as she fought, she danced, she drank both blood and wine, and the Asuras fled from her in every direction.

They fled from Skanda, too, for Siva's son killed as many of them as Bhadrakali did, though he did not eat their flesh or drink their blood. Indeed, it seemed he would exterminate their very race, so many Danavas did Subrahmanya kill with tides of arrows from his bow brilliant as an arc of the sun in his hands. Only Vrishaparva, Viprachitti, Dambha and Vikampana still faced the blazing Kumara, and the fearless Mahamari as well. Seeing the Daitya legions run, the Devas showered down fragrant petals on Karttikeya and Bhadrakali, and soon their host streamed back into battle again.

Then, Sankhachuda himself arrived to fight, mounted on an unknown beast. He covered the Deva legions with such a terror of arrows, like the night after the pralaya, that they turned and ran again, even Nandiswara. Only Karttikeya stood firm, and the Danava covered him in a swathe of missiles. Serpentine narachas, astras, showers of lava, even mountain peaks and solid walls of water!

Siva's son withstood all these, he blew them all to dust with his nitid archery. Then, in a dark inspiration of marksmanship, Sankhachuda cut the magical quiver from Skanda's back. Skanda cast a recalescent shakti at the Demon's mount, and killed it; but, the Danava replied with a smoking shakti of his own, which stunned both Kumara and his mount, and they fainted.

But in a moment, Karttikeya recovered and, seizing up the quiver Vishnu had given him of old, resumed the battle. He climbed into a chariot now, and shot a blazing white shakti straight into Sankhachuda's chest. It erupted there like a volcano, and the Danava fell stunned. But Krishna's kavacha protected him, and next moment he rose and fought again.

Now he fought with maya, and even the Lord Karttikeya was deceived by his sorcery. At the heart of a thousand hallucinations, Sankhachuda cast another shakti like a flaming star at Siva's son. This missile took Kumara deep in his chest, and he fell dead! A howl of dismay went up from the Devas, they stood petrified. But Bhadrakali swooped down on Karttikeya, swept him up in her bloody arms, and bore him off the field to where Siva still sat serene under the vata vriksha, beside the murmurous river.

Siva laid his palm briefly on his son's cold brow, and Karttikeya lived again! The great wound in his chest healed in a moment, even as if no weapon had torn it. Siva kissed the top of his splendid boy's head, and blessed him to be more powerful than ever. Kumara rose, shining, before his father.

Bhadrakali came storming back into battle, in wrath, and Nandiswara and the other Sivaganas, and the Devas, Gandharvas, Kinnaras, Yakshas, and her own Rakshasas followed her. A thousand drums rolled like thunder in the sky, and the Devi Kali flew back into battle, drinking deeply of the wine she carried, and so did her fearsome legion of Dakinis, Pisachis and Bhutinis drink.

She threw back her head, and gave a roar to dislodge the sky from its moorings! The Danava legion nearest her fainted just to hear that sound. Then she laughed horribly, peal after echoing peal. She sang and danced upon the crimson field. Ugra Damishtra, Ugrachanda, lewd and lovely Kotavi, the Yoginis, Dakinis, and even the Devas all swilled wine now. The Asuras trembled. But their king Sankhachuda came among them, crying exhortation to his soldiers, swearing to annihilate the enemy, come what may, reminding them that he was invincible and that their race was the firstborn and master race of creation, and they were emboldened.

Just then, Kali loosed an agneyastra at the Danava legions, and it swept at them like an apocalypse. But, unflappable, Sankhachuda put out that inferno in a moment with a Varunastra. Now Kali shot a Varunastra at the Demon, but he cut it down with a Gandharvastra. The black Devi invoked a Mahesvarastra, but Sankhachuda subdued even that great weapon, easily, with Vaishnavastra. Shrewdly, the Devi summoned a Narayanastra, which only grows fiercer when it is resisted. But Sankhachuda, Lord of the three realms, was a most knowing Danava. He threw down his bow and prostrated himself before the Narayanastra, hanging fire in the sky! At which, the astra grew mild at once and vanished.

Bhadrakali summoned a Brahmastra, an ayudha more powerful than any she had used yet. But the Asura subdued it with a Brahmastra of his own. The two missiles locked in the sky, and put each other out in a cataract of sparks. Kali invoked every weapon she knew, but the Danava had the answer for each one: for the shakti she extruded from her own body, a yojana long, and for countless more.

At last, in a frothing rage, the Devi Bhadrakali invoked the final weapon, the one that would consume the universe if Sankhachuda withstood it. She began to chant the mantra for the Pasupatastra. Suddenly, an asariri spoke to her out of heaven, 'As long as Sankhachuda wears Krishna's kavacha, and as long as Tulasi's chastity protects him, not even the Pasupata can kill the Danava.'

Bhadrakali stopped herself from summoning the final astra, she knew it would makes ashes of the universe in fury if it could not have Sankhachuda's life. Instead, she devoured a few thousand Asuras to cool her wrath. Then she rushed at Sankhachuda again, all manner of missiles streaming from her eight hands. She cast a glinting battle-axe at him, but he smashed it into dust with a wishlike astra.

Howling by now, she was so frustrated, Kali leapt at the Asura and wanted to eat him alive! But, using the siddhi of mahima, he grew bigger than the Himalaya, and all she managed to bite off was a minuscule bit of his flesh. Beside herself, she bunched a black fist and shattered his chariot and crushed his sarathy's head like a melon. She cast a burning sula at the Demon, but he caught it in his left hand, at which she struck him squarely with her fist and he fell over.

But, next moment, he jumped up again and would not fight her hand to hand because she was a woman. Instead, he bowed deeply to her. She loosed another rill of arrows at him, but Krishna's kavacha was impenetrable, and burning astras vanished when they struck it, even as if they had fallen into the void. The black Goddess darted forward, seized the Demon and, whirling him round over her head, flung him down violently enough to shatter his body. But he was unhurt, and rose smiling, and bowed to her again.

Another chariot arrived for him to fight from, and he climbed into it and battled on, razing the Devas' legions at will. And Kali hunted in another part of the field, quenching her frustration with the blood of another thousand demons, whose heads she plucked off with her nails, and then drank thirstily at their naked throats. Then she seemed to tire of battle for the moment, and went to Siva, and told him everything that had happened on the field.

When Siva heard of her exploits among the Danavas, he began to laugh. She said, 'Only the Asuras who jumped out of my mouth, whilst I was chewing, are left alive. These are about a hundred thousand. As for Sankhachuda, he is invincible. He never attacked me, but only cut down any astra I shot at him.'

When she had finished, Siva rose slowly and his body shone like a sun under that vata vriksha. He said softly, 'Let me go and see if I can kill him.'

Mounted on Nandiswara and with his army of ganas around him, white Siva came into battle, and when Sankhachuda saw him that Demon got down from his chariot set aside his weapons and armour, and prostrated himself before the Lord. Siva blessed him, and the Danava arose again, and armed himself once more. He climbed into his chariot, and they began to fight, the Asura of darkness, and the gracious three-eyed Lord Maheswara," said Narayana to Narada, in a certain kalpa,' Muni Vyasa told the king," says Suta Romaharshana.

SEVENTY-ONE

"'NARAYANA SAID, "THEY FOUGHT FOR A HUNDRED YEARS, THE GOD AND the Demon, and neither prevailed. Thousands of soldiers perished on both sides, and Siva restored life to his dead. But Sankhachuda he could not kill.

Then one evening, an old and wizened Brahmana, who seemed very distraught, came to the Danava and said, 'Lord of the worlds, invincible Sankhachuda, will you grant an old Brahmana a small boon?'

'I have always given a Brahmana anything he asked for,' replied the generous Demon.

'You are sure you will give me anything I ask for?'

'Anything at all, old one. Only ask.'

'It is not for me, but for your sake that I have come to beg this gift. Invincible Sankhachuda, you haven't perhaps heard what the three worlds you rule are saying about you. They say Sankhachuda is no great warrior, he only seems to be because he owns a magical kavacha that protects him. My blood boils when I hear this, everywhere I go. So I have come to prove the wretches who say this wrong. Give me your kavacha, great Emperor, that is the gift I seek from you.'

And, having given his word, Sankhachuda stripped off Krishna's subtle armour, which was a golden amulet he wore around his neck, which contained a sliver of bhurja bark with Krishna's mantra carved on it. The Brahmana took the mystic kavacha and left. Sankhachuda was not in the least perturbed, for he remembered Brahma's boon to him well, and he trusted Tulasi's chastity even more than he did Krishna's kavacha.

But the same night Tulasi, who had waited a hundred years in prayer for her lord, heard the dundubhi of victory being beaten at her gates. She jumped out of bed and ran to her window and saw her husband stepping out of his vimana! In joy, she went to bathe before he arrived in her bedroom. She perfumed herself with the musks and scents that were his favourites. Tulasi waited in quivering eagerness for Sankhachuda, the fragrant betel leaf ready, with camphor in it.

After what seemed a lifetime, she heard his knock at her door. She ran into his arms and he embraced her tightly, so his precious kavacha cut into her delicate skin. Something deep inside her gave a lurch at his embrace, but she thought it was only a pang of joy. Crying for happiness, she washed his feet and peeled his clothes away tenderly, her hands like butterflies on his tired flesh, while he sat exhausted in a silken chair with his feet immersed in a silver vessel of warm water.

She kneaded him expertly where he was knotted with the tenseness of battle. She drew a bath with steaming water and medicinal herbs and, having anointed his magnificent body with scented oils, she led him in to it herself as shyly and excitedly as she had on their first night together. She put aside her own clothes on the way, so she could minister to him intimately in the water.

In the bath, her fine hands were upon him again, and his touched her in the perfumed water so her breath grew shallow. Desire rose in her body like a comet after the long night of his absence. As she traced a thousand kisses down his smooth chest and belly, she whispered, 'Tell me how you have come back alive from a war with Siva. I did not hope to see you again.'

Stroking her, stroking her, lost in the fantasies of her perfect body, her flanks, her arched slender back, the triangle of soft night and peace between her legs of water and fire, he said sadly, 'Oh, such killing there was, such killing. He and I fought for a year. Karttikeya and Bhadrakali slew all my Asuras, and yet we fought on. Then Brahma came down to the field to make peace between us. And, with all my people dead and you waiting here for me, I agreed. The Devas have their kingdom back and I have you!'

Joining his great hands around her slender waist, he lifted her up. And then, as she bit her lip and shut her eyes, he lowered her on to his body so she cried out as he was in her like dark fire. Then, Tulasi's eyes flew open and a scream rose to her lips, for she knew by the feel of him inside her body that he was not her husband! But holding her helpless, he moved her effortlessly above him and thrust at her from below. And who could tell if her cries were of rapture, of horror, or of both, as so quickly in that frenzy he spent himself deep in her womb?

He heard her sob, beating her fist on his chest, 'Wretched cheat, who are you?'

And he was himself again before her wondering eyes, blue and four-armed, smiling and awesome, stroking her flushed face. With a cry she tore herself from him and, standing naked and dripping, she cursed him.

'Ruthless Vishnu, you shall be a stone, as hard as your heart is!'

Suddenly Siva appeared there, incandescent. He said to Tulasi, 'Dry your tears, this is just the fruit of your own karma of the past. For, only karma brings joy and sorrow. This is the fruit of your own tapasya that you have forgotten. Cast off your body. You are Hari's now, let your flesh be a river of love for Him. Be the sacred Gandaki, and be you in Swarga, Bhumi, and Patala, the holiest of the plants of worship. And from now on, be Vishnu's love for ever!'

After Tulasi's curse, Vishnu became a mountain in Bharatavarsha on the banks of the Gandaki. And with tiny teeth, the insects of the ground carved slow rings of torture into his body of stone, they carved strange and sacred sculptures there. And the pieces he was carved in that fell into the river are the holiest of all Saligramas. And thus, Vishnu took unto himself Tulasi's anguish at her separation from Sankhachuda, whose wife she had been for a whole manvantara.

The next morning, Sankhachuda attacked Siva again on the distant battlefield. Siva cried to the Danava, 'Where is your pretty kavacha today? Won't you be killed without it?'

Sankhachuda roared back, 'I have other kavacha which protects me well, Rudra, an invisible kavacha of love!'

'Are you certain you have not lost that kavacha also in the night?'

'That kavacha can never be taken from me. It not mine to give.'

'I think it has been given, Sankhachuda.'

The trisula blazed in Rudra's hand, it was a thousand dhanus long and a hundred hands wide. It was light, it was the universal Atman embodied. It was eternal, pristine and un-created. Siva whirled it above him thrice and, with a touch of it on Sankhachuda's head, made him whispering ashes. In his last moment, the great Danava screamed in anguish, for, before his dying eyes he saw a vision of his beloved Tulasi in Vishnu's arms. And then he was free. Sudaman was himself again, even on that field, and he mounted a shimmering vimana which flew down to him and Krishna's gopa returned to him in Goloka.

By Siva's blessing, Sankhachuda's skeleton fell into the ocean, and every holy conch-shell in the sea is made from that Asura's bones. And water from any tirtha is offered in a conch-shell made of Sankhachuda's bones, while worshipping every God, except Siva. The sacred conch is Krishna's own body, for Sudaman, who became Sankhachuda, is not apart from him. Which is why if the Devi Lakshmi hears a woman blow on a holy sankha, she shuts her ears in anger!

O Narada, this story destroys torment, it confers deep gyana and bhakti. The Brahmana who hears it is a Brahmana indeed, the Kshatriya a conqueror, the Vaishya wealthy, and the Sudra the most excellent of men!" explained Narayana to the avid Narada.

Narada asked, "How is the Tulasi the most sacred plant in creation?"

"Even after she cursed him for destroying her chastity, Vishnu reminded Tulasi, mystically, of who she actually was, and how she had come to be here in first place. Then he blessed her, saying, 'Your hair shall turn into the most holy plant in all creation, and it shall be named after you. In Goloka, on the banks of the Viraja, in the Raasa mandala, in the bhandria vana, in the champaka vana, the fragrant chandana vana, and in groves of madhavi, ketaki, kunda, mallika and malati, you will grow, and spread grace wherever you are.

All the tirthas shall dwell in essence beneath the Tulasi plant, and he who is initiated with water mixed with the Tulasi's leaf, will have the punya of a great yagna. And I shall be more pleased with a single Tulasi leaf, especially in the Kartika masa, than with even a thousand jars of tirtha-jala. He who dies after sipping Tulasi jala, is rid of all his sins and finds himself in Vishnuloka. The Tulasi will be auspicious for every holy ritual, and you, my love, will live with me even as Lakshmi does, for ever.' "

Narada asked, "And the Saligramas, Guru, what are they?"

"Vishnu also said to Tulasi, 'You will bless Bhumi by flowing as the Gandaki upon her, and I shall stand as a mountain beside where that river springs. By your curse, for deceiving you, countless insects will carve my flesh of stone with their teeth, and that pain will be my expiation, and the carved pieces of rock will be Saligramas, the holiest stones in creation.'

Saligramas that have one door and four whorls, bearing the marks of a vanamala, and the colour of a fresh rain-cloud, are called Lakshmi Janardhana murtis. Others, just like these but without the vanamala, are known as Vishnu Janardhana chakras. Some with two dwarfs, four whorls, and marks like those of the cow's hoof, are Raghunatha chakras. Little Saligramas with two whorls, the colour of clouds, but no other marking are Vamana chakras.

Small Saligramas, which have the mark of the garland, as well, are called Sridhara chakras. These are said to fetch great prosperity into the household where they are. Large, round Saligramas, without the mark of the vanamala, but with two whorls, are called Damodaras. And those that are medium-sized, and have two whorls, which appear to be pierced through by an arrow, and which bear the mark of a cane bow, are Rana Ramas.

Then, there are Saligramas that are neither big nor small, but have seven whorls, and the marks of an umbrella and jewels; these are the Rajarajeswaras. They bestow the fortune of the Rajalakshmi upon those that own them. And those that have seven chakras and the colour of the fresh raincloud, and are big as well, are the Anantas; and they give dharma, artha, kama, and moksha too.

The other Saligramas, each one bearing its own special features, are the Sudarshanas, the Gadhadharas, whose whorls are hidden, the horse-headed Hayagrivas, the fierce-looking Narasimhas, the Lakshmi Narasimhas, the bounteous Vasudevas, the delicate Pradyumnas, the dual Samkarshanas which bring joy to every grihasta, the round, yellowish and exquisite Aniruddhas.

Muni, where there is a Saligrama, there Vishnu himself dwells, and where he is Lakshmi is, too, and so are all the tirthas. Worshipping a Saligrama sila can destroy the most heinous sins, even Brahmahatya. But even among these sacred stones of great power, there are those that bring adversity. Saligramas formed like carts, Sakatas, inevitably cause sorrow, those formed like Sulas bring death swiftly, those whose facets are crooked will fetch poverty, and yellow stones are inauspicious too, bringing all kinds of afflictions. Saligramas which have cracked chakras bring disease, and those whose chakras are torn apart bring a swift death.

Auspicious deeds are specially blessed if they are performed before a Saligrama sila, whether taking a vow, giving a gift, installing a sacred image, performing a sraddha, worshipping the Devas. Worshipping a Saligrama confers the benediction of bathing at all the tirthas, and performing a great yagna. A man who worships a Saligrama every day acquires the wisdom of one who knows the Vedas.

Indeed, the wise have said that the tirthas themselves are eager to be touched by the man who worships a Saligrama! And such a man becomes a jivanmukta, and Bhumidevi herself is purified by the touch of his feet. If a man sips water touched by a Saligrama, as he is dying, all his sins are forgiven him, and he attains Vishnuloka, and nirvana. He is absorbed forever into the feet of holy Narayana.

A Saligrama must be worshipped with the leaves of the Tulasi, and he who does not do so will be separated from his wife in his next birth; indeed, for seven births thereafter. A Saligrama must be offered water from a conch-shell that contains Tulasi.

And so it was that Tulasi abandoned her body and became the eternal love of Sri Hari. And so, Narayana has four wives in Vaikuntha—Lakshmi, Saraswati, Ganga and Tulasi. The moment Tulasi's spirit left her body, it turned into a crystalline, redolent river and flowed upon the earth. And she was called the Gandaki. And Hari stood as a great massif on her banks, and the needle-toothed insects began their long, agonising work of carving the precious Saligramas out of his rock body. And the pieces of him that fall into the river are all blue and most auspicious, and those that fall onto the ground turn yellow, and they are not fit to be worshipped, for they bring evil fortune upon the bhakta," said Narayana Muni to Narada,' my master Vyasa said to me."

SEVENTY-TWO

" 'NARADA ASKED NARAYANA, "LORD, TELL ME MORE ABOUT HOW TULASI Devi is worshipped, tell me about all who worshipped her."

The immaculate Muni replied, "Mahavishnu worshipped the Devi Tulasi even as he did Lakshmi, ah, he enjoyed her to his heart's content. Ganga and Sri made no objection to this, but Saraswati was furious. She once struck Tulasi in Hari's very presence, over some trifle, and at once Tulasi, who is the Iswari of all siddhis, vanished before their eyes so even Narayana could not see her anymore.

In anguish, the Blue God arrived in Vrindavana. He bathed in the blue river that flowed through it, and worshipped the vanished Devi with a butter lamp, and offerings of sandal, sindura, food and flowers. When he had sat in dhyana for a while, chanting her mantra, **Srim Hrim Klim Aim Vrindavanyai Svaha** she appeared again out of a Tulasi plant.

Vishnu was overwhelmed, and said to her, 'You will be worshipped by all the world. I will keep you in my heart from now, and the Devas shall have you in their heads.'

And she, who appeared in that sacred forest, is called Vrinda and Vrindavani. She is also called Viswapujita, for she is worshipped in every universe, and Viswapavani, since she purifies them all. The Devas say she is the essence of all green plants and their flowers, and they are pleased only when her leaves are offered at their worship; for this she is called Pushpasara. She is delighted with worship, so she is Nandini. Krishna loves her, always, hence she is Krishnajivani.

Vishnu could not live without her, and he took her back to Vaikuntha where Lakshmi, Ganga and, now, even Saraswati received her lovingly. The

Devi Tulasi is worshipped by her seven sacred names, Vrinda, Vrindavani, Viswapujita, Viswapani, Tulasi, Pushpasara, Nandini and Krishnajivani, and chanting these names sets a bhakta free from all his sins.

Especially on the purnima night of the month of Kartika, Tulasi is worshipped; for, he who does so attains Vishnuloka, because this Devi is a sacred flame who burns away his worst sins from a man. She is incomparable, why, she bestows jivanmukti on those that know and adore her. Never doubt this, O Muni, for I speak only the truth: the Devi Tulasi purifies the very universe, she is so pure herself," said Narayana Muni.

Narada was silent for a while, then he asked, "Guru, tell me about Savitri now. Who worshipped her first? And who did, later?"

Narayana said, "Brahma worshipped the Devi Savitri first, then the Vedas did, and the Rishis. Then king Asvapati worshipped her in Bharatavarsha, and after him the four varnas did."

"Who, Lord, was Asvapati? Tell me more about Savitri, O Narayana. Why, I feel her presence near me and I am eager to hear about her."

Narayana Muni, who was Vishnu's own amsa, beyond doubt, said "Asvapati was the invincible king of Bhadradesa, who, it was told, took all their power from his enemies, and their pain from his friends. His queen was called Malati, and she was as lovely and virtuous as another Sri Lakshmi. But she was barren, and yearned for a child.

Vasishta Muni told her to worship the Devi Savitri. Malati did so in her palace, but had no vision or even a dream of the Goddess. She grew dispirited, and Asvapati took her to Pushkara, and there they sat in tapasya to the Devi for a hundred years. Still, Savitri Devi did not appear before them. But then, one day, an asariri spoke to the fervent king and his queen, 'Repeat the Gayatri mantra a million times, and you shall have your hearts' desire.'

The king and his wife, however, were uncertain how to chant that holiest mantra. But, then, as if to echo that unearthly voice, Parasara Muni arrived in Pushkara, and he said to Asvapati and Malati, 'Chanting the Gayatri mantra just once destroys the sins of a day. Ten japas of the Gayatri makes ashes of the sins of both the day and night. A hundred japas of the Gayatri incinerates a month's sins, a thousand a year's. A hundred thousand Gayatris remove the sins of the present birth, and a million Gayatris those of other births. Ten times as many Gayatris burn up the sins of every birth, from the beginning, and ten times that many bestows nirvana, and jivanmukti.'

Asvapati asked great Parasara, 'Muni, how do we chant the Devi's holy mantra?'

Brahma's son, the Maharishi, replied, 'Form your right hand into a mudra to resemble a striking cobra's hood, be sure there are no gaps between the fingers, and bend the fingertips down. Then, quieten your breath and your heart, and facing east begin chanting. Thread a rosary of white lotus seeds or crystals through your fingers, and count the number of japams from the ring finger, right-handedly to the index finger. The rosary should be smeared in cowdung, set for a time upon a banyan leaf, and then washed clean, or else cleansed with panchagavya, milk, curd, clarified butter, cow urine and cowdung, and consecrated as well.

Then, O Rajarishi, perform a million japams, at dawn, noon, and dusk, the three sandhyas, and your sins of the three times, past, present and future, will be as ashes in the wind, and you will see the Devi Savitri. He who does not observe the sandhyas is no longer worthy of being called a man, while he who does becomes as lustrous as a sun by his tapasya, for his sins fly away from his spirit like serpents at the sight of Garuda. Why, the very earth is purified by the touch of the feet of such a man.'

Saying this, and teaching Asvapati and his queen many precious mantras, specially the Gayatri, Parasara went back to his own asrama."

Narada wanted to know, "What were the mantras the Maharishi taught the king and queen, and how did they worship the Devi Savitri? What is the great mystery of this Devi and her mantra, Lord?"

Narayana said, "On the thirteenth day of the dark fortnight, the trayodasa tithi of the month of Jyestha, the Muni told them their vow must be taken, earnestly, immaculately. Fourteen fruits and fourteen salvers of food must be offered. Ganesha, Surya, Agni, Vishnu, Siva and Sivaa are to be worshipped. The mangala ghatam, the magical pot is placed in an auspicious position, and then the vow must be observed for fourteen years, without blemish.

They invoked Savitri Devi in the consecrated ghatam, and worshipped her, who is the mother of the Veda, whose nature is Pranava, whose skin is like burnished gold, who burns with Brahmatejas, refulgent like a noonday summer sun, who gives joy and mukti, who is perfectly serene. They meditated upon her, they offered naivedyam, and then offered the fourteen offerings, invoking the Devi once more in the ghatam.

The fourteen offerings were the asana, the throne for her to sit on, the padya water to wash her feet with, the arghya rice and darbha grass, the snaniya water for her ablution, the anulepana of sandalwood paste and other sweet unguents, the dhupa incense, the dipa lamps, the naivedya of food, the tambula betel leaf, pavitra jala to drink, garments, ornaments, and malas, garlands for her to adorn herself with. With each offering, they intoned an ancient mantra, as Parasara taught them to.

O Narada, the Devi whom the king and queen worshipped was she who was in the pristine times given in Goloka, the highest realm, to be Brahma's wife. But, at first, she would not leave Goloka and go with the four-faced Creator of the worlds. Brahma worshipped her, rather as Asvapati and his Malati did, and only then did Savitri come to Brahmaloka.

So, too, when Asvapati had adored the Devi as the Muni told him to, she appeared before that king and his queen in majesty and grace, radiant as suns, and blessed them. She said to them lovingly, even as a mother to her children, 'Malati, you will have the daughter you crave for, and you Asvapati shall have the son you want.'

She raised her hand over them in blessing and vanished, while they stood rooted for a long time, trembling in ecstasy. Soon, Malati conceived, and her first child was a lovely daughter, and Asvapati called her Savitri after the Devi. She grew, day by day, and her beauty grew with her even like the face of the moon during the bright fortnight.

When Savitri was a young woman, her father arranged a swayamvara for her, and she chose the exiled king Dyumat Sena's splendid and always truthful son Satyavan for her husband. They spent a joyful year together in the forest, and their love was so complete that it seemed to be too perfect for this mortal world. Why, it seemed time could hardly endure such a blemishless love.

One day, Satyavan went into the deep forest on a task his father sent him on, and Savitri went with him. Satyavan climbed up to the crown of a great tree to pluck some fine-looking fruit that hung from its loftiest branches. But the branch under his feet snapped and he plunged down to the ground, and died. Yama, the Lord Death arrived there, saw Satyavan's soul, the size of a man's thumb, issue from his broken body and, taking it in his hands, made to leave for his own realm. But Savitri followed him!

Yama turned to the young princess, and said, 'Where are you coming, child? You cannot come where I am going until you leave your mortal elements behind you. Your husband's time to die had arrived. Now, he comes to my world to reap the harvest of his karma. And according to the life he has lived, he shall know pleasure and pain, joy and sorrow, and then be born again as a man, a Deva, a king, or even a Ganapathy or a Siva! Or he may be a Muni, a Kshatriya, a Vaishya, a mleccha, a beast, a bird, a fish, an insect, a tree or a stone, a Rakshasa or an Asura, depending entirely on his karma. Otherwise, he may not even be born again, and dwell in Vishnu Salokya, if he has Hari's blessing to be free of birth and death.'

But, Savitri wanted to know, earnestly, 'Dharmaraja, what is this karma? What is its cause? What is the body, and what is death? What is knowledge and what is enjoyment? What is buddhi and prana? What are the indriyas? How does one escape karma? Tell me, great Lord, about the jivatma and the Paramatman.'

A little surprised, Dharma said smiling, 'Karma is of two kinds, good and evil. Karma, which results in dharma, is punya, and leads the doer towards bhakti and moksha. This karma is performed with relinquishment, no desire for its fruits. The other kind of karma, done selfishly, is paapa, and it binds the soul in darkness.

The seed of all karma, and of this world, is the Bhagavan, the Lord. He who does the karma is the dehi, the embodied soul, and the subtle prompter within is the Atman. Bhoga, enjoyment, is the experience of pleasure and pain, which results from karma, and knowledge or gyana is the discrimination between the Soul and illusion. Buddhi is the intelligence by which this discrimination comes about, it is the right way of seeing the world and oneself, it is the seed of gyana, and gyana is its final fruit.

Prana is the many vayus, the breaths of the body. This prana is the strength of the embodied soul. The mind is the highest indriya, and its uncertainty and intrinsic scepticism are its chief characteristics. It is naturally restless, and impels the body to all manner of actions. Indeed, it obstructs true knowledge. The other senses are sight, hearing, smell, touch and taste. These are like the subtle limbs of the jivatma, they too are impellers to karma. Invariably, they bestow pain when they are attached to objects of desire, and pleasure when they are devoted to the things of virtue.

Surya, Vayu, Bhumi, Brahma and the other Devas are the lords of the indriyas, even as they are of the elements in nature. The jivatma sustains the life-breath in each embodied creature, and the Paramatman is beyond nature and its gunas. He is immutable, the cause of all causes, he is Brahma himself. Now, child, go home in peace, and let me go where I must.'

But she, the extraordinary, irresistible young woman would not let him go so easily, and he, the God of justice and death, was so taken with her transparent purity, her luminous spirit, that he allowed himself to tarry.

Savitri said to Yamaraja, 'Where is my home now, O Ocean of gyana, that you have taken my husband from me? I beg you, stay a while and answer a few questions that rise in my heart. What are the karmas by which jivas are born in women's wombs, and what are those by which they gain the Swargas or Narakas for themselves? What are the karmas that lead to mukti? Tell me what karma bestows bhakti? Which ones give one a long life, or a short one, which karma brings disease, which ones bring joy, and which grief? Lord Dharma, which are the deeds that fetch a jiva the life of a cripple, or a blind man, a mad man or an idiot? Which karmas make one greedy or a thief, and which bestow siddhis upon a man?

Which deeds give a man the four Salokyas, which make him a Brahmana or a Muni? Which take him into Vaikuntha, and which into Goloka? And, Lord Dharmaraja, tell me about the Narakas, as well. What are they called? How many are they, and what are they like? What torments does a sinner face in each one?'

The Lord Yama was astonished at the questions she asked. He saw how unafraid she was, and how true her spirit. He smiled more than ever, and, entirely charmed by her, said, 'You are scarcely more than a child, yet your questions are those that the greatest gyanis hardly dream of! But then, I know who you are. You are Savitri, and your father Asvapati had you after performing the perfect tapasya. Ah, you are indeed what all the Munis say you are, an amsavatara of the Devi herself. And I see your love for your Satyavan is no less than the love Lakshmi bears Narayana, or Uma does Siva, which Aditi has for Kashyapa Muni, Ahalya for Gautama, Sachi for Devendra, Rohini for Soma Deva, Rati for Kama, Svaha for Agni, Svadha for the Pitrs, Sanjana for the Sun, Varunani for Varuna, Dakshina for Yagna, Bhumidevi for Varaha, Devasena for Karttikeya.

And now, without your asking me, I will give any boon you want, only ask me for it.'

Savitri replied, 'Noble Deva, let me have a hundred sons by my Satyavan. And let my father, who longs for a son, have a hundred sons as well. Let my father-in-law Dyumat Sena have his lost sight back, and his lost kingdom. And, finally my lord, let me dwell for a hundred thousand years in Vaikuntha with Satyavan, in this very body of mine.'

Dharma Deva bowed solemnly to her, and said, 'You are the chastest of the chaste, young Savitri, and you shall have all the boons you have asked me for.'

She said, 'Lord, you have not answered my questions on karma, dharma and moksha. I beg you, enlighten me now, for I did not ask them lightly.'

And so the Lord Yama, lord of death, lord of truth, discoursed on the Sanatana dharma, on karma and its fruits; of the Swargas he spoke, and of the Narakas, at length, of Gods and Demons, and of the vast cycles of time. Of rebirth and death, of moksha too, he told the young girl, the embodiment of purity. He spoke of the many paths to salvation, of the worship of the Gods and of the highest Devi. Indeed, he spoke at great length, and for a day and a night, of all things and wisdom.

Then, he restored Satyavan to her, alive, for meanwhile the time of that prince's death had passed. As Yama began to leave, suddenly, Savitri fell at his feet and began to sob loudly, like a child! In some amazement, the Lord Dharma said gently, 'What is it now? I have granted you all the boons you wanted. I have given you back your Satyavan. Why are you crying?'

Tears streaming down her lovely face, she wailed, 'Because you are going away! I have enjoyed your company so much, O Dharma, and now you are leaving me and going away.'

And when he heard this, the Lord Death had tears in his own eyes! Tenderly, he raised her up, and, laying his palm upon her head, blessed her. Then, he said, 'Precious child, live in the sacred Bharatavarsha for a hundred thousand years with your Satyavan, then go into Devaloka and from there to Mani dwipa, too. I, Yama, bless you.'

And so it happened. Savitri is the Devi of the Suryamandala, she dwells at the heart of the Parabrahmam in the Sun. She is called Savitri because the Vedas have come from her, and she is the embodiment of the pristine Gayatri, the mother of all mantras," said Narayana Muni to Narada,' Muni Vyasa said to the king," says Romaharshana.

SEVENTY-THREE

"VYASA CONTINUED HIS DEVI BHAGAVATAM, 'NARADA THEN ASKED THE Muni, "Lord, tell me now about the Devi Lakshmi. Who worshipped Sri first, and with what mantra?"

"In the beginning, in the Raasa mandala, from the left side of Krishna's body, there appeared a delectable Devi. She was fair as a lotus, a moonbeam; her form was perfect and the lustre of her face was that of a thousand full moons of autumn. By Krishna's will, this Goddess clove herself in two. She became two relucent Devis, each one a mirror image of the other, each as lovely and as auspicious as the other.

The Devi who stood on Krishna's right now was called Radha, and she who was on his left was Mahalakshmi. Radha desired Krishna, and so did the Devi Lakshmi, in Goloka, first of all the worlds. So Krishna also clove himself in two. From his right side came a two-armed Krishna, and from his left a four-armed one. Radha had the two-armed Lord for herself, and Lakshmi Devi the four-armed one.

It is told that Sri Lakshmi casts a soft gaze over all creation, cool as moonlight, and hence she has her name. And since she is immeasurably great, as well, she is called Mahalakshmi. Krishna remained in Goloka, while the four-armed Narayana he had become took the Devi Lakshmi to Vaikuntha. In cosmic time, the Devi Lakshmi was to become many Goddesses in many realms. She remains her pristine self in Vaikuntha, perfectly sattvika, in Devaloka she is Swarga Lakshmi whom Indra's people worship, in Patala she is Naga Lakshmi whom the Nagas adore, for kings she is Raja Lakshmi, and in the world she is the blessed Devi of fortune in every home, Griha Lakshmi.

Of cows, she is Surabhi who was churned from the Kshirasagara, she is that pale ocean's daughter Lakshmi, too; she is Padmini, the lustre of the Sun and the Moon. She is also the light of every precious jewel in creation, from the most rare and exalted gems to the lowliest ones. She is the radiance in fruit, of kings and queens, of Devastris and Apsaras, of grains in the field, of water that flows and of the sacred lakes of the earth.

She is the grace in every tirtha, in sacred idols, in flowers and garlands, in milk, in fragrant sandal, in trees and plants, in the fresh raincloud, in the rainbow and in every colour seen in Swarga, Bhumi, and the mysterious nether worlds.

She was worshipped, first, by Narayana in Vaikuntha, then by Brahma and by Siva too. Vishnu worshipped her in the Kshirasagara, then Svayambhuva Manu did, and every Rishi, Muni, grihastha, Gandharva, Kinnara, and Indra and his Devas. Mangala Deva worshipped her on a Tuesday, and so did Kedara, Nila, Subala, Dhruva, Uttanapada, Sakra, Bali, Kashyapa, Daksha, Kardama, Surya, Priyavrata, Chandra, Vayu, Kubera, Varuna, Yama, Hutasana, and all, all good men down the winding ages.

The Devi Lakshmi is she who presides over fortune, and, indeed, over wealth!"

Narada would know, "Muni, tell me how Devi Lakshmi came down into the world first, and rose out of the Kshirasagara."

"Once, the Rishi Durvasa, who is said to be an amsavatara of the Lord Siva, cursed Indra that he and his Devas would become mortal, and lose their kingdom in heaven. For, Indra draped a garland of undying lotuses from Vishnu, which Durvasa gave him, on his elephant Airavata's head, and the bees that buzzed around the precious blooms stung the beast, and Airavata flung the garland down and trampled on it in a frenzy.

At Durvasa's curse the Devas fell, they came down to the earth. Swarga Lakshmi, whom Indra's people worshipped and who dwelt in heaven, also left Devaloka in rage at what Indra had done, and arrived in Vaikuntha, seeking refuge in Narayana. And when she left Devaloka, so did the Devas' fortune depart.

The Devas invoked Brahma, and with him they came to Vaikuntha as well, and sought Vishnu's blessing, for the Asuras had driven them from their home in Amravati. The Devas said they could not face the legions of darkness in battle, for by Durvasa's curse they were not immortal any more. It was then that Vishnu told them to churn the Kshirasagara, why, to churn the sea of milk with the help of the Asuras, for the pale sea would yield the amrita of immortality to them. And not only that, but Sri Lakshmi would return, embodied, born again as the Ocean's daughter.

And so it was that the sworn and eternal enemies, the Asuras and the Devas, embarked on the great enterprise together! For, Vishnu told the Devas to tempt the Asuras with greed for the nectar of immortality, even like a serpent does a mouse from its hole. He said that neither the Devas by themselves, nor the demons on their own, could hope to churn the white sea on the bed of which the amrita lay. But if the races of darkness and light combined their strength, yes, then surely the awesome task could be accomplished.

Indra asked in some alarm, 'But, Lord, if Bali's Asuras drink the amrita, they will also become immortal. How shall we ever hope to vanquish them then?'

Narayana replied mysteriously, 'Be humble with Bali's demons, be even servile if you have to, until the amrita rises from the waves. I promise you the Asuras shall not drink a drop of the nectar, but only you Devas.'

Agni asked, 'How will we churn the sea?'

Vishnu said, 'Use golden Sumeru for your churning rod, and let Vasuki be the rope you wind around the mountain, and I shall be there in the sea you churn, and your enterprise will not fail.'

And with that, he vanished. The Devas went, humbly indeed, to the Asuras; and it was not hard to tempt Bali and his people with some glittering descriptions of the priceless jewels and gold that lay buried beneath the sea of milk. The Asuras agreed to join hands with their enemies, and they decided among themselves that, if indeed the immortal nectar was churned to the surface, the Devas, who they knew were under the Rishi's curse, would not get a drop of the amrita.

Combining their untold strength, the two races uprooted golden Sumeru and fetched that stupendous mountain to the sea. Then Bali and Indra flew down to the seventh Patala, where Vasuki, Lord of serpents, dwelt, and they tempted the emerald Naga emperor of a thousand coils by offering him an equal share of the amrita.

So winged Vasuki also flew to the shore of fate, and was wound around the thousand shimmering peaks of golden Meru. The Devas made to take his throat and upper parts to begin the churning, for they were naturally arrogant, the ones of light. But Bali's people cried, 'We are the eldest race in creation, we are the masters of the worlds. We will hold the serpent's head, let the vain Devas hold his tail!'

A hot protest rose to Indra's lips, but just in time he remembered Vishnu's counsel that he must be humble, even servile, with the Asuras until the amrita was churned up. The Devas took Vasuki's tail, and the Asuras the great Naga's throat, and they began to haul him to and fro, so golden Meru spun round and round, first one way, then the other.

But the mountain was heavy, and it began to sink into the waves. Vishnu appeared there as the strangest beast, as a gigantic tortoise, the primal Kurma big as a continent, and he swam under Meru and held it upon his awesome shell. Now the mountain was buoyant, and the Devas and the Asuras hauled Vasuki's interminable length across the momentous shore, swifter and swifter, crying loud challenge and exhortation to one another, like milkmaids making cheese. And Vishnu the Kurma chuckled softly, because the churning tickled his back!

But the mountain was lofty and it wobbled about, and the churning was hardly as effectual as it could be. Now Vishnu appeared as a great Purusha, his head in the Sun, and held the golden mountain steady with four vast hands. The Devas and the Asuras churned quicker than ever, but still it seemed they did not churn hard enough, and the sea did not yield its treasure. Vishnu appeared as another towering Purusha on the shore, and he lent his divine strength to the snake-haulers!

Meru spun quick as a top, with a magnificent whirring, and waves stood up around the mountain, tall as other mountains themselves. But now Vasuki was being hauled about so quickly that he grew dizzy and began to vomit fire from the thousand jaws on his thousand hoods. And Vishnu smiled at the Devas, who had the Naga by the tail, for the haughty Asuras had their faces singed, and dropped the serpent in a hurry. Vishnu doused the flames from Vasuki's jaws with a fragrant shower from his hands, and the churning resumed.

It was like prodigious lightning now, as Vishnu poured his infinite strength into it, while he held the mountain steady from above and below. Unsettled from the deeps, teeming schools of fish swam helplessly to the surface, whales, dolphins and sharks, swordfish and tuna, sea serpents and sea horses, sea elephants and alligators, colourful as another world. But they swam up in terror because the effervescent venom, the Halahala, stirred from its long slumber beneath the ocean floor and rose to the surface, smoking, staining the white waves dark. Spiralling ever higher the Kalakuta swirled straight up into the air, threatening to put out the Sun in the sky, to burn up creation in a day!

Deva, Asura and Rishi flew to Siva, Narayana himself at their head, he the one who first cried, 'Only Siva can save us from the Halahala!'

'God of Gods,' they begged him, high on Kailasa, 'only you can deliver us from the Kalakuta, O Pranava!'

In their dire need, all this was said not just to worship him, but to placate Bhavani at his side. She did not seem pleased at her husband having to subdue the virulent Kalakuta. Siva glanced at her from the corner of his eye.

Vishnu said, 'O Siva, with Agni for your mouth, the Earth for your feet, time your motion, the cardinal points your ears, O Soul of all the Devas, the sky your navel, Vayu your breath, Surya your eyes, Soma your mind, the Swargas your imagination, the primal ocean your semen, the first sea your belly, the mountains your bones, the dharma your heart, the advent of evil your shadow...'

So that of course it seemed that no poison, even the terrible Halahala, could affect such a One. Yet, Parvati shifted at her Lord's side and looked askance at his petitioners.

Siva said, 'It pleases Hari to help the Devas and the Asuras to churn the sagara, and what pleases Hari pleases me.'

Restraining Bhavani from her protest by laying a hand on her arm, Siva rose from Kailasa. Cupping his lotus white hands he drained the steaming poison from sky and sea. He quaffed it in a gulp, smiling! But that dreadful leaven burned even him, it burned his throat forever blue. And from then on, he wore it as an ornament on his neck, and Siva has been called Nilakanta since.

A few drops of the poison that dribbled from his lips were shared between the serpents, scorpions, spiders, lizards and insects of the earth, to be their venom.

The Devas, the Asuras and Vishnu returned to their churning, and now, at last, the sagara yielded its treasures. First from the churned waters came Surabhi, Kamadhenu dappled and bright, the cow of wishes. The Devas stood staring at her, and the Asuras unblinking.

Then Varuni, the Goddess of wine, rose from the foam, so lovely, and her eyes rolling drunk. Next rose the lambent Parijata tree and, in a moment, swept the worlds with heady fragrance, seducing the minds of the Devastris.

Then came Ucchaisravas, the original irradiant horse. From the spray of the amrita, rising slow and majestic from the deeps, from the very drops of flying nectar, arose the Apsaras of matchless beauty, bright as fire, their skins translucent, maddening the world with their bewitching eyes. To shine on them and upon the earth the Moon rose, and Sura, wine embodied, and the bow Saringa, the sea-conch Panchajanya, foam-made, and the scintillant jewel Kaustubha. Last of all, brilliant blue and long-armed like Vishnu himself, his eyes of the hue of the red lotus, youthful, richly adorned, clad in flaming yellow, rose Dhanvantari the physician, bearing in his hands the chalice brimming with the amrita.

But every wonder that rose paled when Sri, perfect Lakshmi, came forth from the Kshirasagara, exquisite, naked and vibrant! A shining lotus of a thousand petals in her hand, she stood before them, all stunned by her, she lit up the quarters with her effulgence. She was utterly auspicious, she who is worshipped as fortune and affluence! The Devas were smitten, Indra himself offered her his throne. The Asuras lost their reason seeing her, the Rishis were beside themselves, and they hymned her loudly, babbling the inspired Srisukta. There was subtle music in the air.

The embodied rivers, led by Ganga, came bearing their waters in golden pitchers for the Devi's ablution. Airavata-sired elephants poured those sacral waters over her from pale trunks, while Bhumidevi appeared herself to bring ineffable Lakshmi the five precious ablutionaries. Vasantha brought her fruit and flowers of the vernal months Chaitra and Visaka. The Gandharvas arrived and sang, inspired, while the Apsaras danced as they were born to, this first time ever just for her, to pulsating rhythms of mridanga, panava, murga, anaka and gomukha. The Vedas were chanted while Sri bathed, laughing softly at the joy of it all, the rapture of being. The amrita was quite forgotten when Lakshmi was born again.

When she had bathed, Varuna brought two pieces of silken yellow raiment for her as offering. He gave her the original Vaijayanti garland, made from unfading blue ocean lotuses. Viswakarman brought ornaments for her perfect body, now anointed with sandalwood and saffron. Lakshmi rose out of her bath, clad in Varuna's silks, resplendent in divine jewellery, the garland of wild lotuses in her hand.

And now she looked around her for a home, a sanctuary for herself. And she saw Hari before her, standing blue and perfect, and waiting for her with a quizzical and infinitely tender smile on his face. She walked unhesitatingly to Him, and placed the Vaijayanti around his neck, resting her face, herself, against his chest. He put an arm around her, taking her for his own forever more. And the heavens rained soft flowers down on them.

The Rishis took Kamadhenu, the Asuras took Sura, and the humans took Dhanvantari. Vishnu took Lakshmi, the divine longbow Saringa, the sankha Panchajanya, and the Kaustubha, which he wore round his neck on a golden cord. Surya took the marvellous horse Ucchaisravas, Indra the Parijata tree, and Siva took the Moon and he wore it in his jata as a crescent ornament. Varuna took Varuni for himself, the amrita-born Apsaras were shared by Deva and Asura alike hereafter, depending on which race ruled the worlds.

When Sri walked up to Narayana and wreathed the Vaijayanti around him, the Asuras woke rudely from their daydream of keeping the Goddess for themselves. Bali snatched the chalice of amrita out of Dhanvantari's hands. But, inevitably, the demons began to fight among themselves about who should have how much of the nectar, who should drink it first, and who last. They snatched the chalice, one from the other, and the Devas joined eagerly in the fray. Suddenly, a woman, such as they had not dreamt of, appeared among them. No, not even Sri could match her beauty or seductiveness. While Lakshmi was a vision of purity, this dusky one came among the Asuras with undisguised lasciviousness.

In contrast to fair Lakshmi, the seductress was as blue as the lotus of the vana. Her dark skin was a dream of grace, her breasts heavy, straining against each other in the bursting fullness of youth. Her waist was a reed, her behind ample and rolling, her hair of jet was profuse and adorned with white mallika. Her nose, her bones, her cheeks, her ears were all perfect; her neck, her bare arms were dreams. Her navel showed deep as a well above a golden girdle draped sensuously over flaring, maddening hips. For all her loveliness, her eyes were like frightened birds, darting this way and that, insanely heightening her warm appeal. The Asuras gaped at her, the Devas stood spellbound; they stared, hearts on fire.

At last, quite out of his mind, Bali cried hoarsely, 'Vision of perfection, tell us who you are! Who are you, whose daughter? Surely, you are no man's child. You are not defiled by the touch of Deva or Asura, Gandharva or Siddha, else you could not be so perfect. Peerless one, solve this dispute among us, sons of Kashyapa all: share this amrita out evenhandedly among us brothers, Asura and Deva!'

And the chalice of nectar was handed to Mohini, for so she was, an enchantress! But she laughed at him when she took the precious thing from Bali's hands that trembled just to brush against hers. In her breathy torment of a voice, she said, 'How do you, O sons of great Kashyapa, come near a wanton woman like me? Haven't you heard the friendship of loose women is just for the moment?'

Grinning vacantly, Bali still thrust the amrita at her. Throwing back her head, she laughed huskily, maddening them further! With an ambiguous, coquettish smile, she said, 'Only if all of you accept whatever I do, whether it seems right or wrong, will I divide the amrita among you.'

'Be it so!' cried the Asuras in one voice. And she sent them to bathe, to purify themselves before the nectar was shared out. When they returned from their ablutions, gaudily dressed and bejewelled, she made them sit in an incense-fragrant sabha, which had appeared there miraculously. She sat them on seats of kusa grass, the blades of which pointed to the auspicious east. When they were all silent in the sabha lit with soft butter lamps, she came among them, enchanting them with her gait slowed by the weight of her hips and her breasts. Shy, yet somehow brazen, were her glances, her very presence was stunning, and the nectar was in her hands.

Her anklets sang like a forest of birds in that awestruck, lustful quiet. She made them sit in separate places, Devas and Asuras, across the sabha from each other. As she showed the Asuras where they should sit, as if by accident the silken cloth fell off her naked breasts. She took it up again, but not too quickly, and, with a velvet giggle, full of promises, she whispered to them, 'Let the niggardly Devas drink first, I'll save the most for the end!'

She winked at them, promising not only the amrita, but everything. Then, hips swaying, she crossed to the Devas, and, smiling and glancing back at the demons, she began to pour out all the amrita just for the ones of light. She took her time about it. Though they grew restive, the Asuras dared not cross her and were content to wait.

All of them, except Rahu who, with maya, assumed the raiment and form of a Deva and stole to the other side of the sabha and into the line of nectar drinkers between the Sun and the Moon. Mohini served Rahu, but Surya and Soma silently indicated that he was not what he seemed to be. But Rahu had drunk the nectar and Vishnu, becoming himself in a flash, for he was Mohini, lopped off Rahu's head with the Sudarshana chakra before the amrita went down his throat.

Chakra-borne, Rahu's head flew immortal into the sky while his body fell dead on the ground. Vishnu granted planethood to Rahu. But each day of the new and full moon Rahu assails both Surya and Soma, between whom he sat to drink the amrita.

All the nectar had been drunk by the Devas and, smiling in triumph, Vishnu was himself again. Roaring that they had been tricked, the Asuras attacked the Devas. But Vishnu beat them back and down into Patala with the Sudarshana chakra, killing countless demons. The Devas were now immortal, so even if they were hewn down in battle they rose again to fight. Terror-stricken, the Asuras fled to the underworlds," said Narayana,' Vyasa said."

SEVENTY-FOUR

"VYASA CONTINUED, 'NARAYANA MUNI SAID, "SOME SAY THAT WHEN SIVA heard of the trick Vishnu played on the Asuras, he came with Uma to Narayana's garden in Vaikunta, and said to the Blue God, 'O Hari, I have seen all your Avataras, Narayana, but not this one of the woman Mohini.'

Vishnu laughed, 'I took that form to excite the Asuras so they would lose their judgement. My Lord, what would you do seeing Mohini, who was the embodiment of seduction?'

But Siva, with Uma at his side, insisted, and Vishnu vanished before their eyes in that garden. Siva and Uma waited there for a while but there was no sign of either Vishnu or Mohini. They were about to leave disappointed, when suddenly Siva saw her under some flowering trees, amidst red foliage, playing with a ball Mohini, the enchantress of the Asuras, only now for his sake a thousand times as lovely, a thousand times as seductive as she had been before. With each step, she appeared to break in two at her waist, so slender was it; and so full her breasts, throbbing with youth, while a string of pearls covered them like small moons. Her eyes swimmingly followed the ball, always bouncing out of her grasp.

Those who tell this tale say that, seeing Mohini, Siva lost control of himself. When the blue ball bounced away from her, she stood fidgeting with her dishevelled braids and her silken garment, which had fallen away before the Asuras. As in a dream, helpless Siva detached himself from Parvati and his ganas to retrieve the ball for Mohini. A thing of enchantment itself, that ball bounced and rolled a long way and, chasing it, Siva and Mohini were soon at some remove from the others, who stood dumbfounded.

When Siva picked up the ball for her, in one hot gust the wind blew the diaphanous garment she wore clean off her, and her girdle slipped away from her waist around her ankles. The scent of her naked body pierced him like a weapon, and Siva was in the grip of a lust he could not resist. He seized the enchantress. He bared himself feverishly and tried to ravish her even as his wife stood watching!

But Mohini vanished out of his embrace. She reappeared behind a nearby tree, laughing in her tinkling way, and Siva ran towards her, insanely aroused now, completely under her spell. Behind the tree, like a wild beast he embraced her again. He pierced her with a thrust of fire, then moved in lightning flashes while she screamed, the great Lord Siva groaning like any lost man.

She cried out shrilly. She wove out of his embrace and ran from him, her hair now loose and streaming behind her ravishing nakedness. Like the wind, she ran from him. And Rudra chased her witlessly, his seed spilling in great spurts. Over the mountains she flew, with him hot on her heels, across rivers and their soft banks, with him ejaculating in geysers now in the heat of pursuit. Until his golden seed was all spilt on to the earth, and, panting, he suddenly remembered himself and stopped the panicked careen. And Mohini was Vishnu again, radiant, and confronted Hara! At once, Siva was without desire or shame, and began to roar with laughter, ah, how the both of them laughed and embraced each other in mirth. So say those who tell this tale.

There are those who also say that Mohini did not run far from Siva. But that he caught her and, from their loving and from Vishnu's thigh, Ayappan the tiger-rider was born, the bachelor God of Sabarimala, Hari-Hara Putra.

But others say that, at first, the Apsaras were shared by Deva and Asura alike. But when Lakshmi attached herself to Vishnu, Bali's demons forcibly took all the nymphs for themselves, and they wrested the amrita from Dhanvantari's grasp. And certain of imminent immortality, the demons swore, 'If we are vanquished by the Devas we will never touch these women.'

When Mohini tricked them and only the Devas drank the amrita, the demons bayed for blood, and they attacked Vishnu and the Devas. After the Asuras were routed and fled down to Patala, Vishnu became intensely aware of the exquisite, haughty nymphs! It is said he dallied at will with those nectar maidens very willing to make love with the Blue God, so they could tutor to perfection the genius they were born with.

He loved them all, say those who tell this tale, and begot on them myriad sons, every one blue, a Kshatriya, and a master of knowledge and war like him. Vishnu was lost to the worlds, he went down into the Patalas with his harem of Apsaras, and wasted himself at endless passion.

Brahma came to Kailasa and begged Siva, 'Pervador of the universe, Vishnu no longer protects the worlds. He is lost in the lust of the Apsaras. His sons run riot through the mandalas, and only you can save us.'

They say Siva became a mighty Bull and, bellowing so the sky quaked, he confronted the sons of Narayana. Those Kshatriyas, arrogant by their birth, were furious that this mere animal dared challenge them. They rushed at the Bull with fierce cries, they rained arrows on him, they smote him with sword, spear and mace, but he was proof against their every attack. Rudra the Bull turned on those Apsaras' sons. He kicked them with awesome hooves, he rent their divine bodies with his horns, and he swiftly killed the lot.

Hearing the uproar of this battle, Vishnu rose from his Patala of passion, and attacked the Bull with arrows of light and time. He covered the Vrishabha with a storm of shafts that fell harmlessly off the animal's hide. Then the beast charged Hari and felled him. It gored his chest open, spilling his blood on to the earth like rain; and only then, Mahavishnu remembered himself. Hands folded, he said to Siva, 'I did not know it was you, Ocean of mercy! Forgive me my vanity.'

Smiling a little, Siva said, 'You were surely not yourself for a while, O Uplifter of the universe.'

But, meanwhile, Vishnu had already advised the other celestials that among the Patalas lived the Apsaras who had been born for the enjoyment of all, and that they were mistresses of pleasure like no other women before them. And the Devas, as a man, had plunged down to the nether realms to seek untold satisfaction with the nymphs. But, after bringing Mahavishnu back to his senses and Lakshmi's arms, Siva warned them, 'Any except a quiescent Rishi, or a Danava born of my body, who enters the Apsaras' realms, will find his death.'

So, following Vishnu back into heaven, streamed all the forlorn Vidyadharas, Yakshas, Rakshasas, Kinnaras, Gandharvas, Pichasas, Guhyakas, Siddhas and Bhutas. And all was well in the worlds again. So they say who tell the story of Siva the Bull," said Narayana.

Narada now asked, "Rishi, tell me about the Devi Lakshmi's dhyana and the stotra with which she is hymned."

"When Lakshmi rose from the sea, she was with the Devas again, and she was root of their fortune once more. And when the Asuras had been driven down into Patala, and Indra and his Devas had resumed sovereignty over Devaloka, Indra worshipped both Hari and the Devi Lakshmi. He bathed in the waters of the Kshirasagara, wore a clean fire-purified garment around his waist, and set an earthen jar on the sands, a ghatam beside the holy waves.

Indra, lord of the Devas of light, worshipped Ganapathy, Surya, Agni, Vishnu, Siva and Sivaa, he made offerings of incense and flowers to those six Deities. Now, he invoked the Devi Sri Lakshmi in the ghatam, and worshipped her as Brahma, who was the presiding ritvik at Indra's yagna. The king of the Devas smeared a single parijata blossom with chandana, sandal-paste, and chanting the Devi Lakshmi's dhyana mantra, he offered it at her feet. The mantra was the very one which Bhagavan Hari first gave to Brahma.

Indra said, 'O Mother, who dwells in the lotus of the thousand petals, the lustre of your face is the light of a million full moons of autumn. And your splendour, O Devi, is your own, just your very own. Devi of the hue of burnished gold, I lay my head at your feet, bless me, sacred Mother! Forgive me if I ever offended you, and bless me forever.'

And Indra worshipped her with the sixteen upacharas, offering each one with a mantra. First, he offered her an asana, saying, 'Mahalakshmi, Maata, this throne was fashioned by Viswakarman. I beg you take this throne from me, sit on it, Devi, and bless me.

Lakshmi, receive this tirtha jala from me. It is water from the holy Ganga, and pure and blessed. I offer it to you with sandal, with flowers, with this darbha grass. Devi, take this amalaki fruit from me, take this length of silk made pure in the fire; take these ornaments, this incense, these lamps that are the symbols of light, the eye of the world and the end of darkness in the three lokas, and in my life.

This grain, this anna, Devi, is Brahma himself, and he preserves the living, keeps their spirits and bodies together. And this paramanna, Mother of worlds, is made from rice, milk and sugar. Sip it, O Mahalakshmi, for my sake, so I have your blessing always. This svastika is made of sugar and ghee; I beg you, take it from me. These pakkannas are made with the purest foods in the world, and this jaggery is sweet as amrita.'

And he offered her a white chamara, betel scented with camphor, cool, clear water to drink, garlands of wildflowers, unguents and perfumes, tirtha jala to rinse her mouth with after she had partaken of his other offerings. And then, Indra chanted Sri Lakshmi's mula mantra a million times, and fervently, since he knew what misery was when he had gone without her grace. And it was Brahma himself who taught Indra Sri Lakshmi's mula mantra, which is **Srim Hrim Klim Aim Kamalavasinyai Svaha**, which is truly like a kalpavriskha.

By chanting this mantra, Kubera the lord of wealth got his nine incomparable Treasures. By the grace of this mantra, Daksha Savarni Manu and Mangala Deva became Lords of the Earth of seven continents and seas. By its power, Priyavrata, Uttanapada and Kedararaja became Siddhas and kings. For, the Devi whose mantra it is, is the Goddess of fortune.

And, when Indra had intoned the mula mantra of the Devi Mahalakshmi a million times, she did indeed appear before him. She came in a majestic vimana; she was fair as the face of the moon, and she was refulgent as a thousand suns. From the aura of her perfect body had the seven dvipas and the seven sagaras been created. Indra looked at her and began to tremble with a joy he had never known before. He wept, the hairs on his body stood on end, and with folded hands, he began to hymn her again, rapturously.

In an ecstasy, the king of the Devas of light called Sri Lakshmi by her many names, he sang those names in fervor, 'O Narayani, Padmasane, Mahalakshmi, Padmadalekshane, Padmanibhanane, Padme, Vaishnavi, Dakshine, Aditi, Kamale, Svahe, Svadhe, Bhumidevi, Sharade!' and a thousand more.

And the Devi blessed Indra and the Devas, and then she flew back to Narayana who rested again upon Anantasesha, his serpent bed upon the sea of eternity. The Devas all returned to their Swargas, and there was grace and fortune again in the three worlds.

Narada, my son, there is never any doubt that the Devi Lakshmi is the root of all fortune in the worlds, and it is her bhaktas who prosper. And if Sri ever leaves a man's home or his life, that man surely falls upon the most wretched times and quickly perishes, until he finds devotion for Lakshmi Devi, the bestower of all boons, in his heart again. And then, like Indra was, that bhakta is restored to prosperity," said Narayana Muni to the itinerant one,' my guru Vyasa told the king."

SEVENTY-FIVE

"VYASA SAID, 'NARADA NOW ASKED, "TELL ME THE SECRET LORE, MUNI, OF the Devis Svaha, Svadha, and of Dakshina."

Narayana began, "The Devas of Swarga have bodies of light, yet they too must have sustenance. So, in the most ancient times, when the four-faced Pitamaha had just recently created them, they came to Brahma and asked him what they could eat, for they were hungry. Brahma began to worship Narayana, and he incarnated himself as Yagna, sacrifice, so the Gods may be fed.

In time, Brahmanas and Kshatriyas poured offerings of ghee into the sacred fire, but the Devas had no access to these because, in those days, Agni was cool and could not convey the offerings to them. They came to Brahma again, and complained that they were hungry. Brahma now went to Krishna in Goloka, and asked for his help. Krishna told him to worship the Mula Prakriti. When Brahma did so, for a long time, a radiant Devi materialised out of the formless Prakriti.

She stood before Brahma, and said gently, 'What boon do you want, O Pitamaha? Ask for anything and you shall have it.'

And Brahma replied, 'Be thou, Devi, the heat of the fire, and let the offerings of every yagna be burnt and, thus, reach the Devas. Be, O Devi, the wife of Agni Deva, be his wealth and fortune, and always be worshipped in the three worlds.'

That Devi, who was an amsa of the Devi Bhagavati herself, was Svaha. But when she heard what Brahma wanted from her, she was sad. She said softly, 'I want Krishna for my husband, and I will sit in tapasya forever to have him.'

And she stood on one leg in dhyana for a hundred thousand divine years. At last, she saw Krishna, and, seeing him, she fainted in rapture, because he was infinitely more splendid and gracious that she had ever imagined.

Krishna said to her, in his voice of ages, 'You shall be my wife in the next Varaha kalpa, when you will be born as the king Nagnajita's daughter. But now, the Devas have dire need of you, O Svaha. Be Agni's consort, and be his love.'

Meanwhile, Brahma sent Agni to where Svaha sat in tapasya. He came a little doubtfully, uncertain whether he wanted a woman for himself. But when he saw her, the Fire-God was smitten and blazed up in excitement. And when Svaha saw him, she felt herself tingling all over her delicate form, and this was love. Brahma appeared there, and Agni and Svaha were married to the chanting of pristine mantras.

And how fiercely their love burned in that solitary place. For a hundred years of the Devas, they were entwined, and then Svaha was pregnant. And, in time, she was delivered of three coruscant sons, Dakshinagni, Grihapatyagni and Ahavaniyagni. And Svaha is the Devi of every yagna, and of every offering made to the sacred fire; offerings that must be burnt before the Devas can partake of it. Her lord, Agni Deva, is he who conveys the burnt offerings to the other Gods on high.

Svaha must be invoked after every mantra which a Brahmana or Kshatriya chants before the holy fire of yagna. And she makes the yagna fruitful. Whereas, if her name is not spoken after each mantra, the sacrifice becomes impotent, barren, like a snake without venom, or a Brahmana who does not know the Vedas or the Shastras, a woman who does not serve her husband, or a tree which bears no fruit.

So, even as Agni Deva did when he took the Devi Svaha to himself for his wife, anyone who performs a yagna, or any sacred rite, first worships Svaha with her mula mantra, **AUM Hrim Vahnijayayai Devyai Svaha**. And he shall certainly have more than his heart desires."

Narada asked, "Tell me about the Devi Svadha, who is the wife of the Pitrs, and worshipped when they are."

"Before he created the three realms, Swarga, Bhumi and Patala, Brahma created the seven Pitrs, the Manes, from his ancestral mind. Four of them had forms and the other three were of the nature of tejas, they were beings of light.

Then, Brahma made the world, and the Brahmanas of the world made their offerings to the Devas and to the Pitrs, as well. But, the Pitrs, too, could not at first receive the oblations the Brahmanas poured onto their sacred fire during their sraddhas. And Brahma created a radiant woman from his mind, to be the bride of the manes. She was white as the champaka flower, forever youthful and lovely; she wore the purest raiment and was adorned with unearthly ornaments.

He called her Svadha, and it is told she had her lotus feet in the petals of a hundred kamala flowers. Her nature was serene, welling infinite contentment. And the manes took her to themselves in joy, and, then on, she conveyed the sraddha offerings to them.

The Devi Svadha is worshipped particularly on the thirteenth day of the dark fortnight in autumn, on the night of the Magha nakshatra. This is the most auspicious night for performing a sraddha to one's ancestors and to the original Pitrs. And anyone who worships the manes must always first worship the Devi Svadha with her mula mantra, **AUM Hrim Srim Klim Svadha Devyai Svaha**.

The wise that know say that the very moment the Svadha mantra is chanted the bhakta receives the punya of bathing in the most holy tirthas. If a man but say the Devi Svadha's name thrice in his heart, he is blessed with the grace of srarddha, tarpana and bali."

"And the Devi Dakshina?" Narada reminded the Muni, who had paused in his Purana.

"In the most ancient days, there was a gopika called Sushila in Goloka. She was a beautiful woman, fortunate, and with a gentle nature. Her complexion was shyama, like burnished gold, she was fawn-eyed, with a perfect body, and there was always a sweet smile on Sushila's face. Her breasts were high and full, her waist slender as a lotus stalk, her hips broad and ample. Her gait was like a swan's, and she was a kalavati, a mistress of the sixty-four arts, and a queen of the art of love. She was a wit, too, and intelligent past all common measure.

Once, wild with love for Krishna, Sushila sat beside him, near him on his left side, while the Devi Radha was there too! In a wink Radha's eyes turned red as scarlet lilies, her lips twitched, and she quivered with anger. Seeing Radha like that, Krishna vanished from there in a flash, and Sushila and the other gopikas trembled in terror of Radha.

With folded hands, they prayed, 'Radhe! Protect us!'

But Radha cursed Sushila, 'If Sushila comes to Goloka again, she shall be ashes!'

Then, Radha, mistress of the Raasa mandala, took herself to the magic circle in search of Krishna. But he was not there. He was not anywhere; it was as if he had vanished forever. Each moment seemed as long as a yuga to her, and she called her Lord's name over and over again, and sobbed piteously.

Sushila, meanwhile, had sought refuge in Mahalakshmi's body; she had melted into that compassionate Devi, from fear of Radha. And, hidden within Sri Lakshmi, Sushila performed an intense tapasya for a long, long time. It was then that the Devas undertook a profound and difficult yagna, but their sacrifice was fruitless, and they came to Brahma in frustration.

Brahma himself worshipped Vishnu with austere devotion, and Narayana appeared before him. Brahma said to the Blue God, the Saviour, 'The yagna of Indra and his people is desolate, for Yagna himself has no Shakti to make his rituals fruitful. What shall I do?'

And Narayana fetched Sushila out from Lakshmi's body, on the night of the full moon of Kartika maasa, in the Raasa mandala, and gave her to Yagna Deva to be his Shakti. Since she emerged from the Devi Lakshmi's right shoulder now, Sushila was called Dakshina, and also because she was possessed of great daksha, intelligence. Brahma brought her before the mournful Yagna, and she was so beautiful, so alluring, and so radiant with her long tapasya, that he fainted just to see her!

Then, the two were given to each other, and they went away to a sequestered mandala, and made love for a hundred years of the Gods. Dakshina became pregnant, and she gave birth to a brilliant son, and he was called Karmaphala. And it was this child who bestowed the fruits of every yagna, thereafter, to those who performed it and gave dakshina to their guru or their priest after. And now the Devas' yagnas were blessed, why, they were awash in plenitude by the grace of the Lord Yagna, the Devi Dakshina, and their son, the bright Karmaphala.

And so it is, that, he who performs any auspicious karma must always pay some dakshina to his guru, if he would enjoy the fruit, the phala, of his karma. And, if he does not pay the needful dakshina, only the righteous Bali, who rules in Patala, enjoys the results of that karma, for, of old Vamana Deva has ordained that it shall be so.

The Devi Dakshina is worshipped with her own mula mantra, just as she was first by Brahma and by her lord Yagna Deva. And that mantra, which purifies every yagna, and confers boundless grace upon the bhakta, is **AUM Srim Hrim Dakshinyai Svaha.**

And the wise know, that when Dakshina Devi is worshipped and dakshina is offered after the yagna, of fire, thought or deed, the man who has no sons is blessed with the best of them, he who has no wife quickly finds an auspicious soul-mate, beautiful and good-natured; he who is indigent finds a treasure, and becomes a wealthy man. And the man who listens to the Dakshina stotra, the hymn of the Devi Dakshina, with which her lord Yagna Deva worshipped her, passes safely over every danger and hardship, and the obstacles in his path disappear miraculously," said the Mahamuni Narayana,' Vyasa said beside the murmuring river."

SEVENTY-SIX

"VYASA CONTINUED, 'NARADA NOW ASKED THE MUNI, "LORD, SASTHI, Mangala Chandi and Manasa are amsas of the Mula Prakriti. Tell me about them, as well."

"Sasthi Devi is the sixth amsa of the Devi Prakriti. She is the Goddess of infants and children; she is the nourisher. She, too, is Vishnu's maya, and the one who blesses women with sons and daughters, and she is counted among the sixteen Matrikas. The Devi Sasthi is called Devasena, and she is the Lord Karttikeya's wife. She is a Siddha Yogini, and all children dwell at her side, even while they are in the world, until they are pubescent.

Dharma Deva told me about Devasena. Listen to her story. As you know, Svayambhuva Manu had one son, Priyavrata, who was a great Yogindra, and never wanted to marry. But, finally, at his grandsire Brahma's behest, he agreed to take a wife. Years went by, and Priyavrata had no son. So, he called Maharishi Kashyapa to perform a putreshti yagna for him. When the rituals were over, Priyavrata took the blessed offerings, the charu, to his wife Malini, and when she ate the charu, she became pregnant.

Her pregnancy lasted twelve years, and then she gave birth to a splendid child, of a golden complexion; but he was stillborn, no breath stirred in his fine, perfectly formed body. Malini fainted away, and Priyavrata picked up his son's body and took it himself to the smasana. There, holding his child in his arms, he began to sob loudly. Why, he would rather die himself than consign his baby to the pyre, which had been stacked for the lifeless little body.

Suddenly, he looked up and saw a scintillant vimana in the sky, flying down towards him. It seemed to be made of the sheerest crystal, and encrusted with incredible jewels. In that vimana sat a radiant Siddha Yogini, completely beautiful, smiling down at him. Priyavrata set his child's body down on the ground, and began to worship the Goddess in the ship of the sky.

He asked her, who shone like the summer sun, 'Devi, who are you, splendid one? Whose daughter? It seems to me you are a great Goddess, yet I do not know your name.'

And she, who had fought once as the Senapati of the Devas in a great war against the Asuras, said, 'I am Sasthi, the sixth amsa of the Devi Bhagavati, and I am Brahma's daughter, born from his mind. I am Skanda's queen, O Priyavrata, and I bless those who have no children with sons and daughters.' She spoke in the most delightful voice, and the blissful smile never left her lips. 'O King, I give wives to the unmarried, wealth to the poor, and work to those who seek it.'

The king stood staring at her, a great hope awakening in him now, at what she said, who had appeared to him at this dreadful moment of fate. The Devi Sasthi alighted from her vimana, she picked up Priyavrata's lifeless child in her arms, and, laying her bright palm on his brow, gave him life. The golden child breathed, he opened his eyes and smiled. Devasena was about to leave with the king's son. Priyavrata's mouth was as dry as a desert, his limbs were weak, and hoarsely he began to hymn her with a stotra that welled spontaneously in his heart.

It seemed he pleased the Devi Devasena, for she said to him, 'Make my name and my worship known through the earth, O Kshatriya. Make the stotra you have just hymned me with renowned, and you shall have your son back from me. He is an amsa of Narayana, and he shall be called Suvrata, and his name will be a legend upon the earth. He will be a trikalagyani, a kavi, and the greatest Kshatriyas of the world will bend their heads at his feet.'

Priyavrata worshipped the Devi himself, and spread her worship throughout his kingdom, specially on the sixth day of the bright fortnight of the month, on the sixth day after the birth of a child, and when giving a child his first ritual taste of rice, when he is six months old. And she was worshipped with her mula mantra, **AUM Hrim Sasthi Devyai Svaha**, and the stotra, the hymn of praise with which Svayambhuva Manu's first son worshipped her. And the Lord Skanda's queen gave his Suvrata back to Priyavrata, and the miracle was celebrated the world over, and the name of the Devi Devasena became renowned."

Narada said, "Tell me about the Devi Mangala Chandi, O Master."

"Mangala is the Earth's son, and Varaha Deva's, and Mangala Chandi is his consort, she is the favourite Goddess of all women in creation, their Ishta Devataa. She is also the Devi of war. Once, during the war against Tripurasura, that Demon cast a huge vimana as a weapon upon Siva's head, and it would have crushed him, except Brahma and Vishnu cried out to him, in the heart of an instant, to worship the Devi Durga.

Siva did so, and she appeared as the Devi Chandi, a sixteen-year-old Goddess, and became his Shakti in battle, so the vimana flashed harmlessly past him. Then, Vishnu became the Lord Sankara's strangest mount, a bull buffalo, and he slew the Asura with the trisula Vishnu gave him. Fragrant petals of light fell out of the sky, and, it is told, Siva worshipped the Devi Mangala Chandi with offerings of padya, arghya, achamaniya, with silk garments, flowers, sandalwood paste, goats, sheep, buffalo, bison, birds, ornaments, garlands, payasa, pistaka, honey, wine, and fruit.

Gandharvas and Apsaras, and mortals, too, danced and sang in her honour, that she had been the Shakti that won the Devasura yuddha for the ones of light. Mahadeva worshipped her with her mantra, **AUM Hrim Srim Klim Sarvapujye Devi Mangala Chandike Hum Phat Svaha**. And she is worshipped particularly on Tuesdays, by all women, and by men too."

"And what of the Devi Manasa?" now Narada Muni asked great Narayana Rishi.

"I heard the legend of the Devi Manasa also from the Lord Dharma Deva. She was Maharishi Kashyapa's daughter, born of his immaculate mind, hence the name Manasa Devi; or, perhaps, she is called that since she is the Goddess who sports with men's minds. Those that know also say that she is the Devi of dhyana, who controls the rapture of the mind. Anyway, for three yugas she sat in tapasya to Sri Krishna, and became a Siddha Yogini.

When Krishna saw her emaciated by penance, he called her Jarata Karu, for she reminded him of that attenuated Rishi. So severe was her tapasya, that not only did she worship Krishna, he, too, worshipped her. This Devi is fair as summer clouds, and her name is known in Swarga, Bhumi, Patala, Nagaloka and Brahmaloka, also, and the beings of all the three realms pray to her. For her exceptionally fair complexion, she is also called Jagad Gauri. And she is known as Saivi, for she is the Lord Siva's bhakta, and as Vaishnavi, as well, for she adores the Lord Vishnu too.

It is told she saved the Nagas at Parikshita's sarpayagna, and she is called Nageswari and Naga Bhagini. Since she can make venom harmless, like water, she is called Vishahari, and she is the sister of Vasuki and his serpents. She is Siddhayogini, for Siva gave her the Siddha yoga; and because he gave her deep knowledge as well, she is Jnanajuta. She can enliven the dead, and is called Mritasanjivani, too. She is the Rishi Astika's mother, and the world knows her as Astika Mata. The Devi Manasa is the Muni Jarat Karu's wife, and she is Jarat Karupriya.

She is worshipped by these twelve names, and the Siddha who chants them and the Manasa mantra, **AUM Srim Hrim Klim Aim Manasa Devyai Svaha**, never has any fear of snakes, why, he can drink serpent venom, and it will do him no harm but make him strong, immortal even, for the poison becomes like amrita to him. And, finally, Manasa Devi's bhakta attains Vishnuloka and the presence of the Lord Hari."

"Tell me how the Devi Manasa became the saviour of the Nagas, Lord."

Narayana said to him, "Dharma Deva told me this tale. Once, the earth was overrun by deadly serpents, and the Rishis of the world had no sanctuary or protection from them. They came to Mahamuni Kashyapa in terror, and begged him to save them from the fear of the Nagas. Kashyapa himself tried to subdue the snakes with his mystic power, but at first, he had no success.

Then, thinking of his father Brahma, and inspired by the Pitamaha, Kashyapa composed a mantra that was founded in the Veda. While he did this, he thought fervently of the Devi Bhagavati, and she was the deity of his mantra. And, by the power of that incantation, and by the purity and the power of Kashyapa Muni's mind, a Goddess materialised before him as he chanted his mantra, and she was the Devi Manasa.

She was born full-grown and entirely beautiful, and, as soon as she had her father's blessing, she took herself to Kailasa parvata, and sat upon it worshipping the Lord Siva. For a thousand years of the Devas, she chanted his mula mantra and sang his stotras, and then Sankara appeared before her in a mass of light, and blessed her with great gyana and great siddhis.

He taught her the Sama Veda, and the Krishna mantra, **Srim Hrim Klim Krishnayah namah**, which is truly a kalpavriksha. Siva gave the Devi Manasa the kavacha that is famed through the three worlds. He told her to go to the Pushkara kshetra, and perform another tapasya. In Pushkara, the Devi Manasa worshipped Krishna for three yugas. It was only then that Krishna appeared before her, and when she prostrated herself before him, macilent as she was with her long privation, he too folded his hands to her, and called her Jarat Karu.

Krishna said to her, 'You will be worshipped throughout the world,' and left.

She returned to her father, and Kashyapa gave her to the Muni Jarat Karu, to be his wife. One afternoon, Jarat Karu Muni fell asleep, after a morning's dhyana, with his head in his wife's lap. Dusk set in, and Manasa grew anxious about her husband not performing the evening sandhya. Gently, she shook him awake.

But the Rishi was furious! He cried, 'How dare you disturb my sleep?'

Tears in her eyes, Manasa said, 'My lord, if a Brahmana does not keep the sandhyas, all his punya is lost. Yet, she who disturbs her husband, when he is at prayer or eating, or asleep, finds the Kalasutra Naraka for herself. What should I have done, my husband? The choice was between your losing your punya or my going to hell.'

And she fell at his feet, and sobbed. But Jarat Karu hardly heard what she said; he was beside himself with anger. Indeed, he was on the point of cursing her, when, suddenly, Surya Deva appeared in that asrama, with Sandhya Devi at his side!

The Sun God said to Jarata Karu, 'Muni, the Brahmana's anger can burn the very earth to a cinder, yet the Brahmana's wrath lasts only for the twinkling of an eye. Your Manasa woke you because I was about to set. If you curse her, then, Muni, you must curse me also, for the fault was mine that your sleep was disturbed. But, I beg you, forgive me!'

Jarat Karu gazed at the brilliant Deva for a moment, then, raised his hand in blessing over the Sun, and that God vanished from there. But Jarat Karu could neither curse his Manasa now, nor could he forgive her. So, he decided to leave her, and was about to abandon their asrama, when Manasa Devi began to wail loudly, she called out to her Ishta Devata, and to the Lord Siva, and to Brahma, Hari and Kashyapa.

The moment she thought of Krishna, the Blue One appeared before the Muni and his wife! Jarat Karu prostrated himself before the Lord, in an ecstasy; he began to hymn him with every stotra he knew.

Brahma said to Krishna, 'Jarat Karu means to abandon Manasa Devi, but he must not do this without first giving her a child, or all his great punya will leave him like water leaking from a sieve.'

At which, Jarat Karu touched the Devi Manasa's navel with his fingertips, and chanted a resonant mantra. He said to her, 'You will have a son, bright as the yagna fire, a devout child who will be the best of all Brahmanas. I am going to Pushkara now, for I mean to sit in dhyana of Sri Krishna's lotus feet.'

But Manasa cried, 'Ah, my Lord, don't be so cruel to me. It is hard to be parted from a friend, and much harder to be parted from a son. Yet, for a woman to be parted from her husband is harder than losing a hundred sons. For a woman, my lord, her husband is the most precious thing in the world. She loves him even as a father does his only son, as a Vaishnava does Sri Narayana, as a one-eyed man does his single eye, as a thirsty man does water, a hungry one does food, as a passionate man does lust, as a thief does the belongings of others, as a libertine does his whore, as the Brahmana does the Shastras, as the Vaishya does his trade. Ah, my lord, take pity on me!'

And she fell senseless at his feet, as if her very life was leaving her. Jarat Karu took her in his arms, and he wept now, and consoled her tenderly. Then, that Rishi enlightened his wife, the Devi Manasa, and, when true gyana arose in both their hearts in tide, fear left them, and every anxiety. A wave of peace swept over their spirits. Finally, the Muni left her, and went away to Pushkara, where he sat in searing tapasya.

When he left, she could not bear her grief. Peace also left her, and she went to Kailasa to her Ishta Devata, the Lord Siva. Siva and Uma both consoled the Devi Manasa as best they could with the eternal wisdom, and their very presence was balm to her anguish. She lived with them upon the sacred mountain, until the day came when she was delivered of a radiant child, who was an amsa of Vishnu himself. He would be the guru of the yogis of the world, the preceptor of the gyanis, for, after all, when he was still in his mother's womb, he had heard the Sanatana Dharma from no less a person than Mahadeva Siva himself!

Sankara performed the child's first karma, and, when he was just a few weeks old, taught him the Vedas and their angas, and gave the brilliant child the mrityunjaya mantra, which conquers death. And they called him Astika, for his mother's perfect bhakti for her husband, and for her Lord Siva. At last, Siva initiated Astika with the maha mantra, the greatest of all mystic incantations. Then, the young Muni went away to Pushkara to worship Sri Vishnu Narayana. He sat in unmoving dhyana for three hundred thousand years of the Devas, and then returned to Kailasa and prostrated himself before his guru Siva.

After being blessed by Siva and Parvati, Manasa Devi came down to her father Kashyapa's asrama again, bringing Astika with her. The Maharishi was beside himself with joy to see his grandson, his wives Diti and Aditi were delighted, and Manasa lived in that asrama for a long, long time," said Narayana Muni,' says Vyasa."

SEVENTY-SEVEN

"JANAMEJAYA ASKED, 'IS THIS THE SAME ASTIKA WHO CAME TO MY SARPA yagna and saved the serpents' lives?'

Dwaipayana Muni, the great Vyasa, replied, 'The very same. When Takshaka fled to Indra for sanctuary when you began your yagna to avenge your father Parikshita's death, the Brahmanas Uttanka and the rest threatened Indra with death if he gave shelter to the serpent king. But Indra sought refuge in the Devi Manasa who is, as we know, Vasuki's sister.

And she sent her son, the magnificent Astika, to your yagna, and you, my lord, asked him what boon he wanted, and said he could have anything from you since he was so illustrious a Muni. He asked you to abandon your sarpa yagna; which is why, O King, you and I are here together, recounting this Purana of the most auspicious Devi Bhagavati!'

By now, Janamejaya's troubled spirit had found deep solace, and the dark thoughts of having revenge on all the serpents in the world had left his heart. For, the Devi Bhagavatam he heard from Vyasa enlightened him. With a wry smile, the king of the Kurus murmured, 'And I am glad he came, O Vyasa, for otherwise I would have been deprived of hearing this wondrous Purana from you. But go on, Muni. Tell me, did Indra worship the Devi Manasa, when her son had saved him and Takshaka from my sarpa yagna?'

'Indeed, he did. He made himself pure by bathing in a sacred river, and performing achamana. He wore fresh, clean clothes, and set the Devi Manasa on a golden throne encrusted with the finest jewels. He then poured ablutionary water over her from the Ganga, from a jewelled urn, and had her body anointed with golden sandal-paste. Then she also put on the raiment Indra gave her, that had been purified in fire.

He offered her tirtha jala to wash her feet, and as arghya. He offered her kusa grass, rice grains and flowers as a first offering. He worshipped the six Devatas, Ganapathy, Surya, Agni, Vishnu, Siva and Sivaa. He chanted the Devi's mula mantra, **AUM Hrim Srim Manasa Devyai Svaha**. And, inspired by the Lord Vishnu, Indra worshipped Manasa Devi, whose son had saved his life, with sixteen precious offerings, and with great joy.

A shower of subtle flowers of light fell out from heaven, onto the Devi Manasa's head, and all the earth was awash with their rapturous scent. And, his body trembling with bliss Indra hymned the Devi Manasa with a spontaneous stotra, which is still used to worship her. The Devas all worshipped Manasa Devi, the Nagas most of all, and, it is told, the cow of wishes Surabhi came down from Goloka, and bathed the Devi Manasa in her milk, which is like amrita, and taught her the occult tattva gyanas, that are the most hermetic secrets in the universe. The Devi rose into Swarga, and there she dwells still, and in the mind of all creatures, most of all, her bhaktas. Any man who chants her mantra five hundred thousand times becomes a Siddha, truly,' said Vyasa Muni.

Janamejaya asked, 'Who was this Surabhi, the cow you spoke of, Rishi?'

'Why, Narada once asked the incomparable Muni Narayana the very same thing. Narayana said, "Once, Krishna and Radha were alone together in the heart of a dark forest in Goloka. They were making love. She had her back to a celestial kadamba, and he was thrusting blue fire at her, for an age. Suddenly, he grew thirsty from his sweet labour, and wanted to drink some milk.

The thought hardly crossed his mind, when a dazzling white cow appeared in that forest grove. She was heavy with unearthly, ambrosial milk, and she had her little calf with her. She was luminous, she was exquisite, she was gentleness and goodness embodied, and she was the Devi Surabhi, that first cow in creation. Sridaman milked her into an earthen jar, and the Lord of the gopis drank thirstily of that frothy, fragrant milk.

It is told, O Muni, that the milk of Surabhi is more nectarine than the amrita which rose from the sea, or the amrita of the Devas. Some drops of Surabhi's precious milk spilled out of the earthen vessel, and a vast sea formed from them! And that sea is called the Kshirasagara, and Radha and her gopikas bathe in it, and play in its white waves. And, by Krishna's blessing, that sea was full of the rarest, most priceless jewels in creation.

Then, by the Lord's grace, and from his delight, from Surabhi's pores there appeared a billion kamadhenus, each a brilliant cow, every one a cow of wishes which gave its owner anything he wanted. Every gopa in Goloka had a kamadhenu of his own. And by Krishna's command, the first cow of all, Surabhi, is worshipped with her own mantra, **AUM Surabhyai namah**, especially on the night after Deepawali, the day after the new moon. And she gives those that worship her everything they want."

Narada asked, "Tell me about the occult worship of Sri Radha and the Devi Durga, as they are in the Veda."

Narayana said, "These are the most secret lores, Narada. Radha is the Devi of Prana, and Durga the Devi of Buddhi, both in their cosmic aspects. From these two Shaktis, the Mulaprakriti has created all the universe. And they must be worshipped, satisfied, before any jiva can have mukti.

The Radha mantra is **Sri Radhayai Svaha**. Krishna was the one who first received this most sacred mantra, and he heard it from an asariri in the Raasa mandala. The Vedas say Krishna is, thus, **Raso Vai Sah**. Vishnu had the mantra from Krishna; Brahma had it from Vishnu, Virata from Brahma, Dharma from Virata, and I from Dharma Deva. All the Devas chant the Radha mula mantra, in bliss, and without worshipping Radha, Krishna can never be worshipped.

Radha is the Devi who is Krishna's very prana, his life-breath that pervades and enlivens all the brahmandas. It is told that, without her Krishna could not live for even a moment. Radha's name is derived from Radhnoti, which means she who fulfils all desires. So, she is the Mulaprakriti herself. And because I chant her mantra, I am called Rishi.

Indeed, I am the Rishi of every mantra save the Durga mantra. The Gayatri is the Chchanda of these mantras, and Radhika is their Devata. Truly, Narayana is the Rishi of all mantras, Gayatri is their Chchanda, their meter, Pranava, the blessed AUM, is their bija, their seed, and Bhuvaneswari is the Shakti.

The bhakta who worships the Devi Radha on the day of the full moon in the month of Kartika has her blessings forever, because she remains with that bhakta, for he has hymned her with her profound stotra, and with her precious mantra," said Narayana Muni to Narada.

Narada asked, in the silence that now fell between them, "And the Devi Durga, Muni?"

Smiling, that greatest Rishi said, "He who worships Durga Devi, his troubles vanish from him like darkness at sunrise. She is the Mother of the universe, of every jiva, and she is Siva's Shakti. She is the Goddess of buddhi, the intellect, and dwells in the hearts of all creatures. She removes danger from life, and is hard to attain, hence her name, Durga. Like the Devi Radha, Durga also is the Mulaprakriti herself.

Her powerful, perfect mula mantra is **Aim Hrim Klim Chamundayai Vichche**. And this is a kalpa vriksha, even like the Radha mantra, and yields every least desire, and it purifies the heart. Brahma, Vishnu and Maheswara are the Rishis of this mantra, Gayatri, Ushnik and Anushtupa are its Chchandas; Mahakali, Mahalakshmi and Saraswati are its Devatas; Raktadantika, Durga and Brahmari are its Bijas. Nanda, Sakambhari and Bhima are its Shaktis, and dharma, artha and kama are its Viniyogas, for which ends the mantra is used.

The head is for the mantra's Rishi, the mouth has the Chchandas, and the Devatas are in the heart. The Shaktis have the right breast and the Bijas the left. Then, the sadamga namaskara, saying, **Aim Hridayaya Namah, Hrim Sirase Svaha, Klim Sikhayam Vasai, Chamundayai Kavachaya Hum, Vichche Netrabhyam Vausat, Aim Hrim Klim Chamundayai Vichche Karatalaprishihahyam Phat.**

Then, touching those parts of the body, **Aim Namah Sikhayam, Hrim Namah,** the right eye; **Klim Namah**, the left eye, **Cham Namah,** the right ear, **Mum Namah,** the left. **Nadam Namah**, the nostrils, **Vim Namah**, the face, **Chchem Namah**, the anus, and at last **Aim Hrim Klim Chamundayai Vichche**, the whole body. Then, the dhyana of the Devi Durga, of Mahalakshmi, then of the Devi Saraswati.

Listen, Muni, to how the occult yantra of the Devi is drawn. First, the bhakta draws a triangle, within that he draws an eight-petalled lotus with twenty-four leaves, within the heart of the lotus he draws the griha, the Devi's home. And here, or in a Saligrama, an image of the Devi or in the consecrated jar of water, or in a banalingam, or in the Sun, he worships her, with his mind controlled thinking of nothing but her.

Then he worships Peetha, and the other Deities enthroned—Jaya, Vijaya, Ajita, Aghora, Mangala and the other Pitha Shaktis. Next, he worships the Deities of the directions, with avarana puja. Brahma and Saraswati in the east, Narayana with Lakshmi in Nairrita's realm, Siva with Uma in Vayu's, the Devi's mount the lion to the north of the Devi, Mahasura on her left, and Mahishasura. He worships Nandaja, Raktadanta, Sakhambari, Sivaa, Durga, Bhimaa and Bhramari.

On the eight petals of the lotus, he worships Brahmi, Maheswari, Kaumari, Vaishnavi, Varahi, Narasimhi, Aindri and Chamundaa. Beginning with the leaf directly before the Devi, on the twenty-four leaves of the lotus, he worships Vishnu Maya, Chetana, Buddhi, Nidra, Chchaya, Shakti, Bhuka, Daaha, Shanti, Jati, Lajja, Sraddha, Kirti, Lakshmi, Saraswati, Uma, Dridhaa, Vriti, Sruti, Karunaa, Tushti, Pushti, Bhranti, and the other Matrikas.

On the corners of the bupura, the portals of the yantra, he worships Ganapathy, the Kshetrapalas, Vatuka and the Yoginis. Beyond that, he prays to Indra and the Devas, all bearing weapons. Then, the bhakta makes his offerings to the Devi, and intones her mula mantra, and the Saptasati Stotra, the Chandi patha.

The one who worships the Devi Durga, thus, every day, has all his desires fulfilled, of dharma, artha, kama and, finally, even moksha comes his way," said the Mahamuni Narayana to Narada,' said Vyasa to the king," says Suta Romaharshana to the Munis of the Naimisa vana.

Saunaka, who was the chief among those Munis of the six clans, who sought nirvana by listening to the immortal Purana, now says, "Peerless Romaharshana, tell us about the Manus, who was the first of them, and who were the others?"

The Suta says, "The Kuru king Janamejaya asked my guru Krishna Dwaipayana the same thing. My master said to the king, 'Once, Narada asked Narayana Muni the names of the Manus who are the sovereigns of the manvantaras.

Narayana said, "The first of all the Manus was Svayambhuva Manu, whom Brahma created from his mind. This Manu made an earthen image of the Devi Bhagavati, and worshipped it. When the Mother appeared before him in glory and blessed him, Manu Svayambhuva set about his task of creation, for which he had been born.

This first Manu had two sons, Priyavrata and Uttanapada, and they also worshipped the Devi Bhagavati, and Priyavrata's son Svarochisa became the second Manu. He worshipped the Devi in an earthen image, on the banks of the Kalindi. And she made him Manu for a manvantara, and thus, she was known as Tarini Jagaddhatri.

Another son of Priyavrata, whose name was Uttama, became the third Manu, when his brother had ruled the earth for a manvantara and then abandoned his body in the final samadhi. Uttama worshipped the Devi Bhagavati on the banks of the Ganga. After him, another son of Priyavrata,

Tamasa, was the fourth Manu. He worshipped the Devi with the Kama bija mantra on the southern bank of the Narmada.

Tamasa's younger brother Raivata was the fifth Manu, and the sixth Manu was Chaksusha, who was Anga's son. You know, O Muni, that the Manus we speak of were more like Gods in the world than mortal men. After Chaksusha, the next Manu was Vaivasvata Sraddha Deva, and after him, the Suryaputra Savarni was the eighth. This Savarni, it is known, was a king of the earth called Suratha in his previous birth during the manvantara of Svarochisa Manu. We have already heard about him, and how he was driven from his kingdom and came to the Muni Sumedha's asrama, and finally had his kingdom back after he worshipped the Devi.

Vaivasvata Manu had six sons, O Narada, and their names were Karusha, Prisadhra, Nabhaga, Dishta, Saryati and Trisankhu. Once, the six of them came together to the banks of the Yamuna and stilled their breath in pranayama. They worshipped the Devi, fervidly. After twelve years, Bhagavati appeared before them, resplendent as a thousand suns! The six princes began to hymn her with stotras that flowed in inspiration from their hearts. Then, they begged her to bless them with boons, and those six became, one after the other, the ninth, tenth, eleventh, twelfth, thirteenth and fourteenth Manus, in other births.

They were called Daksha Savarni, Meru Savarni, Surya Savarni, Chandra Savarni, Rudra Savarni, and the sixth prince Trisankhu became Vishnu Savarni, the great, for the Devi Bhramari did, indeed, bless them," said Narayana,' said Vyasa."

SEVENTY-EIGHT

"AFTER A MOMENT'S PAUSE, VYASA CONTINUED, 'NARADA NOW ASKED THE Muni, "Lord, who was the Devi Bhramari?"

Narayana said, "In time out of mind, the days of which I am telling you, the elder days of the first Manus of the earth, there was in a city of the Daityas in Patala an awesomely powerful Asura called Aruna. His ambition was to crush Indra's Devas, and he came out of Patala, climbed the Himalaya, and sat on the banks of the holy Ganga in an unremitting tapasya. The God he worshipped was his ancestor Brahma.

He held the five vayus, the panchaprana, in perfect control within his body, ate only dry leaves, and chanted the Gayatri mantra for ten thousand years. For another ten thousand, then, he kept himself alive by drinking just a few drops of dew and rainwater that he found in the leaves of the trees around him. He ate nothing anymore.

A wonderful halo enveloped Arunasura's body, and soon that lustre grew so intense it spread like a fire of the spirit, and began to consume the worlds! It spumed up irresistibly into Devaloka, and Indra and his Devas were dismayed, for that tapasya shakti was such a potent thing it would incinerate Swarga, Bhumi and Patala, if the Demon on the Himalaya was not stopped.

Indra and his people came flying to Brahma, and begged him to give Aruna whatever boon he wanted, so the Asura would stop his dhyana. Brahma came on his swan, with Gayatri Devi at his side, to where the Daitya sat in tapasya. Aruna sat with his eyes shut tightly. He was emaciated by his penance, his skin hung loosely on his bones, and hardly any flesh remained on his limbs. Yet, he was like a flame, too bright even to look at.

Brahma said to the Daitya, 'Arunasura, I am pleased with your tapasya. Tell me what boon you want.'

The Asura opened his eyes, and saw the four-faced, splendid Pitama before him, with the Devi Gayatri and the four Vedas, embodied, around him, and a string of beads and a kamandalu in his hands. Overcome, Aruna prostrated himself at the great God's feet, and hymned him with stotras.

Then the Daitya said, 'Lord, bless me that I will never die.'

Brahma smiled. It was not the first time a great Asura had asked for this boon. He said gently, 'Aruna, when Vishnu, even Siva, and I myself are not beyond death, how can I give you this boon? Ask me for a boon that is in my power to grant, ask me for something within the bounds of reason.'

The Asura reflected for a moment, then, said, 'O Lord, grant that I will not be killed in any war, or by any weapon known to men or the Gods, or by a man or a woman, or by any bird or animal, and also grant me that I have an army with which I can conquer the Devas of Indra.'

The Asura's tapasya had been so austere that Brahma had to grant him what he asked. The Pitama said, 'Let it be so,' and vanished.

In great joy, Aruna sent word to all the Asuras that lived in Patala of his boon, and they came swarming up to him, and he was crowned their emperor. When he had collected an oceanic army, Aruna sent messengers to Indra in Devaloka, challenging him to fight.

When Indra heard about the boon the Asura had from Brahma, he flew with his Devas to Brahmaloka. Taking Brahma with them, the Devas came to Vaikuntha, and then, with Vishnu going with them as well, they came to Sivaloka. Meanwhile, Aruna attacked Devaloka with his legions of darkness, and with powerful sorcery, and he assumed sovereignty in heaven. He and his Daityas now ruled the three realms in place of Indra, Agni, Vayu, Surya, Soma, Varuna, Yama and the rest.

On Kailasa, Brahma told the other Gods about the boon he had given Aruna, and they were aghast. None of them could think how Aruna could be killed. Suddenly, an asariri spoke to the Devas out of the sky, 'The lord of the Asuras chants the Gayatri ceaselessly, and the mantra is the root of his power. If he were to stop, he can be killed. Worship the Devi Gayatri Parameswari, only she can help you.'

Indra turned to Brihaspati, and said, 'Guru, you must go the Asura, and somehow make him forsake his bhakti. And we will worship the Devi, and beg her to help us in our need.'

The Devas undertook a great Devi yagna, and worshipped the Devi Gayatri with the maya bija. Brihaspati arrived in Aruna's grand sabha in the guise of a Muni. Aruna looked carefully at the bright ascetic and said to him, 'Why have you come to me, Rishi? I am no friend of your kind, but your enemy.'

Brihaspati replied serenely, 'You also worship the Devi Gayatri just as we do. How can we be enemies? We are the same you and I, for the one we worship is the same.'

Aruna considered this for a moment, then growled, 'I will no longer worship the Devi, if the cowardly Devas also worship her. Now go from here, Brahmana, before I am tempted to drink your blood.'

His mission accomplished, Brihaspati went willingly. Aruna stopped worshipping the Devi, and the Devas still did. A long time elapsed, then one day the Devi appeared before the Devas. She was dazzling, beautiful, her skin many-hued. Her hands were clenched into fists, and from them issued the strangest droning, such as bees make. The garlands she wore around her neck buzzed with swarms of black bees and golden hornets. The droning of those insects was the Hrimkara mantra, the first sacred vibration in creation.

Brahma, Vishnu, Sankara and the Devas praised the Devi with stotras; they sang her thousand names. 'Devi!' they called her, 'O Bhagavati, Kutastha Chaitanya, Durga, Bharga, Kalika, Nila, Saraswati, Ugra Tara, Mahogra, Tripura Sundari, Bhairavi, Matangi, Dhumavati, Chinnamasta, Sakambhari, Rakta Dantika, O Lakshmi, Svaha, Svadha, Dakshina, O Brahmari!' and many names more, each of which is a sacred mantra, whose very echoes are immortal and rule the world.

Smiling, she said to them, in her voice as sweet as a great koyal's, 'Devas, tell me what boon you want from me.'

Indra said, abjectly, 'Devi, Arunasura has driven us from our home and from our thrones of power. Demons rule the three worlds and we are plunged in darkness and evil. No yagnas are performed, no Vedas are chanted for fear of the Daityas. And Aruna has Brahma's boon that no man or God, no bird or beast can kill him.'

The Devi's smile grew wider, she said softly, 'Look, I have brought the killers of Aruna and his demons with me. They are neither man nor God, not bird or animal.'

She opened her hands and from them flew swarms and swarms of bees, wasps and hornets, and the sound they made was deafening, it filled heaven and earth. Then, from her arms, her sides, her faces, her breasts, her yoni, from all over the Devi's body countless bees issued, even like locust swarms, until they covered all the earth and all the sky, and everything was one black night of bees, wasps and hornets.

The insects flew at Aruna and his Asuras, and tore them to shreds. In just an hour all the Asuras died, and the billions of bees, wasps and hornets flew back to the Devi, and vanished into her body. Now the Gandharvas sang her praises, and the Apsaras danced in joy. Siva, Vishnu, Brahma and all the Devas and Rishis were enraptured, they were absorbed in the sea of love that is the Bhagavati.

Sky and earth echoed with the sound of deep conches, with mridangas, murajas, dhakkas, dumarus, bells, vinas, flutes, and all sorts of celebrant instruments that seemed almost to play themselves, though indeed immortal Gandharvas and Vidyadharas and Kinnaras' hands held many of them.

And this, O Narada, was how the Devi Bhagavati came as the Devi Brahmari, the Goddess with the bees, to deliver the Devas from the tyranny of the Asura Aruna," said Narayana to the wanderer,' said my master Veda Vyasa," says the Suta in the Naimisa vana.

SEVENTY-NINE

THE SUTA CONTINUED, "VYASA SAID TO THE KING, 'NARADA SAID TO Narayana, "Bhagavan! You are the Primeval, Eternal One! You are the Lord of all beings that have lived in the past, and of those that will come to be in the deep, deep future. You have told me the wondrous legends of the Devi Bhagavati, and my heart soars. But, Muni, incomparable Narayana, tell me of more earthly, mundane things now; tell me about sadachara, the way of right living, the changeless path of dharma."

Narayana said, "One's deliverance depends upon oneself. So, indeed, one must observe sadachara to earn a goodly store of punya to help one in the next world. With dharma alone does a man cross safely over the sea of sorrow, the ocean of anxiety and fear.

The main dharmas are those laid down by Manu in the Srutis and the Manu Smritis. Only by right conduct are life, prosperity and growth to be had in this world and the next. By righteous living alone does even food come one's way, and by dharma a man's sins are burnt to ashes. It is from good deeds that a man gains knowledge, and knowledge sets him free.

Sadachara is a great tapasya. The Brahmana who has no sadachara may as well be a Sudra. Sadachara is of two kinds—the conduct laid down in the Shastras, and that dictated by popular custom come down the ages, which is called laukika. Both are of equal importance. So, Muni, all men should observe not merely their own dharma but the dharma of the clan, the village, the caste, the country, and of humankind, of the earth, and the very universe of souls.

Wealth that has no dharma in it must be avoided like the deadliest disease. Wealth that accrues from pain caused to any living creature must be avoided like death. You must remember there is no escape from the fruits of what one does, both good and evil. Not in a thousand kalpas is the least karma fruitless."

Narada asked, "But, Muni, the Shastras are many, and they all prescribe different codes of conduct, why, different dharmas, often contradictory. Which Dharma Shastra should one follow?"

"Sruti and Smriti are the two paths of God, and the Purana is his heart! All that the Srutis, the Smritis and the Puranas say is dharma, and, even if they may seem contradictory, each one is flawless for different times and ages. Yet, it is told that the Sruti is higher than the Smriti, and the Smriti is higher than the Purana.

And when the Srutis themselves seem to contradict each other, remember that dharma is also of two kinds. Often, the Puranas describe in detail, even advocate, the Tantra Shastras. But if the Tantra goes against the Veda, always remember the Veda is the elder, and higher, authority.

He who injures another living being, even with a blade of kusa grass, will pay for his crime. For, the justice of the universe is immaculate, just as it is full of mercy and imagination. Heretics and extremists of every kind, whose deeds and words harm either themselves or other living souls, find punishment before they learn the liberal, loving way of the truth, of real dharma, the eternal Sanatana Dharma which is gentle, non-violent, and is harmony with the universe.

Goodness and mercy are the greatest virtues. A man should ask himself every day what good he has done on that day. He should ask himself with relentless honesty what sins he has committed. And during the last quarter of the night, he should meditate upon the Brahmam, the all-lustrous Self of all selves, the ultimate reality whose eyes are everywhere.

He should sit in padmasana, his tongue cleaving to his palate, shutting his eyes, his head erect, utterly quiescent. He should restrain his breath with pranayama, and fix his thought on the sacred light within his heart—**AUM mani padme hum,** the jewel in the lotus of a thousand petals.

Pranayama is the highest yoga, and pranayama is of six kinds: sadhuma, when the breaths are not even; nirdhuma, when they are somewhat steady; sagarbha, when the breath is yoked to one's mantra; agarbha, the pure breathing, without any mantra; salakshva, when the heart is fixed upon one Ishta Devata, and alakshya, when the mind is free and does not attach itself to any Deity.

Pranayama is of the nature of Pranava, the primal syllable, the root of the universe, the blessed, highest **AUM**. The three parts of pranayama, puraka, kumbhaka and reechaka, inhaling, retaining, and exhaling, are indeed the letters of the **AUM**. The ida nadi is the left nostril. Puraka, the drawing in of prana, is done through this nadi. Puraka is of the nature of Vishnu, and is performed to a count of thirty-two. Kumbhaka, retention, so the sacred life-breath permeates the body and the self, is of the nature of Siva, and is performed to the count of sixty-four, and reechaka, exhaling, is done through the pingala nadi, the right nostril, and to the count of sixteen.

When the breath has been fetched under control, the six chakras along the spinal stem are pierced with the kula kundalini, raising the serpent fire from the base of the spine in the muladhara chakra, and it snakes up to the Brahmarandhra, the thousand-petalled lotus of the Soul within the brain.

Now the atman burns like a flame in a windless place, and the yogin meditates upon that which is eternal, beginningless and changeless, in his heart."

Narada wanted to know more about the experience of raising the kundalini shakti through the chakras.

Narayana said, "The chakras are sukshma, they exist in the spiritual dimension. They are like subtle, shining spheres. They are like lotuses, each with its petals. They are profound, O Muni, and at each of them, many visions inundate the sadhaka, many changes occur. All sorts of wonderful insights are obtained, arcane and relucent visions of the universe.

The kundalini shakti slumbers at the base of the spine in the four-petalled muladhara chakra between the anus and the root of the genitals. She is blood red, and is invoked with the mantra Hrim, the mayabija. She is as fine as a fibre of the stalk of a lotus, in truth, far finer. Her face is the Sun, Surya. Agni, the Fire, is her breast. He who sees the kula kundalini awakened even once surely becomes a jivanmukta, though his journey is a long one after his first vision.

He who wants the final blessing of the serpent fire must worship the Devi Bhagavati, whose amsa the kundalini is, who is verily the Kundalini Shakti. He must picture her in his heart, pray to her fervently, and hymn her. The yogin thinks, 'I am the Devi Bhagavati myself. I am the Cause of all causes; I am perfectly free from sorrow. My nature is Satchitananda, everlasting being, intelligence and bliss.

He meditates upon his own self, seeking sanctuary in the kula kundalini, which appears like streak lightning along its ascent to the Brahmarandhra in the brain, and like honeyed nectar on its way down again to the chakra at the base of the spine. He meditates upon his own guru, whom he thinks of as God himself, saying **Gurur Brahma, Gurur Vishnu, Gurur Devo Maheshwara, Gurur Sakshaat Parabrahmam, Tasmayi Sree Gurave namaha!** which is **The Guru is Brahma, he is Vishnu and Siva, too; verily, he is the Parabrahmam, and the Guru full of grace I bow to.**

Even if a man knows the Vedas and their six amgas perfectly, he cannot be without sin if he does not practise sadachara. When young birds' grow wings, they leave their nests. The Vedas leave a man when he dies, if he has no sadachara.

Nitya karma is always a blessing, and all men must observe the rites of nitya, and the three sandhyas of the day, at dawn, noon, and dusk. A man should rise before the sun, and take himself to a place as far from his dwelling as an arrow would travel when shot fiercely from a bow. There he should void his bowels, and cover his excrement with grass or leaves. He must never perform the evacuation on cultivated land, in water, on the site of a pyre, in the ruins of a temple, on an anthill, wherein living creatures dwell, on a roadside where people may see him, or in the hole of any living thing. He must purge himself privately, after praying to the deities of the elements, and the spirits that are abroad, and the holy ones of the earth.

He says, 'O Devas, Munis, O Rishis, O Pisachas, O Uragas, O Rakshasas, all ye that are here, unseen, I beg you to leave while I perform visarjanam!'

He must never void himself while gazing at the Wind, or at Fire, a Brahmana, the Sun, Water or a holy cow.

When he has finished, holding his genital member, he must wash himself thoroughly, or make himself absolutely clean by rubbing his soiled parts with earth or grass. It is told the Brahmana must use white earth, the Kshtariya red, the Vaishya yellow and the Sudra black earth to clean themselves. Of course, no earth, grass or leaves from under water, from a temple or the hole, nest or hill of any living creature should be used for this cleansing. It is also said, Muni, that twice the water, earth, leaves or grass used for cleaning after passing urine must be used for cleaning after defecation, and thrice the water, earth, leaves or grass used for cleaning after defecation must be used to clean one's private parts after sexual intercourse.

After all these, the hands must be washed with even more care. And you know, Narada, that, for cleaning any part of the body below the navel, it is always the left hand that is used, never the right which is used for every sacrifice, for writing, and for eating. Women, too, are to follow a similar procedure, until the last vestige of malodour vanishes from their bodies, after defecation or intercourse. Indeed, their genitals being inner, they must take even greater care than men must.

After his evacuation, the sadhaka must perform achamana, wash his mouth with water twelve times. Then he cleans his teeth with a twig, thick as his little finger, from a tree, either a karanja, an udumbara, a kadamba, lodha, champaka or a badari. The neem is best of all.

When the sadhaka breaks the twig from the tree, he prays to it, thus, 'In you, O Tree, the Moon dwells, as nourisher and protector. May Soma Deva give me strength, honour, wealth, health and fame, and the Brahmagyana.

After he does achamana again, the worshipper intones the blessed Gayatri, mother of all mantras. Then, he comes to the river or the well, and bathes to purify himself. The body is gross, and is always excreting its various filths from its nine dwaras, its apertures. These must be made clean before worship.

Next, the aspirant wears the tilakas on his forehead and his arms and chest and neck, and puts on his rudraksha, which are the most sacred beads on earth, the very tears of Siva. Narada, the wise say that he who wears 251 rudraksha beads on his body becomes like Mahadeva himself. With the rudraksha, the devotee chants the five-lettered Siva mantra, **Namah Sivayah**, and Pranava with it, the pristine **AUM**.

The 108 rudraksha beads worn on a sacred thread across the chest are considered equal to the 108 original Vedas, they signify the Complete Knowledge, and the sixteen digits of the Moon. The beads worn on the arms are the diks, the quarters, on the neck they are the Devi Saraswati and Agni Deva. He who wears rudraksha upon his person is purified of all his sins, whatever they may be; and, indeed, all that man does, says, or thinks become as if the Lord Rudra himself was doing them. That man is set free from the world of grief, from the cycle of birth and rebirth; he becomes a jivanmukta.

Why, it is only by wearing rudraksha that Brahma himself remains Brahma, and the greatest Munis are able to keep their vows!"

Narada wanted to know, "Sinless One, why is the rudraksha seed worshipped, why is it so very sacred?"

Narayana smiled, "His six-faced son Shanmukha asked the Lord Siva this same question once. And Siva said to Karttikeya, 'In the eldest days, there was an Asura, a truly invincible Demon called Tripura. He had put Brahma, Vishnu and the Devas to rout, and they asked me to rid the worlds of his dominion.

But I knew how powerful a Danava this Tripura was, and there was just one weapon in creation by which he could be killed. That immortal ayudha was the Aghora, my own weapon, beautiful and dreadful, which embodies the power of all the Devas in it. Yet it was hard beyond reckoning to summon the Aghora, and I sat in tapasya for a thousand years of the Gods.

I did not sleep, my son, neither did I shut my eyes, or even blink. At the end of a thousand years, suddenly, my staring eyes smarted, and from them some tears leaked onto the earth. From those teardrops, the rudraksha tree sprang, and it is indeed a most holy tree, which gives anyone who wears its seeds upon his body all that his heart desires.

Thirty-eight drops of water fell from my eyes, Shadanana, and there are thirty-eight kinds of rudraksha tree. From my Surya netra, my right eye that is the Sun, twelve tawny-hued rudraksha seeds fell. From my left eye, the Soma netra that is the Moon, sixteen white rudrakshas fell, and from my Agni netra, the third eye on my brow, ten black rudraksha tears fell.

Of these the white rudrakshas are for the Brahmanas, the tawny ones for the Kshatriyas, and the black seeds are for the Vaishyas and Sudras.'

The one-faced rudraksham is Siva himself, and this most powerful bead can make ashes of the most terrible sin, Brahmahatya, killing the most evolved being. The two-faced rudraksha is Mahadeva and the Devi, Ardhanarishwara, it ashes two kinds of sin. The three-faced one is the three Agnis, Dakshinagni, Garhapatya and Ahavaniya; the four-faced Brahma, the five Rudra, who is Siva dwelling in the world, upon the mountain. The six-faceted rudraksha is Shanmukha, the Lord Karttikeya, and is worn on the right hand. The seven-faced rudraksha is Ananga, the Lord Kama Deva, and the seven Matrikas, the Goddesses, the Sun and the Saptarishi, and sets one free of seven venal sins. The eight-faced Rudraksha is Brahmi, the eight Devis, the eight Vasus and the Devi Ganga.

The rudraksha seed with nine faces is Bhairava and Yama as well, and must be worn on the left hand. From it, the wearer shall have both bhoga and moksha. He will be freed even from the sin of committing a hundred abortions, and from the fear of death. The ten-faceted rudraksha is the amsa of Janardhana, the Devadeva, and the ten directions, and this bead wards away the malign influences of the planets, haunting by Pisachas, Vetalas, Brahmarakshasas, and Pannagas. Wearing the eleven-faced rudraksha is like being in the presence and having the grace of the eleven Rudras, the twelve like having the Adityas' blessing always.

The rudraksha of thirteen faces is rare indeed. Any man who finds one becomes himself like the Lord Karttikeya, and the eight mahasiddhis are his to command. He becomes an alchemist who can create gold and silver from base metals, why, from the very air.

The rudraksha of fourteen faces is, verily, Siva Himself. Even the Devas worship the man who wears the rudraksha of fourteen faces. Thus, Siva told his son Kumara about the rudraksha. The Lord said, 'If a man wears 108 rudraksha seeds upon his body, his every moment yields the fruits of an Aswamedha yagna, and blesses twenty-one generations of his family, and, at last, that man finds Sivaloka,' " Narayana Muni said to Narada.

Narada sat absorbed, there was much that he knew already about the holy rudraksha, but so much the peerless Rishi now told him, that he did not.

Narayana continued, "Siva went on, and his son Shadanana listened avidly, 'The face of any rudraksha is Brahma, its summit, or Meru, is Siva, and its base Mahavishnu. And, surely, the rudraksha bestows both bhoga and moksha on him who wears it. Why, it is said that even the grass that grows around a rudraksha tree, touching it, finds moksha! The Devas, the Rishis and the Adipurushas, who were the ancestors of the clans and races of men, all held the rudraksha in deep veneration.

The Rishi Jabala and his followers the Jabala sakhis say that even a dog that dies with a string of rudraksha tied around his neck receives moksha! Then what to say of men? No other rosary has even a sixteenth part of the power of the rudraksha. As the Vishnu is the best of the Puranas, the Ganga of rivers, Kashyapa among Munis, Ucchaisravas among horses, Mahadeva among the Gods, Bhagavati among the Devis, so is the rudraksha, the tears of Siva, among holy beads.

Just wearing the rudraksha yields the fruits of a thousand yagnas, of years of tapasya and absorbing the Vedas and Puranas, and bathing at the holiest tirthas. He who wears the rudraksha as he dies becomes Rudra himself, and is never born again,' said Siva to his son.

Skanda asked, 'Father, did a mule bear the rudraksha once in the Kikata country? Who gave it to him, and what happened?'

Siva said, smiling, 'Once, in the Vindhya mountains, a mule would bear a trader's load of rudraksha beads. One day, the mule fell down on the road and died. His gentle spirit came straight to me, and the mule became a Maheswara, three-eyed and with a trisula in his hands. My son, any creature at all that wears the rudraksha finds salvation for himself, be he a bhakta or not. No sin comes near him, ever, for he has my protection.

Why, the rudraksha bestows bhoga, too, Kumara. Listen to a story. In Kosala, once, there was a Brahmana called Girinatha, a pious, learned and wealthy Brahmana. He had a son called Gunanidhi, who grew into a youth of exceptional, irresistible beauty. So much so, that, his guru's wife fell in love with him. Gunanidhi and his teacher's wife Muktavali became secret lovers. And so strong was their passion that Gunanidhi tired of enjoying her just occasionally, and always furtively, and he poisoned his master.

The lovers said that the guru had died of snakebite, and now they lived together. People thought that the young acolyte stayed on with the widow out of a sense of duty to his dead master. But Gunanidhi's father and mother came to visit them, once, and caught them in the very act of love. Gunanidhi killed his parents, as well, lest the truth come out.

He inherited both his master's and his father's wealth, and lived a luxurious, wasteful, and debauched life. When the money he had quickly ran out, he began to steal from other Brahmanas' homes. He drank heavily by now and, soon, the truth about him and Muktavali was known, and they were banished from Kosala. Seething in anger, Gunanidhi began living in a jungle, and became a bandit. He would waylay travellers through the jungle, especially Brahmanas, whom he hated the most; he killed them and took everything they had on their persons.

Thus some time passed, and then, inevitably, death came for the sinner. Indeed, a thousand Yamadutas arrived to haul Gunanidhi off to the darkest hell. But then, a miracle—a thousand Sivaganas arrived there as well, to take the dead man to Sivaloka!

The Yamadutas were thunderstruck. They cried, "This man is the worst sinner on earth, there is no crime he has not committed. Why, he killed his own parents. Why have you come to take him to the highest heaven?"

The Sivaganas laughed, they replied, "The ways of our Lord are inscrutable, and his reasons are known only to himself. But, fifteen feet below where this man died there grows a most auspicious rudraksha tree.

Gunanidhi cannot but be saved. We mean to take him with us to Siva's realm, Yamadutas; all his sins have been forgiven him!"

And Gunanidhi was to become the lord of the mountain-city Alaka, the master of the Yakshas and Guhyakas, and the Lord of the nine treasures. He became Kubera, Lord of wealth!' said Siva smiling mysteriously," Narayana Muni said to Narada,' Vyasa said to the king."

EIGHTY

"'NARAYANA SAID, "WOULD YOU HEAR OF THE WAY OF BHUTA SHUDDHI, the purifying of the elements?"

"Indeed I would, my Lord."

"First, the sadhaka conceives of the kundalini, rising up through the susumna nadi in the spine, from the Muladhara to the Brahmarandhra chakra. He meditates upon the Hamsa mantra, and thinks of his soul, his jivatman, as being in union with the infinite Soul, the Brahmam. He conceives a square yantra from his legs to his knees, with a vajra, a thunderbolt, in it. This square becomes the earth, golden and signified by Lam, the bija mantra of Bhumi.

Then, from his knees to his navel he conceives a white half-moon, with two great lotuses at either point. This is the realm of water, and Vam is its bija mantra. Then, from his navel to his heart, he conceives a triangle with the sacred svastika at its three corners. This is the red realm of fire, and Ram is its bijamantra. Then, from the heart to the point between the eyebrows, is a realm of six bindus, smoky maroon, the realm of air, its bija mantra Yam. Finally, from the eyebrows to the crown of the head, the ethereal realm, the akasa mandala, perfectly clear and lucid, Hum its bijamantra.

Thus, the sadhaka imagines the earth, which came from water, dissolved in water; he thinks of water dissolved in fire, fire in air, air in its cause, the subtle ether. He thinks of akasa dissolved in ahamkara, ego, which is the source of the ether. And, of ahamkara vanishing into Mahatattva, the Great Principle, and Mahatattva absorbed in Prakriti, the eternal Female, and finally, Prakriti absorbed in the beginningless Brahmam, the Supreme Self.

Now, the sadhaka thinks of himself as only that Final Knowledge, the Brahmagyana. From that height, he then considers the paapa purusha, the 'sinful man', who is the size of a thumb, and dwells in the left side of his abdomen. This creature's head appears as the sin of Brahmahatya, killing a Brahmana, his arms appears as thieves, his heart as being drunk with wine, his genitals as ravishing his guru's wife, why, all his body as being Sin embodied: lust, greed, darkness and rage. The paapa purusha holds all sorts of macabre weapons, and is suffused with wrath, and his head bent low like a beast's, and his entire body horrendous.

The sadhaka, his consciousness lofty, draws a deep breath through his left nostril, chanting the Vam bijamantra of air, and fills his whole body with that prana. He holds that prana in kumbhaka, purifying the paapa purusha with a hurricane. Then, he chants Ram, the bijamantra of fire, and sets searing flames along the breath of air. He burns the paapa purusha to ashes, then exhales those ashes through his right nostril.

Then, he conceives of the ashes of the man embodying every sin, as rolled into a ball with the bija mantra of water, the pale nectar of the Moon. He conceives of this ball as being transformed into a golden egg by chanting Lam, the bhumi mantra, of the Earth. Now, he intones Hum, the bija mantra of akasa and imagines himself as being entirely pure, and his body clear as crystal. He creates himself again, limb by limb, from his precious thought and breath.

He creates afresh the elements, the bhutas from Brahma down, akasa, vayu, agni, jala and bhumi, and locates them in their places. Then, with the mantra Soham he fetches back the Jivatma from the Paramatman, and places the Jivatma in his heart. The Kundalini is also returned to the sacral chakra. When the jivatma, purified by its union with the Paramatman, has been returned to the heart's chamber, the sadhaka now meditates upon the Parashaki...

In a great boat on an interminable ocean, there is a crimson lotus. Upon this lotus the pranashakti sits. She has six hands, holding a trisula, arrows made of sugarcane, a noose, a goad, five other astras and a skull filled with blood. She has three eyes, and perfect breasts, her body is like the rising sun. May she grant us joy. As he conceives of and meditates upon the Parashakti, the sadhaka applies holy ash to his body.

Sirovrata is applying ashes to the forehead. It was by Sirovrata that Brahma and the Devas became the Gods they are. Why, the Trimurti have performed Sirovrata. The vrata of ashes is called Sirovrata in the first part of the Atharva Veda. Elsewhere, it is also called Sivavrata, Pasupatavrata, and by other names. The Sirovrata, marking the brow with holy ash, and making the intelligence firm, is a ritual that burns up sin, turns a whole forest of sins to ashes.

The Atharva Sruti says, Fire is ash, water is ash, earth and air are ash, akasa is ash and so is all the unmanifest universe. This mantra is repeated as the body is smeared with holy ash, during the three sandhya pujas. The Lord hides within the ash, so every Saiva wears them as a blessed adornment, and benediction. The best ashes are from a pure Virajagni. Ashes from other, common fires are lesser, in both their blessedness and their power. The time of the Viraja fire-sacrifice is on the full moon night of Chitra nakshatra.

The Brahmana marks his brow with the curved tripundra of holy bhasma. The first line of every Tripundra is Brahma, the second is Vishnu, and the third, highest line is Mahadeva. The forehead, where the bhasma is laid is the seat of Isvara. Brahma dwells in the head, the ears are where the Aswini Devas sit, and Ganesha in the neck. Only Brahmans must use the tripundra with a mantra, the other castes and the uninitiated wear bhasma on their foreheads, not on all the body, and they do so without a mantra.

The Rishis who smear themselves from head to toe with the sacred ash of burnt cowdung that is caught before it falls to the ground, from the purest kapila cows, call this smearing the agni-snana, the bath of fire! They recite a different mantra for every part of the body that is smeared. Those who wear rudraksha and tripundra with perfection, attain moksha. For, the bhasma they wear burns away their sins of every life, and, at last, makes them entirely pure. Desire leaves them like a spirit does a corpse, and their lives shine forth with knowledge and bliss.

All the Devas and Devis anoint themselves with bhasma every day, so also the Yakshas, Gandharvas, Rakshasas, Siddhas, Vidyadharas and Rishis. Tripundra belongs to Siva, and the man who would seduce the Devi Mukti must have the jewel of the Siva lingam, and the mantra **AUM Namah Sivayah**! Why, he who uses bhasma inherits the blessing of studying the Vedas, the Srutis and Puranas, and performing great yagnas, aswamedhas and rajasuyas, of visiting the holiest tirthas. It is even said that he who wears the Tripundra has Bhola Natha under control, be he a Brahmana or a Chandala!

O Narada, there is no mantra higher than the Siva mantra, **AUM Namah Sivayah**, there is no God higher than Mahadeva Siva, there is no worship greater than the worship of Siva, and there is no tirtha greater than Siva's bhasma. For, this bhasma is no common thing, O Muni, it is truly the retas, the semen, of Agni, and has the nature of the Lord Rudra himself. He who wears the sacred bhasma even has what the Lord Brahma wrote on his head and the palms of his hands erased, because, when Siva Himself first put this bhasma on, he chanted the Sadyo Jata, the five primeval mantras, and blessed the holy bhasma forever. There is no ablution holier than the bath of ashes, for the very bonds of nature, of pleasure and pain, are burnt away by the bhasma-snana. Bathing in water cleans the body; bathing in ashes purifies the very spirit.

The yati who bathes in ashes is called a bhasmanishta, and an atmatnishta, and Bhutas, Pretas, Pisachas, and Rakshasas and dread diseases of every kind flee at the very approach of such a man. Because sacred ashes reveal the Brahmagyana, they are called bhasita, because they burn sins away, they are called bhasma, because bhasma strengthens the eight subtle siddhis of anima, mahima, and the others, it is called vibhuti, and because it protects the man who wears it, it is called raksha.

So, let the wise man be far keener to gather the ashes born of agni, than he is to gather gold and jewels. You know the famous story of how the great Saiva Rishi Durvasa peered down into the dreadful hell, Kumbhipaka, when he heard the piteous groaning of the sinners who were being tormented there by Yamaraja's horrible servants. Rishi Durvasa happened to be wearing Tripundra and bhasma upon his person, and, at once, O Narada, that most terrible Naraka was transformed into the sweetest place, and, its sinners' sins all made ashes, they began to live in ecstasies that exceeded the delights of Devaloka! All the Gods came there, in wonder. Then Siva and Parvati arrived there to explain the mystery. Siva said, laughing, 'A particle of the bhasma that Durvasa wore on his brow was blown into the city of sinners. That shred of ash set the sinners free.'

A linga and yoni were installed in that once infernal city, and it was transformed from a Naraka into a blessed tirtha. Finally, the sinners rose to Kailasa in a splendid vimana, and dwell there still with the Lord Siva, and even today they are known as Bhadras. Since that day, the Devas are careful that no Saiva goes anywhere near any Naraka, or even peers into one.

And, you know Muni that, even as Siva's bhaktas wear the tripundra horizontally across their brows, the Vaishnavas wear Urdhpundra vertically on theirs," said the immortal Rishi Narayana to an avid Narada, upon the blessed mountain.

Narada was quiet for a while, absorbing all he had heard, then he asked, "Munivara, Lord, tell me now about Sandhyopasana, and how the Devi Gayatri is worshipped during the three twilights of the day." ' Vyasa told the king," the great Suta says to the Rishis of the six clans in the Naimisa vana, which, once, Brahma himself sanctified for Pauranik revelations.

EIGHTY-ONE

"'NARAYANA SAID, "YES, THE DEVI GAYATRI IS THE DEVI OF THE THREE sandhyas of the day—of morning, noon, and dusk—and of the dvijas, the twice born. The morning sandhya is observed before the sun rises, when the stars are still in the sky. The noon sandhya is observed when the sun is at his zenith, and as the sun sinks into the horizon, the third, evening sandhya. The Brahmanas are said to be the root of sandhya vandanam, the Vedas are its branches, and dharma its leaves. Sandhya may be performed in one's home, on the banks of a river or in a temple, especially the Devi's, for it is her very worship. Why, Brahma and the Devas worship the Devi Gayatri, who is the mother of the Vedas.

Pranayama and achamana are performed, and the Gayatri is recited, ***AUM Bhuur Bhuvah Svah/Tat Savitur Varenyam/Bhargo Devasyah Dhimahi/Dhiyo Yo Nah Prachodayaat***...The Surya mantra is repeated, and the paapa purusha dwelling in the belly fetched out with a mantra through the nostril, into the holy water in cupped palms. Without looking at the water, the sadhaka throws it away onto a stone to his left. Arghya is offered to the Sun, and, while offering it during the morning sandhya, the sadhaka bends himself a little, at noon, he stands upright, and in the evening, he sits.

Listen, Muni, to why this arghya is offered to the Sun. There are, O Narada, thirty crores of Rakshasas called the Mandehas, who range the Sun's path, always. They are powerful demons, and assuming horrible shapes, they are forever trying to devour Surya Deva, the splendent one. The water offered to Surya as arghya by the Rishis and bhaktas is transformed into subtle thunderbolts that strike off the heads of the monstrous forms the demons assume in the sky, their mouths yawning like ravines.

While performing the sandhya upasana, the sadhaka chants the sandhya mantras, saying to himself, I am the Sun, I am the Atman, and I am the light of the Atman and of the Sun. I am Siva, crystalline and lucid. O Devi Gayatri, who are of Brahma's nature, I implore you, come and fill my heart with your presence. And now perform the nyasa, to be free of the three curses that Gayatri Devi incurred, from Brahma, from Viswamitra and from Vasishta. Before saying the nyasa, the sadhaka remembers the highest Self, the immortal Person who dwells in the lotus of the heart, who is the Truth, who is the Universe, and who can never be known by words, but only with bhakti. Then, perform the amganyasa.

First, say **AUM**, then touch the two feet, chanting **AUM Bhuh padabhyam namaha**. Touch the knees, chanting **AUM Bhuva janubhyam namaha**. Touch the hips saying **AUM Svah katibhyam namaha**. Touch the navel intoning **AUM Maharnabhyai namah**. Touch the heart saying **AUM Janah hridayahah namaha**. Touch the throat saying **AUM Tapah kanthaya namaha**. Touch the brow, saying **AUM Satyam lalatayah namaha.**

Then, perform the Vyarhiti nyasa. Then, the karamganyasa, for the hands, digit by digit, and so on every nyasa, for every limb, for every organ, for every member of the body. Though, some japakas do not adhere to the nyasa, and indeed disapprove of them.

Next, the japaka sits in dhyana of the Devi Gayatri, whose form is like a java flower in full bloom. She sits on a hamsa, a swan, in a scarlet lotus. She, too, is red, and wears a crimson garland around herself. She has four faces, and in her four hands, she holds a wreath of flowers, a yagna ladle, a rosary of beads and a kamandalu. She is resplendent with every manner of blazing ornament.

The Rig Veda first came from the virgin Devi Gayatri. She has eight bellies, which are the eight directions of the firmament. She has seven sirsas, her subtle heads, all of them aspects of knowledge—vyakarana, siksha, kalpa, nirukta, jyotisha, ithihasa, purana and upanishad. Her mouth is Agni, her sikha is Rudra, her gotra is Smakhayyana, her heart Vishnu, and Brahma her kavacha. Conceiving of the Devi Gayatri in the midst of the Sun during sandhyopasana, the bhakta forms the auspicious and hermetic mudras with his fingers, to invoke the Devi, to please her, to worship her: Samputa, Vitata, Vistrita, Dvimukha, Trimukha,

Chaturmukha, Panchamukha, Sanmukha, Saptamukha, Adhomukha, Vyapaka, Anjali, Sakata, Yamapasa, Vilamba, Mustika, Matsya, Kurma, Varaha, Simhakranta, Mahakranta, Mudgara and Pallava. The Rishi for the morning sandhya is Viswamitra, Savita is the Devata.

Then he performs the Gayatri japam. Yet, the Gayatri and the method of chanting it must preferably be learnt from a guru, else it can have adverse effects, for it is indeed an all-powerful mantra. Indeed, the morning sandhya is the Gayatri, and the Gayatri the sandhya, there is no difference between the two. Both are complex, and must be acquired from a true master, an evolved acharya. Most of all, the sandhyopasana and the Gayatri japa must be done with love, and with bhakti, which transcends everything else.

The tarpana for the morning sandhya is as follows:

AUM Bhuh Rigveda Purusham tarpayami; AUM Bhuvah Yajurveda Purusham tarpayami; AUM Svah Samaveda Purusham tarpayami; AUM Mahah Atharvaveda Purusham tarpayami; AUM Janah Ithihasapurana Purusham tarpayami; AUM Tapah Sarvagama Purusham tarpayami; AUM Satyam Satyaloka Purusham tarpayami; AUM Bhuh Bhurloka Purusham tarpayami; AUM Bhuvah Bhuvoloka Purusham tarpayami; AUM Svah Svarloka Purusham tarpayami; AUM Bhuvo Rekhapadim Gayatrim tarpayami; AUM Bhuvo Vitiyapadam Gayatrim tarpayami; AUM Svastripadam Gayatrim tarpayami; AUM Bhurbhuvah Svaschatuspadam Gayatrim tarpayami."

Narada, the Vishnu-bhakta, asked, "Tell me, holy one, is the worship of the Devi Bhagavati as efficacious as they say?"

Narayana said, smiling, "The mother loves her child, naturally. And we are all the Devi's children, and she is the original mother, from whom motherhood itself has come. The Devi Gayatri is called Savitri during the second sandhya, at midday. She is fair, three-eyed. She holds a rosary in one of four hands, a trisula in another, and with the other two makes mudras that dispel her bhaktas' fear, and grant them boons.

She recites the Yajur Veda. She rides a bull, for she is the Rudra Shakti, of tamo guna, and dwells in Brahmaloka. She rides the path of the Sun, every day. She is the beginningless Mayadevi, and she is worshipped in the orb of the meridian Sun.

The tarpana with which Savitri Devi is appeased is: **AUM Bhuvah Purusham tarpayami namo namah; AUM Yajurvedam tarpayami namo**

namha; AUM Mandalam tarpayami namo namah; AUM Hiranyagarbham tarpayami namoh namah; AUM Anataratmanam tarpayami namo namah; AUM Savitrim tarpayami namoh namah; AUM Devamataram tarpayami namo namah; AUM Samkritim tarpayami namo namah; AUM Yuvatim sandhyam tarpayami namo namah; AUM Rudranim tarpayami namo namah; AUM Nimrijam tarpayami namo namah; AUM bhurbhuvah Svah Purusham tarpayami namo namah.

For the evening sandhya, Gayatri Devi is called Saraswati. She is old, black, wearing the most ordinary yellow raiment. In her four hands, she holds the sankha, chakra, gada, and padma. She wears anklets, tinkling sweetly whenever she moves, around her waist she wears a golden thread. She sits on Garuda, and is crowned with a priceless coronet. At her throat, she wears a necklace of stars. Her brow shines with the tatamka, and her nature is of eternal knowledge and bliss. The Devi Saraswati intones the Sama Veda. She is worshipped in the heart of the vermilion setting Sun.

Vasishta is the Rishi of the evening tarpana, Vishnu as Saraswati is the Devata. The main tarpana is as follows: **AUM Svah Purusham tarpayami; AUM Samavedam tarpayami; AUM Suryamandalam tarpayami; AUM Hiranyagarbham tarpayami; AUM Paramatmanan tarpayami; AUM Saraswatim tarpayami; AUM Devamataram tarpayami; AUM Samkritim tarpayami; AUM Vriddham sandhyam tarpayami; AUM Vishnurupinim Ushasim tarpayami; AUM Nirmrijim tarpayami; AUM Sarvasiddhikarinim tarpayami; AUM Sarvamantra dipatikam tarpayami; AUM Bhurbhuvah Svah Purusham tarpayami.**

When the sins of the three sandhyas have been destroyed by sandhyopasana, Muni, moksha comes to the sadhaka, for the Devi Bhagavati makes his worship fruitful.

Auspicious places, Narada, for performing Gayatri purascharanam, chanting the name of a God and making burnt offerings after reciting the Gayatri, are on mountain-tops, the banks of rivers, the roots of bel trees, beside clear tanks, in temples, near cows, beneath aswattha trees, in open gardens, in tulasi groves, in the punya kshetras and tirthas, in the presence of one's guru, or, indeed wherever the mind feels delight and exaltation.

There are yagnas, O Narada, like the Devayagna, the Brahmayagna, the Bhutayagna, the Pitryagna and the Manusyayagna. You know how intricate they are, and how exacting. Then, there are the great vratas, even harder, and perhaps hardly suited to the Kali yuga. The Parjapatya Krichchra, the Santapana, the Paraka Krichchra and the Chandrayana. There are more, but they are esoteric and secret, and a man must be a great master of himself before he can even think of attempting them."

"If they are indeed so hard, O Guru, what can an ordinary man do to nurture his soul?"

"Chanting the Gayatri mantra sets a man free. The Gayatri is the mother of all mantras, of all worship. He who worships the Devi Bhagavati with the twenty-four syllables of the Gayatri mantra, which is Satchitananda, shall certainly find every joy, and moksha for himself."

"Blessed Muni, I have heard about the Rishis, the Chchandas and the Devatas of the twenty-four syllables of the Gayatri. Can you name them for me, Mahamuni?"

Narayana said, "The Rishis, in their order, are Vamadeva, Atri, Vasishta, Sukra, Kanva, Parasara, the fiery Viswamitra, Kapila, Saunaka, Yagnavalkya, Bharadvaja, the ascetic Jamadagni, Gautama, Mudgala, Vyasa, Lomasa, Agastya, Kaushika, Vatsya, Pulastya, Manduka, Durvasa the great, you Narada, and Kashyapa."

Narada asked, "And the Chchandas?"

"Gayatri, Ushnika, Anushtup, Brihati, Pankti, Trishnup, Jagati, Ati Jagati, Sakkari, Ati Sakkari, Dhriti, Ati Dhriti, Virata, Prastarapankti, Kriti, Prakriti, Akriti, Vikriti, Samkriti, Aksharapantki, Bhuh, Bhuvah, Svah and Jyotishmati."

"And the Devatas, Muni?"

"In their proper order, Agni, Prajapati, Soma, Ishana, Savita, Aditya, Brihaspati, Maitravaruna, Bhagadeva, Aryaman, Ganesha, Tvashtra, Pusa, Indragni, Vayu Vamadeva, Maitravaruni, Vishawadeva, Matrika, Vishnu, Vasu, Rudradeva, Kubera, and finally the Aswini Kumaras. But, Narada, it may be that the Devatas for the Gayatri named in the Gayatri Brahma kalpa differ from those I have named."

"There are, I have heard, twenty-four Shaktis also for each sacred syllable of the Mother of mantras."

"Vama Devi, Priya, Satya, Viswa, Bhadravilasini, Prabhavati, Jaya, Santha, Kanta, Durga, Saraswati, Vidruma, Visalesha, Vyapini, Vimala, Tamopaharini, Sukshma, Visawayoni, Jaya, Vasaa, Padmalaya, Parashobha, Bhadra, Tripada.

There are twenty-four colours too, that belong with the twenty-four syllables of the Gayatri: the hue of the champaka and atasi flowers, of vidruma, of crystal, of the lotus, of the rising sun, of the conchshell, of the kunda flower, of prabala and lotus leaves, of padmaraga, of Indranilamani, of pearls, of saffron, of black kohl for the eye, red, of the vaidurya mani, of kshaudra, honey, of turmeric, of milk, of the rays of the sun, of the tail of the suka bird, of Satarupa, of ketaki, of the mallika flower, of the karavira.

And each syllable has its own tattva—earth, water, fire, air, ether, smell, taste, form, sound, touch, linga, mula, legs, hands, speech, prana, tongue, eyes, skin, ears, pana, apana, vyana, samana."

Narada asked, "Tell, me, Muni, about the Gayatri kavacha, which is said to protect a man from every evil."

"He who can cover himself perfectly with the Gayatri kavacha shall have moksha, he shall have his body dissolved in the Devi's! Brahma, Vishnu and Maheswara are the Rishis of the kavacha, the Rik, Yajus, Sama and Atharva Vedas are the Chchandas, the Parama Kalaa Gayatri of Brahma's nature is the Devata, Tat of the Gayatri mantra is the Bija, Bharga is the Shakti, Diya is the Kilaka, and the end for which a bhakta dons this kavacha is moksha!"

"What does the kavacha say, immaculate master?"

"You first conceive the Devi Gayatri with her dhyanam. She appears, five-faced, the frontal face white and the others pearly, of the hue of vidruma, gold and nilakantamani. Each face has three eyes, and she wears a crown of ineffable jewels on her head, and the digit of the Moon scintillates there. Her body is made of the twenty-four great and precious tattvas. She has ten hands, in which she holds two lotuses, a shell, a disk, a rope and a skull, a noose and a goad, and with two she makes the mudras of removing fear and granting boons.

Having conceived the Devi thus, the sadhaka intones the Gayatri kavacha—May the Devi Gayatri protect my front, Savitri my right, Sandhya my back and the Devi Saraswati my left. Let my Mother Parvati protect my quarters, Jalasayini my south-east, Yatudhana Bhayankari my south-west, Pavamanvilasini my north-west, Rudrarupini Rudrani my north-east, Brahmani the sky above me, and Vaishnavi my patalas. May the 'Tat' in the Gayatri watch over my legs, 'Savituh' my knees, 'Varenyam' my loins, 'Bhargah' my navel, 'Devasya' my heart, 'Dhimahi' my neck, 'Dhiyah' my eyes, 'Yah' my forehead, and 'Prachodayat' the tuft on the crown of my head.

The Devi Gayatri's kavacha keeps a million evils and demons away, why, it raises anyone who dons it to being like Brahma himself!"

Narada asked now, "Devadeva, O Trikalagyani, tell about the highest sadhana of all, tell about the secret Gayatri Hridaya, the essence of Gayatri, the Devi's very heart."

Narayana said, "You will find all you want to know about the Gayatri Hridaya in the Atharva Veda, where it is dealt with plainly. But to worship with the Gayatri Hridaya, a man must first conceive of the Devi Gayatri's Viratarupa, her cosmic form, with all the Devas contained within her. In so much as Pinda and Brahmanda are one, he must think of himself as being the Devi Gayatri. No man is an adhikari, who has not made himself like a Deva. So, this he must do.

And the man who knows the Gayatri Hridaya can make himself like all the Devas. The Rishis of the Gayatri Hridaya is Narayana, the Chchanda is Gayatri, and Sri Parameswari is the Devata. The sadhaka performs the nyasa, sits in a sequestered place, and, with his every sense and his breath restrained, fixes his heart on the Devi.

He meditates on the Devata Dayu upon his head, the Aswins on his teeth, the Sandhyas of morning and evening on his lips, Agni in his mouth, Saraswati on his tongue, Brihaspati on his neck, the eight Vasus on his breast, the Vayus on his arms, the Paryanya Deva in his heart, Akasa on his belly, Antariksha on his navel, Indra and Agni, again, on his loins, Prajapati on his hip joints, Kailasa and Malaya on his thighs, the Viswedevas on his knees, Viswamitra on his shanks, Uttarayana and Dakshinayana on his anus, the Pitrs on the backs of his thighs, Bhumi on his feet, Vapaspari on his fingers and toes, the Rishis on his body hair, the muhurtas upon his nails, the grahas in his bones, the ritus, the seasons, as his flesh and blood, the samvatsaras the moment, the Sun and the Moon the day and night.

Having conceived all this on his own person, he should say, 'I seek refuge in the Devi Gayatri, the thousand-eyed, the Mother.'

And then, chant, 'I prostrate myself before Tat Savitur Varenyam, to the rising Sun in the east, to Aditya, Lord of the morning, and to the Devi Gayatri who rides the Morning Sun! I prostrate myself to the All.'

The Gayatri Hridaya is a great destroyer of sins, it bestows the grace of visiting the holiest tirthas of the earth."

Narada asked, "Tell me the stava, the stotra of the Devi Gayatri."

"It says that she is the World-Mother! She favours those who worship her. She is the primal power, omnipresent, omnipotent, and infinite. O Sri Sandhya, I bow to thee! You are Gayatri, Savitri and Saraswati. You are

Brahmi, Vaishnavi and Raudri. You are red, white and black. O Bhagavati! The Rishis meditate upon you as being young in the morning, mature at noon, and old in the twilight.

The tapasvins see you riding the Hamsa as Brahmani, riding on Garuda as Saraswati, and the Vrishabha as Savitri. You have sprung from the eyes and hands, from the sweat and tears of Siva and Sivaa. You are the mother of ecstasy, O Durga, who are called Varenya, Varada, Varishta, Vara varnini, Garishta, Varahaa, Vararohaa, Nilaganga, Sandhya, and Bhoga Mokshada. You are Bhagirathi in the world and Bhogavati in Patala, and the Mandakini, streaming stars as the Milky Way in Swarga.

You are all-enduring Prithvi Devi in this realm, Bhurloka, Vayu Shakti in the middle realm, Bhuvarloka, and the sea of tejas, of energy, on high, in Svarloka. In Maharloka, you are great Siddhi Devi, Jana in Janarloka, Tapasvina in Taparloka, Satya in Satyaloka, Kamala in Vishnuloka, Gayatri in Brahmaloka, and Gauri in Rudraloka. You are Prakriti, the Parashakti, the Paramashakti, and the Trishakti. You are Ganga, Yamuna, Vipasa, Saraswati, Sarayu, Devika, Sindhu, Narmada, Iravati, Godavari, Satadru, Kaveri, Kaushiki, Chandrabhaga, Vitasta, Gandaki, Tapini, Karatoya, Gomati, and Vetravati.

You are the Ida, Pingala and Susumna nadi. You are Gandhari, Hastajihva, Pusa, Apusa, Alambusa, Kuhu, Sankhini, Pranavahini, and all the subtle channels in the body. You are the vital power in the Lotus of the heart. You are Svapnanayikaa in the throat, Sadadharaa upon the palate, and the Bindumalini Shakti between the eyebrows.

You are Kundalini and Muladharaa, Vyapini at the hair-roots. You are Madhyasanaa on the crown of the head, and Manonmani in the Brahmarandhra. Devi, what need is there to say all this, when you are the very universe? You are the Beginning, the Middle and the End of all things, O Sri Sandhya Devi! I bow to You!

This, Muni, is the Gayatri Stotra, which destroys every vestige of sin. He who chants this stotra has the blessings of all the tirthas, of all tapasya, he gains the joys of artha, kama, and finally he finds moksha as well. Why, even the one who but listens to the Gayatri-stotra with devotion is liberated," said Narayana Muni in the forest to Narada,' said Vyasa."

EIGHTY-TWO

"VYASA SAID, 'NARADA NOW ASKED THE IMMACULATE NARAYANA, "GURU, how can one be free of death?"

Narayana replied, "By chanting the thousand and eight names of the Devi Gayatri, in a state of purity."

"Tell me those names, Muni."

"She is Achintya Lakshanaa, Avyaktaa, Arthamatrimaheswari, Amritarnavamadhasthaa, Ajitaa, Aparijitaa, Animadigunadharaa, Arkamandalasamsthithaa, Ajaraa, Ajaa, Aparaa, Adharmaa, Akshasutradharaa, Adharaa, Akaradikshakarantaa, Arishadvargabhedini, Anjandripratikasaa, Anjanadrinivasini, Aditi, Ajapaa, Avidyaa, Aravindanibhekshanaa, Antarvahihsthithaa, Avidyadhvamsini, Antaratmikaa.

She is Ajamukhavasaa, Aravindanibhananaa, Ardhamatraa, Arthadanajnaa, Arindmandalamrdini, Asuraghni, Amavasyaa, Alakasinghini, and Antyajarchitaa. All these are her names that begin with 'a'.

Now, those that begin with 'aa'—Aadi Lakshmi, Aadi Shakti, Aakriti, Aayatananaa, Aadityapadaricharaa, Aadityaparisevitaa, Aacharyaa, Aavartanaa, Aacharaa, Aadimuritnivasini, Aagneyi, Aamai, Aadyaa, Aaradhyaa, Aasanathithaa, Aadharanilayaa, Aadharaa, Aakasanthanivasini, Aadiyaksharaasamyktaa, Aantarksharupini, Aadityamandalagataa, Aantaradhvantanasini.

Those that begin with 'i'—Indiraa, Ishtadaa, Ishtaa, Indivaranivekshanaa, Iravati, Indrapadaa, Indrani, Indrarupini, Ikshukodandasamyuktaa, Ishusandhanakarini, Indranilasamakaraa, Idapingalarupini, Indrakshi, Iswari, Ihatrayavivarjitaa.

She is Uma, Usha, Udunibhaa, Urvarukaphalananaa, Uduprabhaa, Udumati, Udupaa, Udumadhyagaa, Urdhaa, Urdhakesi, Urdhadhogatibhedini, Urdhavahupriyaa, and Urmimalavagranthadayini. She is Ritaa, Rishi, Ritumati, Rishidevanamskritaa, Rigvedaa, Rinahatri, Rishimandalacharini, Riddhidaa, Rijumargasthaa, Rijadharmaa, Rijupradaa, Rigvedanilayaa, and Rijvi.

She is Luptadharmapravartini, Lutarivarasambhutaa, Lutadivishaharini.

Ekakasharaa, Ekamatraa, Ekaa, Ekakanishthithaa, Aindri, Airavatarudhaa, Aihikamushmikapradaa, Omkaraa, Osadhi, Otaa, Otaprotavasini, Aurbbaa, Aushadhasampannaa, Aupasanaphalapradaa, Aundamadhyashtithaa, Aukaramanurupini. These are her names that begin with the vowels of the sacred alphabet. Now, the consonants.

She, the Mother Gayatri, is Katyayani, Kalaratri, Kamakshi, Kamasundari, Kamalaa, Kamini, Kantaa, Kamadaa, Kalakanthini, Karikaa, Kumbha Sthanabharaa, Karavira Suvasini, Kalyani, Kundalavati, Kurukshetranivasini, Kuruvindaa, Kudalkaraa, Kundali, and Kumudalayaa.

And Kaalajibhaa, Karalasyaa, Kalikaa, Kalarupini, Kamaniyagunaa, Kanti, Kaaladharaa, Kumudvati, Kausiki, Kamalakaraa, Kamacharaprabhanjini, Kaumari, Karunapangi, Kakubantaa, Karipriyaa, Kesari, Kesavanutaa, Kadamba kusumapriyaa, Kalindi, Kalikaa, Kanchi, Kalasodhbhavasamstutaa, Kamamataa, Kratumati, Kamarupaa, Kripavati, Kumari, Kunda Nilayaa, Kirati, Kiravahanaa, Kaikeyi, Kiokilalapaa, Ketaki Kusumapriyaa, Kamandaludharaa, Kali, Karmanirmulakarini, Kalahamsagati, Kakshaa, Kiritaa, Kautukamangalaa, Kasturitilakaa, Kamraa, Karindra Gamanaa, Kuhu, Karpuralepanaa, Krishnaa, Kapilaa, Kuharsarayaa, Kutasthaa, Kudhraa, Kuksishta Akhilavisthapaa.

Khadgaa, Khetadaraa, Kharbbaa, Khechari, Khagavahanaa, Khattangadharini, Khyataa, Khagarajo Paristhithaa, Khalagni, Khanditarajaa, Khadakshyana Pradaynini, Khandendu Tilakaa.

Ganga, Ganesha Guhapujitaa, Gayatri, Gomati, Gita, Gandharaa, Ganalolupaa, Gautami, Gamini, Gadhaa, Gandharvapsara Sevitaa, Govinda Charana Krantaa, Gunatreya Vibhavitaa, Gandharvi, Gahvari, Gotraa, Girisaa, Gahanaa, Gami, Guhavasaa, Gunavati, Guhyaa, Goptavyaa, Gunadayini, Girijaa, Guhyamatangi, Garudadhvaja Vallabhaa, Garvapaharini, Godaa, Gokulasthaa, Gadadharaa, Gokarna Nilaya Saktaa, Guhayamandalavartini.

Gharmadaa, Ghanadaa, Ghantaa, Ghora Danava Marddini, Ghrini Mantra Mayi, Ghoshaa, Ghanasampatadayini, Ghantaranarimandalaa, Ghurnaa, Ghritachi, Ghanavegini, Gyanadhatu Mayi.

Charchaa, Charchitaa, Charuhasini, Chatulaa, Chandika, Chitra, Chitramalyavi Bhishitaa, Chaturbhujaa, Charu Dantaa, Charuri, Charitapradaa, Chulikaa, Chitravasrantaa, Chandramah Karna Kundalaa, Chandrahasaa, Charudatri, Chakori, Chandrahasini, Chandrika, Chandrahatri, Chauri, Charu Chandana Liptangi, Chancha Chamara Bijitaa, Charumadhyaa, Chakrabahukaa, Chandramandala Madhyasthaa, Chandramandala Darpanaa, Chandravati, Chandramaa, Chandanapriyaa, Chodayitri, Chiraprajnaa, Chetakaa, Charuhetuki.

Chhatrayataa, Chhatradharaa, Chhayaa, Chhandhahparichhadaa, Chhayathantaa, Chhidrapadrava Bhedini, Chheda, Chhatreswari, Chhinnaa, Chhurikaa, Chhelanpriyaa.

Janani, Jaganmayi, Jahnavi, Jatilaa, Jatri, Jetri, Jaramarana Varjitaa, Jambudvipavati, Jvalaa, Jayanti, Jalasalini, Jitendriyaa, Jitakrodhaa, Jitamitraa, Jagatpriyaa, Jatarupamayi, Jihvaa, Janaki, Jagati, Jaraa, Jayaa, Janitri, Jahnutanayaa, Jagatrayahitaisini, Jvalamuli, Japavati, Jvaraghni, Jaladaa, Jyesthaa, Jyaghosha Sphota Dinmukhi, Jambhini, Jrimbhanaa, Jrumbhaa, Jvalanmanikya Kundalaa.

Jhinjhikaa, Jhananirghosaa, Jhanjha Maruta Veghini, Jhallakivadya Kusalaa. Nrupaa, Nbhujaa. Tanka Bhedini, Tanka Bhanasamyuktaa, Tankini, Tankigana Kritaghoshaa, Tankaniya Mahoraasaa, Tankara Karini, Tha Tha Shavdaninadini.

Damari, Dakini, Dimbhaa, Dundamaraikanirjitaa, Damaritantra Margasthaa, Danda Damarunadini, Dindiravasahaa, Dimbhalasat Kridhaparayanaa.

Dhundi Vighnesha Janani, Dhakka Hastaa, Dhilivraja, Nityajananaa, Nirupamaa, Nirgunaa, Narmadaa.

Trigunaa, Tripada, Tantri, Tulasi, Tarunaa, Taru, Trivikrama Pada Krantaa, Turiyapadagamini, Tarunaditya Samkasaa, Tamasi, Tuhinaa, Turaa, Trikala Jnana Sampannaa, Trivali, Trilochanaa, Trishakti, Tripuraa, Tungaa, Turanga Vadanaa, Timingilagilaa, Tibraa, Trisrotaa, Tamasadini, Tantra Mantra Visesagynaa, Tanimadhyaa, Trivistapaa, Trisandhyaa, Trishtani, Tosasanthaa, Talapratapini, Tatankini, Tusarabhaa, Tuhinachala Vasini, Tantujala Samayuktaa, Tarahara Valipriyaa, Tilahomapriyaa, Tirthaa, Tamala Kusuma Kriti, Tarakaa, Triyutaa, Tanvi, Trisam Kuparivaritaa, Talodari, Tirobhasaa, Tatamka Priyavadini, Trijataa, Tittiri, Trishnaa, Tribidhaa, Taruna Kriti, Tanta Kanchanasamkasaa, Tapta Kanchana Bhushanaa, Traiyambakaa, Trivargaa, Trikalagyanadayini, Tarpanaa, Triptidaa, Triptaa, Tamasi,

Tumvarustutaa, Taraksyasthaa, Trigunakaraa, Tribhangi, Tanuvallari, Thatkari, Tharavaa, Thantaa.

Dohini, Dinavatsalaa, Danavanta Kari, Durga, Durgasura Nivahrini, Devariti, Divaratri, Draupadi, Dundabhisvanaa, Devayani, Duravasaa, Daridriya Bhedini, Divaa, Damodarapriyaa, Diptaa, Digvasaa, Digvimohini, Danda Karanyanilayaa, Dandini, Devapujitaa, Devavandyaa, Divisalaa, Dvesini, Danavakriti, Dinanathastuthaa, Dikshaa, Daivadisvarupini, Dhatri, Dhanurdharaa.

Dhenur Dharini, Dharmacharini, Dhurndharaa, Dharadharaa, Dhanadaa, Dhanya Dohini, Dharmasilaa, Dhyanadhyakshaa, Dhanurveda Visaradaa, Dhriti, Dhanyaa, Dhritapadaa, Dharmarajapriyaa, Dhruvaa, Dhumavati, Dhumakesi, Dharmashastra Prakasini.

Nandaa, Nandapriyaa, Nidraa, Nrinutaa, Nandanatmikaa, Narmadaa, Nalini, Nilaa, Nilakantha Samsrayaa, Narayanapriyaa, Nityaa, Nirmalaa, Nirgunaa, Nidhi, Niradharaa, Nirupamaa, Nityasuddhaa, Niranjanaa, Nadabindu Kalatiti, Nadabindu Kalatmikaa, Narasimhini, Nagadharaa, Nripanaga Vibhushitaa, Naraka Klesanasini, Narayana Padodbhavaa, Niravadyaa, Nirakaraa, Naradapriyakarini, Nanajyoti, Nidhidaa, Nirmalaatmikaa, Navasutradharaa, Niti, Nirupa Drava Karini, Nandajaa, Navaratnadhyaa, Naimisaranya Vasini, Navanitapriyaa, Nari, Nila Jimuta Nisvanaa, Nimesini, Nadirupaa, Nilagrivaa, Nisisvari, Namavali, Nisumbhagini, Nagaloka Nivasini, Navajambhu Nadaprakhyaa, Nagaloka Niveditaa, Nupura Krantacharanaa, Narachitta Pramodini, Nimagna Rakta Nayanaa, Nirghata Sama Nishvanaa, Nandanodya Nilayaa, Nirvyuhoparicharini.

Parvati, Paramodaraa, Parabrahmatmikaa, Paraa, Panchakosavinirmuktaa, Panchapataka Nasini, Parachitta Vidhanajnaa, Panchikaa, Pancharupini, Purnimaa, Parama Priti, Parateja Prakasini, Purani. Paurusi, Punya, Pundari Kanibhekshana, Patala Talanirmagna, Pritaa, Pritivivardhini, Pavani, Pada Sahitaa, Pesalaa, Pavanasini, Prajapati, Parisrantaa, Parvatasthana Mandalaa, Padmapriyaa, Padmasamsthaa, Padmakshi, Padmasambhavaa, Padmapatraa, Padmapadaa, Padmini, Priyabhashini, Pasupaasa Vinirmuktaa, Purandhri, Puravasini, Pushkalaa, Purushaa, Parbbaa, Parijata Kusumapriyaa, Pativrataa, Pavitrangi, Pushpabhasa Parayanaa, Prajnavatisutaa, Pautri, Putrapujyaa, Payasvini, Pattipasadhaara, Pankti, Pitriloka Pradayini, Purani, Punyasilaa, Pranatarti Vinasini, Pradyumna Janani, Pustaa, Pitamahaparigrahaa, Pundarikapuravasaa, Pundarikasamananaa, Prithujanghaa, Prithubhujaa,

Prithupadaa, Prithudhari, Pravalasobhaa, Pingakshi, Pitavasahah, Prachapalaa, Praasavaa, Pushtidaa, Punya Pratishtaa, Pranavaa, Pati, Panchavarnaa, Panchavani, Panchikaa, Panjarasthitaa, Paramayaa, Parajyotih, Parapriti, Paragati, Parakashthaa, Paresani, Pavani, Pavaka Dyuti, Punyabhadraa, Paricchedyaa, Pushpahasaa, Prithudaraa, Pitangi, Pitavasanaa, Pitasayaa, Pisachini, Pitakriyaa, Pisachagni, Patalakshi, Patukriyaa, Panchabhakshaa, Priyacharaa, Putana Pranaghatini, Punnagavana Madhyasthaa, Punyatirthani Sevitaa, Panchagni Vistapaa, Panapriyaa, Panchasikhaa, Pannagoparisayini, Panchamatratmikaa, Prithvi, Pathikaa, Prithudohini, Purananyaya Mimamsaa, Patali, Pushpagandhini, Punyaprajaa, Paradatri, Paramargaika Gocharaa, Pravasobhaa, Purnasaa, Pallabodari.

She is Phalini, Phaladaa, Phalgu, Phutkari, Phalakakriti, Phanindra Bhogasayanaa, Phanimandala Manditaa, Balabalaa, Bahumataa, Balatapani, Bhamsukaa, Balabhadrapriyaa, Bandyaa, Badavaa, Buddhisamstutaa, Bandidevi, Bilavati, Badisanghini, Balipriyaa, Bandhavi, Bodhitaa, Buddhirbandhuka Kusumapriyaa, Balabhanu Prabhakaraa, Brahmi, Brahmana Devataa, Brihaspatistutaa, Brindaa, Brindavana Viharini, Balakini, Bilaharaa, Bilavasaa, Bahudakaa, Bahunetraa, Bahupadaa, Bahukarna Vatamsikaa, Bahubahuyutaa, Bijarupini, Bahurupini, Bindunada Kalatitaa, Bindunada Svarupini, Badhagodha Angulitranaa, Badariyasrama Vasini, Brindarakaa, Brihatskandhaa, Brihati, Banapatini, Brindadhyakshaa, Bahunutaa, Banitaa, Bahuvikramaa, Baddhapadmasanasinaa, Bilvapatra Talasthithaa, Bodhidrumani Javasaa, Badishthaa, Bindu Darpanaa, Balaa, Banasanavati, Badayanalavegini, Brahmanda Bahrirantasthaa, Brahma Kankanasutri, Bhavani, Bhisanavati, Bhavini, Bhayaharini, Bhadrakali, Bhujangakshi, Bharati, Bharatasayaa, Bhairavi, Bhishanakaraa, Bhutidaa, Bhutimalini, Bhamini, Bhoganirataa, Bhadradaa, Bhurivikramaa, Bhutavasaa, Bhrigulataa, Bhargavi, Bhusurachitaa, Bhagirathi, Bhogavati, Bhavasanthaa, Bhisagvaraa, Bhamini, Bhigini, Bhasaa, Bhavani, Bhuridakshinaa, Bhargatmikaa, Bhimavati, Bhavabandha Vimochini, Bhajaniyaa, Bhutadhatri Ranjithaa, Bhuvaneswari, Bhujangavalayaa, Bhimaa, Bherundaa, Bhagadheyini.

Mataa, Maya, Madhumati, Madhujihvaa, Manupriyaa, Mahadevi, Mahabhagyaa, Malini, Minalochanaa, Mayatitaa, Madhumati, Madhumansaa, Madhudravaa, Manavi, Madhusambhutaa, Mithilapuravasini, Maithili, Madhukaitabha Samhartri, Medini, Meghamalini, Mandodari, Maha Mayaa, Masrinapriyaa, Mahalakshmi, Mahakali, Mahakanyaa, Maheswari, Mahedri,

Merutanayaa, Mandara Kusumarchitaa, Majumajirarchanaa, Mokshadaa, Manjubhashini, Madhuradravini, Mudraa, Malayaa, Malayanvitaa, Medhaa, Marakatasyamah, Magadhi, Menakatmajah, Mahamari, Mahaviraa, Mahasyamaa, Manustutaa, Matrikaa, Mihirabhasaa, Mukundapada Vikramaa, Muladharaasthitah, Mugdhaa, Manipuranivasini, Mrigakshi, Mahisarudhaa, Mahishasuramardini.

Yogasanaa, Yogamayaa, Yogaa, Yauvanksharayaa, Yauvani, Yuddha Madhyasthaa, Yamuna, Yugadharini, Yakshini, Yogayuktaa, Yaksharajaprasutini, Yatraa, Yana Bidhaujanaa, Yaduvamsha Samsudhbhavaa, Yakaradi-Ha Karantaa, Yajushi, Yagnarupini, Yamini, Yoganirataa, Yatudhanaa.

Rukmini, Ramani, Rema, Revati, Renuka, Rati, Raudri, Raudrapriyakaraa, Rama Matraa, Ratipriyaa, Rohini, Rajyadaa, Reva, Raasaa, Rajivalochanaa, Rakeshi, Rupasampannaa, Ratnasimhasanasthitaa, Raktamalyambaradharaa, Raktagandbanu Lepanaa, Raja Hamsa Samarudhaa, Rambha, Raktavalipriyaa, Ramaniya Yugadharaa, Rajitakhila Bhutalaa, Rurucharma Paridbanaa, Rathini, Ratnamallikaa, Rogesi, Ravanachhedakarini, Romaharshini, Ramachandra Pada Krantaa, Rogashmanani, Ravini, Ratnavastra Parichhinvaa, Rathasthaa, Rukmabhushanaa.

Lajjadhi Devataa, Lola, Lalita, Lingdharini, Lakshmi, Luptavisaa, Lokini, Lokavisrutaa, Lajja, Lambodari, Lalanaa, Lokadharini.

Varachaa, Vanditaa, Vidyaa, Vaishnavi, Vimalakriti, Varahi, Virajaa, Varshaa, Varalakshmi, Vilasini, Vinataa, Vyomadhyasthaa, Varijasana Samsthithaa, Varuni, Venusambhutaa, Vitihotraa, Virupini, Vayumandala Madhyasthaa, Vishnurupaa, Vidhikriyaa, Vishnupatni, Vishnumati, Visalakshi, Vasundharaa, VamaDevapriyaa, Velaa, Vajrini, Vasudohini, Vedakshara Paritamgi, Vajapeya Phalapradaa, Vasavi, Vamajanani, Vaikunthanilayaa, Varaa, Vyasapriyaa, Varmadhaaraa, Valmikiparisevitaa.

Sakhambari, Sivaa, Santaa, Saradaa, Saranagati, Satodari, Subhacharaa, SumbhAsuramardini, Shobhavati, Sivakaraa, Sankarardha Saririni, Sonaa, Subhasayaa, Subhra, Sirahsandhana Karini, Saravati, Saranandaa, Sarajyotsanaa, Subhananaa, Sarabhaa, Sulini, Suddhaa, Sabari, Sukavahanaa, Srimati, Sridharanandaa, Sravana Nandadayini, Sarvani, Sarvarivandyaa, Sadbahasaa, Sadritupriyaa, Sadaharasthita Devi, Sanmukha Priyakarini, Sadamgarupa Sumati, SuraAsura Namaskritaa.

Saraswati, Sadadhaara, Sarvamangalakarini, Samagana Priyaa, Sukshmaa, Savitri, Samasambhavaa, Sarvavasaa, Sadanandaa, Sustani, Sagarambaraa,

Sagarambaraa, Sarvaisyaryapriyaa, Siddhi, Sadhubandha Parakramaa, Saptarshimanadaagataa, Somamandala Vasini, Sarvajanaa, Sandrakarunaa, Samanadhi Kavarijitaa, Sarvottungaa, Sangahinaa, Sadgunaa, Sakaharini.

Hrimkari, Hamsavahini, Kshaumavastra Paritangi, Kshirabdhi Tanayaa, Kshamaa, Vedagarbhaa, Vararohaa, Sri Gayatri and Parambikaa. These are the thousand names of the Devi, that set a man free from the bonds of samsara, they liberate him, O Narada.

No fear enters a house where the Devi Gayatri's thousand names are kept written. And Sri Lakshmi, the Goddess of wealth, who is notoriously fickle, remains steadfastly in that house. And a thousand sins are made ashes by chanting the Devi's holy names," said Narayana Muni to the great wanderer.

Now Narada asked Narayana Muni to describe the sacred covenant between a guru and his sishya, and how the sishya is initiated into a mula mantra, and given the ritual diksha. Narayana Muni described this hermetic ceremony in some detail. But this is a most secret ritual, O Kshatriya,' said Veda Vyasa to Janamejaya of the Kurus on the banks of the whispering river," the Suta said.

EIGHTY-THREE

THE SUTA SAID, "JANAMEJAYA ASKED VYASA, 'MUNI, WHY HAS BHAKTI waned in the world of men?'

Vyasa replied, 'It was from Siva's ancient curse and the Rishi Gautama's curse, that in Kali yuga the Brahmanas of the world would be born without the inner knowledge of the Vedas and the sandhyas, and that, since they were the upholders of dharma in the world, dharma would decay. And so would the spirits of men dwindle.'

Janamejaya asked, 'Tell me a little more about Manidvipa, where the Devi dwells.'

Vyasa said, 'The Srutis and the Sabalopanishad speak of the Sarvaloka which is higher than Brahmaloka. This, O king, is Manidvipa where the Devi Bhagavati lives. The shadow of this loftiest realm falls over the rest of the universe, and removes its sins. The Sudha sagara surrounds Manidvipa, and the Lords of the four seasons dwell on the perimeter of that most auspicious world with their consorts, and with countless other unearthly beings and creatures, all enraptured by the very air of the transcendent isle. Also, the Lords of the different quarters of the universe, the Dikpalas, dwell on Manidvipa with their women. All these are the masters of the universe, who live under the Devi Bhagavati's grace. The Devas, too, in their most pristine forms dwell nowhere but here, with the Devi; and their women, the Apsaras, Gandharvas, Kinnaras, Siddhas, Charanas and all the others.

The sixty-four Kalaas dwell here, in this final mandala—each one powerful enough to lick up a thousand brahmandas with their lolling tongues! Past them lives Sri Bhuvaneswari Devi, then the Matrikas: Brahmi, Maheswari, Kaumari, Vaishnavi, Varahi, Indrani, Chamunda and Mahalakshmi.

Still nearer the heart of Manidvipa, there is a great lotus of sixteen petals, and the Devi Bhagavati's sixteen Shaktis live on each splendid, incomparable petal. Beyond this, the Devi's eight sakhis, her companions, dwell.

Still nearer the heart of Manidvipa, four-faced Brahma lives with Gayatri Devi, Vishnu with Savitri Devi and Maha Rudra with Saraswati Devi. All their endless avataras, who rule the myriad universes, dwell here with them. And, then, there is a palace at the very heart of Manidvipa, a palace made of Chintamani, and with an infinity of pillars and rooms. There are four mantapas within this peerless palace—the Sringara mantapa, the Mukti mantapa, the Gyana mantapa and the Ekanta mantapa. The Devi Bhagavati, the Mula Prakriti, the Goddess of all the Gods and Goddesses, dwells here.

But, mostly, she is in the Chintamani Griha, and her bhaktas from all the ages, and from every part of the universe, are here with her, in everlasting bliss. Why attempt, O King, to describe that mandala, which is past my powers of description, save to say that it is the loftiest jewel in the universe, where the Devi Bhagavati lives.'

Janamejaya grew humble, he said, 'I beg you, O Guru, give me deeksha. Bless me, teach me the Devi's mula mantra. Let me perform the Navaratra puja in the name of the Devi Bhagavati.'

And Krishna Dwaipayana, the Muni Vyasa, did teach that sad king the blessed Devi's mantra, and Janamejaya the Kuru, Parikshita's son, performed the Navaratra puja in his father's name. As the ritual was ending, he saw a brilliant path grow lucid in the sky, and down it Vyasa saw a smiling, brilliant Devarishi fly down right to the king's side!

Janamejaya folded his hands to the immortal wanderer, for it was Narada who came to his puja. The king took the auspicious dust from the itinerant Muni's feet. He said, 'Mahamuni, my Navaratra puja is thrice blessed that you have come here. But, tell me, Narada, why you have come. Is there anything I can do for you?'

Devarishi Narada said, smiling blithely, 'I came to tell you of a wonderful thing I saw in Devaloka today, Janamejaya. O Kshatriya, I saw your father Parikshita, and, ah, he had a body of light and grace and he was flying up from Yama's realm into the Lord Indra's, and beyond, in a pushpaka vimana! All the Devas were singing his praises, and he sat among heaven's Apsaras. I heard that he was on his way to Manidvipa, where the Devi dwells! And I heard the reason was he had been forgiven the sin he committed, that you kept the Navaratra vrata, and that you heard the Devi Bhagavatam from the Muni Vyasa.

Janamejaya, you have delivered your father from hell, and your name is being whispered throughout Devaloka!'

Janamejaya trembled with delight. He prostrated himself at Vyasa's feet, and tears of joy flowed down his face. The king cried, 'Ah Dwaipayana, Guru, you have blessed me! I beg you, Kaviraja, let your blessing always be upon me.'

Vyasa said kindly to the Kuru, 'It is the Devi who has blessed you, Janamejaya. Her Purana saved your father's soul. So worship Devi Bhagavati, and keep her Purana near you and read it always.'

'Bless me, Lord, that I may,' said Janamejaya.

Vyasa, Narada, Dhaumya and the other holy ones who had gathered there to hear the incomparable Devi Bhagavatam, all laid their palms in blessing on the Kuru king's head, and then they left," the Suta Romaharshana said to Saunaka and his Rishis of the Naimisa vana.

The Suta now ended his ancient legend of revelation, "O Munis, in time out of mind, near the very beginning, this precious Devi Bhagavatam emerged from the Devi Bhagavati's own face, as half a sloka, and it was the epitome and the conclusion to all the Vedas. She said this half-sloka, wistfully, to Vishnu who lay upon his pipal leaf, at the kalpa's end, upon the Ekarnava, the single sea of the dissolution.

And, at hearing those resonant syllables in a tongue that was the very universe and the face of she who is its Mother, an inspired Brahma expanded the sacred half-sloka into a hundred billion slokas, in a few moments. But most of them are no longer available in a world that has become too impure for their revelation in it. That pristine Devi Bhagavatam was, verily, the universe and all that is in it. It is still heard, sung and read in Devaloka.

Krishna Dwaipayana, Veda Vyasa, wanted his son Suka Deva to hear the Devi Bhagavatam, and Vyasa condensed Brahma's awesome Purana into a mere eighteen thousand slokas. There is no other Purana even a sixteenth part as powerful as the Devi Bhagavatam. Every line of it you read yields the fruits of performing a few Aswamedhas. And if you write it with your own hand, there is no doubt, Munis, you will find the realms of the Devi for yourself, and her grace as if she laid her palm on your head and blessed you.

Hearing this sacred Purana will make ashes of many lives of sins, and confer everything you desire upon you. Lakshmi and Saraswati dwell in the home where the Devi Bhagavatam is kept and read. No evil spirit, no Dakini, Vetala or Rakshasi can even cast a sidelong glance at a bhakta of the Devi's.

He who reads just a chapter of this Purana, regularly, quickly acquires true gyana. If it is read during the Navaratra or the Durga puja, the Devi blesses the one who reads or hears it many times over.

AUM, I bow to the Devi Gayatri whose nature is **Hrim**, who is Satchitananda, being, intelligence and bliss, who is the cause of all causes, and of ours as well."

Here the blessed Suta Romaharshana, greatest of Pauranikas, ended the Devi Bhagavatam. The Rishis of the Naimisaranya prostrated themselves before him in gratitude. For, he had told them the entire Devi Bhagavatam, and they could feel its grace inside their bodies, within their hearts. They could see its subtle light, the light of truth, upon themselves and each other. They felt as if they were feathers afloat on the great wind of the Devi's love.

Romaharshana, the great, blessed those Munis, and then went his mysterious way, through deep jungles, over jagged mountains full of the Brahmam, and only God and he knew where else, into which other realms, taking his invaluable treasure of the Puranas with him. And the other Rishis, who heard the immortal Devi Bhagavatam from his lips, in time, became immortal themselves. They became the Devi; they were absorbed into her. They lived with her forever after.

AUM TAT SAT.
AUM SANTI SANTI SANTIHI AUM.
AUM HARI AUM.